Brief Contents

Eric J. Simon • Jean L. Dickey • Jane B. Reece

Campbell Essential Biology with Physiology
Volume 1

Custom Edition for Houston Community College

Taken from:
Campbell Essential Biology with Physiology, Fourth Edition
by Eric J. Simon, Jean L. Dickey, and Jane B. Reece

Cover Art: Courtesy of Photodisc/Getty Images.

Taken from:

Campbell Essential Biology with Physiology, Fourth Edition
by Eric J. Simon, Jean L. Dickey, and Jane B. Reece
Copyright © 2014, 2013, 2010, 2007 by Pearson Education, Inc.
Boston, Massachusetts 02116

This special edition published in cooperation with Pearson Learning Solutions.

Pearson Learning Solutions, 501 Boylston Street, Suite 900, Boston, MA 02116
A Pearson Education Company
www.pearsoned.com

Printed in the United States of America

7 8 9 10 11 VOUD 19 18 17 16 15

000200010271886506

NC

ISBN 10: 1-269-75336-3
ISBN 13: 978-1-269-75336-4

About the Authors

ERIC J. SIMON

is an associate professor in the Department of Biology and Health Science at New England College, in Henniker, New Hampshire. He teaches introductory biology to science majors and nonscience majors, as well as upper-level courses in genetics, microbiology, tropical marine biology, and careers in science.

Dr. Simon received a B.A. in biology and computer science and an M.A. in biology from Wesleyan University and a Ph.D. in biochemistry from Harvard University. His research focuses on innovative ways to use technology to improve teaching and learning in the science classroom, particularly for nonscience majors. Dr. Simon is also a coauthor of *Campbell Biology: Concepts & Connections*, 7th Edition.

To Marshall, an intellectual role model, a source of data and wisdom, an organizational tour de force, a hardcore bicyclist, a bona fide Deadhead, a great father, and one cool dude

JANE B. REECE

has worked in biology publishing since 1978, when she joined the editorial staff of Benjamin Cummings. Her education includes an A.B. in biology from Harvard University (where she was initially a philosophy major), an M.S. in microbiology from Rutgers University, and a Ph.D. in bacteriology from the University of California, Berkeley. At UC Berkeley, and later as a postdoctoral fellow in genetics at Stanford University, her research focused on genetic recombination in bacteria. Dr. Reece taught biology at Middlesex County College (New Jersey) and Queensborough Community College (New York). During her 12 years as an editor at Benjamin Cummings, she played a major role in a number of successful textbooks. She is the lead author of *Campbell Biology*, 9th Edition, and *Campbell Biology: Concepts & Connections*, 7th Edition.

To my wonderful coauthors, who have made working on our books a pleasure

JEAN L. DICKEY

is a professor of biology at Clemson University in South Carolina. She had no idea that science was interesting until her senior year in high school, when a scheduling problem landed her in an advanced biology course. Abandoning plans to study English or foreign languages, she enrolled in Kent State University as a biology major. After receiving her B.S. in biology, she went on to earn a Ph.D. in ecology and evolution from Purdue University. Since joining the faculty at Clemson in 1984, Dr. Dickey has specialized in teaching nonscience majors, including a course designed for pre-service elementary teachers and workshops for in-service teachers. She also developed an investigative laboratory curriculum for general biology. Dr. Dickey is the author of *Laboratory Investigations for Biology*, 2nd Edition, and is a coauthor of *Campbell Biology: Concepts & Connections*, 7th Edition.

To my mother, who taught me to love learning, and to my daughters Katherine and Jessie, the twin delights of my life

NEIL A. CAMPBELL

(1946–2004) combined the inquiring nature of a research scientist with the soul of a caring teacher. Over his 30 years of teaching introductory biology to both science majors and nonscience majors, many thousands of students had the opportunity to learn from him and be stimulated by his enthusiasm for the study of life. While he is greatly missed by his many friends in the biology community, his coauthors remain inspired by his visionary dedication to education and are committed to searching for ever-better ways to engage students in the wonders of biology.

Detailed Contents

UNIT 2: Genetics

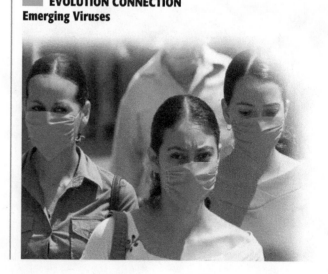

11 How Genes Are Controlled 198
CHAPTER THREAD: CANCER

12 DNA Technology 218
CHAPTER THREAD: DNA PROFILING

To the Student: How to use this book

Each chapter is built around three features connected by a unifying thread.

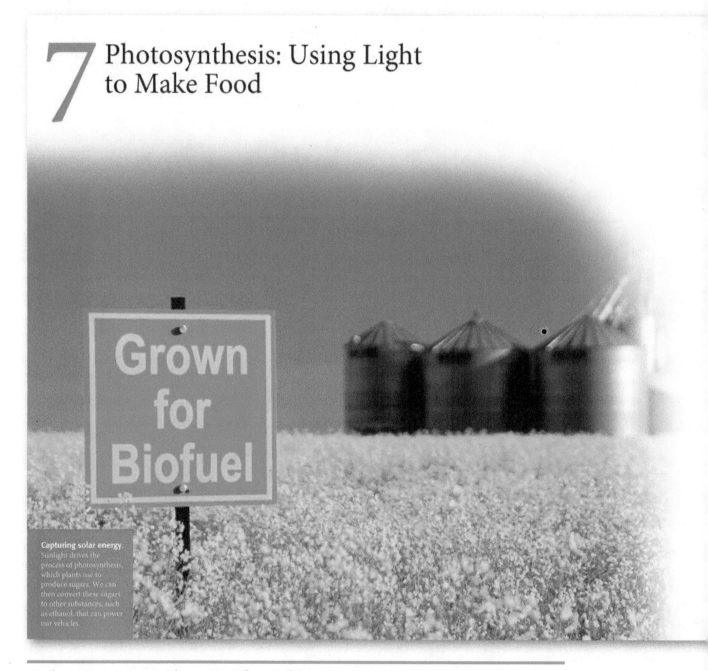

7 Photosynthesis: Using Light to Make Food

Grown for Biofuel

Capturing solar energy. Sunlight drives the process of photosynthesis, which plants use to produce sugars. We can then convert these sugars to other substances, such as ethanol, that can power our vehicles.

Other Exciting Chapter Thread Topics:

- Global Climate Change
- Athletic Endurance
- Steroid Abuse
- Controlling Your Weight
- Cancer
- DNA Profiling
- The Deadliest Virus
- Antibiotic-Resistant Bacteria

Chapter Thread

The chapter thread weaves a single compelling topic throughout the chapter. For example, here the thread is Green Energy, and you'll find this thread consistently at the beginning, middle, and end of each chapter.

 Green Energy BIOLOGY AND SOCIETY

Biofuels

What's old is sometimes new again. Throughout our early history, people relied on plants as our primary source of energy, burning wood to produce heat and light. Then, as societies became industrialized, wood was largely displaced as an energy source by fossil fuels such as coal, gas, and oil. But now, as fossil fuel supplies dwindle and concerns are raised about global climate change, spiking oil prices, and the need for a domestic energy source, scientists are researching better ways to harness energy from biomass (living material). Some researchers focus on burning plant matter directly (for example, wood pellet boilers), while others focus on using plant material to produce biofuels that can be burned.

There are several types of biofuels. Bioethanol is a type of alcohol (the same type found in alcoholic drinks) that is made from wheat, corn, sugar beets, sugarcane, and other food crops. Starch made naturally by plants is converted to glucose and then fermented to ethanol by microorganisms (such as single-celled algae). Bioethanol can be used directly as a fuel source in specially designed vehicles, but it is more commonly used as a gasoline additive that can increase fuel efficiency while decreasing vehicle emissions. You may have noticed a sticker on the gas pump that declares the percentage of ethanol in the gas you are pumping; most cars today run on a blend of 85% gasoline and 15% ethanol. Many car manufacturers are producing flexible-fuel vehicles that can run on any combination of gasoline and bioethanol.

Cellulosic ethanol is a form of bioethanol made through the same fermentation process as bioethanol, but its primary ingredient is cellulose from nonedible plant material such as wood or grass. Biodiesel, the most common biofuel in Europe, is made from plant oils such as re-cycled frying oil. Like bioethanol, it can be used on its own or as an additive to standard diesel.

Whatever its form, when we derive energy from biomass or biofuels, we are actually tapping into the energy of the sun, which drives the process of photosynthesis in plants. Biofuels are just one way that people take advantage of plants' ability to capture solar energy. The topic of this chapter is photosynthesis, the process whereby plants use light to make sugars from carbon dioxide—sugars that are food for the plant and the starting point for most of our own food. First, we'll examine some basic concepts of photosynthesis; then we'll look at the specific mechanisms involved.

 Green Energy BIOLOGY AND SOCIETY

BIOLOGY AND SOCIETY relates biology to your life and interests. For example, in this chapter, you'll learn about the types of biofuels, their sources, and their everyday uses.

 Green Energy THE PROCESS OF SCIENCE

THE PROCESS OF SCIENCE gives you real-world examples of how the scientific method is applied. For example, in this chapter, you'll learn how a researcher discovered which wavelengths of light are primarily responsible for photosynthesis.

 Green Energy EVOLUTION CONNECTION

EVOLUTION CONNECTION concludes the chapter by demonstrating how the theme of evolution runs throughout all of biology. For example, in this chapter, you'll learn how plants have adapted in different environments.

Orient yourself and find content

Find the chapter you want
Use the tabs on the left-hand page and quickly locate units by the color of the tabs.

Locate study questions
Checkpoint questions in the margins help you assess your understanding of the content you just read.

Visual organizers
See important categories at a glance.

Identify the subject of the figure by glancing at the heading.

Spot the categories at once by looking at the subheadings.

The Basics of Photosynthesis

Photosynthesis is a process whereby plants, algae (which are protists), and certain bacteria transform light energy into chemical energy, using carbon dioxide and water as starting materials. The chemical energy produced via photosynthesis is stored in the bonds of sugar molecules. Organisms that generate their own organic matter from inorganic ingredients are called autotrophs (see Chapter 6). Plants and other organisms that do this by photosynthesis—photosynthetic autotrophs—are the producers for most ecosystems (Figure 7.1). This section presents an overview of photosynthesis, focusing on plants. Later, we'll take a closer look at some details of this process.

Chloroplasts: Sites of Photosynthesis

You have already learned that photosynthesis in plants and algae occurs within light-absorbing organelles called **chloroplasts** (see Chapter 4). All green parts of a plant have chloroplasts and can carry out photosynthesis. In most plants, however, the leaves have the most chloroplasts (about 500,000 per square millimeter of leaf surface) and are therefore the major locations of photosynthesis. Their green color is fro[m] **chlorophyll**, a light-absorbing molecule (a pigmen[t]) the chloroplasts that plays a central role in converti[ng] solar energy to chemical energy.

Chloroplasts are concentrated in the interior cells [of] leaves (Figure 7.2), with a typical cell containing 30–40 chloroplasts. Carbon dioxide (CO_2) enters a leaf, and oxygen (O_2) exits, by way of tiny pores calle[d] **stomata** (singular, *stoma*, meaning "mouth"). In add[ition] to carbon dioxide, photosynthesis requires water, wh[ich] is absorbed by the plant's roots and transported to th[e] leaves, where veins carry it to the photosynthetic cell[s].

Membranes within the chloroplast form the fram[e]work where many of the reactions of photosynthesi[s] occur. Like a mitochondrion, a chloroplast has a double-membrane envelope. The chloroplast's inne[r] membrane encloses a compartment filled with str[oma, a] thick fluid. Suspended in the stroma are interconne[cted] membranous sacs called **thylakoids**. The thylakoid[s are] concentrated in stacks called **grana** (singular, *gran[um*]). The chlorophyll molecules that capture light energ[y are] built into the thylakoid membranes. The structure [of a] chloroplast—with its stacks of disks—aids its functi[on] by providing a large surface area for the reactions o[f] photosynthesis. ☑

☑ CHECKPOINT
Photosynthesis takes place within organelles called _____ using gases that are exchanged via pores called _____.

Answer: chloroplasts; stomata

▼ Figure 7.1 **A diversity of photosynthetic autotrophs.**

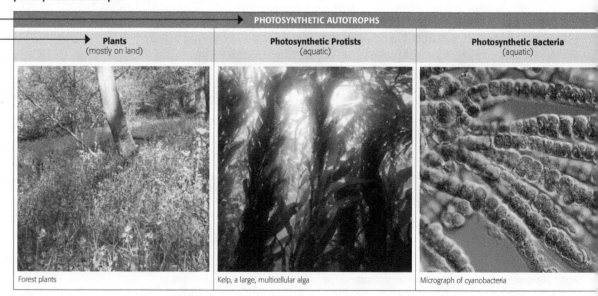

PHOTOSYNTHETIC AUTOTROPHS

Plants (mostly on land) — Forest plants

Photosynthetic Protists (aquatic) — Kelp, a large, multicellular alga

Photosynthetic Bacteria (aquatic) — Micrograph of cyanobacteria

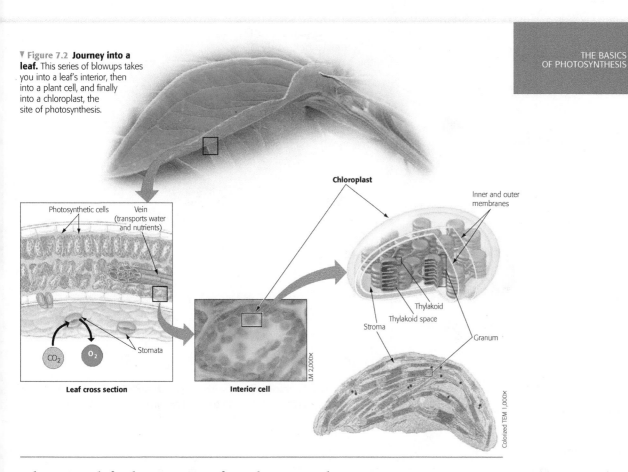

▼ Figure 7.2 **Journey into a leaf.** This series of blowups takes you into a leaf's interior, then into a plant cell, and finally into a chloroplast, the site of photosynthesis.

Remember the main topic
Colored tabs at the top corner of each right-hand page help you to remember what you're studying.

Chloroplast

Inner and outer membranes

Thylakoid

Thylakoid space

Stroma

Granum

Photosynthetic cells

Vein (transports water and nutrients)

Stomata

CO_2

O_2

Leaf cross section

LM 2,000x

Interior cell

Colorized TEM 1,000x

The Simplified Equation for Photosynthesis

The following chemical equation, simplified to highlight the relationship between photosynthesis and cellular respiration, provides a summary of the reactants and products of photosynthesis:

Light energy

$6\ CO_2$ + $6\ H_2O$ → → → $C_6H_{12}O_6$ + $6\ O_2$

Carbon dioxide   Water   **Photosynthesis**   Glucose   Oxygen gas

Notice that the reactants of photosynthesis—carbon dioxide (CO_2) and water (H_2O)—are the same as the waste products of cellular respiration (see Figure 6.2). Also notice that photosynthesis produces what respiration uses—glucose ($C_6H_{12}O_6$) and oxygen (O_2). In other words, photosynthesis recycles the "exhaust" of cellular respiration and rearranges its atoms to produce food and oxygen. Photosynthesis is a chemical transformation that requires a lot of energy, and sunlight absorbed by chlorophyll provides that energy.

You learned in Chapter 6 that cellular respiration is a process of electron transfer. A "fall" of electrons from food molecules to oxygen to form water releases the energy that mitochondria can use to make ATP (see Figure 6.5). The opposite occurs in photosynthesis: Electrons are boosted "uphill" and added to carbon dioxide to produce sugar. Hydrogen is moved along with the electrons being transferred from water to carbon dioxide. This transfer of hydrogen requires the chloroplast to split water molecules into hydrogen and oxygen. The hydrogen is transferred along with electrons to carbon dioxide to form sugar. The oxygen escapes through stomata in leaves into the atmosphere as O_2, a waste product of photosynthesis. ☑

In what sense do photosynthesis and cellular respiration form a complementary cycle?

Intriguing questions
These questions help you relate core content to topics that pique your interest.

☑ **CHECKPOINT**
What molecules are the inputs of photosynthesis? What molecules are the outputs?

Answer: CO_2 and H_2O; glucose and O_2

109

Tools to help you study

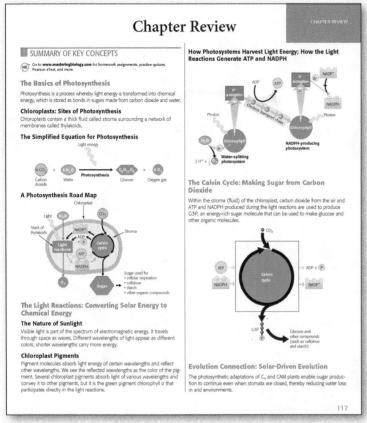

◀ **Chapter Review**

Words and images work together to help you review the key concepts of the chapter.

▼ **Pearson eText**

Pearson eText, within MasteringBiology™, gives you access to the text whenever and wherever you can access the Internet.

Highlight Function lets you highlight what you want to remember.

Annotation Function allows you to take notes.

Google®-based search function.

Zoom lets you zoom in and out for better viewing.

Interactive Glossary provides pop-up definitions and terms.

Teacher Notes allows your teacher to share his or her notes and highlights with the class.

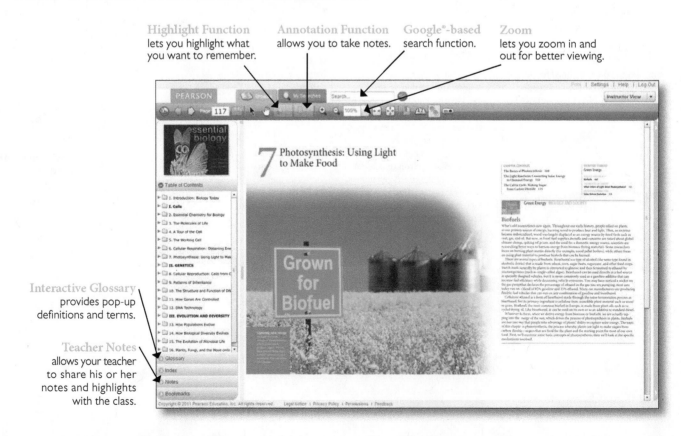

MasteringBiology®

www.masteringbiology.com

The MasteringBiology online homework and tutoring system delivers self-paced tutorials that provide you with individualized coaching set to your teacher's class objectives. MasteringBiology helps you arrive prepared for class and offers additional study tools for you to use wherever you are!

BioFlix® Animation ▶

Dynamic 3-D animations help you to visualize and learn the toughest topics in biology covered in the coaching activity tutorial.

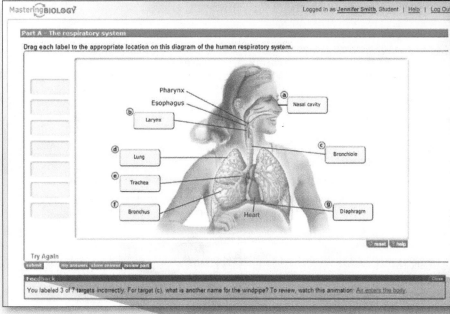

◀ BioFlix Coaching Activity

Interactive activities provide coaching and feedback.

Wrong-Answer Feedback ▶

Gain a better understanding of the toughest topics with specific wrong-answer feedback.

Feedback   Close

You labeled 3 of 7 targets incorrectly. For target (c), what is another name for the windpipe? To review, watch this animation: Air enters the body.

Author-Created Assignments

More than 100 new MasteringBiology® activities written
by the author team help you arrive prepared for class
and provide you with feedback and coaching.

**Video Tutor Sessions and ▶
MP3 Tutor Sessions**

Get help with key
concepts and vocabulary
with on-the-go tutorials
hosted by co-author
Eric Simon.

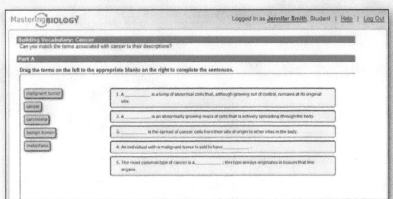

**◀ Building
Vocabulary
Activities**

Practice the new
vocabulary you are
learning in class.

**Learning Through ▶
Art Activities**

Connect the art to
the concepts using
activities that enhance
the text's visual approach
to learning biology.

MasteringBiology®

www.masteringbiology.com

Connecting the Concepts Activities

Link the concepts you learned and see how they work together.

You Decide Activities ▶

Explore the data behind hot topics so you can make informed decisions.

Interpreting Data Activities

Receive coaching on how to read and interpret data and graphs.

How to Access MasteringBiology

Access to MasteringBiology is provided with textbook purchases. Students, ask your teachers for access. Teachers, see page xxvii for more information.

To the Teacher: MasteringBiology®

The Mastering platform is the most effective and widely used online tutorial, homework, and assessment system for the sciences. It was developed by scientists for science students and teachers and has a proven history with more than 10 years of student use.

Gradebook

Get easy-to-interpret insights into student performance using the gradebook.

- Every assignment is automatically graded.
- Shades of red highlight vulnerable students and challenging assignments.

Student Performance Data ▶

Learn how students are doing compared to a national average and which topics they're struggling with.

◀ Track student performance against your learning outcomes:

- Add your own or use the publisher-provided learning outcomes to track student performance.
- View class performance against the specified learning outcomes.
- Export results to a spreadsheet that you can further customize.
- Mastering offers a data-supported measure to quantify students' learning gains and to share those results quickly and easily.

One-click Diagnostics ▶

Show where students are struggling or progressing.

Upon textbook purchase, students and teachers are granted access to MasteringBiology. High school teachers can obtain preview or adoption access for MasteringBiology in one of the following ways:

Preview Access

- Teachers can request preview access online by visiting PearsonSchool.com/Access_Request, using Option 2. Preview access information will be sent to the teacher via email.

Adoption Access

- With the purchase of this program a Pearson Adoption Access Card, with codes and complete instructions, will be delivered with your textbook purchase. (ISBN: 0-13-034391-9)

- Ask your sales representative for a Pearson Adoption Access Code Card. (ISBN: 0-13-034391-9)

  OR

- By visiting PearsonSchool.com/Access_Request, using Option 3. Adoption access information will be sent to the teacher via email.

Preface

This is a wonderful time to teach and learn biology. Opportunities to marvel at the natural world and the life within it abound. It's difficult to peruse a news website without finding stories that touch on biology and its intersection with society. In addition, the world of pop culture is rich with books, movies, TV shows, comic strips, and video games that feature biological wonders and challenge us to think about important biological concepts and their implications. Although some people *say* that they don't like biology (or, more often, science in general), nearly everyone will admit to an inborn biophilia. After all, most of us keep pets, tend a garden, enjoy zoos and aquariums, or appreciate time spent outdoors. Furthermore, nearly everyone realizes that the subject of biology has a significant impact on his or her own life through its connections to medicine, biotechnology, agriculture, environmental issues, forensics, and myriad other areas. But despite the inborn affinity that nearly everyone has for biology, it can be a struggle for nonscientists to delve into the subject. Our primary goal in writing *Campbell Essential Biology with Physiology* is to help teachers motivate and educate the next generation of citizens by tapping into the inherent curiosity about life that we all share.

Goals of the Book

Although our world is rich with "teachable moments" and learning opportunities, the explosion of knowledge threatens to bury a curious person under an avalanche of information. "So much biology, so little time" is the universal lament of biology educators. Neil Campbell conceived of *Campbell Essential Biology with Physiology* as a tool to help teachers and students focus on the most important areas of biology. To that end, the book is organized into six core areas: cells, genes, evolution, ecology, animals, and plants. His vision, which we carry on and extend in this edition, has enabled us to keep *Campbell Essential Biology with Physiology* manageable in size without being superficial in developing the concepts that are most fundamental to understanding life. We take the "less is more" mantra in education today to mean fewer topics and more focused explanations, not content that is more diluted.

In countless conversations with teachers and students, we have noticed some important trends in how biology is taught. In particular, many teachers voice a desire to achieve three goals: (1) to engage students by relating the core content to their lives and the greater society; (2) to clarify the process of science by showing how it is applied in the real world; and (3) to demonstrate how evolution serves as biology's unifying theme. To help achieve these goals, every chapter of this book includes three important features. First, a chapter-opening section called Biology and Society highlights a connection between the chapter's core content and students' lives. Second, a section called The Process of Science describes how the scientific process has illuminated the topic at hand, using a classic or modern experiment as an example. Third, a chapter-closing Evolution Connection section relates the chapter to biology's unifying theme of evolution. To maintain a cohesive narrative for each topic, the content of each chapter is tied together with a unifying chapter thread, a relevant high-interest topic that is woven throughout the three chapter essays and throughout the entire chapter. In this way, the unifying chapter thread ties together the three pedagogical goals of the course using a topic that is compelling and relevant to students.

New to This Edition

We hope that this latest edition of *Campbell Essential Biology with Physiology* goes even further to help students relate the material to their lives, understand the process of science, and appreciate how evolution is the unifying theme of biology. To this end, we've added significant new features and content to this edition:

- **New high-interest topics** Every chapter in *Campbell Essential Biology with Physiology* has its own unifying chapter thread—a high-interest topic that helps to demonstrate the relevance of the chapter content. The chapter thread is incorporated into the three main essays of each chapter (Biology and Society, The Process of Science, and Evolution Connection) as well as throughout the chapter text. In this edition, we significantly updated many of these topics and essays. For example, Chapter 2 (Essential Chemistry for Biology) includes a new chapter-opening essay on the causes and impacts of droughts. Chapter 7 (Photosynthesis: Using Light to Make Food, a potentially difficult-to-relate-to topic for many students) has the new unifying chapter thread "Green Energy" and includes a new chapter-opening essay on biofuels. Chapter 23 (Circulation and Respiration) has the new unifying chapter thread "Athletic Endurance," along with three new essays in the chapter that emphasize the role of training on athletic performance, a topic of great interest to many students.

- **Updated content** As with every edition, we introduce timely, high-interest topics into the chapter content. For example, Chapter 6 (Cellular Respiration: Obtaining Energy from Food) mentions ethanol biofuels; Chapter 15 (The Evolution of Microbial Life) discusses the recent success that Craig Venter's team has had in "rebooting" one bacterial species with the lab-synthesized genome of another; Chapter 18 (An Introduction to Ecology and the Biosphere) notes the Deepwater Horizon oil spill; and Chapter 29 (The Working Plant) discusses the use of sunflowers to detoxify soil around the Fukushima nuclear disaster site.

- **Intriguing questions** Most people have questions about the subject of biology that are both relevant and highly illuminating. New to this edition, we have tapped into this innate curiosity by including a series of intriguing questions in large-type font within every chapter. Each chapter has from three to seven of these attention-grabbing questions, always placed alongside the text that answers them. We hope that as students read the chapter, they will be drawn in by such questions and motivated to read the surrounding content to discover the answers. For example, Chapter 3 (The Molecules of Life) asks, "Why does chocolate melt in your mouth but not in the package?" as a hook to discuss the different properties of saturated and unsaturated fats. In Chapter 11 (How Genes Are Controlled), the question "Can cloning reverse extinction?" relates the process of nuclear transplantation to a discussion of ethical questions that surround it. Chapter 13 (How Populations Evolve), poses the question "If your parents spend a lot of money on orthodontia for you, will your children inherit nice, straight teeth?" to make students consider the heritability of phenotypic traits. Chapter 18 (An Introduction to Ecology and the Biosphere) asks, "Are vampire devices consuming electricity while you sleep?" to draw students' attention to actions they can take to reduce their carbon footprints. We expect these questions to pique students' curiosity and deepen their engagement with the content.

- **MasteringBiology™ updates** Many teachers wish to encourage and assess student learning outside the classroom. To this end, we have created a new version of MasteringBiology that features more than 100 new interactive activities: Building Vocabulary exercises that ask students to place key terms within sentences and paragraphs, Learning Through Art activities that help students learn through labeling of important illustrations, Interpreting Graphs and YouDecide exercises that challenge students to assess quantitative information in ways that promote critical thinking, and Connecting the Concepts activities that help students see the relationship between different content areas. To make it easier for teachers to incorporate MasteringBiology into their classes, we have included a prebuilt course (SimonBiology: Bio-1010) that includes multiple assignments for each chapter. Each assignment is a mix of multimedia, interactive, and multiple-choice questions, which take between 20 and 40 minutes to complete. For each chapter, at least one assignment is written as pre-class preparation, and at least one more is intended as an applications-oriented summative assessment. Teachers can copy the entire course (and then simply change due dates to very quickly deploy the course) or pick and choose individual assignments. In addition, there are several new ways of assessing student achievement in key content areas in MasteringBiology,

including an Evolution Quiz that enables the teacher to track assumptions and measure learning gains and remedial exercises that can help students who struggle with the chemistry or math.

- **Teaching the issues** Many educators, including the authors, like to use current events to demonstrate the relevance of core content to students' lives. For this edition of *Campbell Essential Biology with Physiology,* we have created a series of PowerPoint presentations that focus on important issues such as cancer, HIV, and global climate change. Each PowerPoint presentation topic has an associated MasteringBiology homework assignment that can be used to demonstrate learning gains, check comprehension, and root out misconceptions.

- **Instructor Exchange** We know that educators often struggle to find new ways to engage and excite students, but many lack opportunities for interaction with like-minded colleagues. To tap into the tremendous wealth of talent that exists among biology educators, we have created an Instructor Exchange blog and website (available through the Instructor Resources area within MasteringBiology) as a means of discussing and distributing proven strategies from the classroom. We invite teachers to view the site, search for activities that can help their students, and contribute their own ideas.

- **Demonstrating learning outcomes** Teachers are often asked to demonstrate fulfillment of the learning outcomes that have been established for their class. The latest version of MasteringBiology greatly simplifies this process by keying individual questions and activities to one or more prewritten chapter-specific learning outcomes. In addition, teachers can add their own learning outcomes and associate them with specific tasks. Teachers can use the learning outcomes feature to generate a report that shows how student participation in MasteringBiology has fulfilled the goals established by these learning outcomes, allowing each teacher to assess student completion of the designated outcomes with greater ease.

Attitudes about science and scientists are often shaped by a single required science class—*this* class. We hope to tap into the innate appreciation of nature we all share and nurture this affection into a genuine love of biology. In this spirit, we hope that this textbook and its supplements will encourage all readers to make biological perspectives a part of their personal worldviews. Please let us know how we are doing and how we can improve the next edition of *Campbell Essential Biology with Physiology.*

ERIC SIMON
Department of Biology
and Health Science
New England College
Henniker, NH 03242
esimon@nec.edu

JEAN DICKEY
Department of Biology
Clemson University
Clemson, SC 29634
dickeyj@clemson.edu

JANE REECE
C/O Pearson Education
1301 Sansome Street
San Francisco, CA 94111
JaneReece@cal.berkeley.edu

Acknowledgments

Throughout our time writing *Campbell Essential Biology with Physiology*, the author team has had the great fortune of collaborating with an extremely talented group of publishing professionals and educators. Although the responsibility for any shortcomings lies solely with us, the merits of the book and its supplements reflect the contributions of a great many dedicated colleagues.

First and foremost, we must acknowledge our huge debt to Neil Campbell, the original author of this book and a source of ongoing inspiration for each of us. Although this edition has been carefully and thoroughly revised—to update its science, its connections to students' lives, its pedagogy, and its currency—it remains infused with Neil's founding vision and his commitment to share biology with introductory students.

This book could not have been completed without the efforts of the *Campbell Essential Biology with Physiology* team at Pearson Science. The leading visionary of that team remains executive editor Chalon Bridges. All of us are continually inspired by Chalon's limitless positive energy, clear vision, and unwavering dedication to the nonmajors course, its students, and its instructors. The book team is lucky to be supported by the entire Pearson Science executive team. We are grateful to Linda Davis, president of Pearson Math and Science, and Paul Corey, president of Pearson Science, for the leadership they provide to the entire company. Further guidance was provided by editorial director Michael Young, editor-in-chief Beth Wilbur, executive director of development Deborah Gale, director of production Erin Gregg, and director of media development Lauren Fogel. All Pearson Science authors benefit from such supportive leadership.

It is no exaggeration to say that the fingerprints of the best editorial team in the industry appear on every page of this book. In dealing with the complexities of creating this book, the authors were masterfully and kindly guided by senior editorial manager Ginnie Simione Jutson. Our three development editors—Evelyn Dahlgren, Debbie Hardin, and Kim Krummel—worked tirelessly to hone the words that convey our love of biology. We owe this editorial team—including the wonderfully capable and friendly editorial assistant Rachel Brickner—a deep debt of gratitude for their talents, hard work, and seemingly limitless patience.

Once we formulated our words and images, the production and manufacturing teams transformed them into the book you hold in your hands. Assistant managing editor Shannon Tozier and managing editor Mike Early oversaw the production process and kept everyone and everything on track (a task that is much more daunting than it may sound). We hope you will agree that every edition of *Campbell Essential Biology with Physiology* is distinguished by unique and beautiful photography. For that we thank senior photo editor Donna Kalal and photo researcher Kristin Piljay, who constantly dazzle us with their keen ability to locate stunning images.

For the production and composition of the book, we thank senior project editor Emily Bush of S4Carlisle Publishing Services, whose professionalism and commitment to the quality of the finished product is visible throughout. The authors owe much to copyeditor Janet Greenblatt and proofreader Pete Shanks for polishing our words and making us seem like better writers. We thank design manager Marilyn Perry and the artists at Precision Graphics for developing the beautiful interior design and illustrations. The striking cover on this book can be credited to the cover designers at Riezebos Holzbaur Design Group. We also thank permissions editors Sue Ewing and Beth Keister and permissions manager Beth Wollar for keeping us on the straight and narrow. In the final stages of production, the talents of manufacturing buyer Michael Penne shone.

Most instructors view the textbook as just one piece of the learning puzzle. Filling in the gaps are this book's supplements and media. We are lucky to have a *Campbell Essential Biology with Physiology* supplements team that is fully committed to the core goals of accuracy and readability. Senior supplements project editor Susan Berge, with assistance from associate editor Logan Triglia, expertly coordinated the supplements, a difficult task given their number and variety; and production supervisor Jane Brundage handled the production of these materials (no small feat!). We also thank associate media project manager Shannon Kong for her work on the excellent Instructor Resources DVD set that accompanies the text.

We owe particular gratitude to the supplements authors, especially the indefatigable and eagle-eyed Ed Zalisko, of Blackburn College, who wrote the Instructor Guide and the PowerPoint® Lectures; the highly skilled and multitalented Tom Kennedy, of Central New Mexico Community College, who revised the Quiz Shows and Clicker questions and contributed to the Instructor Guide; Cindy Klevickis, of James Madison University, who worked on the Quizzes; and Jennifer Yeh, who helped with the exhaustive revision of the Test Bank. Kelly Hogan, of the University of North Carolina Chapel Hill, created the Instructor Exchange and brought her creativity and tremendous teaching talent to every aspect of the site. Jean DeSaix, of the University of North Carolina Chapel Hill; Jennifer Katcher, of Pima College; Calvin Young, of Fullerton College; and Lisa Urry, of Mills College, carefully crafted the Evolution Quiz. The author team is grateful for the hard work, talent, and teaching experience of these contributors. Thank you, all!

We wish to thank the talented group of publishing professionals who worked on the comprehensive media program that accompanies *Campbell Essential Biology with Physiology*, starting with director of media strategy Stacy Treco. The team members dedicated to MasteringBiology™ are true "game changers" in the field of biology education and are led by director of editorial content Natania Mlawer and developmental editor Sarah Jensen. We thank senior media producer Jonathan Ballard for exhibiting the Zen-like patience necessary to bring our collective vision to fruition. Vital contributions were also made by project editor Juliana Tringali, senior media producer Katie Foley, and associate Web developer Pete Ratkevich.

As educators and writers, we are very lucky to have a crack marketing team. Director of marketing Christy Lesko, executive marketing manager Lauren Harp, and marketing manager Lauren Rodgers seemed to be everywhere at once as they helped us achieve our authorial goals by keeping us constantly focused on the needs of students and instructors. For their amazing efforts, we also thank executive marketing manager Scott Dustan, creative director Lillian Carr, copywriter supervisor Jane Campbell, copywriter Jessica Perry, and designer Jessica Tree.

We also thank the Pearson Science sales reps, district/regional managers, and product specialists for representing *Campbell Essential Biology with Physiology* on campuses. These representatives are our lifeline to the greater educational community, telling us what you like (and don't like) about this book and the accompanying supplements and media. Their enthusiasm for helping students makes them not only ideal ambassadors but also our partners in education.

Eric Simon would like to thank his colleagues at New England College for their support and for providing a model of excellence in education. Eric would also like to acknowledge the contributions of Jim Newcomb for lending his keen eye for accuracy; Elyse Carter Vosen for providing much-needed social context; Jamey Barone for her sage sensitivity; and Amanda Marsh for her expert eye, sharp attention to detail, tireless commitment, constant support, compassion, and wisdom.

At the end of these acknowledgments, you'll find a list of the many instructors who provided valuable information about their courses, reviewed chapters, and/or conducted class tests of *Campbell Essential Biology with Physiology* with their students. All of our best ideas spring from the classroom, so we thank them for their efforts and support.

Most of all, we thank our families, friends, and colleagues, who continue to tolerate our obsession with doing our best for science education.

ERIC SIMON, JEAN DICKEY, JANE REECE

REVIEWERS OF THIS EDITION

Megan E. Anduri
California State University, Fullerton

Maitreyee Chandra
Diablo Valley College

Renee L. Engle-Goodner
Merritt College

Angela M. Foster
Wake Technical Community College

Brandon Lee Foster
Wake Technical Community College

Wendy Jean Garrison
University of Mississippi

Tamar L. Goulet
University of Mississippi

Robert A. Holmes
Hutchinson Community College

Scott Johnson
Wake Technical Community College

Lisa Maranto
Prince George's Community College

Maryanne Menvielle
California State University, Fullerton

Andrew Miller
Thomas University

Dawn Michelle Rogers
Austin Peay State University

Pamela Sandstrom
University of Nevada, Reno

Susmita Sengupta
City College of San Francisco

Michael Anthony Thornton
Florida Agriculture and Mechanical University

Leonard Vincent
Fullerton College

Daryle Waechter-Brulla
University of Wisconsin, Whitewater

Sean E. Walker
California State University, Fullerton

Arthur C. Washington
Florida Agriculture and Mechanical University

Bethany Williams
California State University, Fullerton

Jo Wen Wu
Fullerton College

Calvin Young
Fullerton College

REVIEWERS OF PREVIOUS EDITIONS

Marilyn Abbott
Lindenwood College

Tammy Adair
Baylor University

Felix O. Akojie
Paducah Community College

Shireen Alemadi
Minnesota State University, Moorhead

William Sylvester Allred, Jr.
Northern Arizona University

Estrella Z. Ang
University of Pittsburgh

David Arieti
Oakton Community College

C. Warren Arnold
Allan Hancock Community College

Mohammad Ashraf
Olive-Harvey College

Heather Ashworth
Utah Valley University

Bert Atsma
Union County College

Yael Avissar
Rhode Island College

Barbara J. Backley
Elgin Community College

Gail F. Baker
LaGuardia Community College

Neil Baker
Ohio State University

Kristel K. Bakker
Dakota State University

Andrew Baldwin
Mesa Community College

Linda Barham
Meridian Community College

Charlotte Barker
Angelina College

Verona Barr
Heartland Community College

S. Rose Bast
Mount Mary College

Sam Beattie
California State University, Chico

Rudi Berkelhamer
University of California, Irvine

Penny Bernstein
Kent State University, Stark Campus

Suchi Bhardwaj
Winthrop University

Donna H. Bivans
East Carolina University

Andrea Bixler
Clarke College

Brian Black
Bay de Noc Community College

Allan Blake
Seton Hall University

Karyn Bledsoe
Western Oregon University

Judy Bluemer
Morton College

Sonal Blumenthal
University of Texas at Austin

Lisa Boggs
Southwestern Oklahoma State University

Dennis Bogyo
Valdosta State University

David Boose
Gonzaga University

Virginia M. Borden
University of Minnesota, Duluth

James Botsford
New Mexico State University

Cynthia Bottrell
Scott Community College

Richard Bounds
Mount Olive College

Cynthia Boyd
Hawkeye Community College

Robert Boyd
Auburn University

B. J. Boyer
Suffolk County Community College

Mimi Bres
Prince George's Community College

Patricia Brewer
University of Texas at San Antonio

Jerald S. Bricker
Cameron University

Carol A. Britson
University of Mississippi

George M. Brooks
Ohio University, Zanesville

Janie Sue Brooks
Brevard College

Steve Browder
Franklin College

Evert Brown
Casper College

Mary H. Brown
Lansing Community College

Richard D. Brown
Brunswick Community College

Steven Brumbaugh
Green River Community College

Joseph C. Bundy
University of North Carolina at Greensboro

Carol T. Burton
Bellevue Community College

Rebecca Burton
Alverno College

Warren R. Buss
University of Northern Colorado

Wilbert Butler
Tallahassee Community College

Miguel Cervantes-Cervantes
Lehman College, City University of New York

Bane Cheek
Polk Community College

Thomas F. Chubb
Villanova University

Reggie Cobb
Nash Community College

Pamela Cole
Shelton State Community College

William H. Coleman
University of Hartford

Jay L. Comeaux
McNeese State University

James Conkey
Truckee Meadows Community College

Karen A. Conzelman
Glendale Community College

Ann Coopersmith
Maui Community College

Erica Corbett
Southeastern Oklahoma State University

James T. Costa
Western Carolina University

Pat Cox
University of Tennessee, Knoxville

Laurie-Ann Crawford
Hawkeye Community College

Pradeep M. Dass
Appalachian State University

Paul Decelles
Johnson County Community College

Galen DeHay
Tri County Technical College

Cynthia L. Delaney
University of South Alabama

Jean DeSaix
University of North Carolina at Chapel Hill

Elizabeth Desy
Southwest State University

Edward Devine
Moraine Valley Community College

Dwight Dimaculangan
Winthrop University

Deborah Dodson
Vincennes Community College

Diane Doidge
Grand View College

Don Dorfman
Monmouth University

Richard Driskill
Delaware State University

Lianne Drysdale
Ozarks Technical Community College

Terese Dudek
Kishawaukee College

Shannon Dullea
North Dakota State College of Science

David A. Eakin
Eastern Kentucky University

Brian Earle
Cedar Valley College

Ade Ejire
Johnston Community College

Dennis G. Emery
Iowa State University

Virginia Erickson
Highline Community College

Carl Estrella
Merced College

Marirose T. Ethington
Genesee Community College

Paul R. Evans
Brigham Young University

Zenephia E. Evans
Purdue University

Jean Everett
College of Charleston

Dianne M. Fair
Florida Community College at Jacksonville

Joseph Faryniarz
Naugatuck Valley Community College

Phillip Fawley
Westminster College

Lynn Fireston
Ricks College

Jennifer Floyd
Leeward Community College

Dennis M. Forsythe
The Citadel

Brandon Foster
Wake Technical Community College

Carl F. Friese
University of Dayton

Suzanne S. Frucht
Northwest Missouri State University

Edward G. Gabriel
Lycoming College

Anne M. Galbraith
University of Wisconsin, La Crosse

Kathleen Gallucci
Elon University

Gregory R. Garman
Centralia College

Gail Gasparich
Towson University

Kathy Gifford
Butler County Community College

Sharon L. Gilman
Coastal Carolina University

Mac Given
Neumann College

Patricia Glas
The Citadel

Ralph C. Goff
Mansfield University

Marian R. Goldsmith
University of Rhode Island

Andrew Goliszek
North Carolina Agricultural and Technical State University

Tamar Liberman Goulet
University of Mississippi

Curt Gravis
Western State College of Colorado

Larry Gray
Utah Valley State College

Tom Green
West Valley College

Robert S. Greene
Niagara University

Ken Griffin
Tarrant County Junior College

Denise Guerin
Santa Fe Community College

Paul Gurn
Naugatuck Valley Community College

Peggy J. Guthrie
University of Central Oklahoma

Henry H. Hagedorn
University of Arizona

Blanche C. Haning
Vance-Granville Community College

Laszlo Hanzely
Northern Illinois University

Reba Harrell
Hinds Community College

Sherry Harrel
Eastern Kentucky University

Frankie Harris
Independence Community College

Lysa Marie Hartley
Methodist College

Janet Haynes
Long Island University

Michael Held
St. Peter's College

Consetta Helmick
University of Idaho

J. L. Henriksen
Bellevue University

Michael Henry
Contra Costa College

Linda Hensel
Mercer University

Jana Henson
Georgetown College

James Hewlett
Finger Lakes Community College

Richard Hilton
Towson University

Juliana Hinton
McNeese State University

Phyllis C. Hirsch
East Los Angeles College

W. Wyatt Hoback
University of Nebraska at Kearney

Elizabeth Hodgson
York College of Pennsylvania

A. Scott Holaday
Texas Tech University

R. Dwain Horrocks
Brigham Young University

Howard L. Hosick
Washington State University

Carl Huether
University of Cincinnati

Celene Jackson
Western Michigan University

John Jahoda
Bridgewater State College

Dianne Jennings
Virginia Commonwealth University

Richard J. Jensen
Saint Mary's College

Tari Johnson
Normandale Community College

Tia Johnson
Mitchell Community College

Greg Jones
Santa Fe Community College

John Jorstad
Kirkwood Community College

Tracy L. Kahn
University of California, Riverside

Robert Kalbach
Finger Lakes Community College

Mary K. Kananen
Pennsylvania State University, Altoona

Thomas C. Kane
University of Cincinnati

Arnold J. Karpoff
University of Louisville

John M. Kasmer
Northeastern Illinois University

Valentine Kefeli
Slippery Rock University

Dawn Keller
Hawkeye College

John Kelly
Northeastern University

Cheryl Kerfeld
University of California, Los Angeles

Henrik Kibak
California State University, Monterey Bay

Kerry Kilburn
Old Dominion University

Joyce Kille-Marino
College of Charleston

Peter King
Francis Marion University

Peter Kish
Oklahoma School of Science and Mathematics

Robert Kitchin
University of Wyoming

Cindy Klevickis
James Madison University

Richard Koblin
Oakland Community College

H. Roberta Koepfer
Queens College

Michael E. Kovach
Baldwin-Wallace College

Jocelyn E. Krebs
University of Alaska, Anchorage

Ruhul H. Kuddus
Utah Valley State College

Nuran Kumbaraci
Stevens Institute of Technology

Holly Kupfer
Central Piedmont Community College

Gary Kwiecinski
The University of Scranton

Roya Lahijani
Palomar College

James V. Landrum
Washburn University

Lynn Larsen
Portland Community College

Brenda Leady
University of Toledo

Siu-Lam Lee
University of Massachusetts, Lowell

Thomas P. Lehman
Morgan Community College

William Leonard
Central Alabama Community College

Shawn Lester
Montgomery College

Leslie Lichtenstein
Massasoit Community College

Barbara Liedl
Central College

Harvey Liftin
Broward Community College

David Loring
Johnson County Community College

Eric Lovely
Arkansas Tech University

Lewis M. Lutton
Mercyhurst College

Maria P. MacWilliams
Seton Hall University

Mark Manteuffel
St. Louis Community College

Lisa Maranto
Prince George's Community College

Michael Howard Marcovitz
Midland Lutheran College

Angela M. Mason
Beaufort County Community College

Roy B. Mason
Mt. San Jacinto College

ACKNOWLEDGMENTS

John Mathwig
College of Lake County

Lance D. McBrayer
Georgia Southern University

Bonnie McCormick
University of the Incarnate Word

Katrina McCrae
Abraham Baldwin Agricultural College

Tonya McKinley
Concord College

Mary Anne McMurray
Henderson Community College

Ed Mercurio
Hartnell College

Timothy D. Metz
Campbell University

David Mirman
Mt. San Antonio College

Nancy Garnett Morris
Volunteer State Community College

Angela C. Morrow
University of Northern Colorado

Patricia S. Muir
Oregon State University

James Newcomb
New England College

Jon R. Nickles
University of Alaska, Anchorage

Jane Noble-Harvey
University of Delaware

Michael Nosek
Fitchburg State College

Jeanette C. Oliver
Flathead Valley Community College

David O'Neill
Community College of Baltimore County

Sandra M. Pace
Rappahannock Community College

Lois H. Peck
University of the Sciences, Philadelphia

Kathleen E. Pelkki
Saginaw Valley State University

Jennifer Penrod
Lincoln University

Rhoda E. Perozzi
Virginia Commonwealth University

John S. Peters
College of Charleston

Pamela Petrequin
Mount Mary College

Paula A. Piehl
Potomac State College of West Virginia University

Bill Pietraface
State University of New York Oneonta

Gregory Podgorski
Utah State University

Rosamond V. Potter
University of Chicago

Karen Powell
Western Kentucky University

Martha Powell
University of Alabama

Elena Pravosudova
Sierra College

Hallie Ray
Rappahannock Community College

Jill Raymond
Rock Valley College

Dorothy Read
University of Massachusetts, Dartmouth

Nathan S. Reyna
Howard Payne University

Philip Ricker
South Plains College

Todd Rimkus
Marymount University

Lynn Rivers
Henry Ford Community College

Jennifer Roberts
Lewis University

Laurel Roberts
University of Pittsburgh

April Rottman
Rock Valley College

Maxine Losoff Rusche
Northern Arizona University

Michael L. Rutledge
Middle Tennessee State University

Mike Runyan
Lander University

Travis Ryan
Furman University

Tyson Sacco
Cornell University

Sarmad Saman
Quinsigamond Community College

Leba Sarkis
Aims Community College

Walter Saviuk
Daytona Beach Community College

Neil Schanker
College of the Siskiyous

Robert Schoch
Boston University

John Richard Schrock
Emporia State University

Julie Schroer
Bismarck State College

Karen Schuster
Florida Community College at Jacksonville

Brian W. Schwartz
Columbus State University

Michael Scott
Lincoln University

Eric Scully
Towson State University

Lois Sealy
Valencia Community College

Sandra S. Seidel
Elon University

Wayne Seifert
Brookhaven College

Patty Shields
George Mason University

Cara Shillington
Eastern Michigan University

Brian Shmaefsky
Kingwood College

Rainy Inman Shorey
Ferris State University

Cahleen Shrier
Azusa Pacific University

Jed Shumsky
Drexel University

Greg Sievert
Emporia State University

Jeffrey Simmons
West Virginia Wesleyan College

Frederick D. Singer
Radford University

Anu Singh-Cundy
Western Washington University

Kerri Skinner
University of Nebraska at Kearney

Sandra Slivka
Miramar College

Margaret W. Smith
Butler University

Thomas Smith
Armstrong Atlantic State University

Deena K. Spielman
Rock Valley College

Minou D. Spradley
San Diego City College

Robert Stamatis
Daytona Beach Community College

Joyce Stamm
University of Evansville

Eric Stavney
Highline Community College

Bethany Stone
University of Missouri, Columbia

Mark T. Sugalski
New England College

Marshall D. Sundberg
Emporia State University

Adelaide Svoboda
Nazareth College

Sharon Thoma
Edgewood College

Kenneth Thomas
Hillsborough Community College

Sumesh Thomas
Baltimore City Community College

Betty Thompson
Baptist University

Paula Thompson
Florida Community College

Linda Tichenor
*University of Arkansas,
Fort Smith*

John Tjepkema
University of Maine, Orono

Bruce L. Tomlinson
State University of New York, Fredonia

Leslie R. Towill
Arizona State University

Bert Tribbey
California State University, Fresno

Nathan Trueblood
California State University, Sacramento

Robert Turner
Western Oregon University

Michael Twaddle
University of Toledo

Virginia Vandergon
California State University, Northridge

William A. Velhagen, Jr.
Longwood College

Jonathan Visick
North Central College

Michael Vitale
Daytona Beach Community College

Lisa Volk

*Fayetteville Technical Community
College*

Stephen M. Wagener
Western Connecticut State University

James A. Wallis
St. Petersburg Community College

Helen Walter
Diablo Valley College

Kristen Walton
Missouri Western State University

Jennifer Warner
University of North Carolina at Charlotte

Dave Webb
St. Clair County Community College

Harold Webster
Pennsylvania State University, DuBois

Ted Weinheimer
California State University, Bakersfield

Lisa A. Werner
Pima Community College

Joanne Westin
Case Western Reserve University

Wayne Whaley
Utah Valley State College

Joseph D. White
Baylor University

Quinton White
Jacksonville University

Leslie Y. Whiteman
Virginia Union University

Rick Wiedenmann
New Mexico State University at Carlsbad

Peter J. Wilkin
Purdue University North Central

Daniel Williams
Winston-Salem University

Judy A. Williams
Southeastern Oklahoma State University

Dwina Willis
Freed Hardeman University

David Wilson
University of Miami

Mala S. Wingerd
San Diego State University

E. William Wischusen
Louisiana State University

Darla J. Wise
Concord College

Michael Womack
Macon State College

Bonnie Wood
University of Maine at Presque Isle

Mark L. Wygoda
McNeese State University

Shirley Zajdel
Housatonic Community College

Samuel J. Zeakes
Radford University

Uko Zylstra
Calvin College

1 Introduction: Biology Today

Biology is all around us. Like this student in New York City's Central Park, we are all surrounded by biology.

Biology in Our Everyday Lives BIOLOGY AND SOCIETY

Biology All Around Us

We are living in a golden age of biology. A large and diverse community of scientists is studying a myriad of questions that are as relevant to our lives as they are interesting: How can errors in cell growth lead to cancer? How do plants trap solar energy, and what might this teach us about global climate? How do living creatures form ecological networks, and how do human activities disrupt them? How did the great diversity of life on Earth evolve from the first microbes, and how does such evolution have an impact on human health? How do mutations in genes lead to disease? How can DNA—the molecular basis of heredity—be used in forensic investigations? These are just a few examples of how biology is woven into the fabric of society as never before. If you try, you can easily think of a dozen ways that biology affects your life each day. Welcome to the big adventure of the 21st century!

We wrote this book to help you—a student with little or no college-level science experience—develop an appreciation for biology and apply that understanding to your own life and to the society in which you live. We believe that such a biological perspective is essential for any educated person, which is why we named our book *Essential Biology*. So, whatever your reasons for taking this course, even if only to fulfill your school's science requirement, you'll soon discover that exploring life has never been more important or exhilarating.

To help you get started, this first chapter of *Essential Biology* defines biology and then expands on important concepts within this definition. First, we'll survey the properties of life and the scope of life. Next, we'll introduce evolution as the theme that unifies all of biology. Finally, we'll set the study of life in the broader context of science as a process of inquiry. Throughout this chapter (and, indeed, throughout all of *Essential Biology*), we'll provide examples of how biology intersects your everyday life, highlighting the relevance of this subject to society and everyone in it.

The Scope of Life

Biology is the scientific study of life. It's a subject of enormous scope that gets bigger all the time. To start our investigation of life, let's look at some properties that are shared by all living things.

The Properties of Life

How can you tell if something is alive?

Our definition of biology as the scientific study of life raises the obvious question: What is life? Or, to put it another way, what distinguishes living things from nonliving things? The phenomenon of **life** seems to defy a simple, one-sentence definition. Yet even a small child knows that a dog or a bug or a plant is alive, while a rock is not. We recognize life mainly by what living things do.

Figure 1.1 highlights seven of the properties and processes associated with life: (a) *Order*. All living things exhibit complex but ordered organization, as seen in the structure of a pinecone. (b) *Regulation*. The environment outside an organism may change drastically, but the organism can adjust its internal environment, keeping it within appropriate limits. When it senses its body temperature dropping, a lizard can bask on a rock to absorb heat. (c) *Growth and development*. Information carried by DNA controls the pattern of growth and development in all organisms, including the ostrich. (d) *Energy processing*. Organisms take in energy and use it to perform all of life's activities; they emit energy as heat. A puffin obtains energy by eating fish and then uses this energy to power swimming and other work. (e) *Response to the environment*. All organisms respond to environmental stimuli. A carnivorous Venus flytrap closes its leaves rapidly in response to the environmental stimulus of an insect touching the plant's sensory hairs. (f) *Reproduction*. Organisms reproduce their own kind. Thus, hippos reproduce only hippos—never snakes or puffins. (g) *Evolution*. Reproduction underlies the capacity of populations to change (evolve) over time. For example, the katydid has evolved in a way that provides camouflage in its environment. Evolutionary change is a central, unifying phenomenon of all life.

Life at Its Many Levels

One of the aspects of biology that makes it so interesting is the incredible range that the subject covers. To illustrate this point, **Figure 1.2** takes you on a tour that spans the full scope of life. The top of the figure shows the global scale of the entire **biosphere**, which consists of all the environments on Earth that support life—including soil; oceans, lakes, and other bodies of water; and the lower atmosphere. At the other extreme of biological size and complexity are microscopic molecules such as DNA, the chemical responsible for inheritance. Going from bottom to top in the figure, you can see that it takes many molecules to build a cell, many cells to make a tissue, multiple tissues to make an organ, and so on. At each new level, novel properties emerge from the specific arrangement and interactions of the parts in an increasingly sophisticated system. Such properties are called emergent properties because they emerge as complexity increases. For example, life emerges at the level of the cell; a test tube full of molecules is not alive. The familiar saying that "the whole is greater than the sum of its parts" captures this idea.

From the interactions within the biosphere to the molecular machinery within cells, biologists are investigating life at its many levels. In the next section, we'll take a closer look at two biological levels near opposite ends of the size scale: ecosystems and cells. ☑

☑ CHECKPOINT

1. Define biology.
2. Which properties of life apply to a car? Which do not?
3. What is the smallest level of biological organization that can display all the characteristics of life?

Answers: 1. Biology is the scientific study of life. 2. A car demonstrates order, regulation, energy utilization, and response to the environment. But a car does not grow, reproduce, or evolve. 3. a cell

---

▼ Figure 1.1 **Some properties of life.**

(a) Order

(b) Regulation

(c) Growth and development

(d) Energy processing

▼ Figure 1.2 **Zooming in on life.**

1 Biosphere
Earth's biosphere includes all life and all the places where life exists.

2 Ecosystems
An ecosystem consists of all living organisms in a particular area and all the nonliving components of the environment with which life interacts, such as soil, water, and light.

3 Communities
All organisms in the tide pool (iguanas, crabs, seaweed, bacteria, and others) are collectively called a community.

4 Populations
Within communities are various populations, groups of interacting individuals of one species, such as a group of iguanas.

5 Organisms
An organism is an individual living thing, like this iguana.

6 Organ Systems and Organs
An organism's body consists of several organ systems, each of which contains two or more organs. For example, the iguana's circulatory system includes its heart and blood vessels.

10 Molecules and Atoms
Finally, we reach molecules, the chemical level in the hierarchy. Molecules are clusters of even smaller chemical units called atoms. Each cell consists of an enormous number of chemicals that function together to give the cell the properties we recognize as life. DNA, the molecule of inheritance and the substance of genes, is shown here as a computer graphic. Each sphere in the DNA model represents a single atom.

← Atom

9 Organelles
Organelles are functional components of cells, such as the nucleus that houses the DNA.

— Nucleus

7 Tissues
Each organ is made up of several different tissues, such as the heart muscle tissue shown here. A tissue consists of a group of similar cells performing a specific function.

8 Cells
The cell is the smallest unit that can display all the characteristics of life.

(e) Response to the environment

(f) Reproduction

(g) Evolution

Ecosystems

Life does not exist in a vacuum. Each organism interacts continuously with its environment, which includes other organisms as well as physical (nonliving) factors. Together, all the living organisms in a specific area, along with all the nonliving factors with which they interact, form an **ecosystem**. The roots of a tree, for example, absorb water and minerals from the soil. Leaves take in carbon dioxide gas from the air. Chlorophyll, the green pigment of the leaves, absorbs sunlight, which drives the plant's production of sugar from carbon dioxide and water. The tree releases oxygen to the air, and its roots help form soil by breaking up rocks. Both organism and environment are affected by the interactions between them. The tree also interacts with other living things, including microscopic organisms in the soil that are associated with the plant's roots and animals that eat its leaves and fruit.

The dynamics of any ecosystem depend on two main processes (**Figure 1.3**). The first major process is the recycling of chemical nutrients (represented by the light blue circle in the figure). For example, minerals that plants absorb from the soil can eventually be recycled to the soil by microorganisms that decompose leaf litter and other organic refuse. Within most ecosystems, there are three modes of nutrition: Producers are photosynthetic organisms, such as plants; consumers are the organisms, such as animals, that feed on plants, either directly (by eating plants) or indirectly (by eating animals that eat plants); decomposers, such as fungi and many bacteria, break down waste products and the remains of deceased organisms, changing complex dead material into simple nutrients that are recycled. The action of decomposers ensures that nutrients are recycled within an ecosystem.

How is an ecosystem like a recycling plant?

The second major process in an ecosystem is the flow of energy. Unlike chemical nutrients, energy doesn't get recycled. In fact, an ecosystem gains and loses energy constantly. Most ecosystems are solar powered (represented by the yellow, wavy arrow in the figure). The energy that enters an ecosystem as sunlight is captured by producers when plants and other photosynthesizers absorb the sun's energy and convert it to the chemical energy of sugars and other complex molecules (orange arrow). Chemical energy is then passed through a series of consumers and, eventually, decomposers, powering each organism in turn. In the process of these energy conversions between and within organisms, some energy is converted to heat, which is then lost from the system (red arrow). Thus, energy flows through an ecosystem, entering as light and exiting as heat.

The biosphere is enriched by a great variety of ecosystems. Examples include a tropical rain forest in South America, the deserts of the southwestern United States, the Great Barrier Reef off the eastern coast of Australia, and even a small pond that may exist on your campus or in your city. Even a woodland patch in New York's Central Park qualifies as an ecosystem, although it is small and artificial and may be overrun by human visitors. The fact is, humans are organisms that now have some presence, often disruptive, in all ecosystems throughout the biosphere. And the collective clout of 7 billion people and their machines affects the entire biosphere. For example, our fuel burning and forest chopping are changing the atmosphere and the planet's climate in ways that we do not yet fully understand, though we already know that our actions jeopardize the diversity of life on Earth. ☑

☑ CHECKPOINT

Within an ecosystem, _____ are recycled, whereas _____ flows through.

Answer: nutrients; energy

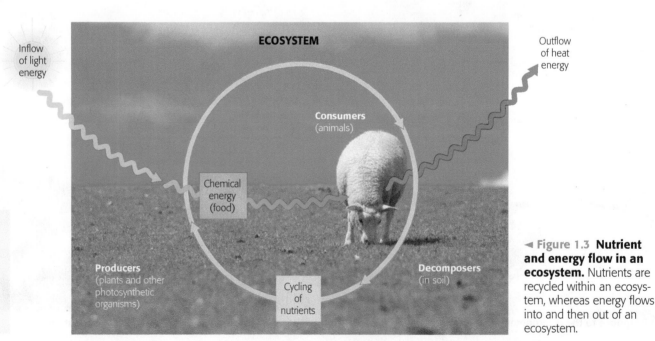

ECOSYSTEM

Inflow of light energy

Outflow of heat energy

Consumers (animals)

Chemical energy (food)

Producers (plants and other photosynthetic organisms)

Decomposers (in soil)

Cycling of nutrients

◀ Figure 1.3 **Nutrient and energy flow in an ecosystem.** Nutrients are recycled within an ecosystem, whereas energy flows into and then out of an ecosystem.

Prokaryotic cell (bacterium)
- Smaller
- Simpler structure
- DNA concentrated in nucleoid region, which is not enclosed by membrane
- Lacks most organelles

Organelles

Nucleoid region

Colorized TEM 25,000×

Eukaryotic cell
- Larger
- More complex structure
- Nucleus enclosed by membrane
- Contains many types of organelles

Nucleus

Colorized TEM 11,250×

◄ **Figure 1.4 Two main kinds of cells: prokaryotic and eukaryotic.** The number near the bottom right corner of each image represents the magnification. In this case, the image of the eukaryotic cell shown is approximately 11,250 times bigger than the actual cell.

Cells and Their DNA

Let's downsize now from ecosystems to cells. The cell has a special place in the hierarchy of biological organization: It is the level at which the properties of life emerge—the lowest level of structure that can perform all activities required for life.

All organisms are composed of cells. They occur singly as a great variety of unicellular (single-celled) organisms, such as amoebas and bacteria. Cells are also the subunits that make up multicellular organisms, such as humans and trees. In all cases, the cell is life's basic unit of structure and function. The ability of cells to divide to form new cells is the basis for all reproduction and for the growth and repair of multicellular organisms.

All cells share many characteristics. For example, every cell is enclosed by a membrane that regulates the passage of materials between the cell and its surroundings. And every cell uses DNA as its genetic information. But we can distinguish two basic types of cells: prokaryotic and eukaryotic **(Figure 1.4)**. The **prokaryotic cell** is much simpler and usually much smaller than the eukaryotic cell. The cells of bacteria are prokaryotic. Most other forms of life, including plants and animals, are composed of eukaryotic cells. In contrast to prokaryotic cells, a **eukaryotic cell** is subdivided by internal membranes into different functional compartments called organelles. For example, the nucleus houses DNA, the inherited material that directs the

cell's activities. Prokaryotic cells also have DNA, but it is not packaged within a nucleus.

All cells use DNA as the chemical material of **genes**, the units of inheritance that transmit information from parent to offspring. Of course, bacteria and humans inherit different genes, but that information is encoded in a chemical language common to all organisms. In fact, the language of life has an alphabet of just four letters. The chemical names of DNA's four molecular building blocks are abbreviated as A, G, C, and T **(Figure 1.5)**.

An average-sized gene may be hundreds or thousands of chemical "letters" long. A gene's meaning to a cell is encoded in its specific sequence of these letters, just as the message of a sentence is encoded in its arrangement of letters selected from the 26 letters of the English alphabet.

► **Figure 1.5 The language of DNA.** Every molecule of DNA is constructed from four kinds of chemical building blocks that are chained together, shown here as simple shapes and letters.

A
G
C
T

The four chemical building blocks of DNA

A DNA molecule

One gene may be translated as "Build a blue pigment in a bacterial cell." Another gene may mean "Make human insulin in this cell." Insulin is a chemical that helps regulate your body's use of sugar as a fuel. Some people who have the disease diabetes must regulate their sugar levels by injecting themselves with insulin, which is produced by genetically engineered bacteria. These bacteria can make insulin because a gene for human insulin production has been transplanted into their DNA. This example of genetic engineering was one of the earliest successes of biotechnology, a field that has transformed the pharmaceutical industry and extended millions of lives (Figure 1.6). And it is only possible because biological information is written in the universal chemical language of DNA.

The entire "book" of genetic instructions that an organism inherits is called its genome. The nucleus of each human cell packs a genome that is about 3 billion chemical letters long. In recent years, scientists have tabulated virtually the entire sequence of these letters, and the news media and world leaders have acclaimed this international achievement as one of the greatest scientific triumphs ever. But unlike past cultural zeniths, such as the landing of Apollo astronauts on the moon, the sequencing of the human genome is more a commencement than a climax. As the quest continues, biologists will learn the functions of thousands of genes and how their activities are coordinated in the development and functioning of an organism. Additionally, the genomes of other organisms (such as *E. coli* bacteria, dogs, and monkeys) have been sequenced, allowing scientists to compare the genomes of different species. The emerging field of genomics—a branch of biology that studies whole genomes—is a striking example of human curiosity about life at its many levels. ☑

☑ CHECKPOINT

Name the two major kinds of cells. Which kind is your body made up of?

Answer: prokaryotic and eukaryotic; eukaryotic.

Life in Its Diverse Forms

Diversity is a hallmark of life. The fish shown in Figure 1.7 is just one of about 1.8 million species that biologists have identified and named (the scientific name for this fish is *Plectorhinchus polytaenia*). The diversity of known life includes at least 290,000 plants, 52,000 vertebrates (animals with backbones), and 1 million insects (more than half of all known forms of life). Biologists add thousands of newly identified species to the list each year. Estimates of the total number of

How many different species are there on Earth?

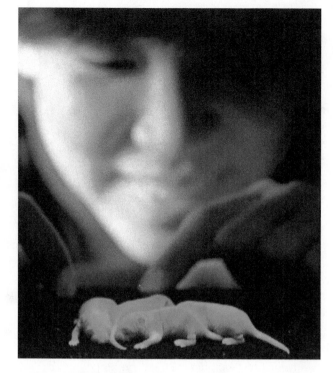

▲ Figure 1.6 **Biotechnology.** These mice were genetically engineered to contain a gene for a glowing protein extracted from a jelly (jellyfish).

species range from 10 million to over 100 million. Whatever the actual number, the enormous diversity of life presents organizational challenges to biologists who study it.

Grouping Species: The Basic Concept

Biological diversity can be something to relish and preserve, but it can also be a bit overwhelming.

▼ Figure 1.7 **A small sample of biological diversity.** A fish called a yellow-ribbon sweetlip swims around a coral reef in Indonesia.

People have a tendency to group diverse items according to similarities. We may speak of "squirrels" and "butterflies," even though we recognize that each group actually includes many different species. We may even sort groups into broader categories, such as rodents (which include squirrels) and insects (which include butterflies). Taxonomy, the branch of biology that names and classifies species, is the arrangement of species into a hierarchy of broader and broader groups. Here we consider only the broadest units of classification.

The Three Domains of Life

On the broadest level, biologists divide the diversity of life into three domains: Bacteria, Archaea, and Eukarya (Figure 1.8). The first two domains, Bacteria and Archaea, identify two very different groups of organisms that have prokaryotic cells. All the eukaryotes (organisms with eukaryotic cells) are grouped into the domain Eukarya, which includes three kingdoms—Plantae, Fungi, and Animalia. Most members of the three kingdoms are multicellular. The kingdoms are distinguished partly by how the organisms obtain food. Plants produce their own sugars and other foods by photosynthesis. Fungi are mostly decomposers, obtaining food by digesting dead organisms and organic wastes. Animals obtain food by ingesting (eating) and digesting other organisms. (This, of course, is the kingdom to which we belong.) Those eukaryotes that do not fit into any of the three kingdoms are referred to as the protists. Most protists are single-celled; they include microscopic protozoans, such as amoebas. But protists also include certain multicellular forms, such as seaweeds. Scientists are in the process of organizing protists into multiple kingdoms, although they do not yet agree on exactly how to do this.

Unity in the Diversity of Life

If life is so diverse, how can biology have any unifying themes? What, for instance, can a tree, a mushroom, and a human possibly have in common? As it turns out, a great deal! Underlying the diversity of life is a striking unity, especially at the lower levels of biological organization. One of biology's major goals is to explain how such diversity arises while also accounting for characteristics common to different species. We have already seen one example: the universal genetic language of DNA. That fundamental language connects all kingdoms of life, even uniting prokaryotes such as bacteria with eukaryotes such as humans. What can account for this combination of unity and diversity in life? The scientific explanation is the biological process called evolution, which is our next topic. ☑

▼ Figure 1.8 **The three domains of life.**

DOMAIN BACTERIA

Colorized TEM 10,000X

DOMAIN ARCHAEA

TEM 18,500X

DOMAIN EUKARYA

Kingdom Plantae

Kingdom Fungi

Kingdom Animalia

Protists (multiple kingdoms)

LM 150X

9

Evolution: Biology's Unifying Theme

The history of life, as documented by fossils and other evidence, is a saga of a constantly changing Earth billions of years old, inhabited by an evolving cast of living forms (Figure 1.9). Life evolves. Just as you have a family history, each species is one twig of a branching tree of life extending back in time through ancestral species more and more remote. Species that are very similar, such as the brown bear and the polar bear, share a common ancestor that represents a relatively recent branch point on the tree of life (Figure 1.10). But through an ancestor that lived much farther back in time, all bears are also related to squirrels, humans, and all other mammals. Hair and milk-producing mammary glands are two uniquely mammalian traits. Such similarities are what we would expect if all mammals descended from a common ancestor, a prototypical mammal. And mammals, reptiles, and all other vertebrates share a common ancestor even more ancient. Evidence of a still broader relationship can be found in similarities that are seen within all eukaryotic cells. Trace life back far enough, and there are only fossils of the primeval prokaryotes that inhabited Earth over 3 billion years ago. All of life is connected. And the basis for this kinship is evolution, the process that has transformed life on Earth from its earliest beginnings to the extensive diversity we see today. Evolution is the fundamental principle of life and the theme that unifies all of biology; it is the one idea that makes sense of everything we know about living organisms.

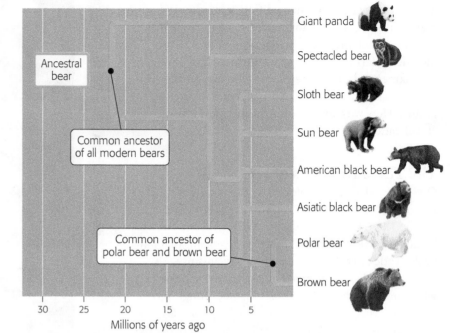

▲ Figure 1.10 **An evolutionary tree of bears.** This tree is a hypothesis (a tentative model) based on both the fossil record and a comparison of DNA sequences among modern bears.

CHECKPOINT

What is the modern term for what Darwin called "descent with modification"?

Answer: *evolution*

▼ Figure 1.9 **Digging into the past.** A paleontologist excavates mammoth bones from a site in South Dakota.

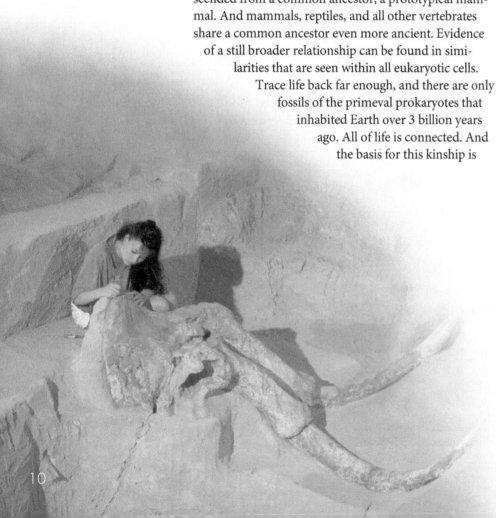

The Darwinian View of Life

The evolutionary view of life came into focus in 1859 when English naturalist Charles Darwin published one of the most important and influential books ever written: *On the Origin of Species by Means of Natural Selection*. His book developed two main points. First, Darwin presented a large amount of evidence in support of the evolutionary view that species living today descended from a succession of ancestral species. Darwin called this process "descent with modification." It is an insightful phrase, as it captures the duality of life's unity (descent) and diversity (modification). In the Darwinian view, for example, the diversity of bears is based on different modifications of a common ancestor from which all bears descended. As the second main point in *The Origin of Species*, Darwin proposed a mechanism for descent with modification. He called this process natural selection. ✓

Natural Selection

Charles Darwin gathered important evidence for his theories during an around-the-world voyage. He was particularly struck by the diversity of animals on the Galápagos Islands, off the coast of Ecuador (Figure 1.11). Darwin regarded adaptation to the environment and the origin of new species as closely related processes. If some geographic barrier—an ocean separating islands, for instance—isolated two populations of a single species from each other, the populations could diverge more and more in appearance as each adapted to local environmental conditions. Over many generations, the two populations could become dissimilar enough to be designated separate species. The labeled branch point near the lower right of Figure 1.10 represents the point in time when two populations of one bear species began to diverge from each other, adapting to different climates and resulting in the evolution of the brown bear and the polar bear as two distinct species. Darwin realized that explaining such adaptation was the key to understanding descent with modification, or evolution. This focus on adaptation helped Darwin envision his concept of natural selection as the mechanism of evolution.

Darwin's Inescapable Conclusion

Darwin synthesized the theory of natural selection from two observations that by themselves were neither profound nor original. Others had the pieces of the puzzle, but Darwin saw how they fit together. Let's look at his logic:

Observation 1: Overproduction and competition.
Any population can produce far more offspring than the environment can possibly support with available resources such as food and shelter. This overproduction leads to competition among the individuals of a population for these limited resources.

Observation 2: Individual variation.
Individuals in a population of any species vary in many inherited traits. No two individuals in a population are exactly alike. You know that no two humans are exactly alike; careful observers find this kind of variation in populations of all species.

Conclusion: Unequal reproductive success.
In the struggle for existence, those individuals with heritable traits best suited to the local environment are more likely to have the greatest reproductive success: They will survive and leave the greatest number of surviving, fertile offspring. Therefore, the very traits that enhance survival and reproductive success will be disproportionately represented in the next generation.

▶ Figure 1.11 **Charles Darwin (1809–1882),** *The Origin of Species,* **and blue-footed boobies on the Galápagos Islands.**

ON
THE ORIGIN OF SPECIES
BY MEANS OF NATURAL SELECTION,
OR THE
PRESERVATION OF FAVOURED RACES IN THE STRUGGLE
FOR LIFE.

By CHARLES DARWIN, M.A.,

LONDON:
JOHN MURRAY, ALBEMARLE STREET.
1859.

It is this unequal reproductive success that Darwin called **natural selection** because the environment "selects" only certain heritable traits from those already existing. And the product of natural selection is adaptation, the accumulation of favorable variations in a population over time. Returning to the example of bear evolution in Figure 1.10, one familiar adaptation is fur color. Polar bears and brown (grizzly) bears, as closely related as they are, each display an evolutionary adaptation (white and brown fur, respectively) that resulted from natural selection operating in their respective environments. Presumably, natural selection tended to favor the fur color that provided each bear lineage with the best camouflage in its home territory.

As the process leading to adaptation, natural selection is the mechanism of evolution. **Figure 1.12** presents a hypothetical example of a beetle population that colonizes a location where the soil has been blackened by a recent brush fire. Notice that natural selection works on preexisting variation (in shell color, in this case), enhancing the reproductive success of individuals with beneficial traits.

Observing Artificial Selection

Darwin found convincing evidence for the power of unequal reproduction in examples of artificial selection, the purposeful breeding of domesticated plants and animals by humans. People have been modifying other species for millennia by selecting breeding stock with certain traits. The plants we grow for food bear little resemblance to their wild ancestors; this is because we have customized crop plants through many generations of artificial selection by selecting different parts of the plant to accentuate as food. All the vegetables shown in **Figure 1.13a** (and more) have a common ancestor in one species of wild mustard (shown in the center of the figure). The power of selective breeding is especially apparent in our pets, which have been bred for looks and *Why is there such a wide variety of dog breeds?* to be useful. For example, people in different cultures have customized hundreds of dog breeds as different as basset hounds and Saint Bernards, all descended from wolves **(Figure 1.13b)**. The tremendous variety of modern dogs reflects thousands of years of artificial selection. Darwin could see that in artificial selection, people take the place of the environment in screening the heritable traits of populations.

Observing Natural Selection

If artificial selection could achieve so much change so rapidly, Darwin reasoned, then natural selection should be capable of considerable adaptation of species over hundreds or thousands of generations. We now recognize many examples of natural selection in action. A classic example involves the finches (a kind of bird) of the Galápagos Islands. Over a span of two decades,

▼ **Figure 1.12 Natural selection.**

Population with varied inherited traits. Initially, the population varies extensively in the coloration of individual beetles, from very light gray to a dark charcoal color.

Elimination of individuals with certain traits. For hungry birds that prey on the beetles, it is easiest to spot the beetles that are lightest in color.

Reproduction of survivors. The selective predation favors survival and reproductive success of the darker beetles. Thus, genes for dark color are passed along to the next generation in greater frequency than genes for light color.

Increasing frequency of traits that enhance survival and reproductive success. Generation after generation, the beetle population adapts to its environment through natural selection.

researchers measured changes in beak size in a population of a species of ground finch that eats mostly small seeds. In dry years, when all seeds are in short supply, the birds must eat more large seeds. Birds with larger, stronger beaks have a feeding advantage and greater

▼ Figure 1.13 **Examples of artificial selection.**

(a) Vegetables descended from wild mustard

Wild mustard

Cabbage from end buds

Brussels sprouts from side buds

Kohlrabi from stems

Kale from leaves

Broccoli from flowers and stems

Cauliflower from flower clusters

(b) Domesticated dogs descended from wolves

Gray wolves

Domesticated dogs

reproductive success, and the average beak depth for the population increases. During wet years, smaller beaks are more efficient for eating the abundant small seeds, and the average beak depth decreases. Such changes are measurable evidence of natural selection in action. At the end of this chapter, you'll read about another example: how the evolution of antibiotic resistance among bacteria is changing the way doctors prescribe drugs.

Darwin's publication of *The Origin of Species* fueled an explosion in biological research and knowledge that continues today. Over the past century and a half, a tremendous amount of evidence has accumulated in support of Darwin's theory of evolution by natural selection, making it one of biology's best-demonstrated, most comprehensive, and longest-lasting theories. At the end of every chapter of *Essential Biology*, we will highlight connections to evolution—the unifying theme of biology. ☑

☑ **CHECKPOINT**

What mechanism did Darwin propose for evolution? What three-word phrase summarizes this mechanism?

Answer: natural selection; unequal reproductive success

The Process of Science

Recall the first definition from the start of this chapter: Biology is the scientific study of life. Now that we have explored the question *What is life?* we can turn our attention to the next obvious question: *What is science?* How do we tell the difference between science and other ways of trying to make sense of nature?

The word *science* is derived from a Latin verb meaning "to know." **Science** is a way of knowing, an approach to understanding the natural world that is based on inquiry—a search for information, explanations, and answers to specific questions. It developed from our curiosity about ourselves and the world around us. This basic human drive to understand is manifest in two main scientific approaches: discovery science, which is mostly about *describing* nature, and hypothesis-driven science, which is mostly about *explaining* nature. Most scientists practice a combination of these two forms of inquiry.

Discovery Science

Scientists seek natural causes for natural phenomena. This limits the scope of science to the study of structures and processes that we can observe and measure, either directly or indirectly with the help of tools, such as microscopes. This dependence on observations that other people can confirm demystifies nature and distinguishes science from belief in the supernatural. Science can neither prove nor disprove that angels, ghosts, deities, or spirits, whether benevolent or evil, cause storms, rainbows, illnesses, or cures, for such explanations are outside the bounds of science.

Verifiable observations and measurements are the data of **discovery science** (Figure 1.14). In our quest to describe nature accurately, we discover its structure. In biology, discovery science enables us to describe life at its many levels, from ecosystems down to cells and molecules. Darwin's careful description of the diverse plants and animals he collected in South America is an example of discovery science. A more recent example is the sequencing of the human genome, a detailed dissection and description of our genetic material.

Hypothesis-Driven Science

The observations of discovery science stimulate us to ask questions and seek explanations. Ideally, such investigation makes use of a process of inquiry called the scientific method. As a formal process of inquiry, the **scientific method** consists of a series of steps (Figure 1.15). These steps provide a loose guideline for scientific investigations, but working scientists typically do not follow them rigidly; different scientists proceed through the scientific method in different ways.

Most modern scientific investigations can be described as **hypothesis-driven science**. A **hypothesis** is a tentative answer to a question—an explanation on trial. Although we don't think of it in those terms, we all use hypotheses in solving everyday problems. Let's

▼ Figure 1.14 **Careful observation and measurement: the raw data for discovery science.** Dr. Jane Goodall spent decades recording her observations of chimpanzee behavior during field research in the jungles of Tanzania.

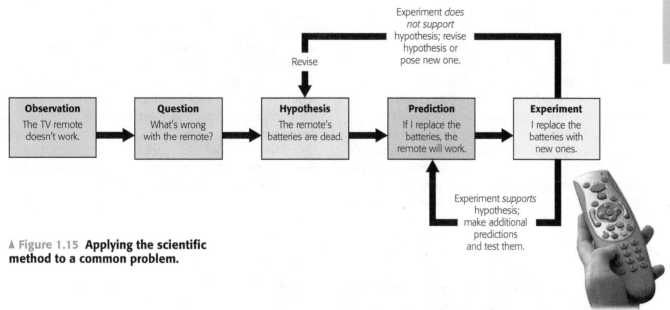

Experiment *does not support* hypothesis; revise hypothesis or pose new one.

Revise

Observation
The TV remote doesn't work.

Question
What's wrong with the remote?

Hypothesis
The remote's batteries are dead.

Prediction
If I replace the batteries, the remote will work.

Experiment
I replace the batteries with new ones.

Experiment *supports* hypothesis; make additional predictions and test them.

▲ Figure 1.15 **Applying the scientific method to a common problem.**

say, for example, that your TV remote fails to turn on your TV. That's an observation. The question is obvious: Why doesn't the remote work? An observation may give rise to many hypotheses, but we need to focus on one to begin an investigation. In this case, a reasonable hypothesis based on past experience is that the batteries in the remote are dead.

Once a hypothesis is formed, an investigator can use logic to test it. In the process of science, this logic usually takes the form of predictions about what experimental results or observations we should expect if a particular hypothesis (premise) is correct. We then test the hypothesis by performing an experiment to see whether or not the results are as predicted. This logical testing takes the form of "If . . . then" logic:

Observation: The TV remote doesn't work.

Question: What's wrong with the remote?

Hypothesis: The remote's batteries are dead.

Prediction: If I replace the batteries, then the remote will work.

Experiment: I replace the batteries with new ones.

Predicted result: The remote should work.

Let's say the remote still doesn't work. We can test an alternative hypothesis. Perhaps, for example, the TV is unplugged. We could also blame the dead remote on supernatural spirits, but that hypothesis is untestable and therefore outside the realm of science. ☑

☑ CHECKPOINT

If you spend a summer observing the squirrels on your campus and collecting data on their dietary habits, what kind of science are you performing? If you come up with a tentative explanation for their dietary behavior and then test your idea, what kind of science are you performing?

Answer: discovery science; hypothesis-driven science

Biology in Our Everyday Lives THE PROCESS OF SCIENCE

Are Trans Fats Bad for You?

One way to better understand the process of science is to examine a case study, an in-depth examination of an actual investigation. This particular case study is about the effects of one kind of dietary fat. Later chapters will include other case studies in the process of science, illustrating how discovery and hypothesis-driven science have been used in experiments both modern and classic. To

emphasize how the scientific method has been employed in each case, the key steps will be highlighted in blue text.

Dietary fat, a major component of the food we eat, comes in several different forms. Trans fats are a non-natural form of fat produced through a manufacturing process called hydrogenation (as in partially hydrogenated vegetable oil, which is often used in fried foods). Because trans fats add texture, increases shelf life, and is inexpensive to prepare, it was added to foods (such as margarine and shortening) in increasing amounts throughout the 1900s.

Fat was one dietary component examined in the Nurses' Health Study, a landmark study of over 120,000 female U.S. nurses begun in 1976. Every two years, the study participants completed questionnaires about their health status and dietary habits. In 1994, researchers examining the trove of collected data discovered that study participants who ate high levels of trans fats had nearly double the risk of heart disease compared with participants who ate little trans fats. This is a good example of discovery science: examination of a set of data gathered without a preconceived notion of what it might reveal.

While the data were suggestive, some researchers remained skeptical about the link between trans fats and health. In a hypothesis-driven study published in 2004, a research team started with the observation that human body fat (adipose tissue) retains traces of consumed dietary fats. This observation raised a question: Would the adipose tissue of heart attack patients be measurably different from the adipose tissue of a similar group of healthy patients? The researchers' hypothesis was that it would be, leading to the prediction that the body fat of healthy patients would contain less trans fats than the body fat of heart attack victims.

The researchers then set up an experiment to determine the amounts of different kinds of fat in the adipose tissue of 79 patients who had experienced a heart attack. These amounts were compared with data for 167 patients who had not experienced a heart attack but were similar to the first group in most other respects. Since trans fats are not produced by the body, the researchers assumed that any trans fats found in the adipose tissue had been consumed in the diet. Their results showed significantly

higher levels of trans fats in the bodies of the heart attack patients than in the healthier group (Figure 1.16). Although other risk factors are also involved, these results added to the growing body of evidence that trans fats are unhealthy and should be avoided. Indeed, such evidence has led several countries (such as Australia and Denmark), some states (such as California), and some cities (such as New York City) to ban trans fats altogether. Trans fats have been eliminated from many foods, but you would do well to read nutrition labels and avoid trans fats as much as possible in your own diet.

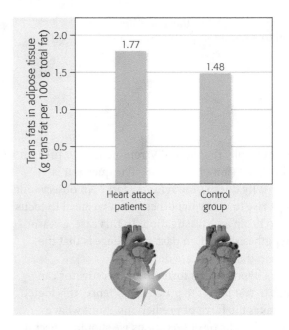

▲ Figure 1.16 **Levels of trans fats.** Results of an experiment that measured the levels of trans fats in the adipose tissue of 79 patients who had experienced a heart attack and 167 patients who had not (control group).

Place the following steps of the scientific method in their proper order: experiment, hypothesis, observation, prediction, results, question, revise/repeat.

Answer: observation, question, hypothesis, prediction, experiment, results, revise/repeat

The trans fats study described in the Process of Science section is an example of a **controlled experiment**. An experiment of this type is designed to compare an experimental group (the patients who had a heart attack, in this case) with a control group (patients who did not have a heart attack). Ideally, the control group and the experimental group differ only in one factor the experiment is designed to test—in our example, the occurrence of a heart attack. Other factors—such as age, weight, and sex of the patients—were matched between the two sets of patients. Thus, the control group canceled out the effects of all variables other than the one being tested. The use of a controlled experiment enabled researchers to draw conclusions about the effect of just one variable—trans fats—on heart attack risk. ✓

Theories in Science

Many people associate facts with science, but accumulating facts is not the primary goal of science. A telephone book is an impressive catalog of factual information, but it has little to do with science. It is true that facts, in the form of verifiable observations and repeatable experimental results, are the prerequisites of science. What really advances science, however, are new theories that tie together a number of observations that previously seemed unrelated. The cornerstones of science are the explanations that apply to the greatest variety of phenomena. People like Newton, Darwin, and Einstein stand out in the history of science not because they discovered a great many facts, but because their theories had such broad explanatory power.

What is a scientific theory, and how is it different from a hypothesis? A scientific **theory** is much broader in scope than a hypothesis. This is a hypothesis: "White fur is an evolutionary adaptation that helps polar bears survive in an Arctic habitat." But this is a theory: "Adaptations to the local environment evolve by natural selection."

Because theories are so comprehensive, they only become widely accepted in science if they are supported by an accumulation of extensive and varied evidence. The use of the term *theory* in science for a comprehensive explanation supported by abundant evidence contrasts with our everyday usage, which equates theories more with speculations or hypotheses. Natural selection qualifies as a scientific theory because of its broad application and because it has been validated by a huge number of observations and experiments.

Scientific theories are not the only way of knowing nature, of course. A comparative religion course would be a good place to learn about the diverse legends that tell of a supernatural creation of Earth and its life. Science and religion are two very different ways of trying to make sense of nature. Art is still another way. A broad education should include exposure to all these different ways of viewing the world. Each of us synthesizes our worldview by integrating our life experiences and multidisciplinary education. As a science textbook and part of that broad education, *Essential Biology* showcases life in the scientific context of evolution, the one theme that continues to hold all of biology together, no matter how big and complex the subject becomes. ☑

The Culture of Science

It is not unusual for several scientists to ask the same questions. Such overlap contributes to the progressive and self-correcting qualities of science. Scientists build on what has been learned from earlier research, and they pay close attention to contemporary scientists working on the same problem. Scientists share information through publications, seminars, meetings, websites, blogs, and personal communication.

Both cooperation and competition characterize the scientific culture (Figure 1.17). Scientists working in the same research field subject one another's work to careful scrutiny. It is common for scientists to check the conclusions of others by attempting to repeat experiments. This obsession with evidence and confirmation helps characterize the scientific style of inquiry. Scientists are generally skeptics.

We have seen that science has two key features that distinguish it from other styles of inquiry: (1) a dependence on observations and measurements that others can verify and (2) the requirement that ideas

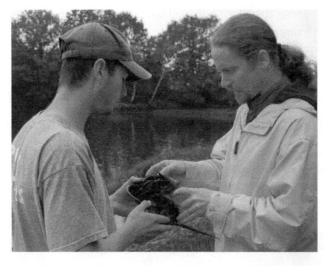

▲ Figure 1.17 **Science as a social process.** New England College neurobiologist Jim Newcomb (right) mentors a student in the methods of marine biology.

(hypotheses) are testable by experiments that others can repeat.

Science, Technology, and Society

Science and technology are interdependent. New technologies, such as more powerful microscopes and computers, advance science. And scientific discoveries can lead to new technologies. In most cases, technology applies scientific discoveries to the development of new goods and services. For example, about 60 years ago, two scientists, James Watson and Francis Crick, discovered the structure of DNA through the process of science. Their discovery eventually led to a variety of DNA technologies, including genetic engineering (see Figure 1.6) and the use of DNA profiling for investigating crimes (Figure 1.18). Perhaps Watson and Crick envisioned that their discovery would someday inform new technologies, but they could not have predicted exactly what the applications would be.

☑ CHECKPOINT

You arrange to meet a friend for dinner at 6 P.M., but she is not there. You wonder why. Another friend says, "My theory is that she forgot." If your friend were speaking like a scientist, what should she have said?

Answer: *"My hypothesis is that she forgot."*

► Figure 1.18 **DNA technology and the law.** In 2007, DNA evidence helped to exonerate Jerry Miller of rape and kidnapping, crimes for which he spent 25 years wrongly imprisoned.

☑ **CHECKPOINT**

How does modern genetic engineering reflect a common ancestry for all life on Earth?

Answer: Genetic engineering is possible because all life uses chemically identical DNA, a result of our evolution from a common ancestor.

Technology has improved our standard of living in many ways, but it is a double-edged sword. Technology that keeps people healthier has enabled the population to grow more than tenfold in the past three centuries and to more than double to 7 billion in just the past 40 years. The environmental consequences are sometimes devastating. Acid rain, deforestation, global climate change, nuclear accidents, toxic wastes, and extinction of species are just a few of the repercussions of more and more people wielding more and more

technology. Science can help us identify such problems and provide insight about what course of action may prevent further damage. But solutions to these problems depend upon politics, economics, culture, and the values of societies. Now that science and technology have become such powerful aspects of our culture, each of us has the responsibility to develop a reasonable amount of scientific literacy. The crucial relationship between science, technology, and society is a central theme of this book. ☑

Biology in Our Everyday Lives EVOLUTION CONNECTION

Evolution in Our Everyday Lives

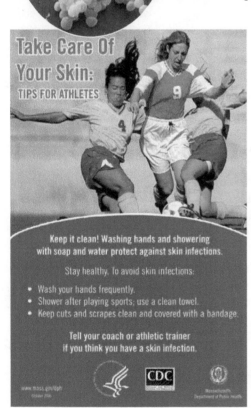

Colorized SEM 3,400x

▲ Figure 1.19 Natural selection in action. Strains of the common bacterium *Staphylococcus aureus* (inset) that have evolved resistance to multiple antibiotics pose a significant health threat, particularly to hospitalized patients and college athletes.

To emphasize evolution as the core theme of biology, we end each chapter of *Essential Biology* with an Evolution Connection section. Evolution teaches us that the environment is a powerful selective force for traits that best adapt populations to their environments. But how does this affect your life? Our world is rich with examples of natural selection in action. One example that may directly affect you is the development of resistance to antibiotics in disease-causing bacteria.

Antibiotics are drugs that help cure certain infections by impairing the bacteria that cause them. Antibiotics have saved millions of human lives, but there's a dark side to their widespread use: It has driven the evolution of antibiotic-resistant populations of the very bacteria the drugs are meant to kill.

When an antibiotic is taken by a patient, it will usually kill most, but not all, of the infecting bacteria. The few bacteria among the varying members of a population that can survive the drug will have a survival advantage. In some cases, the mechanism of resistance in the bacteria is an ability to destroy the antibiotic—or even use the drug as food! Even though the drug kills most of the bacteria, those few bacteria that

are resistant may soon multiply and become the norm in the population rather than the exception.

The evolution of antibiotic-resistant bacteria is a huge problem in public health. For example, methicillin-resistant *Staphlococcus aureus*, or MRSA, is a strain of a relatively common bacterium that has evolved resistance to several of the most potent antibiotics used to treat bacterial infections. Although most commonly spread in hospitals, MRSA is becoming an increasing problem among college athletes because of its potential to spread via skin-to-skin contact in locker rooms and during contact sports **(Figure 1.19)**.

The problem of antibiotic-resistant bacteria is influencing the way many physicians prescribe antibiotics. Doctors who understand that the abuse of these drugs is speeding the evolution of resistant bacteria are less likely to prescribe antibiotics needlessly—for instance, for a patient complaining of a common cold or flu, diseases caused by viruses (not bacteria), against which antibacterial drugs are powerless. Additionally, many farmers are reducing the use of antibiotics in animal feed, and many consumers are choosing to buy meats from animals raised without antibiotics. Some health professionals wonder if the increased use of antibacterial soaps contributes to the problem.

It is important to note that adaptation of bacteria to an environment containing an antibiotic does not mean that the drug *created* the antibiotic resistance trait. Instead, the environment screened the variations that already existed among individuals of a population and favored the individuals best suited to the present conditions. Throughout *Essential Biology*, you will learn more about how natural selection works and see other examples of how natural selection affects your life.

Chapter Review

 Go to **www.masteringbiology.com** for homework assignments, practice quizzes, Pearson eText, and more.

The Scope of Life

Biology is the scientific study of life. The study of biology encompasses a wide scale of size and a huge variety of life, both past and present.

The Properties of Life

All life displays a common set of characteristics:

Order

Regulation

Growth and development

Energy processing

Response to the environment

Reproduction

Evolution

Life at Its Many Levels

Within ecosystems, nutrients are recycled, but energy flows through. Cells are either prokaryotic (simple, small, and lacking membrane-enclosed organelles, such as the nucleus) or eukaryotic (more complex, larger, and containing a nucleus and other membrane-enclosed organelles). Both types of cells contain genes, the molecular units of inheritance.

Life in Its Diverse Forms

Biologists organize living organisms into three domains. The domain Eukarya is further divided into three kingdoms (distinguished partly by their means of obtaining food) and one catch-all group:

Life		
Prokaryotes	**Eukaryotes**	
Domain Bacteria	**Domain Archaea**	Plantae Fungi Animalia Protists (all other eukaryotes) — Three kingdoms — **Domain Eukarya**

Evolution: Biology's Unifying Theme

The Darwinian View of Life

Charles Darwin established the ideas of evolution ("descent with modification") via natural selection (unequal reproductive success) in his 1859 publication *The Origin of Species*.

Natural Selection

Darwin formulated the theory of natural selection through a logical inference: Natural selection leads to adaptations to the environment, which—when passed from generation to generation—is the mechanism of evolution.

Observations

| Overproduction and competition |
| Individual variation |

Conclusion

| Unequal reproductive success (natural selection) |

The Process of Science

Discovery Science

Describing the natural world with verifiable data is the hallmark of discovery science.

Hypothesis-Driven Science

A scientist formulates a hypothesis (tentative explanation) to explain observations of the natural world. The hypothesis may then be tested via the steps of the scientific method:

Revise and repeat

Observation → Question → Hypothesis → Prediction → Experiment

Theories in Science

A theory is a broad and comprehensive statement about the world that is supported by the accumulation of a great deal of verifiable evidence.

The Culture of Science

Scientists build on each other's work by always remaining skeptical and by seeking reproducible evidence to confirm ideas.

Science, Technology, and Society

Scientific advances promote new technologies, which in turn enable further scientific advances and useful applications to our lives.

1. Which of the following is *not* a characteristic of all living organisms?
   a. capable of self-reproduction
   b. composed of multiple cells
   c. complex yet organized
   d. energy utilization

2. Place the following levels of biological organization in order from smallest to largest: atom, biosphere, cell, ecosystem, molecule, organ, organism, population, tissue. Which is the smallest level capable of demonstrating all of the characteristics of life?

3. Plants use the process of photosynthesis to convert the energy in sunlight to chemical energy in the form of sugar. While doing so, they consume carbon dioxide and water and release oxygen. Explain how this process functions in both the cycling of chemical nutrients and the flow of energy through an ecosystem.

4. For each of the following organisms, match its description to its most likely domain and/or kingdom:

a. A foot-tall organism capable of producing its own food from sunlight

1. Bacteria

b. A microscopic, simple, nucleus-free organism found living in a riverbed

2. Eukarya/Animalia

c. An inch-tall organism growing on the forest floor that consumes material from dead leaves

3. Eukarya/Fungi

d. A thimble-sized organism that feeds on algae growing in a pond

4. Eukarya/Plantae

5. How does natural selection cause a population to become adapted to its environment over time?

6. Why is it difficult to draw a conclusion from an experiment that does not include a control group?

7. Which of the following best describes the logic of the scientific method?
a. If I generate a testable hypothesis, tests and observations will support it.
b. If my prediction is correct, it will lead to a testable hypothesis.
c. If my observations are accurate, they will support my hypothesis.
d. If my hypothesis is correct, I can expect certain test results.

8. Which of the following statements best distinguishes hypotheses from theories in science?
a. Theories are hypotheses that have been proved.
b. Hypotheses are tentative guesses; theories are correct answers to questions about nature.
c. Hypotheses usually are narrow in scope; theories have broad explanatory power.
d. Hypotheses and theories mean essentially the same thing in science.

9. _____ is the core idea that unifies all areas of biology.

10. Match each of the following terms to the phrase that best describes it.
a. Natural selection
b. Evolution
c. Hypothesis
d. Biosphere

1. A testable idea
2. Descent with modification
3. Unequal reproductive success
4. All life-supporting environments on Earth

Answers to these questions can be found in Appendix: Self-Quiz Answers.

THE PROCESS OF SCIENCE

11. The graph below shows the results of an experiment in which mice learned to run through a maze.

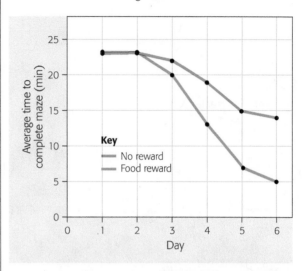

a. State a hypothesis and prediction that you think this experiment may have been designed to test.
b. Which was the control group and which the experimental group? Why was a control group needed?
c. List some variables that must have been controlled so as not to affect the results.
d. Do the data support the hypothesis you chose? Explain.

12. The fruits of wild species of tomato are tiny compared with the giant beefsteak tomatoes available today. This difference in fruit size is almost entirely due to the larger number of cells in the domesticated fruits. Plant biologists have recently discovered genes that are responsible for controlling cell division in tomatoes. Why would such a discovery be important to producers of other kinds of fruits and vegetables? To the study of human development and disease? To our basic understanding of biology?

BIOLOGY AND SOCIETY

13. The news media and popular magazines frequently report stories that are connected to biology. In the next 24 hours, record all such stories you hear or read about from three different sources and briefly describe the biological connections you perceive in each story.

14. If you pay attention, you will find yourself conducting many hypothesis-driven experiments each day. Over the next day, try to think of a good example where you performed a simple experiment to test a hypothesis about some observation. Write the experience out as a story, and then rewrite it using the steps of the scientific method (observation, question, hypothesis, prediction, and so on).

Unit 1 Cells

Chapter 2: Essential Chemistry for Biology

Chapter Thread: **Life's Dependence on Water**

Chapter 3: The Molecules of Life

Chapter Thread: **Lactose Intolerance**

Chapter 4: A Tour of the Cell

Chapter Thread: **Antibiotic-Resistant Bacteria**

Chapter 5: The Working Cell

Chapter Thread: **Nanotechnology**

Chapter 6: Cellular Respiration: Obtaining Energy from Food

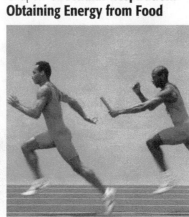

Chapter Thread: **Aerobic versus Anaerobic Lifestyles**

Chapter 7: Photosynthesis: Using Light to Make Food

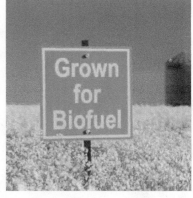

Chapter Thread: **Green Energy**

2 Essential Chemistry for Biology

Human dependence on water.
All life, and the health of human civilization, depends on the availability of water.

Life's Dependence on Water BIOLOGY AND SOCIETY

More Precious than Gold

Drought is one of the most devasting natural disasters. A drought is a sustained period of abnormally dry weather that lasts long enough to change the environment. The effects of drought can include severe crop damage, shortages of drinking water, dust storms, famine, habitat loss, and mass migration. Even a mild drought can produce disruptions; most of us have experienced government-mandated water-saving measures, such as prohibitions on watering lawns and washing cars. In some areas, particularly in the southwestern United States, such water conservation measures have been in place for years.

Throughout human history, droughts have helped wipe out societies and even whole civilizations. A study of growth rings from a 1,100-year-old tree in Mexico suggests that a 25-year-long drought may have hastened the demise of the Mayan civilization. In the 1930s, a seven-year-long drought across the American prairie produced the Dust Bowl, resulting in millions of acres of lost farmland and a large westward migration of displaced people. More recently, a drought that lasted from 1987 to 1989 is considered the costliest natural disaster in our country's history, with agricultural losses totaling $39 billion. Certain parts of Africa, although historically lush, have experienced severe drought in the 21st century. The country of Sudan, for example, has suffered widespread famine, contributing to the ongoing social and political unrest in its drought-plagued Darfur region. As recently as 2009, a drought in the American Southwest (which hit California and Texas the hardest) caused more than $5 billion in agricultural losses. In the future, as global climate change accelerates, our most precious resource may be neither gold nor oil but fresh water.

Why are droughts so catastrophic? The reason is simple: Life cannot exist without water. Living organisms use water as the medium for the chemical reactions necessary to sustain life. Many questions about life are actually questions about chemicals and their interactions, making knowledge of chemistry essential to understanding biology. In this chapter, you will learn some essential chemistry that you can apply throughout your study of life. In the last section, we'll return to the crucial role that water plays in sustaining life on Earth.

Some Basic Chemistry

Why would a biology textbook include a chapter on chemistry? Well, take any biological system apart, and you eventually end up at the chemical level. In fact, you could think of your body as one big container of watery chemicals undergoing a continuous series of chemical reactions. Beginning at this basic biological level, let's explore the chemistry of life.

Matter: Elements and Compounds

All organisms and everything around them are made of matter, the physical "stuff" of the universe. Defined more formally, **matter** is anything that occupies space and has mass. Matter is found on Earth in three physical states: solid, liquid, and gas.

All matter is composed of chemical elements. An **element** is a substance that cannot be broken down into other substances by chemical reactions. There are 92 naturally occurring elements; examples are carbon, oxygen, and gold. Each element has a symbol derived from its English, Latin, or German name. For instance, the symbol for gold, Au, is from the Latin word *aurum*. All the elements—the 92 that occur naturally and several dozen that are human-made—are listed in the periodic table of the elements, a familiar fixture in any chemistry or biology lab (**Figure 2.1**; see Appendix: Periodic Table of Elements for a full version).

Of the 92 naturally occurring elements, 25 are essential to people (other organisms need fewer; plants, for example, typically need 17). Four of these elements—oxygen (O), carbon (C), hydrogen (H), and

Mercury (Hg)

Copper (Cu)

Lead (Pb)

► **Figure 2.1 Abbreviated periodic table of the elements.** In the full periodic table (see Appendix: Periodic Table of Elements), each entry contains the element symbol in the center, with the atomic number above and the mass number below (both of these numbers are discussed on the facing page). The element highlighted here is carbon (C).

Carbon (C): 18.5%
Oxygen (O): 65.0%
Calcium (Ca): 1.5%
Phosphorus (P): 1.0%
Potassium (K): 0.4%
Sulfur (S): 0.3%
Sodium (Na): 0.2%
Chlorine (Cl): 0.2%
Magnesium (Mg): 0.1%
Hydrogen (H): 9.5%
Nitrogen (N): 3.3%

Trace elements: less than 0.01%
Boron (B)   Manganese (Mn)
Chromium (Cr) Molybdenum (Mo)
Cobalt (Co)   Selenium (Se)
Copper (Cu)   Silicon (Si)
Fluorine (F)   Tin (Sn)
Iodine (I)   Vanadium (V)
Iron (Fe)   Zinc (Zn)

▲ **Figure 2.2 Chemical composition of the human body by weight.** Notice that just 4 elements make up 96% of your weight.

nitrogen (N)—make up about 96% of the weight of most cells (**Figure 2.2**). Much of the remaining 4% is accounted for by 7 elements, most of which are probably familiar to you, such as calcium (Ca) and phosphorus (P). Calcium, important for building strong bones and teeth, is found abundantly in milk and dairy products as well as sardines and green, leafy vegetables (kale and broccoli, for example). Phosphorus, a component of DNA, can be obtained by eating eggs, beans, and nuts.

Less than 0.01% of your weight is made up of 14 trace elements. **Trace elements** are required in only very small amounts, but you cannot live without them. The average person, for example, needs only a tiny speck of iodine each day. Iodine is an essential ingredient of a hormone produced by the thyroid gland, located in the neck. An iodine deficiency causes the thyroid gland to enlarge, a condition called goiter. Therefore, consuming foods that are naturally rich in iodine—such as kelp, green vegetables, and dairy products—prevents goiter. The addition of iodine to table salt ("iodized salt") has nearly eliminated goiter in industrialized nations, but many thousands of people in developing countries are still affected (**Figure 2.3**). Another trace element is fluorine, which (in the form of fluoride) is added to dental products and drinking water and helps maintain healthy bones and teeth. Many prepared foods are fortified with trace mineral elements. Look at the side of a cereal box and you'll probably see iron listed; you can actually see the iron youself if you crush the cereal and stir a magnet through it.

Elements can combine to form **compounds**, substances that contain two or more elements in a fixed ratio. In everyday life, compounds are much more common than pure elements. Familiar examples include table salt and water. Table salt is sodium chloride, NaCl, consisting of equal parts of the elements sodium (Na) and chlorine (Cl). A molecule of water, H_2O, has two atoms of hydrogen and one atom of oxygen. Most of the compounds in living organisms contain several different elements. DNA, for example, contains carbon, nitrogen, oxygen, hydrogen, and phosphorus. ☑

Atoms

Each element consists of one kind of atom, which is different from the atoms of other elements. An **atom**, named from a Greek word meaning "indivisible," is the smallest unit of matter that still retains the properties of an element. In other words, the smallest amount of the element carbon is one carbon atom. Just how small is this "piece" of carbon? It would take about a million carbon atoms to stretch across the period at the end of this sentence.

The Structure of Atoms

Atoms are composed of subatomic particles, of which the three most important are protons, electrons, and neutrons. A **proton** is a subatomic particle with a single unit of positive electrical charge (+). An **electron** is a subatomic particle with a single negative charge (−). A **neutron** is electrically neutral (has no charge).

Figure 2.4 shows two simplified models of an atom of the element helium (He), the "lighter-than-air" gas used in party balloons. Each atom of helium has 2 neutrons (◯) and 2 protons (⊕) tightly packed into the **nucleus**, the atom's central core. Two electrons (⊖) move around the nucleus in a spherical cloud at nearly the speed of light. The electron cloud is much bigger than the nucleus.

▼ Figure 2.4 **Two simplified models of a helium atom.**

2 ⊕ Protons ⎤
2 ◯ Neutrons ⎦ Nucleus
2 ⊖ Electrons

This model shows the subatomic particles in an atom of helium.

This model, slightly more realistic, shows the electrons as a spherical cloud of negative charge surrounding the nucleus.

▼ Figure 2.3 **The relationship between diet and goiter.**

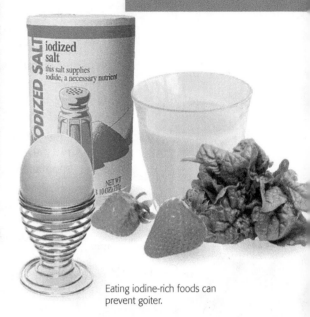

Goiter, an enlargement of the thyroid gland, shown here in a Malaysian woman, can occur when a person's diet does not include enough iodine, a trace element.

Eating iodine-rich foods can prevent goiter.

In fact, if the atom were the size of a baseball stadium, the nucleus would be the size of a pea on the pitcher's mound and the electrons would be two gnats buzzing around the bleachers. The attraction between the negatively charged electrons and the positively charged protons keeps the electrons near the nucleus. When an atom has an equal number of protons and electrons (as helium does), its net electrical charge is zero and so the atom is neutral.

If an atom were the size of a baseball field, how big would its nucleus be?

Elements differ in the number of subatomic particles in their atoms. The number of protons in an atom, called the **atomic number**, determines which element it is. For example, helium always has 2 protons and thus an atomic number of 2. **Mass** is a measure of the amount of material in an object. A proton and a neutron have nearly identical mass. An electron has so little mass—only about 1/2,000 the mass of a proton—that it is usually approximated as zero. Therefore, an atom's **mass number** is just the sum of the number of protons and neutrons in its nucleus. For helium, the mass number is 4 (2 protons + 2 neutrons). Both the atomic number and the mass number can be read from the periodic table (see Figure 2.1 and Appendix: Periodic Table of Elements).

Isotopes

Some elements can exist in different forms called isotopes. The different **isotopes** of an element have the same numbers of protons and electrons but different numbers of neutrons; in other words, isotopes are forms of an element that differ in mass. For example, the

☑ CHECKPOINT

1. How many of the 92 naturally occurring elements are used in your body? Which four are the most abundant in living cells?
2. Which of the following are compounds: water (H_2O), oxygen gas (O_2), methane (CH_4)? Explain your choices.

Answers: 1. 25; oxygen, carbon, hydrogen, and nitrogen. 2. H_2O and CH_4 are compounds, but O_2 is not because a compound must contain at least two different elements.

25

numbers of subatomic particles in three isotopes of carbon are shown in Table 2.1. Carbon-12 (named for its mass number), with 6 neutrons and 6 protons, makes up about 99% of all naturally occurring carbon. Most of the other 1% is carbon-13, with 7 neutrons and 6 protons. A third isotope, carbon-14, with 8 neutrons and 6 protons, occurs in minute quantities. Notice that all three isotopes have 6 protons—otherwise, they would not be carbon. Both carbon-12 and carbon-13 are stable isotopes, meaning that their nuclei remain intact more or less forever. The isotope carbon-14, on the other hand, is unstable, or radioactive. A **radioactive isotope** is one in which the nucleus decays spontaneously, giving off particles and energy.

Radioactive isotopes have many uses in biological research and medicine. Cells use radioactive isotopes the same way they use nonradioactive isotopes of the same element. Once the cell takes up a radioactive isotope, the location and concentration of the isotope can be detected because of the radiation it emits. This makes radioactive isotopes useful as tracers—biological spies, in effect—for monitoring the fate of atoms in living organisms. For example, a medical diagnostic tool called a PET scan works by detecting small amounts of radioactive materials introduced into the body (Figure 2.5).

Although radioactive isotopes can be useful, radiation from decaying isotopes can damage cellular molecules and thus can pose serious health risks. In 1986, the explosion of a nuclear reactor at Chernobyl, Ukraine, released large amounts of radioactive isotopes, killing 30 people within a few weeks and exposing thousands to an increased risk of cancer. Likewise, scientists will carefully monitor the long-term health consequences of the 2011 post-tsunami Fukushima nuclear disaster in Japan.

Natural sources of radiation can also pose a threat. Radon, a radioactive gas, may cause lung cancer. Radon can contaminate buildings in regions where underlying rocks naturally contain the radioactive element uranium. Homeowners can buy a radon detector or hire a company to test their

Why is it a good idea to test your house for radon?

home to ensure that radon levels are safe. Such radon testing is now a standard step in most home purchases.

Electron Arrangement and the Chemical Properties of Atoms

Of the three subatomic particles we've discussed—protons, neutrons, and electrons—only electrons are directly involved in the chemical activity of an atom. Electrons vary in the amount of energy they possess. The farther an electron is from the nucleus, the greater its energy. Electrons do not move around an atom at just any energy level, but only at specific levels called electron shells. Depending on the number of electrons, an atom may have one, two, or more electron shells, with electrons in the outermost shell having the highest energy. Each shell can accommodate up to a specific number of electrons. The innermost shell is full with 2 electrons, while the second and third shells can each hold up to 8 electrons.

The number of electrons in the outermost shell determines the chemical properties of an atom. Atoms whose outer shells are not full tend to interact with other atoms—that is, to participate in chemical reactions. Figure 2.6 shows the electron shells of four biologically important elements. Because the outer shells of all four atoms are not filled, these atoms react readily with other atoms. The hydrogen atom is highly reactive because it has only 1 electron in its single electron shell, which can accommodate 2 electrons. Atoms of carbon, nitrogen, and oxygen are also highly reactive because their outer shells, which can hold 8 electrons, are not filled. In contrast, the helium atom in Figure 2.4 has a single, first-level shell that is full with 2 electrons. As a result, helium is chemically unreactive. ☑

Table 2.1	Isotopes of Carbon		
	Carbon-12	Carbon-13	Carbon-14
Protons	6⎤ mass	6⎤ mass	6⎤ mass
	⎬–number	⎬–number	⎬–number
Neutrons	6⎦ 12	7⎦ 13	8⎦ 14
Electrons	6	6	6

▲ Figure 2.5 **A PET scan.** This monitor shows the images produced by a PET scanner. PET scans can diagnose heart disorders and some cancers.

☑ **CHECKPOINT**

1. By definition all atoms of carbon have exactly 6 _____, but the number of _____ varies from one isotope to another.
2. As two atoms approach each other, which subatomic particles are the first to come into contact?

Answers: 1. protons; neutrons 2. the electrons of the outermost shells

First electron shell (can hold 2 electrons)   Outer electron shell (can hold 8 electrons)

Electron

Hydrogen (H)
Atomic number = 1

Carbon (C)
Atomic number = 6

Nitrogen (N)
Atomic number = 7

Oxygen (O)
Atomic number = 8

◄ Figure 2.6 **Atoms of the four elements most abundant in living matter.** All four atoms are chemically reactive because their outermost electron shells are not filled. The small empty circles (o) in these diagrams represent unfilled "spaces" in the outer electron shells.

Chemical Bonding and Molecules

Chemical reactions enable atoms to give up or acquire electrons, thereby completing their outer electron shells. Atoms do this by either transferring or sharing their outermost electrons. These interactions usually result in atoms staying close together, held by attractions called **chemical bonds**. In this section, we will discuss three types of chemical bonds: ionic, covalent, and hydrogen bonds.

Ionic Bonds

Table salt is an example of how the transfer of electrons can bond atoms together. The two ingredients of table salt are the elements sodium (Na) and chlorine (Cl). When a chlorine atom strips an electron from a sodium atom, the electron transfer results in both atoms having full outer shells of electrons (Figure 2.7). Before the electron transfer, each of these atoms is electrically neutral. Because electrons are negatively charged, the electron transfer moves one unit of negative charge from sodium to chlorine. Both atoms are now **ions**, atoms or molecules that are electrically charged as a result of gaining or losing electrons. The loss of an electron gives the sodium ion a charge of +1, while chlorine's gain of an electron gives it a charge of −1. The sodium ion (Na^+) and chloride ion (Cl^-) are held together by an **ionic bond**, the attraction between oppositely charged ions. Compounds, such as table salt, that are held together by ionic bonds are called ionic compounds. (Note that negatively charged ions often have names ending in "-ide," like "chloride" or "fluoride.") ☑

Covalent Bonds

In contrast to the complete *transfer* of electrons in ionic bonds, a **covalent bond** forms when two atoms *share* one or more pairs of outer-shell electrons. Covalent bonds are the strongest of the various bonds discussed here; they are the ones that hold atoms together in a **molecule**. For example, a covalent bond connects each hydrogen atom to the carbon atom in the molecule CH_4, a molecule called methane (the main component of natural gas). In Figure 2.8, you can see that each of the four hydrogen atoms in a molecule of

▼ Figure 2.7 **Electron transfer and ionic bonding.** When a sodium atom and a chlorine atom meet, the electron transfer between the two atoms results in two ions with opposite charges.

Outer shell has 1 electron

The outer electron is stripped from sodium and completes the chlorine atom's outer shell.

Outer shell has 7 electrons

Complete outer shells

Na Sodium atom

Cl Chlorine atom

Na⁺ Sodium ion

Cl⁻ Chloride ion

The attraction between the ions—an ionic bond—holds them together.

Sodium chloride (NaCl)

☑ **CHECKPOINT**

When a lithium ion (Li^+) joins a bromide ion (Br^-) to form lithium bromide, the resulting bond is a(n) _____ bond.

Answer: ionic

Name (molecular formula)	Electron configuration Shows how each atom completes its outer shell by sharing electrons	Structural formula Represents each covalent bond (a pair of shared electrons) with a line	Space-filling model Shows the shape of a molecule by symbolizing atoms with color-coded balls	Ball-and-stick model Represents atoms with "balls" and bonds with "sticks"
Hydrogen gas (H_2)	Ⓗ Ⓗ	H—H **Single bond** (a pair of shared electrons)		
Oxygen gas (O_2)	Ⓞ Ⓞ	O=O **Double bond** (two pairs of shared electrons)		
Methane (CH_4)	Ⓗ Ⓒ Ⓗ Ⓗ Ⓗ	H—C—H (with H above and below)		

◄ Figure 2.8 **Alternative ways to represent molecules.** A molecular formula, such as CH_4 or H_2O, tells you the number of each kind of atom in a molecule but not how they are attached together. This figure shows four common ways of representing the arrangement of atoms in molecules.

methane shares one pair of electrons with the single carbon atom.

The number of covalent bonds an atom can form is equal to the number of additional electrons needed to fill its outer shell. Note in Figure 2.8 that hydrogen (H) can form one covalent bond, oxygen (O) can form two, and carbon (C) can form four. The single covalent bond in H_2 completes the outer shells of both hydrogen atoms. In contrast, an oxygen atom needs two electrons to complete its outer shell. In an O_2 molecule, the two oxygen atoms share two pairs of electrons, forming a double covalent bond.

Hydrogen Bonds

A molecule of water (H_2O) consists of two hydrogen atoms joined to one oxygen atom by single covalent bonds (the "sticks" represent bonds between the atoms, which are shown as "balls"):

However, the electrons are not shared equally between the oxygen and hydrogen atoms. The two yellow arrows shown here indicate the stronger pull on the shared electrons that oxygen has compared with its hydrogen partners:

The unequal sharing of negatively charged electrons, combined with its V shape, makes a water molecule polar. A **polar molecule** is one with an uneven distribution of charge. In the case of water, the oxygen end of the molecule has a slight negative charge, while the region around the two hydrogen atoms is slightly positive.

The polarity of water results in weak electrical attractions between neighboring water molecules. Because opposite charges attract, water molecules tend to orient such that a hydrogen atom from one water molecule is near the oxygen atom of an adjacent water

molecule. These weak attractions are called **hydrogen bonds** (Figure 2.9). As you will see later in this chapter, the ability of water to form hydrogen bonds has many crucial implications for life on Earth.

Chemical Reactions

The chemistry of life is dynamic. Your cells are constantly rearranging molecules by breaking existing chemical bonds and forming new ones. Such changes in the chemical composition of matter are called **chemical reactions**. A simple example is the reaction between oxygen gas and hydrogen gas that forms water (this is an explosive reaction, which, fortunately, does not occur in your cells):

Let's translate the chemical shorthand: Two molecules of hydrogen gas ($2\,H_2$) react with one molecule of oxygen gas (O_2) to form two molecules of water ($2\,H_2O$). The arrow indicates the conversion of the starting materials, the **reactants** ($2\,H_2$ and O_2), to the **products** ($2\,H_2O$).

Notice that the same numbers of hydrogen and oxygen atoms are present in reactants and products, although they are grouped differently. Chemical reactions cannot create or destroy matter, but only rearrange it.

These rearrangements usually involve the breaking of chemical bonds in reactants and the forming of new bonds in products.

The water molecules we have built here are a good conclusion to this section on basic chemistry. Water is a substance so important in biology that we'll take a closer look at its life-supporting properties in the next section. ☑

☑ **CHECKPOINT**

Predict the formula for the compound that results when a molecule of sulfur trioxide (SO_3) combines with a molecule of water to produce a single molecule of product. (*Hint*: In chemical reactions, no atoms are gained or lost.)

Answer: H_2SO_4 (sulfuric acid), a component of acid rain.

◀ **Figure 2.9 Hydrogen bonding in water.** The charged regions of the polar water molecules are attracted to oppositely charged areas of neighboring molecules. Each molecule can hydrogen-bond to a maximum of four partners.

Water and Life

Life on Earth began in water and evolved there for 3 billion years before spreading onto land. Modern life, even land-dwelling life, is still tied to water. You've had personal experience with this dependence on water every time you seek liquids to quench your thirst. Inside your body, your cells are surrounded by a fluid that's composed mostly of water, and your cells themselves range from 70% to 95% in water content.

The abundance of water is a major reason that Earth is habitable. Water is so common that it is easy to overlook the fact that it is an exceptional substance with many extraordinary properties (Figure 2.10). We can trace water's unique life-supporting properties to the structure and interactions of its molecules.

Water's Life-Supporting Properties

The polarity of water molecules and the hydrogen bonding that results (see Figure 2.9) explain most of water's life-supporting properties. We'll explore four of those properties here: the cohesive nature of water, the ability of water to moderate temperature, the biological significance of ice floating, and the versatility of water as a solvent.

The Cohesion of Water

Water molecules stick together as a result of hydrogen bonding. Hydrogen bonds between molecules of liquid water last for only a few trillionths of a second, yet at any instant, many molecules are hydrogen-bonded to others. This tendency of molecules of the same kind to stick together, called **cohesion**, is much stronger for water than for most other liquids. The cohesion of water is important in the living world. Trees, for example, depend on cohesion to help transport water from their roots to their leaves (Figure 2.11).

Related to cohesion is surface tension, a measure of how difficult it is to stretch or break the surface of a liquid. Hydrogen bonds give water unusually high surface tension, making it behave as though it were coated with an invisible film (Figure 2.12). Other liquids have much weaker surface tension.

Evaporation from the leaves

Flow of water

▲ Figure 2.10 **A watery world.** You can see each of the three physical states of water in this photograph: liquid water (which covers three-quarters of Earth's surface), ice, and water vapor (as fog and clouds).

Microscopic water-conducting tubes

Cohesion due to hydrogen bonds between water molecules

Colorized SEM 150x

▲ Figure 2.11 **Cohesion and water transport in plants.** The evaporation of water from leaves pulls water upward from the roots through microscopic tubes in the trunk of the tree. Because of cohesion, the pulling force is relayed through the tubes all the way down to the roots. As a result, water rises against the force of gravity.

▼ Figure 2.12 **A raft spider walking on water.** The cumulative strength of hydrogen bonds between water molecules allows this spider to walk on pond water without breaking the surface.

How Water Moderates Temperature

If you've ever burned your finger on a metal pot while waiting for the water in it to boil, you know that water heats up much more slowly than metal. In fact, because of hydrogen bonding, water has a stronger resistance to temperature change than most other substances.

Temperature and heat are related but different. A swimmer crossing San Francisco Bay has a higher temperature than the water, but the bay contains far more heat because of its immense volume. **Heat** is the amount of energy associated with the movement of the atoms and molecules in a body of matter. **Temperature** measures the intensity of heat—that is, the average speed of molecules rather than the total amount of heat energy in a body of matter.

When water is heated, the heat energy first disrupts hydrogen bonds and then makes water molecules jostle around faster. The temperature of the water doesn't go up until the water molecules start to speed up. Because heat is first used to break hydrogen bonds rather than raise the temperature, water absorbs and stores a large amount of heat while warming up only a few degrees. Conversely, when water cools, hydrogen bonds form, a process that releases heat. Thus, water can release a relatively large amount of heat to the surroundings while the water temperature drops only slightly.

Earth's giant water supply—the oceans, seas, lakes, and rivers—enables temperatures to stay within limits that permit life by storing a huge amount of heat from the sun during warm periods and giving off heat to warm the air during cold conditions. That's why coastal areas generally have milder climates than inland regions. Water's resistance to temperature change also stabilizes ocean temperatures, creating a favorable environment for marine life.

Another way that water moderates temperature is by **evaporative cooling**. When a substance evaporates (changes physical state from a liquid to a gas), the surface of the liquid remaining behind cools down. This occurs because the molecules with the greatest energy (the "hottest" ones) tend to vaporize first. It's as if the five fastest runners on your track team quit school, lowering the average speed of the remaining team. Evaporative cooling helps prevent some land-dwelling creatures from overheating; it's why sweating helps you dissipate excess body heat (Figure 2.13). And the old expression "It's not the heat, it's the humidity" has its basis in the difficulty of sweating water into air that is already saturated with water vapor.

Why do days that are hot and humid feel so uncomfortable?

▲ Figure 2.13 **Sweating as a mechanism of evaporative cooling.**

The Biological Significance of Ice Floating

When most liquids get cold, their molecules move closer together. If the temperature is cold enough, the liquid freezes and becomes a solid. Water, however, behaves differently. When water molecules get cold enough, they move apart, with each molecule staying at "arm's length" from its neighbors, forming ice. A chunk of ice therefore has fewer molecules than an equal volume of liquid water; it floats because it is less dense than liquid water. Like water's other life-supporting properties, floating ice is a consequence of hydrogen bonding. In contrast to the short-lived and constantly-changing hydrogen bonds in liquid water, those in solid ice last longer, with each molecule bonded to four neighbors. As a result, ice is a spacious crystal (Figure 2.14).

Hydrogen bond

► Figure 2.14 **Why ice floats.** Compare the tightly packed molecules in liquid water with the spaciously arranged molecules in the ice crystal. The less dense ice floats atop the denser water.

Liquid water
Hydrogen bonds constantly break and re-form.

Ice
Stable hydrogen bonds hold molecules apart, making ice less dense than water.

How does the ability of ice to float help support life on Earth? Imagine what would happen if ice was denser than water. If this were true, ice would sink during winter. All ponds, lakes, and even the oceans would eventually freeze solid. During summer, only the upper few inches of the oceans would thaw. Instead, when a deep body of water cools, the floating ice forms an insulating "blanket" over the liquid water, allowing life to persist under the frozen surface.

Water as the Solvent of Life

If you've ever enjoyed a glass of sweetened ice tea or added salt to soup, you know that you can dissolve sugar or salt in water. This results in a mixture known as a **solution**, a liquid consisting of a homogeneous mixture of two or more substances. The dissolving agent is called the **solvent**, and any substance that is dissolved is called a **solute**. When water is the solvent, the resulting solution is called an **aqueous solution**. The fluids of organisms are aqueous solutions. For example, blood, plant sap, and the fluid in and around cells are all aqueous solutions.

Water can dissolve an enormous variety of solutes necessary for life, providing a medium for chemical reactions. For example, water can dissolve salt ions, as shown in **Figure 2.15**. Each ion becomes surrounded by oppositely charged regions of water molecules. Solutes that are polar molecules, such as sugars, dissolve by orienting locally charged regions of their molecules toward water molecules in a similar way.

We have discussed four special properties of water. Next, we'll consider one way that water's unique structure can reveal important clues about the human brain. ☑

☑ CHECKPOINT

1. Explain why, if you pour very carefully, you can actually "stack" water slightly above the rim of a cup.
2. Explain why ice floats.

Answers: 1. Surface tension due to water's cohesion will keep the water from spilling over. 2. Ice is less dense than liquid water because the more stable hydrogen bonds lock the molecules into a spacious crystal.

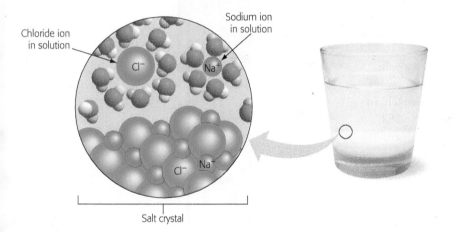

Chloride ion in solution

Sodium ion in solution

Cl⁻

Na⁺

Cl⁻ Na⁺

Salt crystal

◄ Figure 2.15 **A crystal of table salt (NaCl) dissolving in water.** As a result of electrical charge attractions, H_2O molecules surround the sodium and chloride ions, dissolving the crystal in the process.

 Life's Dependence on Water THE PROCESS OF SCIENCE

Can Exercise Boost Your Brain Power?

Biologists use a number of imaging techniques to reveal the body's inner structure. One such technique, magnetic resonance imaging (MRI), depends on the behavior of the hydrogen atoms in water molecules. MRI first aligns the hydrogen nuclei with powerful magnets, then knocks the nuclei out of alignment with a brief pulse of radio waves. In response, the hydrogen atoms give out faint radio signals of their own, which are picked up by the MRI scanner and translated by computer into an image. Since water is a major component of all of our soft tissues, MRI allows doctors to see regions of the body that are invisible to X-rays.

MRI has been particularly useful in studying the brain. One recent study began with the observation that the human brain shrinks as we age: About 20% of our brain matter is lost between ages 30 and 90, and the shrinkage is most prominent in brain areas responsible for memory and learning. Because exercise had been previously associated with improved memory, researchers from the University of Illinois asked the question, Can aerobic exercise slow or even reverse brain loss? Their hypothesis was that MRI scans would reveal differences between the brains of people who regularly exercised and those who did not. They made the prediction that the brains of active people would shrink less than the brains of less active people.

In their experiment, 29 research participants in their 60s and 70s participated for six months in an exercise program of three 1-hour aerobic training sessions per week. A control group of 29 participants (matched for age) engaged in a program of nonaerobic whole-body stretching lasting the same duration. At the start and end of the program, MRI was used to scan the brains of all participants. The **results** of the experiment showed significant increases in brain volume in the aerobic group but not in the non-aerobic controls (Figure 2.16). The researchers concluded that there may be a link between cardiovascular fitness and the retention of memory in aging adults. In other words, regular aerobic exercise may benefit both your body and your mind.

▶ Figure 2.16 **The effect of aerobic exercise on brain size.** The highlighted portion corresponds to regions of the brain that grew in aerobic exercise participants but not in a control group of non-aerobic exercisers.

Acids, Bases, and pH

In aqueous solutions, most of the water molecules are intact. However, some of the water molecules actually break apart into hydrogen ions (H^+) and hydroxide ions (OH^-). A balance of these two highly reactive ions is critical for the proper functioning of chemical processes within organisms.

A chemical compound that releases H^+ to a solution is called an **acid**. One example of a strong acid is hydrochloric acid (HCl), the acid in your stomach. In solution, HCl breaks apart into the ions H^+ and Cl^-. A **base** (or alkali) is a compound that accepts H^+ and removes them from solution. Some bases, such as sodium hydroxide (NaOH), do this by releasing OH^-, which combines with H^+ to form H_2O.

To describe the acidity of a solution, chemists use the **pH scale**, a measure of the hydrogen ion (H^+) concentration in a solution. The scale ranges from 0 (most acidic) to 14 (most basic). Each pH unit represents a tenfold change in the concentration of H^+ (Figure 2.17). For example, lemon juice at pH 2 has 100 times more H^+ than an equal amount of tomato juice at pH 4. Aqueous solutions that are neither acidic nor basic (such as pure water) are said to be neutral; they have a pH of 7. They do contain some H^+ and OH^-, but the concentrations of the two ions are equal. The pH of the solution inside most living cells is close to 7.

Did you drink an acid today?

Even a slight change in pH can be harmful to an organism because the molecules in cells are extremely sensitive to H^+ and OH^- concentrations. Biological fluids contain **buffers**, substances that minimize changes in pH by accepting H^+ when that ion is in excess and donating H^+ when it is depleted. This buffering process, however, is not

▶ Figure 2.17 **The pH scale.** A solution having a pH of 7 is neutral, meaning that its H^+ and OH^- concentrations are equal. The lower the pH below 7, the more acidic the solution, or the greater its excess of H^+ compared with OH^-. The higher the pH above 7, the more basic the solution, or the greater the deficiency of H^+ relative to OH^-.

Basic solution

Increasingly basic (lower H^+ concentration)

Neutral solution

Neutral
H^+ concentration
=
OH^- concentration

Acidic solution

Increasingly acidic (greater H^+ concentration)

14 —
13 — Oven cleaner
— Household bleach
12 — Household ammonia
11 — Milk of magnesia
10 —
9 —
8 — Seawater
— Human blood
7 — **Pure water**
6 — Urine
5 —
— Black coffee
4 — Tomato juice
3 — Grapefruit juice, soft drink
2 — Lemon juice, stomach acid
— Battery acid
1 —
0 —

pH scale

foolproof, and changes in environmental pH can profoundly affect ecosystems. For example, much of the human-made CO_2 released into the atmosphere is absorbed by the oceans. When it combines with seawater, a chemical reaction produces an acid. The resulting ocean acidification can greatly change marine environments. This principle was illustrated by a 2008 study of the Mediterranean Sea near Naples, Italy. There, undersea volcanoes release high levels of CO_2 (Figure 2.18). Researchers found that the resulting acidification caused coral reef collapse and widespread death of marine organisms. This natural system suggests that high levels of dissolved human-made CO_2 could cause similar ecological disaster.

The effects of ocean acidification are daunting reminders that the chemistry of life is linked to the chemistry of the environment. It reminds us, too, that chemistry happens on a global scale, since industrial processes in one region of the world often cause acid precipitation to fall in another part of the world. ✔

◄ **Figure 2.18 The release of volcanic CO_2, causing undersea bubbling off the coast of Italy.**

☑ **CHECKPOINT**

Compared with a solution of pH 8, the same volume of a solution at pH 5 has _____ times more hydrogen ions (H^+). This second solution is considered a(n)_____.

Answer: 1,000; acid

Life's Dependence on Water EVOLUTION CONNECTION

The Search for Extraterrestrial Life

Throughout this chapter, we have highlighted the importance of water to living systems. In fact, water is the substance that makes life as we know it possible.

One of the great questions facing humankind is: Has life evolved elsewhere in the universe? If it has, and if this life is at all similar to ours, then it, too, would depend on water. This explains why the search for water on other planets is such a priority for the U.S. space program.

Researchers at the National Aeronautics and Space Administration (NASA) have found evidence that water was once abundant on Mars. (Although Mars has clearly visible polar ice caps, no liquid water is known to flow there at present.) In January 2004, NASA landed two golf-cart-sized rovers on Mars. These robotic geologists determined the composition of rocks and sent back images of rock formations. One of the rovers detected a mineral that is formed only in the presence of water. Furthermore, pictures revealed physical evidence of the effects of liquid water flowing over the Martian surface in the past.

Images taken by NASA's *Mars Global Surveyor* spacecraft indicate that not only did the red planet have a water-filled ancient past, but liquid water may have flowed recently on its surface. In 2008, an analysis of Martian soil by the *Phoenix Mars Lander* (Figure 2.19) provided evidence that components of the soil had at one time been dissolved in water. As this chapter has shown, where there is water, there may indeed be life. The evidence for water on Mars raises the tantalizing possibility that microbial life may exist below the Martian surface.

Ice

▲ **Figure 2.19 Life on Mars?** The *Phoenix Mars Lander* uncovered a patch of ice (silver rectangle near the bottom of the inset image) while probing for evidence of water on the Martian surface.

Chapter Review

SUMMARY OF KEY CONCEPTS

Some Basic Chemistry

Matter: Elements and Compounds

Matter consists of elements and compounds, which are combinations of two or more elements. Of the 25 elements essential for life, oxygen, carbon, hydrogen, and nitrogen are the most abundant in living matter.

Atoms

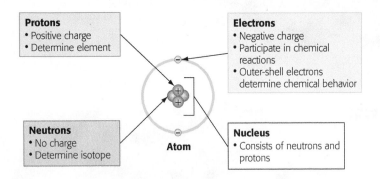

Protons
• Positive charge
• Determine element

Electrons
• Negative charge
• Participate in chemical reactions
• Outer-shell electrons determine chemical behavior

Neutrons
• No charge
• Determine isotope

Atom

Nucleus
• Consists of neutrons and protons

Chemical Bonding and Molecules

Transfer of one or more electrons produces attractions between oppositely charged ions:

Attraction between oppositely charged ions holds the ions in an ionic bond.

Lithium ion   Fluoride ion

Lithium fluoride (ionic compound)

A molecule consists of two or more atoms connected by covalent bonds, which are formed by electron sharing:

Electron sharing

Atoms joined into a molecule via covalent bonds

Water is a polar molecule; the slightly positively charged H atoms in one water molecule may be attracted to the partial negative charge of O atoms in neighboring water molecules, forming weak but important hydrogen bonds:

Hydrogen bond

Chemical Reactions

By breaking bonds in reactants and forming new bonds in products, chemical reactions rearrange matter.

Water and Life

Water's Life-Supporting Properties

The ability of leaves to pull water up microscopic tubes within trunks and stems is an example of how water's cohesion supports life. Water moderates temperature by absorbing heat in warm environments and releasing heat in cold environments. Evaporative cooling also helps stabilize the temperatures of oceans and organisms. Ice floats because it is less dense than liquid water, preventing the oceans from freezing solid. Blood and other biological fluids are aqueous solutions with a diversity of solutes dissolved in water, a versatile solvent.

Liquid water
Hydrogen bonds constantly break and re-form.

Ice
Stable hydrogen bonds hold molecules apart, making ice less dense than water.

Acids, Bases, and pH

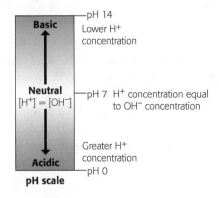

Basic — pH 14 Lower H^+ concentration

Neutral $[H^+] = [OH^-]$ — pH 7 H^+ concentration equal to OH^- concentration

Greater H^+ concentration

Acidic — pH 0

pH scale

SELF-QUIZ

1. An atom can be changed into an ion by adding or removing _____. An atom can be changed into a different isotope by adding or removing _____. But if you change the number of _____, the atom becomes a different element.

2. A nitrogen atom has 7 protons, and the most common isotope of nitrogen has 7 neutrons. A radioactive isotope of nitrogen has 9 neutrons. What are the atomic numbers and mass numbers of the stable and radioactive forms of nitrogen?

3. Why are radioactive isotopes useful as tracers in research on the chemistry of life?

4. A sulfur atom has 6 electrons in its third (outermost) shell, which can hold 8 electrons. As a result, it forms _____ covalent bonds with other atoms. (Provide a number.)

5. What is chemically nonsensical about this structure?

   H—C≡C—H

6. Why is it unlikely that two neighboring water molecules would be arranged like this?

7. Which of the following is not a chemical reaction?
   a. Sugar ($C_6H_{12}O_6$) and oxygen gas (O_2) combine to form carbon dioxide (CO_2) and water (H_2O).
   b. Sodium metal and chlorine gas unite to form sodium chloride.
   c. Hydrogen gas combines with oxygen gas to form water.
   d. Ice melts to form liquid water.

8. Some people in your study group say they don't understand what a polar molecule is. You explain that a polar molecule
   a. is slightly negative at one end and slightly positive at the other end.
   b. has an extra electron, giving it a positive charge.
   c. has an extra electron, giving it a negative charge.
   d. has covalent bonds.

9. Explain how the unique properties of water result from the fact that water is a polar molecule.

10. A can of cola consists mostly of sugar dissolved in water, with some carbon dioxide gas that makes it fizzy and makes the pH less than 7. Describe the cola using the following terms: solute, solvent, acidic, aqueous solution.

Answers to these questions can be found in Appendix: Self-Quiz Answers.

THE PROCESS OF SCIENCE

11. Animals obtain energy through a series of chemical reactions in which sugar ($C_6H_{12}O_6$) and oxygen gas (O_2) are reactants. This process produces water (H_2O) and carbon dioxide (CO_2) as waste products. How might you use a radioactive isotope to find out whether the oxygen in CO_2 comes from sugar or from oxygen gas?

12. The following diagram shows the arrangement of electrons around the nucleus of a fluorine atom (left) and a potassium atom (right). Predict what would happen if a fluorine atom and a potassium atom came into contact. What kind of bond do you think they would form?

Fluorine atom   Potassium atom

BIOLOGY AND SOCIETY

13. Critically evaluate this statement: "It's paranoid and ignorant to worry about industry or agriculture contaminating the environment with chemical wastes; this stuff is just made of the same atoms that were already present in our environment."

14. A major source of the CO_2 that causes ocean acidification is emissions from coal-burning power plants. One way to reduce these emissions is to use nuclear power to produce electricity. The proponents of nuclear power contend that it is the only way that the United States can increase its energy production while reducing air pollution, because nuclear power plants emit little or no acid-precipitation-causing pollutants. What are some of the benefits of nuclear power? What are the possible costs and dangers? Do you think we ought to increase our use of nuclear power to generate electricity? Why or why not? If a new power plant were to be built near your home, would you prefer it to be a coal-burning plant or a nuclear plant? Why?

3 The Molecules of Life

Cheesy pizza.
Lactose digestion results
from interactions
between several classes
of the body's molecules.

Lactose Intolerance BIOLOGY AND SOCIETY

Got Lactose?

You've probably seen ads meant to convince you that a milk mustache represents good health. Indeed, milk is a very healthy food because it's rich in protein, minerals, and vitamins. But for the majority of adults in the world, a glass of milk or a serving of milk-containing foods (such as cheesy pizza or ice cream) can cause bloating, gas, and other discomforts. These are symptoms of lactose intolerance, the inability to digest lactose, the main sugar found in milk.

For people with lactose intolerance, the problem starts when lactose enters the small intestine. To absorb this sugar, digestive cells there must produce a molecule called lactase. Lactase is an enzyme, a protein that helps drive chemical reactions—in this case, the breakdown of lactose into smaller sugars. People with lactose intolerance produce insufficient amounts or a defective version of the enzyme. Lactose that is not broken down in the small intestine passes into the large intestine, where bacteria feed on it and belch out gaseous by-products, producing uncomfortable symptoms. Sufficient lactase can thus mean the difference between delight and discomfort when someone feasts on an ice cream sundae.

What options are there for people with lactose intolerance? There is no treatment for the underlying cause: the decreased production of lactase. But symptoms can be controlled through diet. The first option is avoiding lactose-containing foods. Many substitutes are available, such as milk made from soy or from milk that has been pretreated with lactase. If you are lactose intolerant and pizza is your staple food, lactose-free cheese (made from soy) can be bought at most supermarkets, or you can make your own mozarella from lactose-free milk. Also, lactase in pill form can be taken along with food to ease digestion by artificially providing the enzyme that the body naturally lacks.

Lactose intolerance illustrates one way the interplay of biological molecules can affect your health. Such molecular interactions, repeated in countless variations, drive all biological processes. In this chapter, we'll explore the structure and function of large molecules that are essential to life. We'll start with an overview of carbon and then examine four classes of molecules: carbohydrates, lipids, proteins, and nucleic acids. Along the way, we'll look at where these molecules occur in your diet and the important roles they play in your body.

Organic Compounds

A cell is mostly water, but the rest of it consists mainly of carbon-based molecules. Carbon is unparalleled in its ability to form the skeletons of large, complex, diverse molecules that are necessary for life's functions. The study of carbon-based molecules, which are called **organic compounds**, lies at the heart of any study of life.

Could a cow someday fuel your car?

Carbon Chemistry

Why are carbon atoms so versatile as molecular ingredients? Recall that an atom's bonding ability is related to the number of electrons it must share to complete its outer shell. A carbon atom has 4 electrons in an outer shell that holds 8. Carbon completes its outer shell by sharing electrons with other atoms in four covalent bonds that can branch off in four directions. Because carbon can use one or more of its bonds to attach to other carbon atoms, it is possible to construct an endless diversity of carbon skeletons varying in size and branching pattern (Figure 3.1). Thus, molecules with multiple carbon "intersections" can form very elaborate shapes. The carbon atoms of organic compounds can also use one or more of their bonds to partner with other elements, most commonly hydrogen, oxygen, and nitrogen.

In terms of chemical composition, the simplest organic compounds are **hydrocarbons**, which contain only carbon and hydrogen atoms. And the simplest hydrocarbon is methane: CH_4, a single carbon atom bonded to four hydrogen atoms (Figure 3.2). Methane is one of the most abundant hydrocarbons in natural gas and is also produced by prokaryotes that live in swamps and in the digestive tracts of grazing animals, such as cows. Larger hydrocarbons (such as octane, with eight carbons) are the main molecules in the gasoline we burn in cars and other machines (Figure 3.3). Hydrocarbons are also important fuels in your body; the energy-rich parts of fat molecules have a hydrocarbon structure.

As you will see in subsequent chapters, a recurring theme in biology is the importance of the shape of molecules. Many vital processes within living organisms rely on the ability of molecules to recognize one another based on their shape.

The unique properties of an organic compound depend not only on its carbon skeleton but also on the atoms attached to the skeleton. In an organic compound, the groups of atoms directly involved in chemical

▼ Figure 3.2 **Methane, the simplest hydrocarbon.**

Structural formula   **Ball-and-stick model**   **Space-filling model**

▼ Figure 3.1 **Variations in carbon skeletons.** All of these examples are hydrocarbons, organic compounds consisting only of carbon and hydrogen. Notice that each carbon atom forms four bonds and each hydrogen atom forms one bond. Remember that one line represents a single bond (sharing of one pair of electrons) and two lines represent a double bond (sharing of two pairs of electrons).

Carbon skeletons vary in length

Double bond

Carbon skeletons may have double bonds, which can vary in location

Carbon skeletons may be unbranched or branched

Carbon skeletons may be arranged in rings

Figure 3.3 Hydrocarbons as fuel. Energy-rich hydrocarbons in gasoline provide fuel for machines, and energy-rich hydrocarbons in fats provide fuel for cells.

Octane

Dietary fat

bagels), proteins (such as enzymes and the components of your hair), and nucleic acids (such as DNA)—are gigantic; in fact, biologists call them **macromolecules** (*macro* means "big"). Despite the size of macromolecules, their structures can be easily understood because they are **polymers**, large molecules made by stringing together many smaller molecules called **monomers**. A polymer is like a pearl necklace made by joining together many pearl monomers.

Cells link monomers together to form polymers through a **dehydration** reaction, a chemical reaction that removes a molecule of water (**Figure 3.4a**). For each monomer added to a chain, a water molecule (H_2O) is formed by the release of two hydrogen atoms and one oxygen atom. This same dehydration reaction occurs regardless of the specific monomers and the type of polymer the cell is producing.

Organisms not only make macromolecules but also break them down. For example, many molecules in your food are macromolecules. You must digest these giant molecules to make their monomers available to your cells, which can then rebuild the monomers into the macromolecules that make up your body. Converting macromolecules is like taking apart a car (food) made of Legos and then using the Legos (monomers) to assemble a new car (macromolecule) of your own design. The breakdown of polymers occurs by a process called **hydrolysis** (**Figure 3.4b**). Hydrolysis means to break (*lyse*) with water (*hydro*). Cells break bonds between monomers by adding water to them, a process that is essentially the reverse of a dehydration reaction. You've already heard of one example of a hydrolysis reaction: the breakdown of lactose into its monomers by the enzyme lactase. ☑

reactions are called **functional groups**. Each functional group plays a particular role during chemical reactions. Two examples of functional groups are the hydroxyl group (—OH) and the carboxyl group (—COOH). Many biological molecules have two or more functional groups. Keeping in mind this basic scheme—carbon skeletons with functional groups—we are now ready to see how our cells make large molecules out of smaller ones.

Giant Molecules from Smaller Building Blocks

On a molecular scale, the members of three categories of large biological molecules—carbohydrates (such as those found in starchy foods like French fries and

Figure 3.4 Synthesis and digestion of polymers. For simplicity, the only atoms shown in these diagrams are hydrogens and hydroxyl groups (—OH) in strategic locations.

(a) Building a polymer chain. A polymer grows in length when an incoming monomer and the monomer at the end of the polymer each contribute atoms to form a water molecule. The monomers replace the lost covalent bonds with a bond to each other.

(b) Breaking a polymer chain. Hydrolysis reverses the process by adding a water molecule, which breaks the bond between two monomers, creating 2 smaller molecules from one bigger one.

Large Biological Molecules

The remainder of the chapter will introduce you to the four categories of large biological molecules: carbohydrates, lipids, proteins, and nucleic acids. For each category, we'll explore the structure and function of these large molecules by first learning about the smaller molecules used to build them.

Carbohydrates

Carbohydrates, commonly known as "carbs," are a class of molecules that includes sugars and polymers of sugars. Some examples are the small sugar molecules dissolved in energy drinks and the long starch molecules in spaghetti and bread. In animals, carbohydrates are a primary source of dietary energy and raw material for manufacturing other kinds of organic compounds; in plants, they serve as a building material for much of the plant body.

Monosaccharides

Simple sugars, or **monosaccharides** (from the Greek *mono*, single, and *sacchar*, sugar), are the monomers of carbohydrates; they cannot be broken down into smaller sugars. Common examples are glucose, found in sports drinks, and fructose, found in fruit. Both of these simple sugars are also in honey **(Figure 3.5)**. The

molecular formula for glucose is $C_6H_{12}O_6$. Fructose has the same formula, but its atoms are arranged differently. Glucose and fructose are examples of **isomers**, molecules that have the same molecular formula but different structures. Isomers are like anagrams—words that contain the same letters in a different order, such as *heart* and *earth*. Because molecular shape is so important, seemingly minor differences in the arrangement of atoms give isomers different properties. In this case, the rearrangement of functional groups makes fructose taste much sweeter than glucose.

It is convenient to draw sugars as if their carbon skeletons were linear. In water, however, many monosaccharides form rings when one part of the molecule forms a bond with another part of the molecule **(Figure 3.6)**. You'll notice this ring shape in the structure of many carbohydrates in this chapter.

Monosaccharides, particularly glucose, are the main fuel molecules for cellular work. Like an automobile engine consuming gasoline, your cells break down glucose molecules and extract their stored energy, giving off carbon dioxide as "exhaust." The rapid conversion of glucose to cellular energy is why an aqueous solution of glucose (often called dextrose) is given as an IV to sick or injured patients; the glucose provides an immediate energy source to tissues in need of repair. ☑

► Figure 3.5
Monosaccharides (simple sugars). These molecules have the two trademarks of sugars: several hydroxyl groups (—OH) and a carbonyl group (C=O). Glucose and fructose, which make honey sweet, are isomers.

Glucose
$C_6H_{12}O_6$

Fructose
$C_6H_{12}O_6$

Isomers
(same formula, different arrangements)

▼ Figure 3.6 **The ring structure of glucose.**

(a) Linear and ring structures. The carbon atoms are numbered so you can relate the linear and ring versions of the molecule. As the double arrows indicate, ring formation is a reversible process, but at any instant in an aqueous solution, most glucose molecules are rings.

(b) Abbreviated ring structure. In this book, we'll use this abbreviated ring symbol for glucose. Each unmarked corner represents a carbon and its attached atoms.

Disaccharides

A **disaccharide**, or double sugar, is constructed from two monosaccharides by a dehydration reaction. In the Biology and Society section, you learned about the disaccharide lactose, sometimes called "milk sugar." Lactose is made from the monosaccharides glucose and galactose (Figure 3.7). Another common disaccharide is maltose, naturally found in germinating seeds. It is used in making beer, malt whiskey and liquor, malted milk shakes, and malted milk ball candy. A molecule of maltose consists of two glucose monomers joined together.

The most common disaccharide is sucrose (table sugar), which consists of a glucose monomer linked to a fructose monomer. Sucrose is the main carbohydrate in plant sap, and it nourishes all the parts of the plant. Sugar manufacturers extract sucrose from the stems of sugarcane or the roots of sugar beets. However, sucrose is rarely used as a sweetener in processed foods in the United States. Much more common is high-fructose corn syrup, made through a commercial process that converts natural glucose in corn syrup to the much sweeter fructose. If you read the label on a soft drink can or bottle, you're likely to find that high-fructose corn syrup is one of the first ingredients listed (Figure 3.8).

The United States is one of the world's leading markets for sweeteners, and the average American consumes

Chances are you ate beets today—but in what?

about 45 kilograms (kg)—a whopping 100 pounds—per year, mainly in the form of sucrose and high-fructose corn syrup. This national "sweet tooth" persists in spite of our growing awareness about how sugar can negatively affect our health. Sugar is a major cause of tooth decay. Moreover, high sugar consumption tends to replace eating more varied and nutritious foods. The description of sugars as "empty calories" is accurate in the sense that most sweeteners contain only negligible amounts of nutrients other than carbohydrates. For good health, we also require proteins, fats, vitamins, and minerals. And we need to include substantial amounts of complex carbohydrates—that is, polysaccharides—in our diet. Let's examine these macromolecules next.

▼ Figure 3.7 **Disaccharide (double sugar) formation.** To form a disaccharide, two simple sugars are joined by a dehydration reaction, in this case forming a bond between monomers of glucose and galactose to make the double sugar lactose.

◄ Figure 3.8 **High-fructose corn syrup.** Many processed foods include high-fructose corn syrup, an artificial sweetener made by chemically treating sugars extracted from corn.

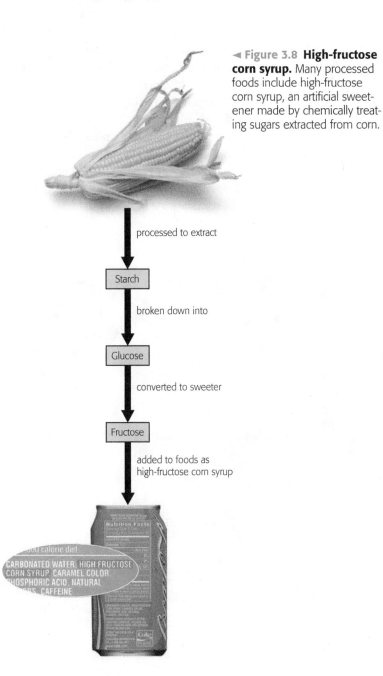

processed to extract

Starch

broken down into

Glucose

converted to sweeter

Fructose

added to foods as high-fructose corn syrup

Polysaccharides

Complex carbohydrates, or **polysaccharides**, are long chains of sugars—polymers of monosaccharides. One familiar example is starch, a storage polysaccharide found in plants. **Starch** consists of long strings of glucose monomers **(Figure 3.9a)**. Plant cells store starch, providing a sugar stockpile that can be broken down when needed. Potatoes and grains, such as wheat, corn, and rice, are the major sources of starch in our diet. Animals can digest starch because their digestive systems break the bonds between glucose monomers through hydrolysis reactions.

Animals store excess sugar in the form of a polysaccharide called **glycogen**. Like starch, glycogen is a polymer of glucose monomers, but glycogen is more extensively branched **(Figure 3.9b)**. Most of your glycogen is stored in liver and muscle cells, which break down the glycogen to release glucose when you need energy. This is why some athletes "carbo load," consuming large amounts of starchy foods the night before an athletic event. The starch is converted to glycogen, which is then available for rapid use during physical activity the next day.

Cellulose, the most abundant organic compound on Earth, forms cable-like fibrils in the tough walls that enclose plant cells and is a major component of wood and other structural components of plants **(Figure 3.9c)**. We take advantage of that structural strength when we use lumber as a building material. Cellulose is also a polymer of glucose, but its glucose monomers are linked together in a unique way. Unlike the glucose linkages in starch and glycogen, those in cellulose cannot be broken by animals. The cellulose in plant foods, which passes unchanged through our digestive tract, is commonly known as dietary fiber (your grandma might call it "roughage"). Because it remains undigested, fiber does not serve as a nutrient, but it does help keep your digestive system healthy. Among other benefits, the passage of cellulose stimulates cells lining the digestive tract to secrete mucus, which allows food to pass smoothly. Most Americans do not get the recommended levels of fiber in their diet. Foods rich in fiber include fruits and vegetables, whole grains, bran, and beans. Grazing animals and wood-eating insects such as termites are able to derive nutrition from cellulose because microorganisms inhabiting their digestive tracts break it down.

Monosaccharides (such as glucose or fructose) and disaccharides (such as sucrose or lactose) dissolve readily in water, forming sugary solutions. In contrast, cellulose does not dissolve in water, but water can adhere to its surface, which is why a fluffy bath towel (high in cellulose) is so water absorbent. Thus, almost all carbohydrates are **hydrophilic** ("water-loving") molecules. As you'll see next, not all biological molecules share this property. ✔

▼ **Figure 3.9 Polysaccharides.**

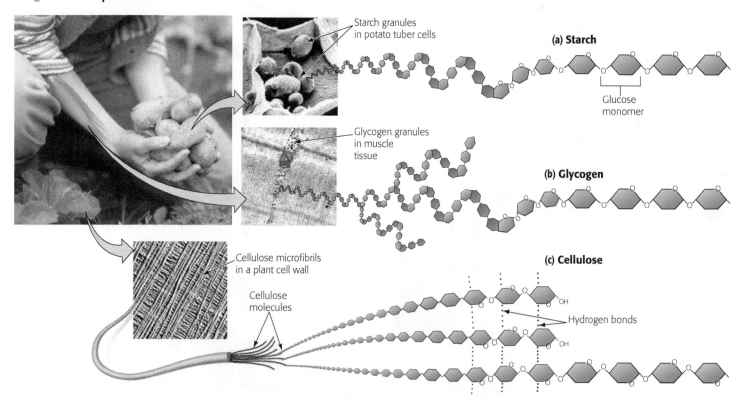

Starch granules in potato tuber cells

(a) Starch

Glucose monomer

Glycogen granules in muscle tissue

(b) Glycogen

Cellulose microfibrils in a plant cell wall

Cellulose molecules

(c) Cellulose

Hydrogen bonds

Lipids

In contrast to most biological molecules, **lipids** are **hydrophobic** ("water-fearing"); they do not mix with water. You've probably seen this chemical behavior when you combine oil and vinegar: The oil, which is a type of lipid, separates from the vinegar, which is mostly water (Figure 3.10). If you shake vigorously, you can force a temporary mixture long enough to douse your salad, but what remains in the bottle will quickly separate.

Unlike carbohydrates, proteins, and nucleic acids, lipids are neither macromolecules nor polymers. In fact, lipids are a diverse group of molecules made from different "building blocks." In this section, we'll look at two types of lipids: fats and steroids.

Fats

A typical **fat** consists of a glycerol molecule joined with three fatty acid molecules via dehydration reactions (Figure 3.11). The resulting fat is called a **triglyceride**, a term you may see on food labels or in the results of a blood test. The major portion of a fatty acid is a long hydrocarbon that stores a lot of energy, like the hydrocarbons of gasoline. In fact, a pound of fat packs more than twice as much energy as a pound of carbohydrate. The downside to this energy efficiency is that it is very difficult for a person trying to lose weight to "burn off" excess fat. It is important to understand that a reasonable amount of body fat is both normal and healthy as a fuel reserve. We stock these long-term food stores in specialized reservoirs called adipose cells, which swell and shrink when we deposit and withdraw fat from them. This adipose tissue, or "body fat," not only stores energy but also cushions vital organs and insulates us, helping maintain a warm body temperature even when the outside air is cold.

Notice in Figure 3.11b that the bottom fatty acid bends where there is a double bond in the carbon skeleton. That fatty acid is said to be **unsaturated** because it has fewer than the maximum number of hydrogens at the double bond. The other two fatty acids in the fat molecule lack double bonds in their hydrocarbon portions. Those fatty acids are **saturated**, meaning that they contain the maximum number of hydrogen atoms, giving them a straight shape. A saturated fat is one with all three of its fatty acid tails saturated. If one or more of the fatty acids is unsaturated, then it's an unsaturated fat, like the one in Figure 3.11b. A polyunsaturated fat has several double bonds within its fatty acids.

Why is it so hard to lose body fat?

◀ Figure 3.10 **The separation of hydrophobic (oil) and hydrophilic (vinegar) components in salad dressing.**

Oil (hydrophobic)

Vinegar (hydrophilic)

▼ Figure 3.11 **The synthesis and structure of a triglyceride molecule.**

Fatty acid

Glycerol

(a) A dehydration reaction linking a fatty acid to glycerol

(b) A fat molecule with a glycerol "head" and three energy-rich hydrocarbon fatty acid "tails"

Most animal fats, such as lard and butter, have a relatively high proportion of saturated fatty acids. The linear shape of saturated fatty acids allows these molecules to stack easily (like bricks in a wall), so saturated fats tend to be solid at room temperature (Figure 3.12). Diets rich in saturated fats may contribute to cardiovascular disease by promoting **atherosclerosis**. In this condition, lipid-containing deposits called plaque build up along the inside walls of blood vessels, reducing blood flow and increasing risk of heart attacks and strokes.

Plant and fish fats are relatively high in unsaturated fatty acids. The bent shape of unsaturated fatty acids makes them less likely to form solids (imagine trying to build a wall using irregularly bent bricks!), so most unsaturated fats are liquid at room temperature. Foods that are primarily unsaturated include vegetable oils (such as corn and canola oil) and fish oils (such as cod liver oil).

Although plant oils tend to be low in saturated fat, tropical plant fats are an exception. Cocoa butter, a main ingredient in chocolate, contains a mix of saturated and unsaturated fat. This gives chocolate a melting point near body temperature. Thus, chocolate stays solid at room temperature but melts in the mouth. This pleasing "mouth feel" is one of the reasons chocolate is so appealing.

Why does chocolate melt in your mouth but not in the package?

Sometimes a food manufacturer wants to use a vegetable oil but needs the food product to be solid, as with margarine or peanut butter. To achieve this, the manufacturer can convert unsaturated fats to saturated fats by adding hydrogen, a process called **hydrogenation**. Unfortunately, hydrogenation also creates **trans fats**, a type of unsaturated fat that is particularly bad for your health. Since 2006, the U.S. Food and Drug Administration (FDA) has required trans fats to be listed on nutrition labels. But even if a label on a hydrogenated product says 0 grams (g) of trans fats per serving, the product might still have up to 0.5 g per serving. Any product with partially hydrogenated vegetable oil contains trans fats. (See the Process of Science section in Chapter 1—"Are Trans Fats Bad for You?"—for an investigation of the health effects of trans fats.) Due to the increased awareness of their unhealthy nature, trans fats are becoming less common as food manufacturers substitute other forms of fat.

Although saturated and trans fats should generally be avoided, it is not true that *all* fats are unhealthy. In fact, some fats perform important functions within the body and are beneficial and even essential to a healthy diet. For example, fats containing omega-3 fatty acids have been shown to reduce the risk of heart disease and relieve the symptoms of arthritis and inflammatory bowel disease. Some sources of these beneficial fats are nuts and oily fish such as salmon. ☑

☑ **CHECKPOINT**

What are "unsaturated fats"? What kinds of unsaturated fat are particularly unhealthy? What kind of unsaturated fats are most healthful?

Answer: fats with less than the maximum number of hydrogens because of double bonds between some carbons; trans fats; fats built from omega-3 fatty acids

▼ Figure 3.12 **Types of fats.**

TYPES OF FATS

Saturated Fats
(unhealthy fats found primarily in meat and full-fat dairy products; solid at room temperature)

Unsaturated Fats
(fats found primarily in fish and plants; usually liquid at room temperature)

BUTTER

Margarine

INGREDIENTS: SOYBEAN OIL, FULLY HYDROGENATED COTTONSEED OIL, PARTIALLY HYDROGENATED COTTONSEED AND SOYBEAN OILS, MONO AND DIGLYCERIDES, TBHO AND CITRIC ACID (ANTIOXIDANTS).

Plant oils
(unhydrogenated; usually liquid at room temperature)

Trans fats
(unhealthy fats in hydrogenated processed foods; solid at room temperature)

Omega-3 fats
(beneficial fats in some fish and plant oils; liquid at room temperature)

Steroids

Although they are also hydrophobic, **steroids** are very different from fats in structure and function. All steroids have a carbon skeleton with four fused rings. Different steroids vary in the functional groups attached to this set of rings, and these chemical variations affect their function. One common steroid is cholesterol, which has a bad reputation because of its association with cardiovascular disease. However, cholesterol is an essential molecule in your body. It is a key component of the membranes that surround your cells. It is also the "base steroid" from which your body produces other steroids, such as the sex hormones estrogen and testosterone (Figure 3.13).

The controversial drugs called anabolic steroids are synthetic variants of testosterone. In human males, testosterone causes buildup of muscle and bone mass during puberty and maintains masculine traits throughout life. Because anabolic steroids resemble testosterone, they mimic some of its effects. Anabolic steroids are prescribed to treat diseases that cause muscle wasting, such as cancer and AIDS. On the flip side, athletes can abuse anabolic steroids to build up their muscles quickly.

In recent years, the discovery that some athletes were using a performance-enhancing anabolic steroid called THG rocked the sports world. THG is a chemically modified ("designer") steroid intended to avoid detection by drug tests (hence its nickname, "the clear"). New tests revealed widespread use of THG and other steroids among athletes in many sports (Figure 3.14) and raised questions about the validity of home run records and other athletic accomplishments.

Using anabolic steroids is indeed a fast way to increase body size beyond what hard work alone can produce. But at what cost? Steroid abuse can cause violent mood swings ("roid rage"), depression, liver damage, high cholesterol, shrunken testicles, reduced sex drive, and infertility. These last symptoms occur because artificial anabolic steroids often cause the body to reduce its output of natural sex hormones. Most athletic organizations ban the use of anabolic steroids because of their many potential health hazards coupled with the unfairness of an artificial advantage. ☑

▼ Figure 3.13 **Examples of steroids.** The molecular structures of the steroids shown here are abbreviated by omitting all the atoms that make up the rings. The subtle difference between testosterone and estrogen influences the development of the anatomical and physiological differences between male and female mammals, including lions and humans.

Cholesterol

can be converted by the body to

Testosterone

A type of estrogen

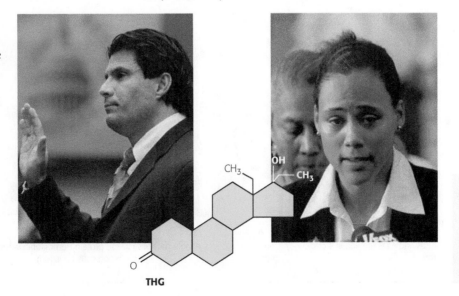

▼ Figure 3.14 **Steroids and the modern athlete.** Baseball player Jose Canseco (left), an admitted user of performance-enhancing steroids, testifies before Congress during an inquiry into the abuse of drugs by professional athletes. After admitting that she had taken performance-enhancing drugs, track-and-field star Marion Jones (right) was stripped of her five Olympic medals. Note the similarity in chemical structure of testosterone (shown above) and THG (shown here).

THG

☑ CHECKPOINT

What steroid acts as the molecular building block of the human steroid hormones?

Answer: cholesterol

45

Proteins

A **protein** is a polymer of amino acid monomers. Proteins are the most elaborate and diverse of life's molecules. Proteins account for more than 50% of the dry weight of most cells, and they are instrumental in almost everything cells do (Figure 3.15). Chances are, if something is getting done in your body, there is a protein doing it. Your body has thousands of proteins, and each protein has a unique three-dimensional shape corresponding to a specific function.

How much protein is on your head?

The Monomers of Proteins: Amino Acids

All proteins are macromolecules, which are made by stringing together a common set of 20 kinds of amino acids. Each **amino acid** consists of a central carbon atom bonded to four covalent partners (carbon, remember, always forms four covalent bonds). Three of those attachments are common to all 20 amino acids: a carboxyl group (—COOH), an amino group (—NH_2), and a hydrogen atom. The variable component of amino acids, the side group (also called an R group, or radical group), is attached to the fourth bond of the central carbon (Figure 3.16a). Each type of amino acid has a unique side group, giving that amino acid its special chemical properties (Figure 3.16b). Some amino acids have very simple side groups; the amino acid glycine, for example, has a single hydrogen as its side group. Other amino acids have more complex side groups, some with branches or rings within them.

▼ **Figure 3.16 Amino acids.** The 20 amino acids vary only in their side groups, which give these monomers their unique properties.

(a) The general structure of an amino acid.

(b) Examples of amino acids with hydrophobic and hydrophilic side groups. The side group of the amino acid leucine is pure hydrocarbon. That region of leucine is hydrophobic because hydrocarbons don't mix with water. In contrast, the side group of the amino acid serine has a hydroxyl group (—OH), which is hydrophilic.

▼ **Figure 3.15 Some types of proteins.**

MAJOR TYPES OF PROTEINS				
Structural Proteins (provide support)	**Storage Proteins** (provide amino acids for growth)	**Contractile Proteins** (help movement)	**Transport Proteins** (help transport substances)	**Enzymes** (help chemical reactions)
Structural proteins give hair and horns their toughness.	Seeds and eggs are rich in storage proteins.	Contractile proteins enable muscles to contract.	The protein hemoglobin within red blood cells transports oxygen.	Some cleaning products use enzymes to help break down molecules.

Proteins as Polymers

Cells link amino acid monomers together by—can you guess?—dehydration reactions. The bond between adjacent amino acids is called a **peptide bond** (Figure 3.17). The resulting long chain of amino acids is called a **polypeptide**. A protein is a polymer consisting of one or more polypeptides.

Your body has tens of thousands of different kinds of proteins. How is it possible to make such a huge variety of proteins from just 20 kinds of amino acids? The answer is arrangement. You know that you can make many different English words by varying the sequence of just 26 letters. Though the protein alphabet is slightly smaller (just 20 "letters"), the "words" are much longer, with a typical polypeptide being at least hundreds of amino acids in length. Just as each word is constructed from a unique succession of letters, each protein has a unique linear sequence of amino acids. This specific amino acid sequence—the "spelling" of a polypeptide—is called the protein's **primary structure** (Figure 3.18).

Changing a single letter can drastically affect the meaning of a word—"tasty" versus "nasty," for instance. Similarly, even a slight change in primary structure can affect a protein's ability to function. For example, the substitution of one amino acid for another at a particular position in hemoglobin, the blood protein that carries oxygen, causes sickle-cell disease, an inherited blood disorder (Figure 3.19). ✓

▼ Figure 3.18 **The primary structure (amino acid sequence) of a protein.** This chain, drawn in serpentine fashion so that it fits on the page, shows the primary structure of a protein called lysozyme. The names of the amino acids are given as their three-letter abbreviations.

▼ Figure 3.17 **Joining amino acids.** A dehydration reaction links adjacent amino acids by a peptide bond.

▼ Figure 3.19 **A single amino acid substitution in a protein causes sickle-cell disease.**

Normal red blood cell | Normal hemoglobin

(a) Normal hemoglobin. Red blood cells of humans are normally disk-shaped. Each cell contains millions of molecules of the protein hemoglobin, which transports oxygen from the lungs to other organs of the body. Next to the micrograph, you can see the first 7 of the 146 amino acids in a polypeptide chain of hemoglobin.

Sickled red blood cell | Sickle-cell hemoglobin

(b) Sickle-cell hemoglobin. A slight change in the primary structure of hemoglobin causes sickle-cell disease. The inherited substitution of one amino acid—valine in place of the amino acid glutamic acid—occurs at the 6th position of the polymer. Such abnormal hemoglobin molecules tend to crystallize, deforming some of the cells into a sickle shape. Someone with the disease suffers from dangerous episodes when the angular cells clog tiny blood vessels, impeding blood flow.

✓ CHECKPOINT

What are the monomers of all proteins?

Answer: amino acids

Protein Shape

At this point, you might be thinking that a polypeptide chain is the same thing as a protein, but that's not quite true. The distinction between the two is like the relationship between a long strand of yarn and a sweater that you could knit from the yarn. A functional protein is one or more polypeptide chains precisely twisted, folded, and coiled into a molecule of unique shape. If we dissect the overall shape of a protein, we can recognize at least three levels of structure: primary, secondary, and tertiary. Proteins with more than one polypeptide chain have a fourth level: quaternary structure. Figure 3.20 shows how the levels of protein structure are related.

▶ **Figure 3.21 A computer model showing a protein (purple) about to bind to its target (red).**

Target

Protein

When a cell makes a polypeptide, the chain usually folds spontaneously to form the functional shape for that protein. It is a protein's three-dimensional shape that enables the molecule to carry out its specific function in a cell. In almost every case, a protein's function depends on its ability to recognize and bind to some other molecule. For example, the specific shape of lactase enables it to recognize and attach to lactose, its molecular target. With proteins, *function follows form*—that is, what a protein does is a consequence of its shape (Figure 3.21).

What Determines Protein Shape?

A protein's shape is sensitive to the surrounding environment. An unfavorable change in temperature, pH, or some other quality of the environment can cause a protein to unravel and lose its normal shape. This is called **denaturation** of the protein. If you cook an egg, the transformation of the egg white from clear to opaque is caused by proteins in the egg white denaturing. As the proteins fall apart, they separate and form a white solid. One of the reasons why extremely high fevers are so dangerous is that some proteins in the body become denatured above 104°F.

The primary structure of a protein—its sequence of amino acids—causes it to fold into its functional shape. Each kind of protein has a unique primary structure and therefore a unique shape that enables it to do a certain job in a cell. What happens if it folds incorrectly? Misfolded proteins are associated with many diseases, including some severe nervous system disorders, such as Alzheimer's disease, mad cow disease, and Parkinson's disease. But what determines a protein's primary structure? As noted earlier, a protein consists of one or more polypeptide chains. The amino acid sequence of each chain is specified by a gene. And this relationship between genes and proteins brings us to this chapter's last category of large biological molecules: nucleic acids. ☑

▼ **Figure 3.20 The four levels of protein structure.**

(a) Primary structure. A protein's primary structure is the unique sequence of amino acids in its polypeptide chain(s).

Phe, Gly, Arg, Cys, Glu, Leu, Ala, Ala, Ala, Met, Lys, Arg, His, Gly, Leu, Asp, Asn

Amino acids

Hydrogen bond

Alpha helix

Pleated sheet

Polypeptide (single subunit)

A protein with four polypeptide subunits

(b) Secondary structure. Certain stretches of the polypeptide form local patterns called secondary structure. Two types are the alpha helix and pleated sheet. Secondary structure is reinforced by hydrogen bonds (dashed lines) along the polypeptide backbone. This drawing shows only the atoms of the polypeptide backbone, not the amino acid side groups.

(c) Tertiary structure. The overall three-dimensional shape of the polypeptide is called tertiary structure. It is reinforced by chemical bonds (not shown here) between the side groups of amino acids in different regions of the polypeptide chain.

(d) Quaternary structure. Proteins with two or more polypeptide chains have a quaternary structure, which results from bonds between the chains.

☑ CHECKPOINT

1. Which of these is *not* made of protein? hair, muscle, cellulose, enzymes
2. Why does a denatured protein no longer function?

Answers: 1. cellulose 2. It has lost its necessary shape.

Nucleic Acids

Nucleic acids are macromolecules that store information and provide the instructions for building proteins. The name *nucleic* comes from the fact that DNA is found in the nuclei of eukaryotic cells. There are actually two types of nucleic acids: **DNA** (which stands for deoxyribonucleic acid) and **RNA** (for ribonucleic acid). The genetic material that humans and other organisms inherit from their parents consists of giant molecules of DNA. The DNA resides in the cell as one or more very long fibers called chromosomes. A **gene** is a specific stretch of DNA that programs the amino acid sequence of a polypeptide. Those programmed instructions, however, are written in a kind of chemical code that must be translated from "nucleic acid language" to "protein language" (Figure 3.22). A cell's RNA molecules help make this translation (see Chapter 10).

Nucleic acids are polymers made from monomers called **nucleotides** (Figure 3.23). Each nucleotide contains three parts. At the center of each nucleotide is a five-carbon sugar (blue in the figure), deoxyribose in DNA and ribose in RNA. Attached to the sugar is a negatively charged phosphate group (yellow) containing a phosphorus atom bonded to oxygen atoms (PO_4^-). Also attached to the sugar is a nitrogen-containing base (green) made of one or two rings. The sugar and phosphate are the same in all nucleotides; only the base varies. Each DNA nucleotide has one of four possible nitrogenous bases: adenine (abbreviated A), guanine (G), cytosine (C), or thymine (T) (Figure 3.24). Thus, all genetic information is written in a four-letter alphabet.

▼ Figure 3.22 **Building a protein.** Within the cell, a gene (a segment of DNA) provides the directions to build a molecule of RNA, which can then be translated into a protein.

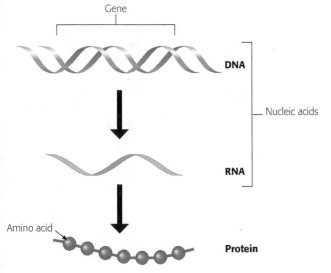

▼ Figure 3.23 **A DNA nucleotide.** A DNA nucleotide monomer consists of three parts: a sugar (deoxyribose), a phosphate, and a nitrogenous (nitrogen-containing) base.

(a) Atomic structure

(b) Symbol used in this book

▼ Figure 3.24 **The nitrogenous bases of DNA.** Notice that adenine and guanine have double-ring structures. Thymine and cytosine have single-ring structures.

Adenine (A)   **Guanine (G)**

Thymine (T)   **Cytosine (C)**

Space-filling model of DNA (showing the four bases in four different colors)

Dehydration reactions link nucleotide monomers into long chains called polynucleotides. In the case of DNA, these are called DNA strands (Figure 3.25a). Nucleotides are joined by covalent bonds between the sugar of one nucleotide and the phosphate of the next. This results in a **sugar-phosphate backbone**, a repeating pattern of sugar-phosphate-sugar-phosphate, with the bases (A, T, C, or G) hanging off the backbone like appendages. With different combinations of the four bases, the number of possible polynucleotide sequences is vast. One long polynucleotide may contain many genes, each a specific series of hundreds or thousands of nucleotides. And each gene stores information in its unique sequence of nucleotide bases. This sequence is a code that provides instructions for building a specific polypeptide from amino acids.

A molecule of cellular DNA is double-stranded, with two polynucleotide strands wrapped around each other to form a **double helix** (Figure 3.25b). In the central core of the helix, the bases along one DNA strand hydrogen-bond to bases along the other strand. The bonds are individually weak—they are hydrogen bonds, like those between water molecules—but collectively they zip the two strands together into a very stable double helix. Because of the way the functional groups hang off the bases, the base pairing in a DNA double helix is specific: The base A can pair only with T, and G can pair only with C. Thus, if you know the sequence of bases along one DNA strand, you also know the sequence along the complementary strand in the double helix. This unique base pairing is the basis of DNA's ability to act as the molecule of inheritance (as discussed in Chapter 10).

There are many similarities between DNA and RNA. Both are polymers of nucleotides, for example, and both are made of nucleotides consisting of a sugar, a phosphate, and a base. But there are three important differences. A first difference: as its name *ribonucleic acid* denotes, its sugar is ribose rather than deoxyribose. A second difference between RNA and DNA is that instead of the base thymine, RNA has a similar but distinct base called uracil (U) (Figure 3.26). Except for the presence of ribose and uracil, an RNA polynucleotide chain is identical to a DNA polynucleotide chain. The third difference is that RNA is usually found in single-stranded form, whereas DNA usually exists as a double helix.

Now that we've examined the structure of nucleic acids, we'll look at how a change in nucleotide sequence can affect protein production. ☑

☑ CHECKPOINT

1. DNA contains _____ polynucleotide strands, each composed of _____ kinds of nucleotides (Provide two numbers.).
2. If one DNA strand has the sequence GAATGC, what is the sequence of the other strand?

Answers: 1. two; four 2. CTTACG

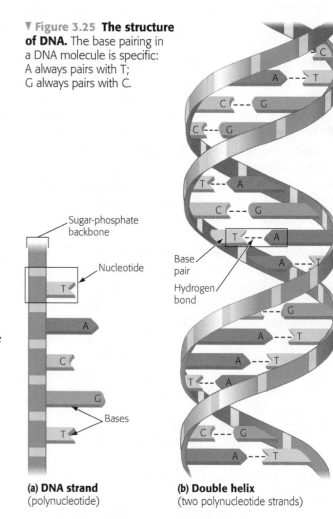

▼ Figure 3.25 **The structure of DNA.** The base pairing in a DNA molecule is specific: A always pairs with T; G always pairs with C.

Sugar-phosphate backbone

Nucleotide

Bases

Base pair

Hydrogen bond

(a) DNA strand
(polynucleotide)

(b) Double helix
(two polynucleotide strands)

▼ Figure 3.26 **An RNA nucleotide.** Notice that this RNA nucleotide differs from the DNA nucleotide in Figure 3.23 in two ways: The RNA sugar is ribose rather than deoxyribose; and the base is uracil (U) instead of thymine (T). The other three kinds of RNA nucleotides have the bases A, C, and G, as in DNA.

Nitrogenous base (A, G, C, or U)

Uracil (U)

Phosphate group

Sugar (ribose)

Does Lactose Intolerance Have a Genetic Basis?

The enzyme lactase, like all proteins, is encoded by a DNA gene. A reasonable hypothesis is that lactose-intolerant people have a defect in their lactase gene. However, this hypothesis is not supported by **observation**. Even though lactose intolerance runs in families, most lactose-intolerant people have a normal version of the lactase gene. This raises the **question**: What is the genetic basis for lactose intolerance?

In 2002, a group of Finnish and American scientists proposed the **hypothesis** that lactose intolerance can be correlated with a single nucleotide at a particular site within one chromosome. Based on their observations, they made the **prediction** that this site would be near, though not within, the lactase gene. In their **experiment**, they examined the genes of 196 lactose-intolerant people from nine Finnish families. Their **results** showed a 100% correlation between lactose intolerance and a nucleotide at a site

Human cell
(DNA in 46
chromosomes)

Chromosome 2
(one DNA molecule)

Section of
chromosome 2

DNA

Lactase gene

14,000 nucleotides

C at this site causes lactose intolerance
T at this site causes lactose tolerance

◄ **Figure 3.27 A genetic cause of lactose intolerance.** A 2002 study showed a correlation between lactose intolerance and a nucleotide at a specific location on one chromosome.

approximately 14,000 nucleotides away from the lactase gene—a relatively short distance in terms of the whole chromosome **(Figure 3.27)**. Other experiments showed that depending on the nucleotide sequence within this region of the DNA molecule, the action of the lactase gene is ramped up or down (in a way that likely involves producing a regulatory protein that interacts with the nucleotides near the lactase gene). This study shows how a small change in a DNA nucleotide sequence can have a major effect on the production of a protein and the well-being of an organism.

The Evolution of Lactose Intolerance in Humans

As you'll recall from the Biology and Society section, most of the world's population are lactose intolerant as adults and thus do not easily digest the milk sugar lactose. In fact, lactose intolerance is found in 80% of African Americans and Native Americans and 90% of Asian Americans but only in about 10% of Americans of northern European descent. And as discussed in the Process of Science section, lactose intolerance appears to have a genetic basis.

From an evolutionary perspective, it is reasonable to infer that lactose intolerance is rare among northern Europeans because the ability to tolerate lactose offered a survival advantage to their ancestors. In northern Europe's relatively cold climate, only one crop harvest a year is possible. Therefore, animals were a main source of food for early humans in that region. Cattle were first domesticated in northern Europe about 9,000 years ago **(Figure 3.28)**. With milk and other dairy products at hand year-round, natural selection would have favored anyone with a mutation that

kept the lactase gene switched on. In other cultures where dairy products were not a staple in the diet, natural selection would not favor such a mutation.

Researchers wondered whether the genetic basis for lactose tolerance in northern Europeans might be present in other cultures that kept dairy herds. To find out, a 2006 study compared the genetic makeup and lactose tolerance of 43 ethnic groups in East Africa. The researchers identified three other genetic changes that keep the lactase gene permanently active. These mutations appear to have occurred beginning around 7,000 years ago, about the time that archaeological evidence shows domestication of cattle in these African regions.

Genetic changes that confer a selective advantage, such as surviving cold winters or withstanding drought by drinking milk, spread rapidly in these early peoples. Evolutionary and cultural history is thus recorded in the genes of such individuals' descendants and in their continuing ability to digest milk.

▲ **Figure 3.28 A prehistoric cave painting in Lascaux, France, of wild cattle.** This species, known as aurochs, became the first domesticated cattle in Europe. Aurochs migrated from Asia about 250,000 years ago but became extinct in 1627.

Chapter Review

SUMMARY OF KEY CONCEPTS

Organic Compounds

Carbon Chemistry

Carbon atoms can form large, complex, diverse molecules by bonding to four partners, including other carbon atoms. In addition to variations in the size and shape of carbon skeletons, organic compounds vary in the presence and locations of different functional groups.

Giant Molecules from Smaller Building Blocks

Short polymer + Monomer → Longer polymer
Dehydration / Hydrolysis

Large Biological Molecules

Large biological molecules	Functions	Components	Examples
Carbohydrates	Dietary energy; storage; plant structure	Monosaccharide	Monosaccharides: glucose, fructose; Disaccharides: lactose, sucrose; Polysaccharides: starch, cellulose
Lipids	Long-term energy storage (fats); hormones (steroids)	Components of a triglyceride	Fats (triglycerides); steroids (testosterone, estrogen)
Proteins	Enzymes, structure, storage, contraction, transport, etc.	Amino acid	Lactase (an enzyme); hemoglobin (a transport protein)
Nucleic acids	Information storage	Nucleotide	DNA, RNA

Carbohydrates

Simple sugars (monosaccharides) provide cells with energy and carbon skeletons for use in building other organic compounds. Double sugars (disaccharides), such as sucrose, consist of two monosaccharides joined by a dehydration reaction. Polysaccharides are long polymers of sugar monomers. Starch in plants and glycogen in animals are storage polysaccharides. The cellulose of plant cell walls is an example of a structural polysaccharide.

Lipids

Lipids are hydrophobic. Fats are the major form of long-term energy storage in animals. A molecule of fat, or triglyceride, consists of three fatty acids joined by a dehydration reaction to a glycerol. Most animal fats are saturated, meaning that their fatty acids have the maximum number of hydrogens. Plant oils contain mostly unsaturated fats, having fewer hydrogens in the fatty acids because of double bonding in the carbon skeletons. Steroids, including cholesterol and the sex hormones, are also lipids.

Proteins

There are 20 types of amino acids, the monomers of proteins. They are linked by dehydration reactions to form polymers called polypeptides. A protein consists of one or more polypeptides folded into a specific three-dimensional shape. Contributing to this shape are four levels of structure:

Primary structure (sequence of amino acids) **Secondary structure** (localized folding) **Tertiary structure** (overall shape) **Quaternary structure** (found in proteins with multiple polypeptides)

Shape is sensitive to environment, and if a protein loses its shape because of an unfavorable environment, its function may also be lost.

Nucleic Acids

Nucleic acids include RNA and DNA. DNA takes the form of a double helix, two DNA strands (polymers of nucleotides) held together by hydrogen bonds between nucleotide components called bases. There are four kinds of DNA bases: adenine (A), guanine (G), thymine (T), and cytosine (C). A always pairs with T, and G always pairs with C. These base-pairing rules enable DNA to act as the molecule of inheritance. RNA has U (uracil) instead of T.

DNA double helix   **DNA strand**   **DNA nucleotide**

SELF-QUIZ

1. Draw the chemical structure of C_2H_4. (*Hint*: Each carbon has four bonds; each hydrogen has one.)

2. Monomers are joined together to form larger polymers through _____ reactions. This reaction releases a molecule of _____. Polymers are broken down into the monomers that make them up through the chemical reaction called _____.

3. Which of the following terms includes all the others in the list?
   a. polysaccharide
   b. carbohydrate
   c. monosaccharide
   d. disaccharide

4. One molecule of dietary fat is made by joining three molecules of _____ to one molecule of _____.

5. Which of the following statements about saturated fats is true?
   a. Saturated fats contain one or more double bonds along the hydrocarbon tails.
   b. Saturated fats contain the maximum number of hydrogens along the hydrocarbon tails.
   c. Saturated fats make up the majority of most plant oils.
   d. Saturated fats are typically healthier for you than unsaturated fats.

6. Humans and other animals cannot digest wood because they
   a. cannot digest any carbohydrates.
   b. cannot chew it fine enough.
   c. lack the enzyme needed to break down cellulose.
   d. get no nutrients from it.

7. Changing one amino acid within a protein could change what about a protein?
   a. the primary structure
   b. the overall shape of the protein
   c. the function of the protein
   d. all of the above

8. Most proteins can easily dissolve in water. Knowing that, where within the overall three-dimensional shape of a protein would you most likely find hydrophobic amino acids?

9. A shortage of phosphorus in the soil would make it especially difficult for a plant to manufacture
   a. DNA.
   b. proteins.
   c. cellulose.
   d. fatty acids.

10. A glucose molecule is to _____ as a nucleotide is to a _____.

11. Name three similarities between DNA and RNA. Name three differences.

12. What is the structure of a gene? What is the function of a gene?

Answers to these questions can be found in Appendix: Self-Quiz Answers.

THE PROCESS OF SCIENCE

13. A food manufacturer is advertising a new cake mix as fat-free. Scientists at the FDA are testing the product to see if it truly lacks fat. Hydrolysis of the cake mix yields glucose, fructose, glycerol, a number of amino acids, and several kinds of molecules with long hydrocarbon chains. Further analysis shows that most of the hydrocarbon chains have a carboxyl group at one end. What would you tell the food manufacturer if you were a spokesperson for the FDA?

14. Imagine that you have produced several versions of lactase, each of which differs from normal lactase by a single amino acid. Describe a test that could indirectly determine which of the versions significantly alters the three-dimensional shape of the protein.

BIOLOGY AND SOCIETY

15. Some amateur and professional athletes take anabolic steroids to help them build strength ("bulk up"). The health risks of this practice are extensively documented. Apart from these health issues, what is your opinion about the ethics of athletes using chemicals to enhance performance? Is this a form of cheating, or is it just part of the preparation required to stay competitive in a sport where anabolic steroids are commonly used? Defend your opinion.

16. Heart disease is the leading cause of death among people in the United States and other industrialized nations. Fast food is a major source of unhealthy fats that contribute significantly to heart disease. Imagine you're a juror sitting on a trial where a fast-food manufacturer is being sued for producing a harmful product. To what extent do you think manufacturers of unhealthy foods should be held responsible for the health consequences of their products? As a jury member, how would you vote?

17. Each year, industrial chemists develop and test thousands of new organic compounds for use as insecticides, fungicides, and weed killers. In what ways are these chemicals useful and important to us? In what ways can they be harmful? Is your general opinion of such chemicals positive or negative? What influences have shaped your feelings about these chemicals?

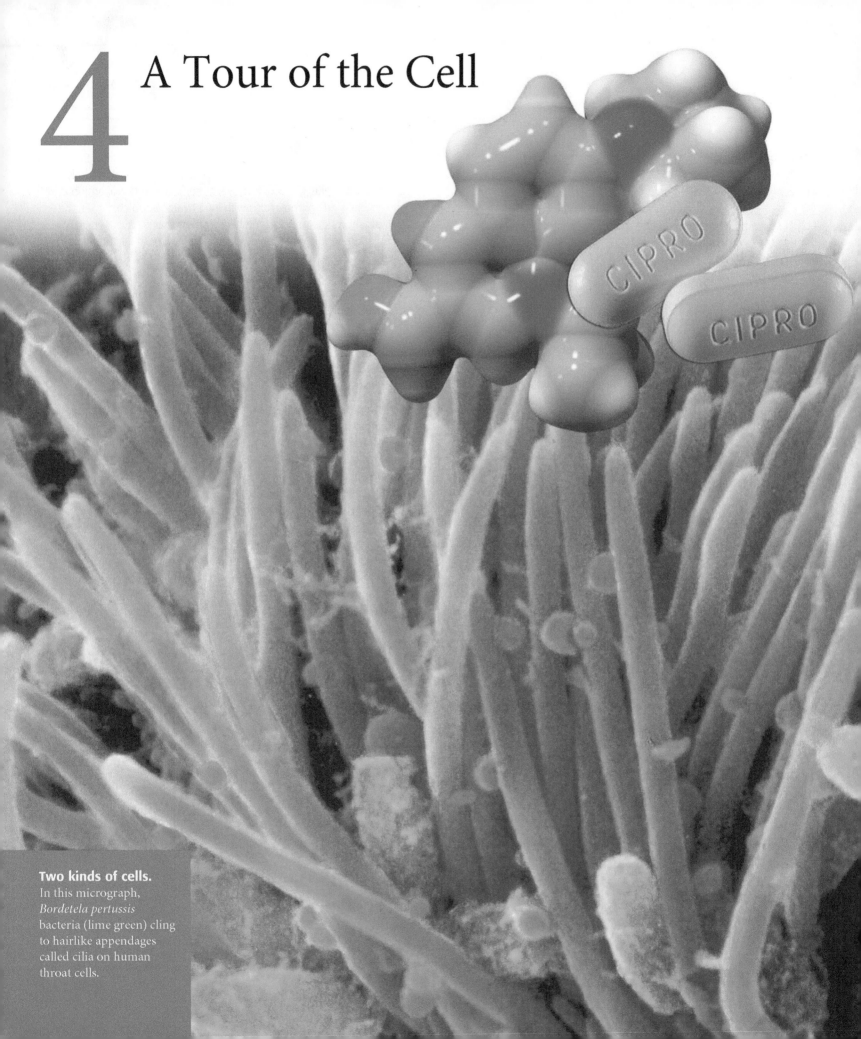

4 A Tour of the Cell

Two kinds of cells.
In this micrograph, *Bordetela pertussis* bacteria (lime green) cling to hairlike appendages called cilia on human throat cells.

Antibiotic-Resistant Bacteria BIOLOGY AND SOCIETY

Antibiotics: Drugs that Target Bacterial Cells

Antibiotics—drugs that disable or kill infectious bacteria—are a marvel of modern medicine. Most antibiotics are naturally occurring chemicals derived from microorganisms. After the isolation of penicillin from mold in 1928, a revolution in human health rapidly followed. Fatality rates of many diseases (such as bacterial pneumonia and surgical infections) fell drastically, saving millions of lives. In fact, the improvement to human health was so fast and so profound that some doctors predicted the end of infectious diseases altogether. Alas, this did not come to pass, for reasons discussed at the end of the chapter.

The goal of antibiotic treatment is to harm invading bacteria while doing no damage to the human host. But how does an antibiotic zero in on its target among trillions of human cells? Most antibiotics achieve such precision by binding to structures found only in bacterial cells. For example, erythromycin and streptomycin bind to the bacterial ribosome, a vital cellular structure responsible for the production of proteins. The ribosomes of people are different enough from those of bacteria that the antibiotics bind only to bacterial ribosomes, leaving human ribosomes unaffected. Ciprofloxacin, the antibiotic of choice against anthrax-causing bacteria, targets an enzyme that bacteria need to maintain their chromosome structure. Your cells can survive just fine without this enzyme because human chromosomes have a sufficiently different makeup. Penicillin, ampicillin, and bacitracin disrupt the synthesis of cell walls, a structural feature found in most bacteria that is absent from the cells of humans and other animals.

The effect of antibiotics underscores the main point of this chapter: To understand how life works—whether in bacteria or in your own body—you first need to learn about cells. Cells are the smallest entities that can display all the characteristics of life. Many living organisms are single-celled; more complex organisms are multicelled. In this chapter, we'll explore the structure and function of cells. Along the way, we'll consider how antibiotics target specific cell structures of infectious bacteria.

The Microscopic World of Cells

Each cell in the human body is a miniature marvel of great complexity. If the space shuttle was reduced to microscopic size, its complexity would pale next to a living cell.

Organisms are either single-celled, such as most prokaryotes and protists, or multicelled, such as plants, animals, and most fungi. Your own body is a cooperative society of trillions of cells of many specialized types. Three examples are the muscle cells that keep your heart beating, the nerve cells that control your muscles, and the red blood cells that carry oxygen throughout your body. Everything you do—every action and every thought—reflects processes that occur at the cellular level. For exploring this world of cells, our main tools are microscopes.

What's the smallest object that can be seen in a microscope?

Microscopes as Windows on the World of Cells

Our understanding of nature often goes hand in hand with the invention and refinement of instruments that extend the human senses. For example, before microscopes were first used in the 1600s, no one knew that living organisms were composed of cells.

The type of microscope used by Renaissance scientists is the same kind of microscope found today in most biology classrooms: a **light microscope (LM)**. Visible light is projected through the specimen, such as a single-celled protist (Figure 4.1). Glass lenses enlarge the image and project it into a human eye or a camera.

Two important factors in microscopy are magnification and resolving power. **Magnification** is an increase in the object's image size compared with its actual size. The clarity of that magnified image depends on **resolving power**, the ability of an optical instrument to show two objects as separate. For example, what appears to the unaided eye as one star may be resolved as twin stars with a telescope. Each optical instrument—be it an eye, a telescope, or a microscope—has a limit to its resolving power. The normal human eye can resolve points as close together as 0.1 millimeter (mm), about the size of a very fine grain of sand. For light microscopes, the resolving power is about 0.2 micrometer (µm), the size of a small bacterial cell. This limits light microscopes to about 1,000× magnification. With greater magnification, an LM image becomes blurry.

Cells were first described in 1665 by the British scientist Robert Hooke, who used a microscope to examine a thin slice of oak tree bark. For the next two centuries, scientists found cells in every organism examined with a microscope. By the mid-1800s, this accumulation of evidence led to the **cell theory**, which states that all living things are composed of cells and that all cells come from other cells.

Our scientific knowledge of cell structure took a giant leap forward as biologists began using electron microscopes in the 1950s. Instead of using light, an

▼ Figure 4.1 **The protist *Paramecium* viewed with three different types of microscopes.** Photographs taken with microscopes are called micrographs. Throughout this textbook, micrographs will have size notations along the side. For example, "LM 1,000×" indicates that the micrograph was taken with a light microscope and the objects are magnified to 1,000 times their original size.

TYPES OF MICROGRAPHS		
Light Micrograph (LM) (for viewing living cells)	**Scanning Electron Micrograph (SEM)** (for viewing surface features)	**Transmission Electron Micrograph (TEM)** (for viewing internal structures)

LM 300×

Light micrograph of a protist, *Paramecium*

Colorized SEM 300×

Scanning electron micrograph of *Paramecium*

Colorized TEM 300×

Transmission electron micrograph of *Paramecium*

electron microscope (EM) uses a beam of electrons to resolve objects. This gives electron microscopes 100-fold better resolution than light microscopes. **Figures 4.1b** and **4.1c** show images made with two kinds of electron microscopes: a **scanning electron microscope (SEM)**—used to study the detailed architecture of the cell surface—and a **transmission electron microscope (TEM)**—to study the internal structure of a cell.

The most powerful modern electron microscopes can distinguish objects as small as 0.2 nanometer (nm) (**Figure 4.2**), which is about a million times smaller than the period at the end of this sentence. The highest-power electron micrographs you will see in this book have magnifications of about 100,000×. Such power can reveal many details within a cell (**Figure 4.3**). However, preparing a specimen for an electron microscope usually requires killing and preserving the cell with a chemical fixative before it can be examined. Thus, the light microscope is still very useful as a window on living cells. ☑

▼ **Figure 4.2 An electron microscope.** An electron micrograph is formed by a beam of electrons that is generated at the top of the microscope's column and travels through the specimen being observed.

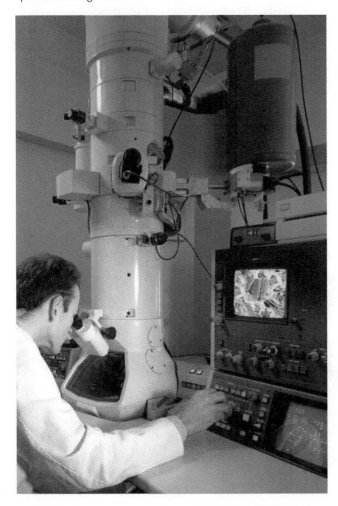

▼ **Figure 4.3 The size range of cells.** Starting at the top of this scale with 10 m (10 meters) and going down, each measurement along the left side marks a tenfold decrease in size.

Measurement Equivalents

1 meter (m) = 100 cm = 1,000 mm = about 39.4 inches

1 centimeter (cm) = 10^{-2} ($\frac{1}{100}$) m = about 0.4 inch

1 millimeter (mm) = 10^{-3} ($\frac{1}{1,000}$) m = $\frac{1}{10}$ cm

1 micrometer (μm) = 10^{-6} m = 10^{-3} mm

1 nanometer (nm) = 10^{-9} m = 10^{-3} μm

☑ **CHECKPOINT**

Identify which type of microscope you would use to study (a) the internal structure of a dead human liver cell; (b) the finest details of surface texture of a human hair; and (c) the changes in shape of a living human white blood cell.

Answers: (a) transmission electron microscope; (b) scanning electron microscope; (c) light microscope

The Two Major Categories of Cells

What do you have in common with a mushroom?

The countless cells that exist on Earth fall into two basic categories: prokaryotic cells and eukaryotic cells.

Prokaryotic cells are found in organisms of the domains Bacteria and Archaea, known as prokaryotes (see Figures 1.4 and 1.8). Organisms of the domain Eukarya—protists, plants, fungi, and animals—are composed of **eukaryotic cells** and are called eukaryotes.

All cells have several features in common. They are all bounded by a barrier called a **plasma membrane**, which regulates the traffic of molecules between the cell and its surroundings. Inside all cells is a thick, jellylike fluid called the **cytosol**, in which cellular components are suspended. All cells have one or more **chromosomes** carrying genes made of DNA. And all cells have **ribosomes** that build proteins according to instructions from the genes. As mentioned in the Biology and Society section, some antibiotics—such as streptomycin—target prokaryotic ribosomes, crippling protein synthesis in the bacterial invaders but not in the eukaryotic host (that is, you).

Although they have many similarities, prokaryotic and eukaryotic cells differ in several important ways. Fossil evidence shows that prokaryotes were the first life on Earth, appearing more than 3.5 billion years ago. In contrast, the first eukaryotes did not appear until around 2.1 billion years ago. Prokaryotic cells are usually much smaller—about one-tenth the length of a typical eukaryotic cell—and are simpler in structure.

The most significant structural difference is that only eukaryotic cells have **organelles** ("little organs"), membrane-enclosed structures that perform specific functions. The most important organelle is the **nucleus**, which houses most of a eukaryotic cell's DNA and is surrounded by a double membrane. A prokaryotic cell lacks a nucleus; its DNA is coiled into a "nucleus-like" region called the **nucleoid**, which is not partitioned from the rest of the cell by membranes.

Consider this analogy: A eukaryotic cell is like an office that is separated into cubicles. Within each cubicle, a specific function is performed, thus dividing the labor among many internal compartments. The cubicle boundaries within eukaryotic cells are made from membranes that help maintain a unique chemical environment inside each cubicle. In contrast, the interior of a prokaryotic cell is like an open warehouse. The spaces for specific tasks are distinct but not separated by barriers.

Figure 4.4 depicts an idealized prokaryotic cell. Surrounding the plasma membrane of most prokaryotic cells is a rigid cell wall, which protects the cell and helps maintain its shape. Recall from the Biology and Society section that bacterial cell walls are the targets of some antibiotics. In some prokaryotes, a sticky outer coat called a capsule surrounds the cell wall. Capsules provide protection and help prokaryotes stick to surfaces. Capsules enable some infectious bacteria to evade engulfment by your immune system cells. Some prokaryotes have short projections called pili, which can also attach to surfaces. Many prokaryotic cells have flagella, long projections that propel them through their liquid environment. ✓

✓ CHECKPOINT

1. How is the nucleoid region of a prokaryotic cell unlike the nucleus of a eukaryotic cell?
2. Name four structures found in both prokaryotic and eukaryotic cells.

Answers: 1. There is no membrane enclosing the prokaryotic nucleoid region. 2. plasma membrane, chromosomes, cytosol, and ribosomes

▼ Figure 4.4 **An idealized prokaryotic cell.**

Colorized TEM 26,000×

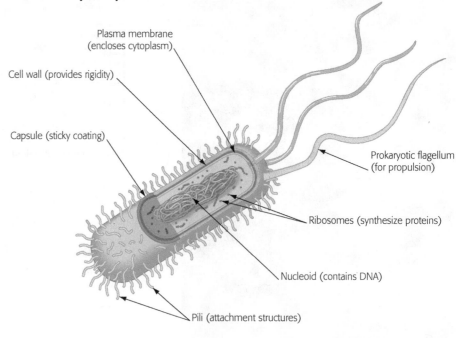

Plasma membrane (encloses cytoplasm)

Cell wall (provides rigidity)

Capsule (sticky coating)

Prokaryotic flagellum (for propulsion)

Ribosomes (synthesize proteins)

Nucleoid (contains DNA)

Pili (attachment structures)

An Overview of Eukaryotic Cells

All eukaryotic cells—whether from animals, plants, protists, or fungi—are fundamentally similar to one another and quite different from prokaryotic cells. **Figure 4.5** provides an overview of an idealized animal cell and plant cell. To keep from getting lost on our tour of the cell, we'll use miniature versions of these diagrams as road maps, highlighting the structure we're discussing. Notice that the structures are color-coded; we'll use this color scheme throughout *Essential Biology*.

The entire region of the cell between the nucleus and plasma membrane is called the **cytoplasm**. (This term is also used to refer to the interior of a prokaryotic cell.) The cytoplasm of a eukaryotic cell consists of various organelles suspended in the liquid cytosol. As you can see in Figure 4.5, most organelles are found in both animal and plant cells. But you'll notice some important differences—for example, only plant cells have chloroplasts (where photosynthesis occurs) and only animal cells have lysosomes (bubbles of digestive enzymes surrounded by membranes). In the rest of this section, we'll take a closer look at the architecture of eukaryotic cells, beginning with the plasma membrane. ☑

▼ **Figure 4.5** **A view of an idealized animal cell and plant cell.** For now, the labels on the drawings are just words, but these organelles will come to life as we take a closer look at how each part of the cell functions.

Idealized animal cell

Idealized plant cell

☑ CHECKPOINT

1. Name three structures in plant cells that animal cells lack.
2. Name two structures that may be found in animal cells but not in plant cells.

*Answers: **1.** chloroplasts, a central vacuole, and a cell wall **2.** centrioles and lysosomes*

Membrane Structure

Before we enter the cell to explore the organelles, let's make a quick stop at the surface of this microscopic world. The plasma membrane is the edge of life, the boundary that separates the living cell from its nonliving surroundings. The plasma membrane is a remarkable film, so thin that you would have to stack 8,000 of these membranes to equal the thickness of the page you're reading. Yet the plasma membrane can regulate the traffic of chemicals into and out of the cell. The key to how a membrane works is its structure.

The Plasma Membrane: A Fluid Mosaic of Lipids and Proteins

The plasma membrane and other membranes of the cell are composed mostly of lipids and proteins. Most of the lipids belong to a special category called **phospholipids**. They are related to dietary fats but have only two fatty acid tails instead of three (see Figure 3.11b). In place of the third fatty acid, a phospholipid has a phosphate group (a combination of phosphorus and oxygen).

The phosphate group is electrically charged, making it hydrophilic ("water-loving"). But the two fatty acid tails are hydrophobic ("water-fearing"). Thus, phospholipids have a chemical ambivalence in their interactions with water. The phosphate group head mixes with water, while the fatty acid tails avoid it. This makes phospholipids good membrane material. By forming a two-layered membrane, or **phospholipid bilayer**, the hydrophobic fatty acid tails of the molecules stay in the membrane interior away from water, while the hydrophilic phospholipid heads remain surrounded by water on the inside or outside of the cell (Figure 4.6a). Embedded in the phospholipid bilayer of most membranes are proteins that help regulate traffic across the membrane and perform other functions (Figure 4.6b). (You'll learn more about membrane proteins in Chapter 5.)

Membranes are not static sheets of molecules locked rigidly in place. The phospholipids and most of the proteins are free to drift about in the plane of the membrane. Thus, a membrane is a **fluid mosaic**—fluid because the molecules can move freely past one another and a mosaic because of the diversity of proteins that float like icebergs in the phospholipid sea. In the Process of Science section, we'll see how some bacteria can cause illness by piercing the plasma membrane. ☑

▼ Figure 4.6 **The plasma membrane structure.**

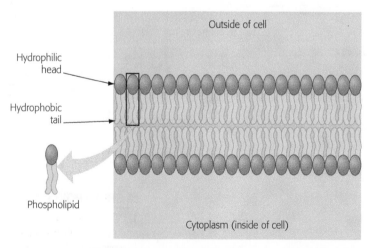

(a) Phospholipid bilayer of membrane. At the interface between two aqueous compartments, phospholipids arrange themselves into a bilayer. The symbol for a phospholipid that we'll use in this book looks like a lollipop with two wavy sticks. The "head" is the end with the phosphate group, and the two "tails" are hydrocarbons. The bilayer arrangement keeps the heads exposed to water while keeping the tails in the oily interior of the membrane.

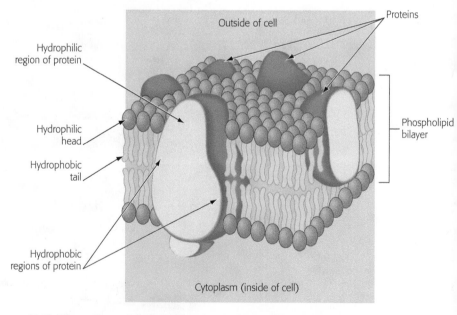

(b) Fluid mosaic model of membrane. Membrane proteins, like the phospholipids, have both hydrophilic and hydrophobic regions.

What Makes a Superbug?

Some bacteria cause disease by rupturing the plasma membrane of human immune cells. One example is a common bacteria called *Staphylococcus aureus*. These bacteria, commonly found on the skin, are usually harmless but may multiply and spread, causing a "staph infection." Staph infections typically occur in hospitals and can cause serious, even life-threatening conditions, such as pneumonia or necrotizing fasciitis ("flesh-eating disease").

Most staph infections can be treated by antibiotics, including one called methicillin. But particularly dangerous strains of *S. aureus*—known as MRSA (for methicillin-resistant *S. aureus* or multi-drug-resistant SA)—are unaffected by these antibiotics. Recently, MRSA infections have become more common and have even turned up in nonhospital settings, such as gyms and schools. In 2007, scientists from the National Institutes of Health (NIH) studied one deadly MRSA strain. They began with the **observation** that other bacteria use a protein called PSM to disable human immune cells by forming holes that rip apart the plasma membrane. This led them to **question** whether PSM plays a role in MRSA infection **(Figure 4.7)**. Their **hypothesis** was that MRSA bacteria lacking the ability to produce PSM would be less deadly than normal MRSA strains.

In their **experiment**, they infected seven mice with a normal MRSA strain and eight mice with an MRSA strain genetically engineered to not produce PSM. The **results** over the next three days were striking: All seven mice infected with the normal MRSA strain died, while five of the eight mice infected with the strain that did not produce PSM survived. Under the electron microscope, immune cells from all of the dead mice showed holes within the plasma membrane. The researchers concluded that normal MRSA strains use the membrane-destroying PSM protein, but other factors must come into play (possibly including other membrane-destroying proteins) because three mice died even in the absence of PSM. Active study of MRSA bacteria and how they interact with human cellular structures continues today.

▼ **Figure 4.7 How MRSA may destroy human immune cells.**

Colorized SEM 1,300×

Methicillin-resistant
Staphylococcus aureus (MRSA)

1 MRSA bacterium producing PSM proteins

2 PSM proteins forming hole in human immune cell plasma membrane

PSM protein

Pore

Plasma membrane

3 Cell bursting, losing its contents through the holes

Cell Surfaces

Surrounding their plasma membranes, plant cells have a cell wall made from cellulose fibers embedded in other molecules (see Figure 3.9c). The walls protect the cells, maintain cell shape, and keep cells from absorbing so much water that they burst. Plant cells are connected via channels that pass through the cell walls, joining the cytoplasm of each cell to that of its neighbors. These channels allow water and other small molecules to move between cells, integrating the activities of a tissue.

Although animal cells lack a cell wall, most of them secrete a sticky coat called the **extracellular matrix**. This layer holds cells together in tissues, and it can also have protective and supportive functions. In addition, the surfaces of most animal cells contain **cell junctions**, structures that connect cells together into tissues, allowing them to function in a coordinated way. ☑

☑ **CHECKPOINT**

What polysaccharide is the primary component of plant cell walls?

Answer: *cellulose*

The Nucleus and Ribosomes: Genetic Control of the Cell

If we think of the cell as a factory, then the nucleus is its executive boardroom. The top managers are the genes, the inherited DNA molecules that direct almost all the business of the cell. Each gene is a stretch of DNA that stores the information necessary to produce a particular protein. Proteins then do most of the actual work of the cell.

Structure and Function of the Nucleus

The nucleus is separated from the cytoplasm by a double membrane called the **nuclear envelope** (Figure 4.8). Each membrane of the nuclear envelope is similar in structure to the plasma membrane. Pores in the envelope allow certain materials to pass between the nucleus and the cytoplasm. Within the nucleus, long DNA molecules and associated proteins form fibers called **chromatin**. Each long chromatin fiber constitutes one chromosome (Figure 4.9). The number of chromosomes in a cell depends on the species; for example, each human body cell has 46 chromosomes, whereas rice cells have 24 and dog cells have 78 (see Figure 8.2 for more examples). The **nucleolus** (shown in Figure 4.8), a prominent structure within the nucleus, is the site where the components of ribosomes are made. We'll examine ribosomes next. ☑

▼ Figure 4.8 **The nucleus.**

Ribosomes · Chromatin fiber · Nuclear envelope · Nucleolus · Nuclear pore

TEM 7,000×

Surface of nuclear envelope

TEM 10,000×

Nuclear pores

▼ Figure 4.9 **The relationship between DNA, chromatin, and a chromosome.**

DNA molecule

Proteins

Chromatin fiber

Chromosome

Ribosomes

The small blue dots in the cells in Figure 4.5 and outside the nucleus in Figure 4.8 represent the ribosomes. As you'll see in the next section, ribosomes are responsible for protein synthesis (Figure 4.10). In eukaryotic cells, the components of ribosomes are made in the nucleus, then transported through the pores of the nucleus into the cytoplasm. It is in the cytoplasm that the ribosomes begin their work. Some are suspended in the cytosol, making proteins that remain within the fluid of the cell (Figure 4.11). Other ribosomes are attached to the outside of the nucleus or an organelle called the endoplasmic reticulum, making proteins that are incorporated into membranes or secreted by the cell. Free and bound ribosomes are structurally identical, and ribosomes can swing their locations, moving between the endoplasmic reticulum and the cytosol.

▼ Figure 4.10 **A computer model of a ribosome synthesizing a protein.**

Ribosome

mRNA

Protein

▼ Figure 4.11 **The locations of ribosomes.**

TEM 50,000×

Ribosomes in cytoplasm

Ribosomes attached to endoplasmic reticulum

How DNA Directs Protein Production

How do the DNA "executives" in the nucleus direct the "workers" in the cytoplasm? Figure 4.12 shows the sequence of events during protein production in a eukaryotic cell (with the DNA and other structures being shown disproportionately large in relation to the nucleus). ❶ DNA programs protein production in the cytoplasm by transferring its coded information to a molecule called messenger RNA (mRNA). Like a middle manager, the mRNA molecule then carries the order to "build this type of protein" from the nucleus to the cytoplasm. ❷ The mRNA exits through pores in the nuclear envelope and travels to the cytoplasm, where it then binds to ribosomes. ❸ The ribosome moves along the mRNA, translating the genetic message into a protein with a specific amino acid sequence. (You'll learn how the message is translated in Chapter 10.) ☑

▼ Figure 4.12 **DNA → RNA → Protein.** Inherited genes in the nucleus control protein production and hence the activities of the cell.

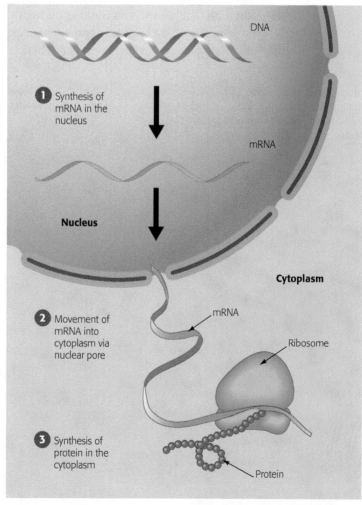

DNA

❶ Synthesis of mRNA in the nucleus

mRNA

Nucleus

Cytoplasm

❷ Movement of mRNA into cytoplasm via nuclear pore

mRNA

Ribosome

❸ Synthesis of protein in the cytoplasm

Protein

☑ **CHECKPOINT**

1. What is the function of ribosomes?
2. What is the role of mRNA in making a protein?

Answers: 1. protein synthesis 2. A molecule of mRNA carries the genetic message from a gene (DNA) to ribosomes that translate it into protein.

The Endomembrane System: Manufacturing and Distributing Cellular Products

The cytoplasm of a eukaryotic cell is partitioned by organelle membranes (see Figure 4.5). Some of the organelles are connected to each other, either directly by their membranes or by transfer of membrane segments between them. Together, these organelles form the **endomembrane system**. This system includes the nuclear envelope, the endoplasmic reticulum, the Golgi apparatus, lysosomes, and vacuoles.

The Endoplasmic Reticulum

The **endoplasmic reticulum (ER)** is one of the main manufacturing facilities within a cell. It produces an enormous variety of molecules. Connected to the nuclear envelope, the ER forms an extensive labyrinth of tubes and sacs running throughout the cytoplasm (Figure 4.13). A membrane separates the internal ER compartment from the cytosol. There are two components that make up the ER: rough ER and smooth ER. These two types of ER are physically connected but differ in structure and function.

Rough ER

The "rough" in **rough ER** refers to ribosomes that stud the outside of its membrane. One of the functions of rough ER is to make more membrane. Phospholipids made by enzymes of the rough ER are inserted into the ER membrane. In this way, the ER membrane grows, and portions of it are transferred to other parts of the cell. The ribosomes attached to the rough ER produce proteins that will be inserted into the growing ER membrane, transported to other organelles, and eventually exported. Cells that secrete a lot of protein—such as the cells of your salivary glands, which secrete enzymes into your mouth—are especially rich in rough ER. Some products manufactured by rough ER are dispatched to other locations in the cell by means of **transport vesicles**, sacs made of membrane that bud off from the rough ER (Figure 4.14).

▼ Figure 4.13 **The endoplasmic reticulum (ER).** In this drawing (top) and micrograph (bottom), the flattened sacs of rough ER and the tubes of smooth ER are connected. Notice that the ER is also connected to the nuclear envelope.

Nuclear envelope

Ribosomes

Rough ER

Smooth ER

TEM 26,500×

Ribosomes

▼ Figure 4.14 **How rough ER manufactures and packages secretory proteins.**

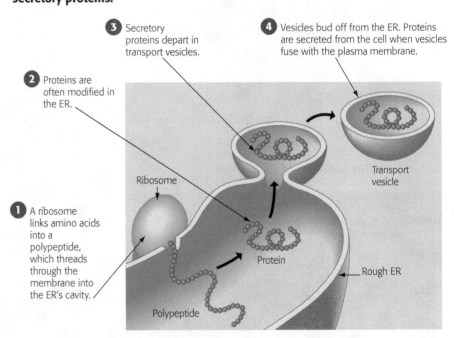

3 Secretory proteins depart in transport vesicles.

4 Vesicles bud off from the ER. Proteins are secreted from the cell when vesicles fuse with the plasma membrane.

2 Proteins are often modified in the ER.

1 A ribosome links amino acids into a polypeptide, which threads through the membrane into the ER's cavity.

Ribosome

Protein

Transport vesicle

Rough ER

Polypeptide

Smooth ER

The "smooth" in **smooth ER** refers to the fact that this organelle lacks the ribosomes that populate the surface of rough ER (see Figure 4.13). A diversity of enzymes built into the smooth ER membrane enables this organelle to perform many functions. One is the synthesis of lipids, including steroids (see Figure 3.13). For example, the cells in ovaries or testes that produce the steroid sex hormones are enriched with smooth ER. In liver cells, enzymes of the smooth ER detoxify circulating sedatives such as barbiturates, stimulants such as amphetamines, and some antibiotics (which is why they don't persist in the bloodstream after combating an infection). As liver cells are exposed to a drug, the amounts of smooth ER and its detoxifying enzymes increase. This can strengthen the body's tolerance of the drug, meaning that higher doses will be required in the future to achieve the desired effect. The growth of smooth ER in response to one drug can also increase tolerance of other drugs. Barbiturate use, such as frequently taking sleeping pills, may make certain antibiotics less effective by accelerating their breakdown in the liver. Furthermore, increased tolerance of drugs is one of the hallmarks of addiction—a potentially serious consequence of the continued use of certain drugs.

How does the liver detoxify drugs from the blood?

The Golgi Apparatus

Working in close partnership with the ER, the **Golgi apparatus**, an organelle named for its discoverer (Italian scientist Camillo Golgi), receives, refines, stores, and distributes chemical products of the cell (**Figure 4.15**). Products made in the ER reach the Golgi apparatus in transport vesicles. The Golgi apparatus consists of a stack of membrane plates. **1** One side of a Golgi stack serves as a receiving dock for vesicles from the ER. **2** Proteins within a vesicle are usually modified by enzymes during their transit from the receiving to the shipping side of the Golgi apparatus. For example, molecular identification tags, such as phosphate groups, may be added that serve to mark and sort protein molecules into different batches for different destinations. **3** The shipping side of a Golgi stack is a depot from which finished products can be carried in transport vesicles to other organelles or to the plasma membrane. Vesicles that bind with the plasma membrane transfer proteins to it or secrete finished products to the outside of the cell. ☑

☑ CHECKPOINT

1. What makes rough ER rough?
2. What is the relationship between the Golgi apparatus and the ER in a protein-secreting cell?

Answers: 1. ribosomes attached to the membrane 2. The Golgi apparatus receives proteins from the ER via vesicles, processes the proteins, and then dispatches them in vesicles.

▼ Figure 4.15 **The Golgi apparatus.** This component of the endomembrane system consists of flattened sacs arranged something like a stack of pancakes. The number of stacks in a cell (from a few to hundreds) correlates with how active the cell is in secreting proteins.

"Receiving" side of the Golgi apparatus

Colorized SEM 130,000×

New vesicle forming

Transport vesicle from rough ER

"Receiving" side of the Golgi apparatus

New vesicle forming

Transport vesicle from the Golgi apparatus

"Shipping" side of the Golgi apparatus

Plasma membrane

Lysosomes

A **lysosome** is a membrane-enclosed sac of digestive enzymes found in animal cells. Lysosomes are absent from most plant cells. Lysosomes develop from vesicles that bud off from the Golgi apparatus. Enzymes within a lysosome can break down large molecules such as proteins, polysaccharides, fats, and nucleic acids. The lysosome provides a compartment where the cell can digest these molecules safely, without unleashing these digestive enzymes on the cell itself.

Lysosomes have several types of digestive functions. Many cells engulf nutrients into tiny cytoplasmic sacs called food vacuoles. Lysosomes fuse with the food vacuoles, exposing the food to enzymes that digest it **(Figure 4.16a)**. Small molecules that result from this digestion, such as amino acids, leave the lysosome and nourish the cell. Lysosomes also help destroy harmful bacteria. For example, our white blood cells ingest bacteria into vacuoles, and lysosomal enzymes that

are emptied into these vacuoles rupture the bacterial cell walls. In addition, lysosomes break down the large molecules of damaged organelles. Without harming the cell, a lysosome can engulf and digest parts of another organelle, essentially recycling it by making its molecules available for the construction of new organelles **(Figure 4.16b)**. Lysosomes also have sculpting functions in embryonic development. In an early human embryo, lysosomes release enzymes that digest webbing between fingers of the developing hand.

The importance of lysosomes to cell function and human health is made strikingly clear by hereditary disorders called lysosomal storage diseases. A person with such a disease is missing one or more of the digestive enzymes normally found within lysosomes. The abnormal lysosomes become engorged with indigestible substances, and this eventually interferes with other cellular functions. Most of these diseases are fatal in early childhood. In Tay-Sachs disease, lysosomes lack a lipid-digesting enzyme. As a result, nerve cells die as they accumulate excess lipids, ravaging the nervous system. Fortunately, storage diseases are rare. ☑

☑ CHECKPOINT

How can defective lysosomes result in excess accumulation of a particular chemical compound in a cell?

Answer: If the lysosomes lack an enzyme needed to break down the compound, the cell will accumulate an excess of that compound.

▼ Figure 4.16 **Two functions of lysosomes.**

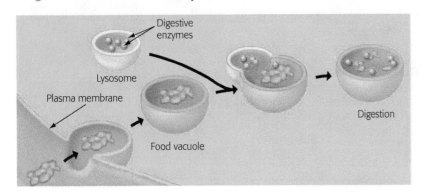

Digestive enzymes

Lysosome

Plasma membrane

Food vacuole

Digestion

(a) A lysosome digesting food

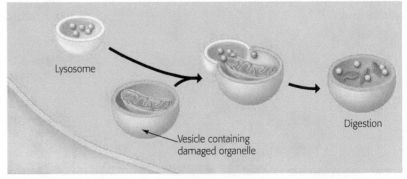

Lysosome

Vesicle containing damaged organelle

Digestion

(b) A lysosome breaking down the molecules of damaged organelles

Organelle fragment

Vesicle containing two damaged organelles

Organelle fragment

TEM 56,250x

Vacuoles

Vacuoles are large sacs of membrane that bud from the ER, Golgi apparatus, or plasma membrane. Vacuoles have a variety of functions. For example, Figure 4.16a shows a food vacuole budding from the plasma membrane. Certain freshwater protists have contractile vacuoles that pump out excess water that flows into the cell from the outside environment (Figure 4.17a).

Another type of vacuole is a **central vacuole**, which can account for more than half the volume of a mature plant cell (Figure 4.17b). The central vacuole of a plant cell is a versatile compartment. It stores organic nutrients, such as proteins stockpiled in the vacuoles of seed cells. It also contributes to plant growth by absorbing water and causing cells to expand. In the cells of flower petals, central vacuoles may contain pigments that attract pollinating insects. Central vacuoles may also contain poisons that protect against plant-eating animals.

▼ Figure 4.17 **Two types of vacuoles.**

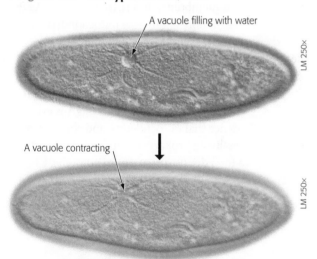

A vacuole filling with water

A vacuole contracting

LM 250×

LM 250×

(a) Contractile vacuole in *Paramecium*. A contractile vacuole fills with water and then contracts to pump the water out of the cell.

Central vacuole

Colorized TEM 1,700×

(b) Central vacuole in a plant cell. The central vacuole (colorized blue in this micrograph) is often the largest organelle in a mature plant cell.

Figure 4.18 will help you review how organelles of the endomembrane system are related. Note that a product made in one part of the endomembrane system may exit the cell or become part of another organelle without crossing a membrane. Also note that membrane made by the ER can become part of the plasma membrane through the fusion of a transport vesicle. In this way, even the plasma membrane is related to the endomembrane system. ☑

▼ Figure 4.18 **Review of the endomembrane system.** The dashed arrows show some of the pathways of cell product distribution and membrane migration via transport vesicles.

Rough ER

Golgi apparatus

Transport vesicle

Plasma membrane

Secretory protein

Transport vesicles carry enzymes and other proteins from the rough ER to the Golgi for processing.

Lysosomes carrying digestive enzymes can fuse with other vesicles.

Some products are secreted from the cell.

Vacuoles store some cell products.

Golgi apparatus

New vesicle forming

Transport vesicle from the Golgi apparatus

Plasma membrane

TEM 31,000×

☑ **CHECKPOINT**

Place the following cellular structures in the order they would be used in the production and secretion of a protein: Golgi apparatus, nucleus, plasma membrane, ribosome, transport vesicle.

Answer: nucleus, ribosome, transport vesicle, Golgi apparatus, plasma membrane

67

Chloroplasts and Mitochondria: Energy Conversion

A cell requires a continuous energy supply to perform the work of life. Two organelles act as cellular power stations: chloroplasts and mitochondria.

Chloroplasts

Most of the living world runs on the energy provided by photosynthesis, the conversion of light energy from the sun to the chemical energy of sugar and other organic molecules. **Chloroplasts**, which are unique to the photosynthetic cells of plants and algae, are the organelles that perform photosynthesis.

A chloroplast is partitioned into three major compartments by internal membranes (Figure 4.19). One compartment is the space between the two membranes that surround the chloroplast. The **stroma**, a thick fluid within the chloroplast, is the second compartment. Suspended in that fluid, the interior of a network of membrane-enclosed disks and tubes forms the third compartment. Notice in Figure 4.19 that the disks occur in interconnected stacks called **grana** (singular, *granum*). The grana are a chloroplast's solar power packs, the structures that trap light energy and convert it to chemical energy. (You'll learn the details of photosynthesis as it occurs within a chloroplast in Chapter 7.)

Mitochondria

Mitochondria (singular, *mitochondrion*) are the organelles of cellular respiration in nearly all cells, harvesting energy from sugars and other food molecules and using it to produce another form of chemical energy called ATP (which stands for adenosine triphosphate). Cells use molecules of ATP as the direct energy source for most of their work. In contrast to chloroplasts, mitochondria are found in almost all eukaryotic cells, including those of plants and those in your body.

An envelope of two membranes encloses the mitochondrion, which contains a thick fluid called the **matrix** (Figure 4.20). The inner membrane of the envelope has numerous infoldings called **cristae**. Many of the enzymes and other molecules that function in cellular respiration are embedded in the inner membrane. By increasing the surface area of this membrane, the cristae maximize ATP output. (You'll learn more about how mitochondria convert food energy to ATP energy in Chapter 6.)

Besides their ability to provide cellular energy, mitochondria and chloroplasts share another feature: They contain their own DNA that encodes some of their own proteins. This DNA is evidence that mitochondria and chloroplasts evolved from free-living prokaryotes in the distant past (see Chapter 15 for a discussion of this hypothesis). ☑

Which organelles have their own genes?

☑ CHECKPOINT

1. What does the process of photosynthesis accomplish?
2. What is cellular respiration?

Answers: 1. the conversion of light energy to chemical energy stored in food molecules 2. a process that converts the chemical energy of sugars and other food molecules to chemical energy in the form of ATP

▼ Figure 4.19 **The chloroplast: site of photosynthesis.**

Inner and outer membranes

Space between membranes

Stroma (fluid in chloroplast)

Granum

TEM 9,750x

▼ Figure 4.20 **The mitochondrion: site of cellular respiration.**

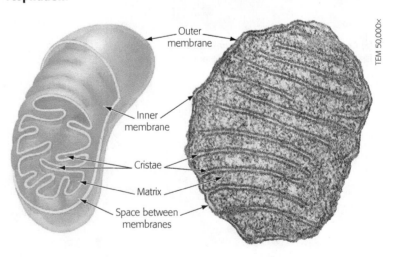

Outer membrane

Inner membrane

Cristae

Matrix

Space between membranes

TEM 50,000x

The Cytoskeleton: Cell Shape and Movement

If someone asked you to describe a house, you would most likely mention the various rooms and their locations. You probably would not think to mention the foundation and beams that support the house. Yet these structures perform an extremely important function. Similarly, cells have an infrastructure called the **cytoskeleton**, a network of fibers extending throughout the cytoplasm. The cytoskeleton serves as both skeleton and "muscles" for the cell, functioning in support and movement.

Maintaining Cell Shape

One function of the cytoskeleton is to give mechanical support to the cell and maintain its shape. This is especially important for animal cells, which lack rigid cell walls. The cytoskeleton contains several types of fibers made from different types of protein. One important type of fiber is the **microtubule** (Figure 4.21a). Microtubules are straight, hollow tubes composed of proteins. The other kinds of cytoskeletal fibers, called intermediate filaments and microfilaments, are thinner and solid.

Just as the bony skeleton of your body helps fix the positions of your organs, the cytoskeleton provides anchorage and reinforcement for many organelles in a cell. For instance, the nucleus is often held in place by a cytoskeletal cage of filaments. Other organelles move along tracks made from microtubules. For example, a lysosome might reach a food vacuole by taking many small "baby steps" along a microtubule track. Microtubules also guide the movement of chromosomes when cells divide.

A cell's cytoskeleton is dynamic: It can quickly dismantle in one part of the cell by removing protein subunits and re-form in a new location by reattaching the subunits. Such rearrangement can provide rigidity in a new location, change the shape of the cell, or even cause the whole cell or some of its parts to move. This process contributes to the amoeboid (crawling) movements of the protist *Amoeba* (Figure 4.21b) and some of our white blood cells. ☑

☑ CHECKPOINT
How is the cytoskeleton able to change the overall shape of a cell?

Answer: by dismantling its subunits in one part of the cell and rebuilding them in another part

▼ Figure 4.21 **The cytoskeleton.**

(a) **Microtubules in the cytoskeleton.** In this micrograph of animal cells, the cytoskeleton microtubules are labeled with a fluorescent yellow dye.

LM 650×

(b) **Microtubules and movement.** The crawling movement of an *Amoeba* is due to the rapid degradation and rebuilding of microtubules.

LM 220×

Cilia and Flagella

In some eukaryotic cells, microtubules are arranged into structures called flagella and cilia. Cilia and flagella are motile appendages—extensions from a cell that aid in movement. Eukaryotic **flagella** (singular, *flagellum*) propel cells through their undulating, whiplike motion. They often occur singly, such as in the sperm cells of humans and other animals **(Figure 4.22a)**, but may also appear in groups on the outer surface of protists. **Cilia** (singular, *cilium*) are generally shorter and more numerous than flagella and promote movement by a coordinated back-and-forth motion, like the rhythmic oars of a crew team. Both cilia and flagella propel various protists through water **(Figure 4.22b)**. Though different in length, number per cell, and beating pattern, cilia and flagella have the same basic architecture, with a core of microtubules wrapped in an extension of the plasma membrane. Although some animal cells have cilia or flagella, many do not, and they are almost never found on plant cells.

Some cilia extend from nonmoving cells that are part of a tissue layer. There, they move fluid over the tissue's surface. For example, cilia lining your windpipe clean your respiratory system by sweeping mucus with trapped debris out of your lungs **(Figure 4.22c)**. Tobacco smoke can inhibit or destroy these cilia, interfering with the normal cleansing mechanisms and allowing more toxin-laden smoke particles to reach the lungs. Frequent coughing—common in heavy smokers—then becomes the body's attempt to cleanse the respiratory system.

Because human sperm rely on flagella for movement, it's easy to understand why problems with flagella can lead to male infertility. Interestingly, some men with a type of hereditary sterility also suffer from respiratory problems. The explanation lies in the similarities between flagella (found in sperm) and cilia (found lining the respiratory tract). Because of a defect in the structure of their flagella and cilia, their sperm cannot swim normally within the female reproductive tract to fertilize an egg (causing sterility) and their cilia do not sweep mucus out of their lungs (causing recurrent respiratory infections). ✓

How can defective flagella lead to male sterility?

✓ CHECKPOINT

Compare and contrast cilia and flagella.

Answer: *Cilia and flagella have the same basic structure and help move cells or move fluid over cells. Cilia are short and numerous and move back and forth. Flagella are longer, often occurring singly, and they undulate.*

▼ Figure 4.22 **Examples of flagella and cilia.**

(a) Flagellum of a human sperm cell. A eukaryotic flagellum undulates in a snakelike motion, driving a cell such as this sperm cell through its fluid environment.

Colorized SEM 5000×

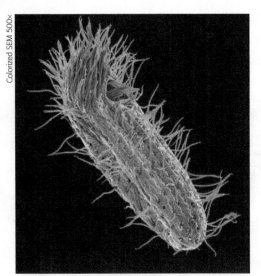

Colorized SEM 500×

(b) Cilia on a protist. Cilia are shorter and more numerous than flagella and move with a back-and-forth motion. As shown here, a dense nap of beating cilia covers *Paramecium*, a freshwater protist that can dart rapidly through its watery home.

Colorized SEM 3,000×

(c) Cilia lining the respiratory tract. The cilia lining your respiratory tract sweep mucus with trapped debris out of your lungs. This helps keep your airways clear and prevents infections.

The Evolution of Antibiotic Resistance

As you read in the Biology and Society section, many antibiotics disrupt the cellular structures of invading microorganisms. This defensive mechanism is quite effective. In fact, when first introduced in the 1940s, penicillin appeared to be such a "wonder drug" that some doctors predicted the end of infections in people (Figure 4.23).

Why hasn't that optimistic prediction come true? The answer is both simple and profound: The rosy outlook does not take into account the force of evolution. Within a population of bacteria, random genetic changes result in slightly different proteins being produced in different bacteria. Some bacteria may produce a protein that reduces the effectiveness of an antibiotic. For example, a random change in a nucleotide sequence might lead to the production of an enzyme that deactivates or breaks down penicillin.

When an environment changes, natural selection favors individuals with beneficial genetic changes. In this case, the introduction of an antibiotic creates a pressure that favors resistant bacteria. Those individuals will survive and multiply, producing more of the same type of bacteria. Over time, drug-resistant bacteria, such as the MRSA strain discussed in the Process of Science section, become more common.

In what ways do we contribute to the problem of antibiotic resistance? Livestock producers add antibiotics to animal feed to promote growth and prevent illness. These practices may favor bacteria that resist standard antibiotics. Some doctors overprescribe antibiotics—for example, to patients with viral infections, which do not respond to such treatment. And some patients misuse prescribed antibiotics by prematurely stopping their medication. This misuse allows mutant bacteria that may be killed more slowly by the drug to survive and multiply.

The evolution of antibiotic-resistant bacteria is a serious public health concern. Nearly 100,000 people die each year in the United States from infections they contract in the hospital, often from antibiotic-resistant bacteria. Penicillin, effective against many bacterial infections in the 1940s, is virtually useless today in its original form. New drugs are developed but also continue to be rendered ineffective as resistant bacteria evolve. The medical community is engaged in an arms race against the powerful force of bacterial evolution. As of now, the ultimate victor remains to be determined.

◄ Figure 4.23 **The changing role of antibiotics.** These two posters illustrate how the early promise of antibiotics (depicted in a poster from 1944) has given way to caution about their overuse (depicted in a poster from 2008).

Chapter Review

Go to **www.masteringbiology.com** for homework assignments, practice quizzes, Pearson eText, and more.

The Microscopic World of Cells

Microscopes as Windows on the World of Cells

Using early microscopes, biologists discovered that all organisms are made of cells. Resolving power limits the useful magnification of microscopes. A light microscope (LM) has useful magnifications up to about 1,000×. Electron microscopes, both scanning (SEM) and transmission (TEM), are much more powerful.

The Two Major Categories of Cells

CATEGORIES OF CELLS	
Prokaryotic Cells	**Eukaryotic Cells**
• Smaller • Simpler • Most do not have organelles • Found in bacteria and archaea	• Larger • More complex • Have organelles • Found in protists, plants, fungi, animals

An Overview of Eukaryotic Cells

Many cellular functions are partitioned by membranes in the complex organization of eukaryotic cells. The largest organelle is usually the nucleus. Other organelles are located in the cytoplasm, the region between the nucleus and the plasma membrane.

Membrane Structure

The Plasma Membrane: A Fluid Mosaic of Lipids and Proteins

Cell Surfaces

Most cells secrete an extracellular coat that helps protect and support the cell. The walls that encase plant cells support plants against the pull of gravity and also prevent cells from absorbing too much water. Animal cells are coated by a sticky extracellular matrix.

The Nucleus and Ribosomes: Genetic Control of the Cell

Structure and Function of the Nucleus

An envelope consisting of two membranes encloses the nucleus. Within the nucleus, DNA and proteins make up chromatin fibers; each very long fiber is a single chromosome. The nucleus also contains the nucleolus, which produces components of ribosomes.

Ribosomes

Ribosomes produce proteins in the cytoplasm.

How DNA Directs Protein Production

Genetic messages are transmitted to the ribosomes via messenger RNA (mRNA), which travels from the nucleus to the cytoplasm.

The Endomembrane System: Manufacturing and Distributing Cellular Products

The Endoplasmic Reticulum

The ER consists of membrane-enclosed tubes and sacs within the cytoplasm. Rough ER, named because of the ribosomes attached to its surface, makes membrane and secretory proteins. The functions of smooth ER include lipid synthesis and detoxification.

The Golgi Apparatus

The Golgi apparatus refines certain ER products and packages them in transport vesicles targeted for other organelles or export from the cell.

Lysosomes

Lysosomes, sacs containing digestive enzymes, aid digestion and recycling within the cell.

Vacuoles

Vacuoles include the contractile vacuoles that expel water from certain freshwater protists and the large, multifunctional central vacuoles of plant cells.

Chloroplasts and Mitochondria: Energy Conversion

Chloroplasts and Mitochondria

The Cytoskeleton: Cell Shape and Movement

Maintaining Cell Shape

Straight, hollow microtubules are an important component of the cytoskeleton, an organelle that gives support to, and maintains the shape of, cells.

Cilia and Flagella

Cilia and eukaryotic flagella are motile appendages made primarily of microtubules. Cilia are short and numerous and move the cell via coordinated beating. Flagella are long, often occur singly, and propel a cell through whiplike movements.

SELF-QUIZ

1. If you wanted to film the movement of chromosomes during cell division, the best choice for a microscope would be a
   a. light microscope, because of its magnifying power.
   b. transmission electron microscope, because of its resolving power.
   c. scanning electron microscope, because the chromosomes are on the cell surface.
   d. light microscope, because the specimen must be kept alive.

2. Using a light microscope to examine a thin section of a large spherical cell, you find that the cell is 0.3 mm in diameter. The nucleus is about one-fourth as wide. What would be the diameter of the nucleus in micrometers? (*Hint*: See Figure 4.3.)

3. You look into a light microscope and view an unknown cell. What might you see that would tell you whether the cell is prokaryotic or eukaryotic?
   a. a rigid cell wall
   b. a nucleus
   c. a plasma membrane
   d. ribosomes

4. Explain how each word in the term *fluid mosaic* describes the structure of a membrane.

5. Identify which of the following structures includes all the others in the list: rough ER, smooth ER, endomembrane system, the Golgi apparatus.

6. The ER has two distinct regions that differ in structure and function. Lipids are synthesized within the _____, and proteins are synthesized within the _____.

7. A type of cell called a lymphocyte makes proteins that are exported from the cell. You can track the path of these proteins within the cell from production through export by labeling them with radioactive isotopes. Identify which of the following structures would be radioactively labeled in your experiment, listing them in the order in which they would be labeled: chloroplasts, Golgi apparatus, plasma membrane, smooth ER, rough ER, nucleus, mitochondria.

8. Name two similarities in the structure or function of chloroplasts and mitochondria. Name two differences.

9. Match the following organelles with their functions:
   a. ribosomes   1. movement
   b. microtubules   2. photosynthesis
   c. mitochondria   3. protein synthesis
   d. chloroplasts   4. digestion
   e. lysosomes   5. cellular respiration

10. DNA controls the cell by transmitting genetic messages that result in protein production. Place the following organelles in the order that represents the flow of genetic information from the DNA through the cell: nuclear pores, ribosomes, nucleus, rough ER, Golgi apparatus.

11. Compare and contrast cilia and flagella.

Answers to these questions can be found in Appendix: Self-Quiz Answers.

THE PROCESS OF SCIENCE

12. The cells of plant seeds store oils in the form of droplets enclosed by membranes. Unlike the membranes you learned about in this chapter, the oil droplet membrane consists of a single layer of phospholipids rather than a bilayer. Draw a model for a membrane around an oil droplet. Explain why this arrangement is more stable than a bilayer.

13. Imagine that you are a pediatrician and one of your patients is a newborn who may have a lysosomal storage disease. You remove some cells from the patient and examine them under the microscope. What would you expect to see? Design a series of tests that could reveal whether the patient is indeed suffering from a lysosomal storage disease.

BIOLOGY AND SOCIETY

14. Doctors at a university medical center removed John Moore's spleen, which is a standard treatment for his type of leukemia. The disease did not recur. Researchers kept the spleen cells alive in a nutrient medium. They found that some cells produced a blood protein that showed promise as a treatment for cancer and AIDS. The researchers patented the cells. Moore sued, claiming a share in profits from any products derived from his cells. The U.S. Supreme Court ruled against Moore, stating that his lawsuit "threatens to destroy the economic incentive to conduct important medical research." Moore argued that the ruling left patients "vulnerable to exploitation at the hands of the state." Do you think Moore was treated fairly? What else would you like to know about this case that might help you decide?

5 The Working Cell

Cellular structures.
This human skin cell
has been stained to
highlight various cellular
structures.

Nanotechnology BIOLOGY AND SOCIETY

Harnessing Cellular Structures

One of the most fascinating applications of modern science is nanotechnology, the manipulation of materials at the molecular scale. When designing devices of such small size, researchers often turn to living cells for inspiration. After all, you can think of a cell as a machine that continuously and efficiently performs a variety of functions, such as movement, energy processing, and production of various products. Let's consider one example of cell-based nanotechnology and see how it relates to three of the main concerns for working cells: energy, enzymes, and the plasma membrane.

Researchers at Cornell University are attempting to harvest the energy-producing capability of human sperm cells. Like other cells, a sperm cell generates energy by breaking down sugars and other molecules that pass through its plasma membrane. Enzymes within the cell carry out a process called glycolysis. During glycolysis, the energy released from the breakdown of glucose is used to produce molecules of ATP. Within a living sperm, the ATP produced during glycolysis and other processes provides the energy that propels the sperm through the female reproductive tract. In an attempt to harness this energy-producing system, the Cornell researchers attached three glycolysis enzymes to a computer chip. The enzymes continued to function in this artificial system, producing energy from sugar. The hope is that a larger set of enzymes can eventually be used to power microscopic robots. Perhaps such nanorobots could use glucose from the bloodstream to power the delivery of drugs to body tissues. This example is just one of many new technologies that may be built some day, inspired by the cells found in all living organisms.

This example of cell-based nanotechnology highlights the three main topics of this chapter. We'll explore how a cell uses energy, enzymes, and the plasma membrane to carry out the work of controlling its internal chemical environment. Along the way, we'll look at some other technologies that mimic the natural activities of living cells.

Some Basic Energy Concepts

Energy makes the world go round—both the larger world outside and the cellular world. But what exactly is energy? Our first step in understanding the working cell is to learn a few basic concepts about energy.

Conservation of Energy

Energy is defined as the capacity to cause change. Some forms of energy are used to perform work, such as moving an object against an opposing force—for example, gravity. In other words, energy is the ability to rearrange a collection of matter.

For example, imagine a diver climbing to the top of a platform and diving off (Figure 5.1). To get to the top of the platform, the diver must perform work to overcome the opposing force of gravity. Specifically, chemical energy from food is converted to **kinetic energy**, the energy of motion. In this case, the kinetic energy takes the form of muscle movement.

What happens to the kinetic energy when the diver reaches the top of the platform? Has it disappeared?

The answer is no. You may be familiar with the principle of conservation of matter, which states that matter cannot be created or destroyed but can only be converted from one form to another. A similar principle, known as **conservation of energy**, states that it is not possible to destroy or create energy. Like matter, energy can only be converted from one form to another. A power plant, for example, does not make energy; it merely converts it from one form (such as energy stored in coal) to a more convenient form (such as electricity). That's what happens in the diver's climb up the steps. The kinetic energy of muscle movement is now stored in a form called potential energy. **Potential energy** is energy that an object has because of its location or structure, such as the energy contained by water behind a dam or by a compressed spring. In our example, the diver at the top of the platform has potential energy because of his elevated location. The act of diving off the platform into the water converts the potential energy back to kinetic energy. Life depends on countless similar conversions of energy from one form to another. ✓

▶ Figure 5.1 **Energy conversions during a dive.**

On the platform, the diver has more potential energy.

Climbing the steps converts kinetic energy of muscle movement to potential energy.

Diving converts potential energy to kinetic energy.

In the water, the diver has less potential energy.

Entropy

If energy cannot be destroyed, where has it gone when the diver hits the water? It has been converted to **heat**, a type of kinetic energy contained in the random motion of atoms and molecules. The friction between the body and its surroundings generated heat in the air and then in the water.

All energy conversions generate some heat. Although heat production does not destroy energy, it does make it less useful. Heat, of all energy forms, is the most difficult to "tame"—the most difficult to harness for useful work. Heat is energy in its most chaotic form, the energy of aimless molecular movement.

Entropy is a measure of the amount of disorder, or randomness, in a system. Every time energy is converted from one form to another, entropy increases. The energy conversions during the climb up the ladder and the dive from the platform increased entropy as the diver emitted heat to the surroundings. To climb up the steps again for another dive, the diver must use additional stored food energy. This conversion will also create heat and therefore increase entropy. ☑

Chemical Energy

How can molecules derived from the food we eat provide energy for our working cells? The molecules of food, gasoline, and other fuels have a special form of potential energy called **chemical energy**, which arises from the arrangement of atoms and can be released by a chemical reaction. Carbohydrates, fats, and gasoline have structures that make them especially rich in chemical energy.

Living cells and automobile engines use the same basic process to make the chemical energy stored in their fuels available for work **(Figure 5.2)**. In both cases, this process breaks organic fuel into smaller waste molecules that have much less chemical energy than the fuel molecules did, thereby releasing energy that can be used to perform work.

For example, the engine of an automobile mixes oxygen with gasoline in an explosive chemical reaction that breaks down the fuel molecules and pushes the pistons that eventually move the wheels. The waste products emitted from the car's exhaust pipe are mostly carbon dioxide and water. Only about 25% of the energy that an automobile engine extracts from its fuel is converted to

What do your cells have in common with a car's engine?

☑ CHECKPOINT

Which form of energy is most randomized and difficult to put to work?

Answer: heat

◄ **Figure 5.2 Energy conversions in a car and a cell.** In both a car and a cell, the chemical energy of organic fuel molecules is harvested using oxygen. This chemical breakdown releases energy stored in the fuel molecules and produces carbon dioxide and water. The released energy can be used to perform work.

Fuel rich in chemical energy

Energy conversion

Waste products poor in chemical energy

Octane (from gasoline)
+
Oxygen

Combustion

Heat energy

Kinetic energy of movement

Carbon dioxide
+
Water

Energy conversion in a car

Glucose (from food)
+
Oxygen

Cellular respiration

Heat energy

ATP

Energy for cellular work

Carbon dioxide
+
Water

Energy conversion in a cell

the kinetic energy of the car's movement. Most of the rest is converted to heat—so much that the engine would melt if the car's radiator and fan did not disperse excess heat into the atmosphere.

Cells also use oxygen in reactions that release energy from fuel molecules. As in a car engine, the "exhaust" is mostly carbon dioxide and water. The combustion of fuel in cells is called cellular respiration, which is a more gradual and efficient "burning" of fuel compared with the explosive combustion in an automobile engine. Cellular respiration is the energy-releasing chemical breakdown of fuel molecules and the storage of that energy in a form the cell can use to perform work. (We will discuss the details of cellular respiration in the next chapter.) You convert about 34% of your food energy to useful work, such as movement of your muscles. About 66% of the energy released by the breakdown of fuel molecules generates body heat. Humans and many other animals can use this heat to keep the body at an almost constant temperature (37°C, or 98.6°F, in the case of humans), even when the surrounding air is much colder. The liberation of heat energy also explains why you feel hot after exercise. Sweating and other cooling mechanisms enable your body to lose the excess heat, much as a car's radiator keeps the engine from overheating.

Why do dieters often feel cold?

Food Calories

Read any packaged food label and you'll find the number of calories in each serving of that food. Calories are units of energy. A **calorie** (cal) is the amount of energy that can raise the temperature of 1 gram (g) of water by 1°C. You could actually measure the caloric content of a peanut by burning it under a container of water to convert all of the stored chemical energy to heat and then measuring the temperature increase of the water.

Calories are tiny units of energy, so using them to describe the fuel content of foods is not practical. Instead, it's conventional to use kilocalories (kcal), units of 1,000 calories. In fact, the Calories (capital C) on a food package are actually kilocalories. For example, one peanut has about 5 kcal. That's a lot of energy, enough to increase the temperature of 1 kg (a little more than a quart) of water by 5°C. And just a handful of peanuts contains enough Calories, if converted to heat, to boil 1 kg of water. In living organisms, of course, food isn't used to boil water but instead to fuel the activities of life. **Figure 5.3** shows the number of Calories in several foods and how many Calories are burned off by some typical activities. ☑

☑ CHECKPOINT

According to Figure 5.3, how long would you have to ride your bicycle to burn off the energy in three slices of pepperoni pizza?

Answer: a little over 1 hour (1 slice = 181 Calories, so 3 slices = 543 Calories; 1 hour of cycling consumes 490 Calories)

▼ Figure 5.3 **Some caloric accounting.**

Food	Food Calories
Cheeseburger	295
Spaghetti with sauce (1 cup)	241
Baked potato (plain, with skin)	220
Fried chicken (drumstick)	193
Bean burrito	189
Pizza with pepperoni (1 slice)	181
Peanuts (1 ounce)	166
Apple	81
Garden salad (2 cups)	56
Popcorn (plain, 1 cup)	31
Broccoli (1 cup)	25

(a) **Food Calories (kilocalories) in various foods**

Activity	Food Calories consumed per hour by a 150-pound person*
Running (7 min/mi)	979
Dancing (fast)	510
Bicycling (10 mph)	490
Swimming (2 mph)	408
Walking (3 mph)	245
Dancing (slow)	204
Playing the piano	73
Driving a car	61
Sitting (writing)	28

*Not including energy necessary for basic functions, such as breathing and heartbeat

(b) **Food Calories (kilocalories) we burn in various activities**

ATP and Cellular Work

The carbohydrates, fats, and other fuel molecules we obtain from food do not drive work in our cells directly. Instead, the chemical energy released by the breakdown of organic molecules during cellular respiration is used to generate molecules of ATP. These molecules of ATP then power cellular work. ATP acts like an energy shuttle, storing energy obtained from food and then releasing it as needed at a later time.

The Structure of ATP

The abbreviation ATP stands for adenosine triphosphate. **ATP** consists of an organic molecule called adenosine plus a tail of three phosphate groups (P) **(Figure 5.4)**. The triphosphate tail is the "business" end of ATP, the part that provides energy for cellular work. Each phosphate group is negatively charged. Negative charges repel each other. The crowding of negative charges in the triphosphate tail contributes to the potential energy of ATP. It's analogous to storing energy by compressing a spring; if you release the spring, it will relax, and you can use that springiness to do some useful work. For ATP power, it is release of the phosphate at the tip of the triphosphate tail that makes energy available to working cells. What remains is **ADP**, adenosine diphosphate (two phosphate groups instead of three, shown on the right side of Figure 5.4).

Phosphate Transfer

When ATP drives work in cells, phosphate groups don't just fly off into space. ATP energizes other molecules in cells by transferring phosphate groups to those molecules. This transfer of phosphate groups helps cells perform three main kinds of work: mechanical work, transport work, and chemical work.

Imagine a bicyclist pedaling up a hill. In the muscle cells of the rider's legs, ATP transfers phosphate groups to motor proteins. The proteins then change shape, causing the muscle cells to contract and perform mechanical work **(Figure 5.5a)**. ATP also enables the transport of ions and other dissolved substances across the membranes of the rider's nerve cells **(Figure 5.5b)**, helping them send signals to his legs. And ATP drives the chemical work of making some of a cell's large molecules **(Figure 5.5c)**. Notice again in Figure 5.5 that all these types of work occur when target molecules accept a phosphate group from ATP.

▼ **Figure 5.4 ATP power.** Each (P) in the triphosphate tail of ATP represents a phosphate group, a phosphorus atom bonded to oxygen atoms. The transfer of a phosphate from the triphosphate tail to other molecules provides energy for cellular work.

▼ **Figure 5.5 How ATP drives cellular work.** Each type of work shown here is powered when an enzyme transfers phosphate from ATP to a recipient molecule.

(a) Motor protein performing mechanical work (moving a muscle fiber)

(b) Transport protein performing transport work (importing a solute)

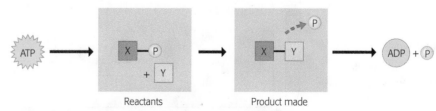

(c) Chemical reactants performing chemical work (promoting a chemical reaction)

The ATP Cycle

Your cells spend ATP continuously. Fortunately, it is a renewable resource. ATP can be restored by adding a phosphate group back to ADP. That takes energy, like recompressing a spring. And that's where food enters the story. The chemical energy that cellular respiration harvests from sugars and other organic fuels is put to work regenerating a cell's supply of ATP. Cellular work spends ATP, which is recycled when ADP and phosphate are combined using energy released by cellular respiration (Figure 5.6). Thus, energy from processes that yield energy, such as the breakdown of organic fuels, is transferred to processes that consume energy, such as muscle contraction and other cellular work.

▼ Figure 5.6 **The ATP cycle.**

The third phosphate group acts as an energy shuttle within the ATP cycle. The ATP cycle can run at an astonishing pace: up to 10 million ATPs are consumed and recycled each second in a working muscle cell. ☑

Enzymes

As you've seen, a living organism contains a vast collection of chemicals, with countless chemical reactions constantly changing the organism's molecular makeup. In a sense, a living organism is a complex "chemical square dance," with the molecular "dancers" continually changing partners via chemical reactions. The total of all the chemical reactions in an organism is called **metabolism**. Interestingly, almost no metabolic reactions occur without help. Most require the assistance of **enzymes**, proteins that speed up chemical reactions. All living cells contain thousands of different enzymes, each promoting a different chemical reaction.

Activation Energy

For a chemical reaction to begin, chemical bonds in the reactant molecules must be broken. (The first step in swapping partners during a square dance is to let go of your current partner's hand.) This process requires that the molecules absorb energy from their surroundings. This energy is called **activation energy** because it activates the reactants and triggers the chemical reaction.

Enzymes enable metabolism to occur by reducing the amount of activation energy required to break the bonds of reactant molecules. If you think of the activation energy as a barrier to a chemical reaction, an enzyme's function is to lower that barrier (Figure 5.7). It does so by binding to reactant molecules and putting them under physical or chemical stress, making it easier to break their bonds and start a reaction. ☑

▼ Figure 5.7 **Enzymes and activation energy.**

(a) **Without enzyme.** A reactant molecule must overcome the activation energy barrier before a chemical reaction can break the molecule into products.

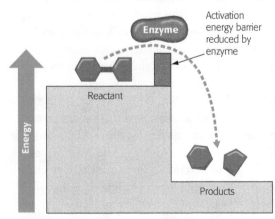

(b) **With enzyme.** An enzyme speeds the chemical reaction by lowering the activation energy barrier.

Can Enzymes Be Engineered?

Like all other proteins, enzymes are encoded by genes. **Observations** of genetic sequences suggest that many of our genes were formed through a type of molecular evolution: One ancestral gene duplicated, and the two copies diverged over time via random genetic changes, eventually becoming distinct genes for enzymes with different functions.

The natural evolution of enzymes raises a **question**: Can laboratory methods mimic this process through artificial selection? A group of researchers at two California biotechnology companies formed the **hypothesis** that an artificial process could be used to modify the gene that codes for the enzyme lactase (which breaks down the sugar lactose) into a new gene coding for a new enzyme with a new function. Their **experiment** used a procedure called directed evolution. In this process, many copies of the gene for the starting lactase enzyme were mutated at random (**Figure 5.8**). The researchers tested the enzymes resulting from these mutated genes to determine which enzymes best displayed a new activity (in this case, breaking down a different sugar). The genes for the enzymes that did show the new activity were then subjected to several more rounds of duplication, mutation, and screening.

After seven rounds, the **results** were clear: Directed evolution had produced a new enzyme with a novel function. Researchers have used similar methods to produce many artificial enzymes with desired properties. Directed evolution is another example of how scientists can mimic the natural processes of cells for useful purposes. Biomedical engineers may someday embed these artificial enzymes in nanotechnology devices with specific functions.

▼ Figure 5.8 **Directed evolution of an enzyme.** During seven rounds of directed evolution, the lactase enzyme gradually gained a new function.

Gene for lactase

Gene **duplicated** and **mutated** at random

Mutated genes (mutations shown in orange)

Mutated genes **screened** by testing new enzymes

Genes coding for enzymes that show new activity

Genes coding for enzymes that do *not* show new activity

Genes **duplicated** and **mutated** at random

Mutated genes **screened** by testing new enzymes

After seven rounds, some genes code for enzymes that can efficiently perform new activity.

Ribbon model showing the polypeptide chains of the enzyme lactase

Induced Fit

An enzyme is very selective in the reaction it catalyzes. This selectivity is based on the enzyme's ability to recognize a certain reactant molecule, which is called the enzyme's **substrate**. And the ability of the enzyme to recognize and bind to its specific substrate depends on the enzyme's shape. A region of the enzyme called the **active site** has a shape and chemistry that fits the substrate molecule. When a substrate slips into this docking station, the active site changes shape slightly to embrace the substrate and catalyze the reaction. This interaction is called **induced fit** because the entry of the substrate induces the enzyme to change shape slightly, making the fit between substrate and active site snugger. Think of a handshake: As your hand makes contact with another hand, it changes shape slightly to make a better fit.

How is your hand like an enzyme?

After the products are released from the active site, the enzyme can accept another molecule of its substrate. In fact, the ability to function repeatedly is a key characteristic of enzymes. **Figure 5.9** follows the action of the enzyme sucrase, which hydrolyzes the disaccharide sucrose (the substrate). Like sucrase, many enzymes are named for their substrates, but with an -*ase* ending.

Enzyme Inhibitors

Certain molecules can inhibit a metabolic reaction by binding to an enzyme and disrupting its function (**Figure 5.10**). Some of these **enzyme inhibitors** are actually substrate imposters that plug up the active site. (You can't shake a person's hand if someone else puts a banana in it first!) Other inhibitors bind to the enzyme at a site remote from the active site, but the binding

☑ **CHECKPOINT**

1. How does an enzyme recognize its substrate?
2. Name two ways that a molecule may inhibit an enzyme.

Answers: **1.** *The substrate and the enzyme's active site are complementary in shape and chemistry.* **2.** *An inhibitor may bind to an enzyme in its active site, or it may bind in an alternate site that affects the active site.*

▼ Figure 5.9 **How an enzyme works.** Our example is the enzyme sucrase, named for its substrate, sucrose.

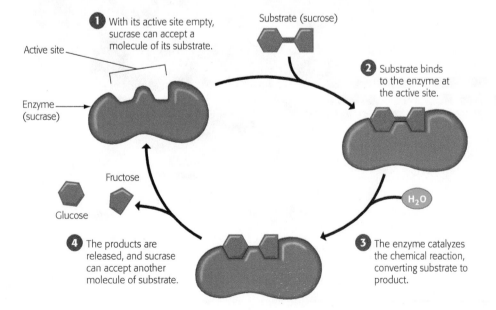

① With its active site empty, sucrase can accept a molecule of its substrate.

Active site

Enzyme (sucrase)

Substrate (sucrose)

② Substrate binds to the enzyme at the active site.

③ The enzyme catalyzes the chemical reaction, converting substrate to product.

H₂O

Fructose

Glucose

④ The products are released, and sucrase can accept another molecule of substrate.

▼ Figure 5.10 **Enzyme inhibitors.**

Substrate

Active site

Enzyme

(a) Enzyme and substrate binding normally

Inhibitor

Active site

Substrate

Enzyme

(b) Enzyme inhibition by a substrate imposter

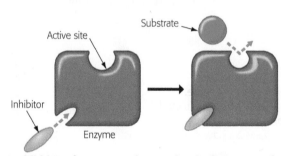

Active site

Substrate

Inhibitor

Enzyme

(c) Inhibition of an enzyme by a molecule that causes the active site to change shape

changes the enzyme's shape so that the active site no longer accepts the substrate. (Imagine trying to shake hands when someone else is tickling your ribs, causing you to clench your hand.) In some cases, the binding is reversible, enabling certain inhibitors to regulate metabolism. For example, if a cell is producing more of a certain product than it needs, that product may reversibly inhibit an enzyme required for its production. This feedback regulation keeps the cell from wasting resources that could be put to better use.

Many beneficial drugs work by inhibiting enzymes. Penicillin, for example, blocks the active site of an enzyme that bacteria use in making cell walls (see Chapter 4). Ibuprofen inhibits an enzyme involved in sending pain signals. Many cancer drugs inhibit enzymes that promote cell division. Many toxins and poisons are irreversible inhibitors. Nerve gases (a form of chemical warfare) bind to the active site of an enzyme vital to transmitting nerve impulses. The inhibition of this enzyme leads to rapid paralysis of vital functions and death. Many pesticides are toxic to insects because they irreversibly inhibit this same enzyme. ☑

Membrane Function

So far, we have discussed how cells control the flow of energy and how enzymes affect the pace of chemical reactions. In addition to these vital processes, cells must also regulate the flow of materials to and from the environment. In Chapter 4, you learned that the plasma membrane consists of a double layer of fat (a phospholipid bilayer) with embedded proteins (see Figure 4.6). **Figure 5.11** describes the major functions of these membrane proteins.

Transport proteins are membrane proteins that help move substances across a cell membrane. In this section, you'll learn about the most important mechanisms of transport across membranes.

Passive Transport: Diffusion across Membranes

Molecules are restless. They constantly vibrate and wander randomly. One result of this motion is **diffusion**, the movement of molecules spreading out evenly into the available space. Each molecule moves randomly, but the overall diffusion of a population of molecules is usually directional, from a region where the molecules are more concentrated to where they are less concentrated. For example, imagine many molecules of perfume inside a bottle. If you remove the bottle top, every molecule of perfume

▼ **Figure 5.11 Primary functions of membrane proteins.** In this diagram of two adjacent membranes, all six types of membrane proteins are shown for convenience. An actual cell may have just a few of these types of proteins.

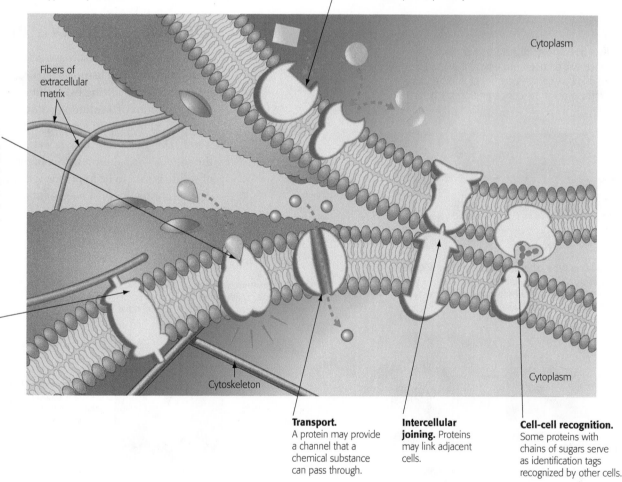

Enzymatic activity. This protein and the one next to it are enzymes, having an active site that fits a substrate. Enzymes may form an assembly line that carries out steps of a pathway.

Cytoplasm

Fibers of extracellular matrix

Cell signaling. A binding site fits the shape of a chemical messenger. The messenger may cause a change in the protein that relays the message to the inside of the cell.

Attachment to the cytoskeleton and extracellular matrix. Such proteins help maintain cell shape and coordinate changes.

Cytoskeleton

Cytoplasm

Transport. A protein may provide a channel that a chemical substance can pass through.

Intercellular joining. Proteins may link adjacent cells.

Cell-cell recognition. Some proteins with chains of sugars serve as identification tags recognized by other cells.

will move randomly about, but the overall movement will be out of the bottle. You could, with great effort, return the perfume to its bottle, but the molecules would never do that spontaneously.

For an example closer to a living cell, imagine a membrane separating pure water from a dye solution (Figure 5.12). Assume that this membrane has tiny holes that allow dye molecules to pass. Although each dye molecule moves randomly, there will be a net migration across the membrane to the side that began as pure water. Movement of the dye will continue until both solutions have equal concentrations. After that, there will be a dynamic equilibrium: Molecules will still be moving, but as many dye molecules move in one direction as in the other.

Diffusion across a membrane is an example of **passive transport**—passive because the cell does not expend any energy for it to happen. However, the cell membrane is selectively permeable, meaning that only certain substances are allowed to pass. For example, small molecules such as oxygen (O_2) generally pass through more readily than larger molecules such as amino acids. But

How does oxygen get from the air into your blood?

the membrane is relatively impermeable to even some very small substances, such as most ions, which are too hydrophilic to pass through the phospholipid bilayer. In passive transport, a substance diffuses down its **concentration gradient**, from where the substance is more concentrated to where it is less concentrated. In our lungs, for example, passive transport is the sole means by which O_2 enters the blood and CO_2 passes out of it.

Substances that do not cross membranes spontaneously—or do cross, but slowly—can be transported via proteins that act as corridors for specific molecules (see Figure 5.11). This assisted transport is called **facilitated diffusion**. For example, water molecules can move through the plasma membrane of some cells via transport proteins—each of which can allow the entry of 3 billion water molecules per second! Other specific transport proteins move glucose across cell membranes 50,000 times faster than diffusion. Even at this rate, facilitated diffusion is a type of passive transport because it does not require the cell to expend energy. As in all passive transport, the driving force is the concentration gradient. ☑

CHECKPOINT

Why is facilitated diffusion a form of passive transport?

Answer: It uses proteins to transport materials down a concentration gradient without expending energy.

Osmosis and Water Balance

The diffusion of water across a selectively permeable membrane is called **osmosis** (Figure 5.13). Imagine a membrane separating two solutions with different concentrations of a solute. A **solute** is a substance that is dissolved in a liquid solvent, such as the salt in salt water. The membrane allows water to pass but not the solute. The solution with a higher concentration of solute is said to be **hypertonic** to the other solution. The solution with the lower solute concentration is said

▼ **Figure 5.12 Passive transport: diffusion across a membrane.** A substance will diffuse from where it is more concentrated to where it is less concentrated. Put another way, a substance tends to diffuse down its concentration gradient.

(a) Passive transport of one type of molecule. The membrane is permeable to these dye molecules, which diffuse down the concentration gradient. At equilibrium, the molecules are still restless, but the rate of transport is equal in both directions.

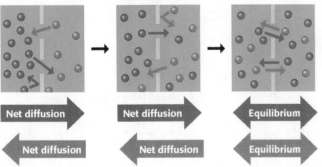

(b) Passive transport of two types of molecules. If solutions have two or more solutes, each will diffuse down its own concentration gradient.

▼ **Figure 5.13 Osmosis.** A membrane separates two solutions with different sugar concentrations. Water molecules can pass through the membrane, but sugar molecules cannot.

to be **hypotonic** to the other. Note that the hypotonic solution, by having the lower solute concentration, has the higher water concentration (less solute = more water). Therefore, water will diffuse across the membrane along its concentration gradient from an area of higher water concentration (hypotonic solution) to one of lower water concentration (hypertonic solution). This reduces the difference in solute concentrations and changes the volumes of the two solutions.

People can take advantage of osmosis to preserve foods. Salt is often applied to meats to cure them; the salt causes water to move out of the food toward the region of greater solute (salt) concentration. Food can also be preserved in honey because a high sugar concentration draws water out of food.

When the solute concentrations are the same on both sides of a membrane, water molecules will move at the same rate in both directions, so there will be no net change in solute concentration. Solutions of equal solute concentration are said to be **isotonic**. For example, many marine animals, such as sea stars and crabs, are isotonic to seawater, so they neither gain nor lose water. You may have seen this term on bottles of contact lens saline solution, which is formulated to have the same solute concentration as the fluid at the surface of the human eye, reducing irritation.

Water Balance in Animal Cells

The survival of a cell depends on its ability to balance water uptake and loss. When an animal cell, such as a red blood cell, is immersed in an isotonic solution, the cell's volume remains constant because the cell gains water at the same rate that it loses water (**Figure 5.14a**, top). But what happens if an animal cell is in contact with a hypotonic solution, which has a lower solute concentration than the cell? Due to osmosis, the cell would gain water, swell, and possibly burst (lyse) like an overfilled water balloon (**Figure 5.14b**, top). A hypertonic environment is also harsh on an animal cell; the cell shrivels from water loss (**Figure 5.14c**, top).

For an animal to survive a hypotonic or hypertonic environment, the animal must have a way to balance the uptake and loss of water. The control of water balance is called **osmoregulation**. For example, a freshwater fish has kidneys and gills that work constantly to prevent an excessive buildup of water in the body. Humans can suffer consequences of osmoregulation failure. Dehydration (consumption of too little water) can cause fatigue and even death. Drinking too much water—called hyponatremia or "water intoxication"—can also cause death by overdiluting necessary ions.

▼ Figure 5.14 **The behavior of animal and plant cells in different osmotic environments.**

Animal cell

Normal | Lysing | Shriveled

Plant cell

Plasma membrane

Flaccid (wilts) | Turgid (normal) | Shriveled

(a) Isotonic solution | **(b) Hypotonic solution** | **(c) Hypertonic solution**

Water Balance in Plant Cells

Problems of water balance are somewhat different for plant cells because of their rigid cell walls. A plant cell immersed in an isotonic solution is flaccid (floppy), and the plant wilts (Figure 5.14a, bottom). In contrast, a plant cell is turgid (very firm) and healthiest in a hypotonic environment, with a net inflow of water (Figure 5.14b, bottom). Although the elastic cell wall expands a bit, the back pressure it exerts prevents the cell from taking in too much water and bursting. Turgor is necessary for plants to retain their upright posture and the extended state of their leaves (**Figure 5.15**). However, in a hypertonic environment, a plant cell is no better off than an animal cell. As a plant cell loses water, it shrivels, and its plasma membrane pulls away from the cell wall (Figure 5.14c, bottom). This process, called plasmolysis, usually kills the cell. ☑

▼ Figure 5.15 **Plant turgor.** Watering a wilted plant will make it regain its turgor.

☑ CHECKPOINT

1. An animal cell shrivels when it is _____ compared with its environment.
2. The cells of a wilted plant are _____ compared with their environment.

Answers: 1. hypertonic 2. isotonic

Active Transport: The Pumping of Molecules across Membranes

In contrast to passive transport, **active transport** requires that a cell expend energy to move molecules across a membrane. Cellular energy (usually provided by ATP) is used to drive a transport protein that pumps a solute *against* the solute's concentration gradient—that is, in the direction that is opposite the way it would naturally flow (Figure 5.16).

Active transport allows cells to maintain internal concentrations of small solutes that differ from environmental concentrations. For example, compared with its surroundings, an animal nerve cell has a much higher concentration of potassium ions and a much lower concentration of sodium ions. The plasma membrane helps maintain these differences by pumping sodium out of the cell and potassium into the cell. This particular case of active transport (called the sodium-potassium pump) is vital to the nervous system. ☑

▲ Figure 5.16 **Active transport.** Transport proteins are specific in their recognition of atoms or molecules. This transport protein (purple) has a binding site that accepts only a certain solute. Using energy from ATP, the protein pumps the solute against its concentration gradient.

Exocytosis and Endocytosis: Traffic of Large Molecules

So far, we've focused on how water and small solutes enter and leave cells by moving through the plasma membrane. The story is different for large molecules such as proteins, which are much too big to fit through the membrane. Their traffic into and out of the cell depends on the ability of the cell to package large molecules inside sacs called vesicles. You have already seen an example of this: During protein production by the cell, secretory proteins exit the cell from transport vesicles that fuse with the plasma membrane, spilling the contents outside the cell (see Figures 4.14 and 4.18). That process is called **exocytosis** (Figure 5.17). When you cry, for

How are tears spilled?

example, cells in your tear glands use exocytosis to export the salty tears.

In **endocytosis**, a cell takes material in via vesicles that bud inward (Figure 5.18). For example, in a process called **phagocytosis** ("cellular eating"), a cell engulfs a particle and packages it within a food vacuole. Other times, a cell "gulps" droplets of fluid into vesicles. Endocytosis can also be triggered by the binding of certain external molecules to specific receptor proteins built into the plasma membrane. This binding causes the local region of the membrane to form a vesicle that transports the specific substance into the cell. In human liver cells, this process is used to take up cholesterol particles from the blood.

▼ Figure 5.17 **Exocytosis.**

▼ Figure 5.18 **Endocytosis.**

The Role of Membranes in Cell Signaling

In addition to transport, the plasma membrane and its embedded proteins play key roles in conveying signals from the external environment into the cell and also between cells. Communication begins when a receptor protein in the plasma membrane receives a stimulus, such as a hormone. This stimulus triggers a chain reaction in one or more molecules that function in transduction (passing the signal along). The proteins and other molecules of this **signal transduction pathway** relay the signal and convert it to chemical forms that can function within the cell. This signal may lead to various responses.

Figure 5.19 shows an example of cell signaling: signal reception, transduction, and response. When a person gets "psyched up" for an athletic contest, certain cells in the adrenal glands secrete a hormone called epinephrine (also called adrenaline) into the bloodstream. When that hormone reaches muscle cells, it is recognized by receptor proteins in the plasma membrane. This recognition triggers responses (such as the breakdown of glycogen into glucose) in the muscle cells without the hormone even entering. This chain of events is part of the "fight-or-flight" response that enables you to attack or run when in danger—or keep alert during an intense competition. ✓

✓ CHECKPOINT

How can a molecule change a cell without entering it?

Answer: It can bind to a membrane protein that triggers a signal transduction pathway.

▼ Figure 5.19 **An example of cell signaling.**

Outside of cell   Cytoplasm

Reception   **Transduction**   **Response**

Receptor protein

Proteins of signal transduction pathway

Hydrolysis of glycogen releases glucose for energy

Epinephrine (adrenaline) from adrenal glands

Plasma membrane

 Nanotechnology EVOLUTION CONNECTION

The Origin of Membranes

Because all cells have a plasma membrane, it is logical to infer that membranes first formed early in the evolution of life on Earth. Phospholipids, their key ingredients, were probably among the first organic compounds that formed from chemical reactions on the early Earth. Once formed, they could self-assemble into simple membranes. When a mixture of phospholipids and water is shaken, for example, the phospholipids organize into bilayers, forming water-filled bubbles of membrane (Figure 5.20). This assembly requires neither genes nor other information beyond the properties of the phospholipids themselves.

The tendency of lipids in water to spontaneously form membranes has led biomedical engineers to produce artificial vesicles called liposomes that can encase particular chemicals. In the future, these liposomes may deliver medications to specific sites within the body. Thus, membranes—like the other cellular components discussed in the Biology and Society and the Process of Science sections—have inspired novel nanotechnologies.

▼ Figure 5.20 **The spontaneous formation of membranes: a key step in the origin of life.**

Water-filled bubble made of phospholipids

Chapter Review

SUMMARY OF KEY CONCEPTS

Some Basic Energy Concepts

Conservation of Energy

Machines and organisms can transform kinetic energy (energy of motion) to potential energy (stored energy) and vice versa. In all such energy transformations, total energy is conserved. Energy cannot be created or destroyed.

Entropy

Entropy is a measure of disorder, or randomness. Every energy conversion releases some randomized energy in the form of heat.

Chemical Energy

Molecules store varying amounts of potential energy in the arrangement of their atoms. Organic compounds are relatively rich in such chemical energy.

Food Calories

Food Calories, actually kilocalories, are units used to measure the amount of energy in our foods and the amount of energy we expend in various activities.

ATP and Cellular Work

Enzymes

Activation Energy

Enzymes are biological catalysts that speed up metabolic reactions by lowering the activation energy required to break the bonds of reactant molecules.

Induced Fit

The entry of a substrate into the active site of an enzyme causes the enzyme to change shape slightly, allowing for a better fit and thereby promoting the interaction of enzyme with substrate.

Enzyme Inhibitors

Enzyme inhibitors are molecules that can disrupt metabolic reactions by binding to enzymes, either at the active site or elsewhere.

Membrane Function

Proteins embedded in the plasma membrane perform a wide variety of functions, including regulating transport.

Passive Transport, Osmosis, and Active Transport

Most animal cells require an isotonic environment. Plant cells need a hypotonic environment, which keeps walled cells turgid. Osmoregulation is the control of water balance within a cell or organism.

Exocytosis and Endocytosis: Traffic of Large Molecules

Exocytosis is the secretion of large molecules within vesicles. Endocytosis is the import of large substances via vesicles into the cell.

The Role of Membranes in Cell Signaling

Receptors on the cell surface trigger signal transduction pathways that control processes within the cell.

SELF-QUIZ

1. Describe the energy transformations that occur when you climb to the top of a stairway.

2. _____ is the capacity to perform work, while _____ is a measure of randomness.

3. The label on a candy bar says that it contains 150 Calories. If you could convert all of that energy to heat, you could raise the temperature of how much water by 15°C?

4. Why does removing a phosphate group from the triphosphate tail in a molecule of ATP release energy?

5. Your digestive system uses a variety of enzymes to break down large food molecules into smaller ones that your cells can assimilate. A generic name for a digestive enzyme is hydrolase. What is the chemical basis for that name? (*Hint*: Review Figure 3.4.)

6. Explain how an inhibitor can disrupt an enzyme's action without binding to the active site.

7. If someone at the other end of a restaurant smokes a cigarette, you may breathe in some smoke. The movement of smoke is similar to what type of transport?
   a. osmosis
   b. diffusion
   c. facilitated diffusion
   d. active transport

8. The total solute concentration in a red blood cell is about 2%. Sucrose cannot pass through a red blood cell's plasma membrane, but water and urea can. Osmosis will cause such a cell to shrink the most when the cell is immersed in which of the following?
   a. a hypertonic sucrose solution
   b. a hypotonic sucrose solution
   c. a hypertonic urea solution
   d. a hypotonic urea solution

9. Explain why it is not enough just to say that a solution is hypertonic.

10. What is the primary difference between passive and active transport in terms of concentration gradients?

11. Which of these types of cellular transport require(s) energy?
    a. facilitated diffusion
    b. active transport
    c. osmosis
    d. a and b

12. A _____ is a process that links the reception of a cell signal to a response within the cell.

Answers to these questions can be found in Appendix: Self-Quiz Answers.

THE PROCESS OF SCIENCE

13. HIV, the virus that causes AIDS, depends on an enzyme called reverse transcriptase in order to multiply. Reverse transcriptase reads a molecule of RNA and creates a molecule of DNA from it. A molecule of AZT, the first drug approved to treat AIDS, has a shape very similar to (but a bit different than) that of the DNA base thymine. Propose a model for how AZT inhibits HIV.

14. Gaining and losing weight are matters of caloric accounting: Calories in the food you eat minus Calories that you spend in activity. One pound of human body fat contains approximately 3,500 Calories. Using Figure 5.3, compare ways you could burn off those Calories. How far would you have to run, swim, or walk to burn the equivalent of 1 pound of fat, and how long would it take? Which method of burning Calories appeals the most to you? The least? How much of each food would you have to consume in order to gain a single pound? How does one pound's worth of food compare with one pound's worth of exercise? Does it seem like an even trade-off?

BIOLOGY AND SOCIETY

15. Obesity is a serious health problem for many Americans. Several popular diet plans advocate low-carbohydrate diets. Most low-carb dieters compensate by eating more protein and fat. What are the advantages and disadvantages of such a diet? Should the government regulate the claims of diet books? How should the claims be tested? Should diet proponents be required to obtain and publish data before making claims?

16. Lead acts as an enzyme inhibitor, and it can interfere with the development of the nervous system. One manufacturer of lead-acid batteries instituted a "fetal protection policy" that banned female employees of childbearing age from working in areas where they might be exposed to high levels of lead. These women were transferred to lower-paying jobs in lower-risk areas. Some employees challenged the policy in court, claiming that it deprived women of job opportunities available to men. The U.S. Supreme Court ruled the policy illegal. But many people are uncomfortable about the "right" to work in an unsafe environment. What rights and responsibilities of employers, employees, and government agencies are in conflict? What criteria should be used to decide who can work in a particular environment?

6 Cellular Respiration: Obtaining Energy from Food

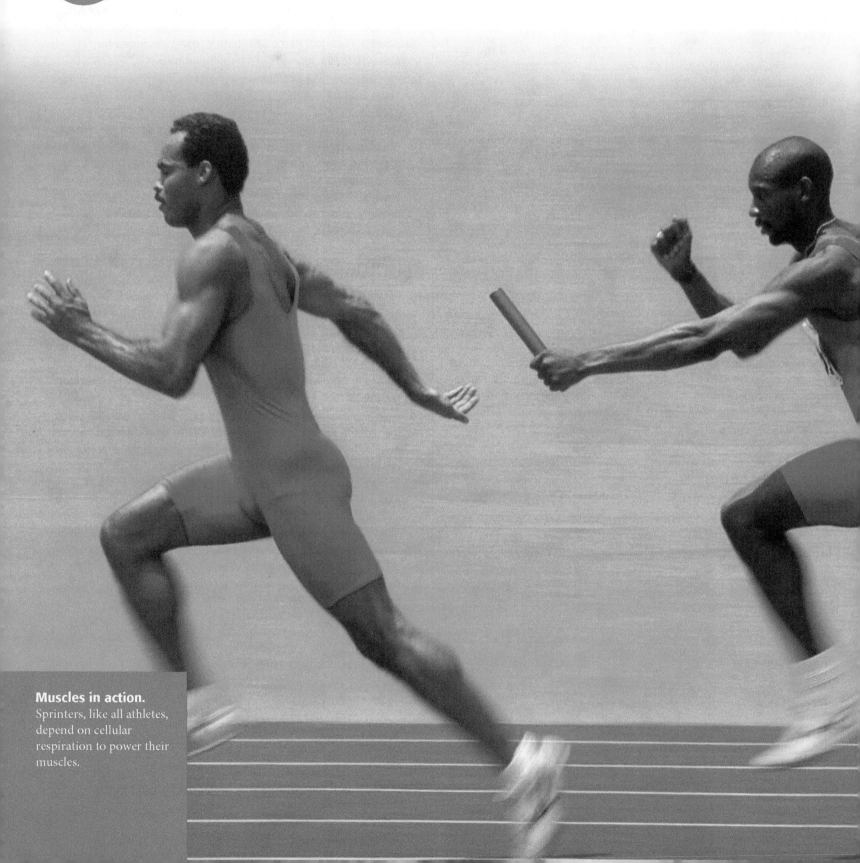

Muscles in action. Sprinters, like all athletes, depend on cellular respiration to power their muscles.

Aerobic versus Anaerobic Lifestyles BIOLOGY AND SOCIETY

Marathoners versus Sprinters

Track-and-field athletes usually have a favorite event in which they excel. Some runners specialize in sprints of 100 or 200 meters. Others excel at longer races of 1,500, 5,000, or even 10,000 m. It is unusual to find a runner who competes equally well in both 100-m and 10,000-m races; most runners are more comfortable running races of particular lengths.

It turns out that there is a biological basis for such preferences. The muscles that move our legs contain two main types of muscle fibers: slow-twitch and fast-twitch. Slow-twitch muscle fibers can contract many times over a longer period but don't generate a lot of quick power for the body. They perform better in endurance exercises requiring slow, steady muscle activity, such as marathons. Fast-twitch muscle fibers can contract more quickly and powerfully than slow-twitch fibers but also fatigue much more quickly. They function best in short bursts of intense activity, such as sprints.

All human muscles contain both slow-twitch and fast-twitch fibers, but the percentage of each fiber type in a particular muscle varies from person to person. For example, the thigh muscles of most marathon runners contain more slow-twitch fibers, whereas sprinters have more fast-twitch fibers. These differences, which are genetically determined, undoubtedly help account for varying athletic capabilities. Thus, to a certain degree, champion marathoners and sprinters are born, not trained!

What makes these two types of muscle fibers perform differently? An important part of the answer is that they use different processes for making ATP, the molecule that supplies the energy for muscle contraction. While the cells in both types of muscle fiber break down glucose and use that chemical energy to produce ATP, slow-twitch fibers do it aerobically (using oxygen, O_2), while fast-twitch fibers can work anaerobically (without oxygen).

The series of chemical reactions that provides energy to muscles is also used by other cells. In fact, all your body cells need a continuous supply of energy for you to walk, talk, think—in short, to stay alive. In this chapter, you'll learn how cells harvest food energy and put it to work.

Energy Flow and Chemical Cycling in the Biosphere

Plants convert the energy of sunlight to the chemical energy of sugars and other organic molecules. This is accomplished via photosynthesis. **Photosynthesis** uses light energy from the sun to power a chemical process that builds organic molecules (as we'll discuss in Chapter 7).

Humans and other animals depend on this conversion for our food and more. You're probably wearing clothing made of a product of photosynthesis—cotton. Most of our homes are framed with lumber, which is wood produced by photosynthetic trees. Even textbooks are printed on a material (paper) that can be traced to photosynthesis in plants. But from an animal's point of view, photosynthesis is primarily about providing food.

Producers and Consumers

Plants and other **autotrophs** ("self-feeders") are organisms that make all their own organic matter—including carbohydrates, lipids, proteins, and nucleic acids—from nutrients that are entirely inorganic: carbon dioxide from the air and water and minerals from the soil. In other words, plants make their own food; they don't need to eat to gain energy to power their cellular processes. In contrast, humans and other animals are **heterotrophs** ("other-feeders"), organisms that cannot make organic molecules from inorganic ones. Therefore, we must eat organic material to get our nutrients and provide energy for life's processes.

Most ecosystems depend entirely on photosynthesis for food. For this reason, biologists refer to plants and other autotrophs as **producers**. Heterotrophs, in contrast, are **consumers**, because they obtain their food by eating plants or by eating animals that have eaten plants (Figure 6.1). We animals and other heterotrophs depend on autotrophs for organic fuel and for the raw organic materials we need to build our cells and tissues. ☑

Chemical Cycling between Photosynthesis and Cellular Respiration

The chemical ingredients for photosynthesis are carbon dioxide (CO_2), a gas that passes from the air into a plant via tiny pores, and water (H_2O), which is absorbed from the soil by the plant's roots (Figure 6.2). Inside leaf cells, tiny structures called chloroplasts use light energy to rearrange the atoms of these ingredients to produce sugars—most importantly glucose ($C_6H_{12}O_6$)—and

▼ Figure 6.1 **Producer and consumer.** A thrush (consumer) eats a fruit produced by a photosynthetic plant (producer).

other organic molecules. A by-product of photosynthesis is oxygen gas (O_2).

Both animals and plants use the organic products of photosynthesis as sources of energy. A chemical process called cellular respiration harvests energy that is stored in sugars and other organic molecules. Cellular respiration uses O_2 to help convert the energy stored in the chemical bonds of organic fuels to another source of chemical energy called ATP. Cells expend ATP for almost all their work. In both plants and animals, the production of ATP during cellular respiration occurs mainly in the organelles called mitochondria (see Figure 4.20).

Notice in Figure 6.2 that the waste products of cellular respiration are CO_2 and H_2O—the very same ingredients used

for photosynthesis. Plants store chemical energy via photosynthesis and then harvest this energy via cellular respiration. (Note that plants perform *both* photosynthesis to produce fuel molecules *and* cellular respiration to burn them, while animals perform *only* cellular respiration.) Plants usually make more organic molecules than they need for fuel. This photosynthetic surplus provides material for the plant to grow or can be stored, as starch in potatoes, for example. People have always taken advantage of plants' photosynthetic abilities by eating them. More recently, engineers have managed to tap into this energy reserve to produce liquid biofuels, primarily ethanol. Analyze nearly any food chain, and you can trace the energy and raw materials for growth back to solar-powered photosynthesis. ☑

Sunlight energy enters ecosystem

Photosynthesis
(in chloroplasts)
converts light energy
to chemical energy

$C_6H_{12}O_6$
Glucose
+
O_2
Oxygen

CO_2
Carbon dioxide
+
H_2O
Water

Cellular respiration
(in mitochondria)
harvests food energy
to produce ATP

ATP   drives cellular work

Heat energy exits ecosystem

◀ **Figure 6.2 Energy flow and chemical cycling in ecosystems.** Energy flows through an ecosystem, entering as sunlight and exiting as heat. In contrast, chemical elements are recycled within an ecosystem.

☑ **CHECKPOINT**

What is misleading about the following statement? "Plants have chloroplasts that perform photosynthesis, whereas animals have mitochondria that perform cellular respiration."

Answer: It implies that cellular respiration does not also occur in plants. It does.

Cellular Respiration: Aerobic Harvest of Food Energy

We sometimes use the word *respiration* to mean breathing. While respiration on the organismal level should not be confused with cellular respiration, the two processes are closely related **(Figure 6.3)**. Cellular respiration requires a cell to exchange two gases with its surroundings. The cell takes in oxygen in the form of the gas O_2. It gets rid of waste in the form of the gas carbon dioxide, or CO_2. Breathing results in the exchange of these same gases between your blood and the outside air. Oxygen present in the air you inhale diffuses

Why do car engines require an air intake?

across the lining of your lungs and into your bloodstream. And the CO_2 in your bloodstream diffuses into your lungs and exits when you exhale. Every molecule of CO_2 that you exhale was originally formed in one of the mitochondria of your body's cells.

Internal combustion engines, like the ones found in cars, use O_2 (via the air intakes) to break down gasoline. A cell also requires O_2 to break down its fuel (see Figure 5.2). Cellular respiration—a living version of internal combustion—is the main way that chemical energy is harvested from food and converted to ATP energy (see Figure 5.6). Cellular respiration is an **aerobic** process, which is just another way of saying that it requires oxygen. Putting all this together, we can now define **cellular respiration** as the aerobic harvesting of chemical energy from organic fuel molecules. ☑

▼ Figure 6.3 **How breathing is related to cellular respiration.** When you inhale, you breathe in O_2. The O_2 is delivered to your cells, where it is used in cellular respiration. Carbon dioxide, a waste product of cellular respiration, diffuses from your cells to your blood and travels to your lungs, where it is exhaled.

Breathing

Lungs

O_2

CO_2

Muscle cells

Cellular respiration

The Simplified Equation for Cellular Respiration

A common fuel molecule for cellular respiration is glucose, a six-carbon sugar with the formula $C_6H_{12}O_6$ (see Figure 3.6). Here is the overall equation for what happens to glucose during cellular respiration:

$$C_6H_{12}O_6 + 6\ O_2 \longrightarrow 6\ CO_2 + 6\ H_2O + ATP$$

Glucose   Oxygen   Carbon dioxide   Water   Energy

The series of arrows indicates that cellular respiration consists of many chemical steps. Remember, the main function of cellular respiration is to generate ATP for cellular work. In fact, the process can produce around 32 ATP molecules for each glucose molecule consumed.

Notice that cellular respiration also transfers hydrogen atoms from glucose to oxygen, forming water. As you'll see next, that hydrogen transfer is the key to why oxygen is so vital to the harvest of energy during cellular respiration.

The Role of Oxygen in Cellular Respiration

In tracking the transfer of hydrogen from sugar to oxygen, we are also following the transfer of electrons. The atoms of sugar and other molecules are bonded together by shared electrons (see Figure 2.8). During cellular respiration, hydrogen and its bonding electrons change partners from sugar to oxygen, forming water as a product.

Redox Reactions

Chemical reactions that transfer electrons from one substance to another substance are called oxidation-reduction reactions, or **redox reactions** for short. The loss of electrons during a redox reaction is called **oxidation**. Glucose is oxidized during cellular respiration, losing electrons to oxygen. The acceptance of electrons during a redox reaction is called **reduction**. (Note that *adding* electrons is called *reduction*; negatively charged electrons added to an atom *reduce* the amount of positive charge of that atom.) Oxygen is reduced during cellular respiration, accepting electrons (and hydrogen) lost from glucose:

Oxidation
Glucose loses electrons (and hydrogens)

$C_6H_{12}O_6$ + 6 O_2 → → → 6 CO_2 + 6 H_2O

Glucose   Oxygen   Carbon dioxide   Water

Reduction
Oxygen gains electrons (and hydrogens)

Water isn't the only thing produced when hydrogen and its bonding electrons change partners from glucose to oxygen; energy is released, too.

Why does electron transfer to oxygen release energy? In redox reactions, oxygen is an "electron grabber." An oxygen atom attracts electrons more strongly than almost any other type of atom. When electrons move (along with hydrogen) from glucose to oxygen, it is as though they are falling. They are not really falling in the sense of an apple dropping from a tree. However, in both cases, potential energy is unlocked. Instead of gravity, it is the attraction of electrons to oxygen that causes the "fall" and energy release during cellular respiration.

Figure 6.4 shows a simple example of a redox reaction: the reaction between hydrogen gas (H_2) and

oxygen gas (O_2), producing water (H_2O). The reaction releases a large amount of energy as the electrons of the hydrogen "fall" into their new bonds with oxygen. This reaction is actually quite explosive, and it would be difficult for a cell to capture such a burst of energy and put it to useful work. As you'll see shortly, cellular respiration is a more controlled "fall" of electrons—more like a stepwise cascade of electrons down an energy staircase. Instead of liberating food energy in a burst, cellular respiration unlocks chemical energy in smaller amounts that cells can put to productive use. ☑

NADH and Electron Transport Chains

Let's take a closer look at the path that electrons take on their way from glucose to oxygen (**Figure 6.5**). The first stop is a positively charged electron acceptor called NAD^+ (n̲icotinamide a̲denine d̲inucleotide) that cells make from niacin, a B vitamin. The transfer of electrons from organic fuel (food) to NAD^+ reduces it to **NADH** (the H represents the transfer of hydrogen along with the electrons). In our staircase analogy, the electrons have now taken one baby step down in their trip from glucose to oxygen. The rest of the staircase consists of an **electron transport chain**.

▼ **Figure 6.5 The role of oxygen in harvesting food energy.** In cellular respiration, electrons e^- "fall" in small steps from food to oxygen, producing water. NADH transfers electrons from food to an electron transport chain. The attraction of oxygen to electrons "pulls" the electrons down the chain.

Electrons from food

NAD^+ NADH

Stepwise release of energy used to make

ATP

2 H^+ 2 e^-

Electron transport chain

2 e^-

2 H^+ $\frac{1}{2}$ O_2

H_2O

Hydrogen, electrons, and oxygen combine to produce water

▼ **Figure 6.4 A simple redox reaction.** An all-at-once redox reaction, such as the reaction of hydrogen and oxygen to form water, releases a burst of energy.

H_2 $\frac{1}{2}$ O_2

Release of heat energy

H_2O

☑ CHECKPOINT

During a redox reaction, the addition of electrons is called _____, while the removal of electrons is called _____.

Answer: reduction; oxidation

95

Each link in an electron transport chain is actually a molecule, usually a protein. In a series of redox reactions, each member of the chain first accepts and then donates electrons. With each transfer, the electrons give up a small amount of energy that can then be used indirectly to generate ATP. The first molecule of the chain accepts electrons from NADH. Thus, NADH carries electrons from glucose and other fuel molecules and deposits them at the top of an electron transport chain. The electrons cascade down the chain, from molecule to molecule, like an electron bucket brigade. The molecule at the bottom of the chain finally "drops" the electrons to oxygen. At the same time, oxygen picks up hydrogen, forming water.

The overall effect of all this transfer of electrons during cellular respiration is a "downward" trip for electrons from glucose to NADH to an electron transport chain to oxygen. During the stepwise release of chemical energy during electron transport, our cells make most of their ATP. It is actually oxygen, the "electron grabber," that makes it all possible. By pulling electrons down the

Why do animals drown so quickly?

transport chain from fuel molecules, oxygen functions somewhat like gravity pulling objects downhill. This is how the oxygen we breathe functions in our cells and why we cannot survive more than a few minutes without it. Viewed this way, drowning is deadly because it deprives cells of the final "electron grabbers" (oxygen) needed to drive cellular respiration.

An Overview of Cellular Respiration

Cellular respiration is an example of a metabolic pathway. That means that it is not a single chemical reaction, but a series of reactions. A specific enzyme catalyzes each reaction in a metabolic pathway. More than two dozen reactions are involved in cellular respiration. We can group them into three main metabolic stages: glycolysis, the citric acid cycle, and electron transport.

Figure 6.6 is a map that will help you follow the three stages of respiration and see where each stage occurs in your cells. During **glycolysis**, a molecule of glucose is split into two molecules of a compound called pyruvic acid. The enzymes for glycolysis are located in the cytoplasm. The **citric acid cycle** (also called the Krebs cycle) completes the breakdown of glucose all the way to CO_2, one of the waste products of cellular respiration. The enzymes for the citric acid cycle are dissolved in the fluid within mitochondria. Glycolysis and the citric acid cycle generate a small amount of ATP directly. They generate much more ATP indirectly, via redox reactions that transfer electrons from fuel molecules to NAD^+, forming NADH. The third stage of cellular respiration is **electron transport**. Electrons captured from food by the NADH formed in the first two stages "fall" down electron transport chains to oxygen. The proteins and other molecules that make up electron transport chains are embedded within the inner membrane of the mitochondria. Electron transport from NADH to oxygen releases the energy your cells use to make most of their ATP. ☑

☑ **CHECKPOINT**

Which stages of cellular respiration take place in the mitochondria?

Answer: the citric acid cycle and electron transport

Cytoplasm
Mitochondrion
Cytoplasm
Cytoplasm
Animal cell
Plant cell
Cytoplasm
Mitochondrion
High-energy electrons via carrier molecules

Glycolysis
Glucose → 2 Pyruvic acid
Citric Acid Cycle
Electron Transport
ATP
ATP
ATP

◄ Figure 6.6 **A road map for cellular respiration.**

The Three Stages of Cellular Respiration

Now that you have a big-picture view of cellular respiration, let's examine the process in more detail. A small version of Figure 6.6 will help you keep the overall process of cellular respiration in plain view as we take a closer look at its three stages.

Stage 1: Glycolysis

The word *glycolysis* means "splitting of sugar." That is exactly what happens (Figure 6.7). ❶ During glycolysis, a six-carbon glucose molecule is broken in half, forming two three-carbon molecules. Notice in Figure 6.7 that the initial split requires an energy investment of two ATP molecules per glucose. ❷ The three-carbon molecules then donate high-energy electrons to NAD⁺, the electron carrier, forming NADH. ❸ In addition to NADH, glycolysis also makes four ATP molecules directly when

enzymes transfer phosphate groups from fuel molecules to ADP (Figure 6.8). Glycolysis thus produces a net of two molecules of ATP per molecule of glucose. (This fact will become important during our discussion of fermentation.) What remains of the fractured glucose at the end of glycolysis are two molecules of pyruvic acid. The pyruvic acid still holds most of the energy of glucose, and that energy is harvested in the second stage of cellular respiration, the citric acid cycle.

▼ **Figure 6.8 ATP synthesis by direct phosphate transfer.** Glycolysis generates ATP when enzymes transfer phosphate groups directly from fuel molecules to ADP.

▼ **Figure 6.7 Glycolysis.** In glycolysis, a team of enzymes splits glucose, eventually forming two molecules of pyruvic acid. After investing 2 ATP at the start, glycolysis generates 4 ATP directly. More energy will be harvested later from high-energy electrons used to form NADH and from the 2 molecules of pyruvic acid.

97

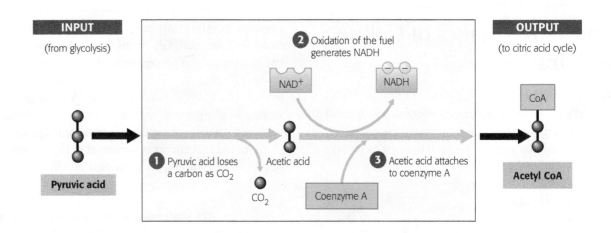

► Figure 6.9 **The link between glycolysis and the citric acid cycle: the conversion of pyruvic acid to acetyl CoA.** Remember that one molecule of glucose is split into two molecules of pyruvic acid. Therefore, the process shown here occurs twice.

Stage 2: The Citric Acid Cycle

The two molecules of pyruvic acid, the fuel that remains after glycolysis, are not quite ready for the citric acid cycle. The pyruvic acid must be "groomed"—converted to a form the citric acid cycle can use (Figure 6.9). ❶ First, each pyruvic acid loses a carbon as CO_2. This is the first of this waste product we've seen so far in the breakdown of glucose. The remaining fuel molecules, each with only two carbons left, are called acetic acid (the acid that's in vinegar). ❷ Oxidation of the fuel generates NADH. ❸ Finally, each acetic acid is attached to a molecule called coenzyme A (CoA), an enzyme derived from the B vitamin pantothenic acid, to form acetyl CoA. The CoA escorts the acetic acid into the first reaction of the citric acid cycle. The CoA is then stripped and recycled.

The citric acid cycle finishes extracting the energy of sugar by dismantling the acetic acid molecules all the way down to CO_2 (Figure 6.10). ❶ Acetic acid joins a four-carbon acceptor molecule to form a six-carbon product called citric acid (for which the cycle is named). For every acetic acid molecule that enters the cycle as fuel, ❷ two CO_2 molecules eventually exit as a waste product. Along the way, the citric acid cycle harvests energy from the fuel. ❸ Some of the energy is used to produce ATP directly. However, the cycle captures much more energy in the form of ❹ NADH and ❺ a second, closely related electron carrier, $FADH_2$. ❻ All the carbon atoms that entered the cycle as fuel are accounted for as CO_2 exhaust, and the four-carbon acceptor molecule is recycled. We have tracked only one acetic acid molecule through the citric acid cycle here. But since glycolysis splits glucose in two, the citric acid cycle actually turns twice for each glucose molecule that fuels a cell. ☑

► Figure 6.10 **The citric acid cycle.**

☑ **CHECKPOINT**

Two molecules of what compound are produced by glycolysis? Does this molecule enter the citric acid cycle?

Answer: Pyruvic acid. No, it is first converted to acetic acid.

Stage 3: Electron Transport

The molecules of electron transport chains are built into the inner membranes of mitochondria (see Figure 4.20). Because these membranes are highly folded, their large surface area can accommodate thousands of copies of the electron transport chain. Each chain functions as a chemical machine that uses the energy released by the "fall" of electrons to pump hydrogen ions (H^+) across the inner mitochondrial membrane. This pumping causes ions to become more concentrated on one side of the membrane than on the other. Such a difference in concentration stores potential energy.

The energy stored by electron transport behaves something like the water behind a dam. There is a tendency for hydrogen ions to gush back to where they are less concentrated, just as there is a tendency for water to flow downhill. The inner membrane temporarily "dams" hydrogen ions.

The energy of dammed water can be harnessed to perform work. Gates in a dam allow the water to rush downhill, turning giant turbines, and this work can be used to generate electricity. Your mitochondria have structures that act like turbines. Each of these miniature machines, called an **ATP synthase**, is constructed from protein built into the inner mitochondrial membrane, adjacent to the proteins of the electron transport chains. **Figure 6.11** shows a simplified view of how the energy previously stored in NADH and $FADH_2$ can now be used to generate ATP. ❶ NADH and ❷ $FADH_2$ transfer electrons to an electron transport chain. ❸ The electron transport chain uses this energy supply to pump H^+ across the inner mitochondrial membrane. ❹ Oxygen pulls electrons down the transport chain. ❺ The H^+ concentrated on one side of the membrane rushes back "downhill" through an ATP synthase. This action spins a component of the ATP synthase, just as water turns the turbines in a dam. ❻ The rotation activates parts of the synthase molecule that attach phosphate groups to ADP molecules to generate ATP.

The poison cyanide produces its deadly effect by binding to one of the protein complexes in the electron transport chain (marked by ☠ in Figure 6.11). When bound there, cyanide blocks the passage of electrons to oxygen. This blockage is like clogging a dam. As a result, no H^+ gradient is generated, and no ATP is made. Cells stop working, and the organism dies. Cyanide was the lethal agent in an infamous case of product tampering: the Tylenol murders of 1982. Seven people in the Chicago area died after ingesting Tylenol capsules that had been laced with cyanide. The perpetrator of that crime was never caught. ☑

☑ CHECKPOINT

What is the potential energy source that drives ATP production by ATP synthase?

Answer: a concentration gradient of H^+ across the inner membrane of a mitochondrion

How does cyanide kill?

▼ Figure 6.11 **How electron transport drives ATP synthase machines.**

The Results of Cellular Respiration

Taking cellular respiration apart to see how all the molecular nuts and bolts of its metabolic machinery work, it's easy to lose sight of its overall function: to generate about 32 molecules of ATP per molecule of glucose (the actual number can vary by a few). Figure 6.12 will help you add up the ATP molecules. Glycolysis and the citric acid cycle each contribute 2 ATP by directly making it. All of the rest of the ATP molecules are produced by the ATP synthase machines, powered by the "fall" of electrons from food to oxygen. The electrons are carried from the organic fuel to electron transport chains by NADH and $FADH_2$. Each electron pair "dropped" down a transport chain from NADH or $FADH_2$ can power the synthesis of a few ATP. To summarize, energy flows from glucose to carrier molecules and ultimately to ATP.

We have seen that glucose can provide the energy to make the ATP our cells use for all their work. The importance of glucose is underscored by the severity of diseases in which glucose balance is disturbed. Diabetes, which affects over 20 million Americans, is caused by an inability to properly regulate glucose levels in the blood due to problems with the hormone insulin. If left untreated, a glucose imbalance can lead to a variety of problems, including cardiovascular disease, coma, and even death.

▼ Figure 6.13 **Energy from food.** The monomers from carbohydrates (polysaccharides and sugars), fats, and proteins can all serve as fuel for cellular respiration.

But even though we have concentrated on glucose as the fuel that is broken down during cellular respiration, respiration is a versatile metabolic furnace that can "burn" many other kinds of food molecules. Figure 6.13 diagrams some metabolic routes for the use of carbohydrates, fats, and proteins as fuel for cellular respiration. ☑

▼ Figure 6.12 **A summary of ATP yield during cellular respiration.**

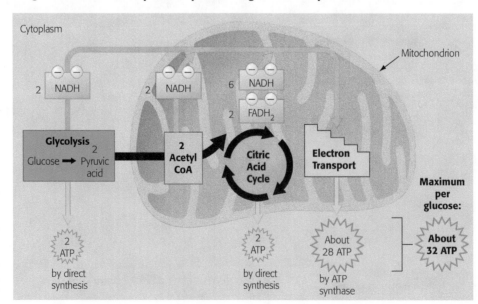

☑ CHECKPOINT

Which stage of cellular respiration produces the majority of ATP?

Answer: electron transport

Fermentation: Anaerobic Harvest of Food Energy

Although you must breathe to stay alive, some of your cells can work for short periods without oxygen. This **anaerobic** ("without oxygen") harvest of food energy is called **fermentation**.

Fermentation in Human Muscle Cells

As your muscles work, they require a constant supply of ATP, which is generated by cellular respiration. As long as your blood provides your muscle cells with enough O_2 to keep electrons "falling" down transport chains in mitochondria, your muscles will work aerobically. But under strenuous conditions, your muscles can spend ATP faster than your bloodstream can deliver O_2; when this happens, your muscle cells begin to work anaerobically. To stay within the aerobic zone, some athletes seek an unfair advantage by blood doping: artificially expanding their capacity to deliver O_2 to muscles by, for example, injecting excess red blood cells previously harvested from themselves or a donor.

After functioning anaerobically for about 15 seconds, muscle cells will begin to generate ATP by the process of fermentation. Fermentation relies on glycolysis, the first stage of cellular respiration. Glycolysis does not require

How does blood doping increase an athlete's aerobic capacity?

O_2 but does produce 2 ATP molecules for each glucose molecule broken down to pyruvic acid. That isn't very efficient compared with the 32 or so ATP molecules each glucose generates during cellular respiration, but it can energize muscles for a short burst. However, your cells will have to consume more glucose fuel per second, since so much less ATP per glucose molecule is generated under anaerobic conditions.

To harvest food energy during glycolysis, NAD^+ must be present as an electron acceptor (see Figure 6.7). This is no problem under aerobic conditions, because the cell regenerates NAD^+ when NADH drops its electron cargo down electron transport chains to O_2 (see Figure 6.5). However, this recycling of NAD^+ cannot occur under anaerobic conditions because there is no O_2 to accept the electrons. Instead, NADH disposes of electrons by adding them to the pyruvic acid produced by glycolysis **(Figure 6.14)**. This restores NAD^+ and keeps glycolysis working.

The addition of electrons to pyruvic acid produces a waste product called lactic acid. The lactic acid by-product is eventually transported to the liver, where liver cells convert it back to pyruvic acid. Exercise physiologists (biologists who study the effects of exercise on the body) have long speculated about the role that lactic acid plays in muscle fatigue, as you'll see next. ☑

☑ CHECKPOINT

How many molecules of ATP can be produced from one molecule of glucose during fermentation?

Answer: 2

▼ Figure 6.14 **Fermentation: producing lactic acid.**
Glycolysis produces ATP even in the absence of O_2. This process requires a continuous supply of NAD^+ to accept electrons from glucose. The NAD^+ is regenerated when NADH transfers the electrons it removed from food to pyruvic acid, thereby producing lactic acid (or other waste products, depending on the species of organism).

What Causes Muscle Burn?

You may have heard that the burn you feel after hard exercise ("Feel the burn! It's a *good* burn!") is due to the buildup of lactic acid in your muscles. This idea originated with the work of a British biologist named A.V. Hill. Considered one of the founders of the field of exercise physiology, Hill won a 1922 Nobel Prize for his investigations of muscle contraction.

In 1929, Hill performed a classic experiment that began with the **observation** that muscles produce lactic acid under anaerobic conditions. Hill asked the **question**, Does the buildup of lactic acid cause muscle fatigue? To find out, Hill developed a technique for electrically stimulating dissected frog muscles in a laboratory solution. He formed the **hypothesis** that a buildup of lactic acid would cause muscle activity to stop.

Hill's **experiment** tested frog muscles under two different sets of conditions (**Figure 6.15**). First, he showed that muscle performance declined when lactic acid could not diffuse away from the muscle tissue. Next, he showed that when lactic acid was allowed to diffuse away, performance improved significantly. These **results** led Hill to the conclusion that "lactic acid accumulation is the primary cause of failure" in muscle tissue.

Given his scientific stature (he was considered the world's leading authority on muscle activity), Hill's conclusion went unchallenged for many decades. Gradually, however, evidence began to accumulate that contradicted Hill's results. For example, the effect that Hill demonstrated did not appear to occur at human body temperature. And certain individuals who are unable to accumulate lactic acid have muscles that fatigue *more* rapidly, which is the opposite of what you would expect. Recent experiments have directly refuted Hill's conclusions. Today, the role of lactic acid in muscle fatigue remains a hotly debated topic.

The changing view of lactic acid's role in muscle fatigue illustrates an important point about the process of science: It is dynamic and subject to constant adjustment as new evidence is uncovered. This would not have surprised Hill, who himself wrote that the "built-in obsolescence" of scientific hypotheses is a necessary feature for the advancement of science.

▼ Figure 6.15 **A. V. Hill's 1929 apparatus for measuring muscle fatigue.**

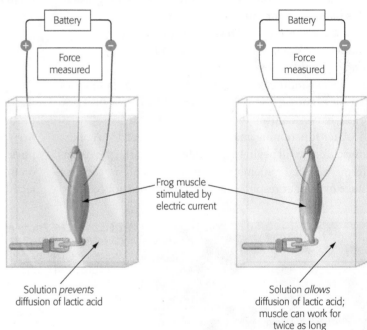

Battery

Force measured

Frog muscle stimulated by electric current

Solution *prevents* diffusion of lactic acid

Battery

Force measured

Solution *allows* diffusion of lactic acid; muscle can work for twice as long

Fermentation in Microorganisms

What gives yogurt its sour flavor?

Our muscles cannot function by lactic acid fermentation for very long. However, the two ATP molecules produced per glucose molecule during fermentation is enough to sustain many microorganisms. We have domesticated such microbes to transform milk into cheese, sour cream, and yogurt. These foods owe their sharp or sour flavor mainly to lactic acid. The food industry also uses fermentation to produce soy sauce from soybeans, to pickle cucumbers, olives, and cabbage, and to produce meat products like sausage, pepperoni, and salami.

Yeast, a microscopic fungus, is capable of both cellular respiration and fermentation. If you keep yeast cells in an anaerobic environment, they are forced to ferment sugars and other foods to stay alive. When yeast ferment,

▲ Figure 6.16 **Fermentation: producing ethyl alcohol.**

they produce ethyl alcohol as a waste product instead of lactic acid (**Figure 6.16**). This alcoholic fermentation also releases CO_2. For thousands of years, people have put yeast to work producing alcoholic beverages such as beer and wine. And as every baker knows, the CO_2 bubbles from fermenting yeast also cause bread dough to rise. (The alcohol produced in fermenting bread is burned off during baking.) ☑

Aerobic versus Anaerobic Lifestyles EVOLUTION CONNECTION

Life before and after Oxygen

In the Biology and Society and Process of Science sections, we have seen that living cells can generate ATP either aerobically (with oxygen via cellular respiration) or anaerobically (without oxygen via fermentation). Both of these processes start with glycolysis, the splitting of glucose to form pyruvic acid. Glycolysis is thus the universal energy-harvesting process of life.

The role of glycolysis in both respiration and fermentation has an evolutionary basis. Ancient prokaryotes probably used glycolysis to make ATP long before oxygen was present in Earth's atmosphere. The oldest known fossils of bacteria date back more than 3.5 billion years, but significant levels of O_2 did not accumulate in the atmosphere until about 2.7 billion years ago (**Figure 6.17**). For almost a billion years, prokaryotes must have generated ATP exclusively from glycolysis.

The fact that glycolysis occurs in almost all organisms suggests that it evolved very early in ancestors common to all the domains of life. The location of glycolysis within the cell also implies great antiquity; the pathway does not require any of the membrane-enclosed organelles of the eukaryotic cell, which evolved more than a billion years after the prokaryotic cell. Glycolysis is a metabolic heirloom from early cells that continues to function in fermentation and as the first stage in the breakdown of organic molecules by cellular respiration.

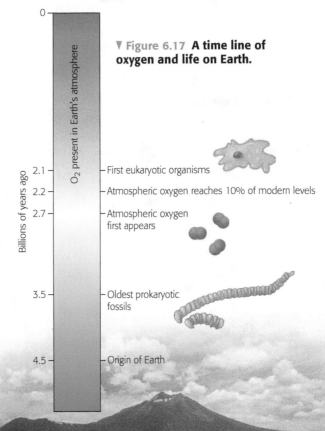

▼ Figure 6.17 **A time line of oxygen and life on Earth.**

Billions of years ago / O_2 present in Earth's atmosphere

- 2.1 — First eukaryotic organisms
- 2.2 — Atmospheric oxygen reaches 10% of modern levels
- 2.7 — Atmospheric oxygen first appears
- 3.5 — Oldest prokaryotic fossils
- 4.5 — Origin of Earth

Chapter Review

SUMMARY OF KEY CONCEPTS

Go to **www.masteringbiology.com** for homework assignments, practice quizzes, Pearson eText, and more.

Energy Flow and Chemical Cycling in the Biosphere

Producers and Consumers

Autotrophs (producers) make organic molecules from inorganic nutrients via photosynthesis. Heterotrophs (consumers) must consume organic material and obtain energy via cellular respiration.

Chemical Cycling between Photosynthesis and Cellular Respiration

Cellular Respiration: Aerobic Harvest of Food Energy

The Simplified Equation for Cellular Respiration

$$C_6H_{12}O_6 + 6\ O_2 \longrightarrow \longrightarrow \longrightarrow 6\ CO_2 + 6\ H_2O + \text{Approx. } 32\ \text{ATP}$$

The Role of Oxygen in Cellular Respiration

Oxidation
Glucose loses electrons (and hydrogens)

Reduction
Oxygen gains electrons (and hydrogens)

Redox reactions transfer electrons from food molecules to an electron acceptor called NAD^+, forming NADH. The NADH then passes the high-energy electrons to an electron transport chain that eventually "drops" them to O_2. The energy released during this electron transport is used to regenerate ATP from ADP. The affinity of oxygen for electrons keeps the redox reactions of cellular respiration working.

An Overview of Cellular Respiration

You can follow the flow of molecules through the process of cellular respiration in the following diagram:

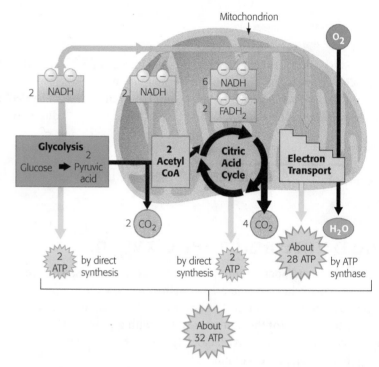

The electron transport chains pump H^+ across the inner mitochondrial membrane as electrons flow stepwise from NADH to O_2. Backflow of H^+ across the membrane powers the ATP synthases, which attach phosphate to ADP to make ATP.

Fermentation: Anaerobic Harvest of Food Energy

Fermentation in Human Muscle Cells

When muscle cells consume ATP faster than O_2 can be supplied for cellular respiration, they regenerate ATP by fermentation. The waste product under these anaerobic conditions is lactic acid. The ATP yield per glucose is much lower during fermentation (2 ATP) than during cellular respiration (about 32 ATP).

Fermentation in Microorganisms

Yeast and some other organisms can survive with or without O_2. Wastes from fermentation can be ethyl alcohol, lactic acid, or other compounds, depending on the species.

SELF-QUIZ

1. Which of the following statements is a correct distinction between autotrophs and heterotrophs?
   a. Only heterotrophs require chemical compounds from the environment.
   b. Cellular respiration is unique to heterotrophs.
   c. Only heterotrophs have mitochondria.
   d. Only autotrophs can live on nutrients that are entirely inorganic.

2. Why are plants called producers? Why are animals called consumers?

3. How is your breathing related to your cellular respiration?

4. Of the three stages of cellular respiration, which produces the most ATP molecules per glucose?

5. In glycolysis, _____ is oxidized and _____ is reduced.

6. The final electron acceptor of electron transport chains in mitochondria is _____.

7. The poison cyanide acts by blocking a key step in the electron transport chain. Knowing this, explain why cyanide kills so quickly.

8. Cells can harvest the most chemical energy from which of the following?
   a. an NADH molecule
   b. a glucose molecule
   c. six CO_2 molecules
   d. two pyruvic acid molecules

9. _____ is a metabolic pathway common to both fermentation and cellular respiration.

10. Sports physiologists at an Olympic training center want to monitor athletes to determine at what point their muscles are functioning anaerobically. They can do this by checking for a buildup of
    a. ADP.
    b. lactic acid.
    c. carbon dioxide.
    d. oxygen.

11. A glucose-fed yeast cell is moved from an aerobic environment to an anaerobic one. For the cell to continue to generate ATP at the same rate, approximately how much glucose must it consume in the anaerobic environment compared with the aerobic environment?

Answers to these questions can be found in Appendix: Self-Quiz Answers.

THE PROCESS OF SCIENCE

12. Your body makes NAD^+ from two B vitamins, niacin and riboflavin. You need only tiny amounts of these vitamins. The U.S. Food and Drug Administration's recommended dietary allowances are 20 mg daily for niacin and 1.7 mg daily for riboflavin. These amounts are thousands of times less than the amount of glucose your body needs each day to fuel its energy requirements. How many NAD^+ molecules are needed for the breakdown of each glucose molecule? Why do you think your daily requirement for these substances is so small?

BIOLOGY AND SOCIETY

13. Nearly all human societies use fermentation to produce alcoholic drinks such as beer and wine. The technology dates back to the earliest civilizations. Suggest a hypothesis for how people first discovered fermentation. In preindustrial cultures, why do you think wine was a more practical beverage than the grape juice from which it was made?

14. The consumption of alcohol by a pregnant woman can cause a series of birth defects called fetal alcohol syndrome (FAS). Symptoms of FAS include head and facial irregularities, heart defects, mental retardation, and behavioral problems. The U.S. Surgeon General's Office recommends that pregnant women abstain from drinking alcohol, and the government has mandated that a warning label be placed on liquor bottles. Imagine you are a server in a restaurant. An obviously pregnant woman orders a strawberry daiquiri. How would you respond? Is it the woman's right to make those decisions about her unborn child's health? Do you bear any responsibility in the matter? Is a restaurant responsible for monitoring the dietary habits of its customers?

7 Photosynthesis: Using Light to Make Food

Capturing solar energy. Sunlight drives the process of photosynthesis, which plants use to produce sugars. We can then convert these sugars to other substances, such as ethanol, that can power our vehicles.

Grown for Biofuel

Green Energy BIOLOGY AND SOCIETY

Biofuels

What's old is sometimes new again. Throughout our early history, people relied on plants as our primary source of energy, burning wood to produce heat and light. Then, as societies became industrialized, wood was largely displaced as an energy source by fossil fuels such as coal, gas, and oil. But now, as fossil fuel supplies dwindle and concerns are raised about global climate change, spiking oil prices, and the need for a domestic energy source, scientists are researching better ways to harness energy from biomass (living material). Some researchers focus on burning plant matter directly (for example, wood pellet boilers), while others focus on using plant material to produce biofuels that can be burned.

There are several types of biofuels. Bioethanol is a type of alcohol (the same type found in alcoholic drinks) that is made from wheat, corn, sugar beets, sugarcane, and other food crops. Starch made naturally by plants is converted to glucose and then fermented to ethanol by microorganisms (such as single-celled algae). Bioethanol can be used directly as a fuel source in specially designed vehicles, but it is more commonly used as a gasoline additive that can increase fuel efficiency while decreasing vehicle emissions. You may have noticed a sticker on the gas pump that declares the percentage of ethanol in the gas you are pumping; most cars today run on a blend of 85% gasoline and 15% ethanol. Many car manufacturers are producing flexible-fuel vehicles that can run on any combination of gasoline and bioethanol.

Cellulosic ethanol is a form of bioethanol made through the same fermentation process as bioethanol, but its primary ingredient is cellulose from nonedible plant material such as wood or grass. Biodiesel, the most common biofuel in Europe, is made from plant oils such as recycled frying oil. Like bioethanol, it can be used on its own or as an additive to standard diesel.

Whatever its form, when we derive energy from biomass or biofuels, we are actually tapping into the energy of the sun, which drives the process of photosynthesis in plants. Biofuels are just one way that people take advantage of plants' ability to capture solar energy. The topic of this chapter is photosynthesis, the process whereby plants use light to make sugars from carbon dioxide—sugars that are food for the plant and the starting point for most of our own food. First, we'll examine some basic concepts of photosynthesis; then we'll look at the specific mechanisms involved.

The Basics of Photosynthesis

Photosynthesis is a process whereby plants, algae (which are protists), and certain bacteria transform light energy into chemical energy, using carbon dioxide and water as starting materials. The chemical energy produced via photosynthesis is stored in the bonds of sugar molecules. Organisms that generate their own organic matter from inorganic ingredients are called autotrophs (see Chapter 6). Plants and other organisms that do this by photosynthesis—photosynthetic autotrophs—are the producers for most ecosystems (Figure 7.1). This section presents an overview of photosynthesis, focusing on plants. Later, we'll take a closer look at some details of this process.

Chloroplasts: Sites of Photosynthesis

You have already learned that photosynthesis in plants and algae occurs within light-absorbing organelles called **chloroplasts** (see Chapter 4). All green parts of a plant have chloroplasts and can carry out photosynthesis. In most plants, however, the leaves have the most chloroplasts (about 500,000 per square millimeter of leaf surface) and are therefore the major locations of photosynthesis. Their green color is from **chlorophyll**, a light-absorbing molecule (a pigment) in the chloroplasts that plays a central role in converting solar energy to chemical energy.

Chloroplasts are concentrated in the interior cells of leaves (Figure 7.2), with a typical cell containing 30–40 chloroplasts. Carbon dioxide (CO_2) enters a leaf, and oxygen (O_2) exits, by way of tiny pores called **stomata** (singular, *stoma*, meaning "mouth"). In addition to carbon dioxide, photosynthesis requires water, which is absorbed by the plant's roots and transported to the leaves, where veins carry it to the photosynthetic cells.

Membranes within the chloroplast form the framework where many of the reactions of photosynthesis occur. Like a mitochondrion, a chloroplast has a double-membrane envelope. The chloroplast's inner membrane encloses a compartment filled with **stroma**, a thick fluid. Suspended in the stroma are interconnected membranous sacs called **thylakoids**. The thylakoids are concentrated in stacks called **grana** (singular, *granum*). The chlorophyll molecules that capture light energy are built into the thylakoid membranes. The structure of a chloroplast—with its stacks of disks—aids its function by providing a large surface area for the reactions of photosynthesis. ☑

▼ Figure 7.1 **A diversity of photosynthetic autotrophs.**

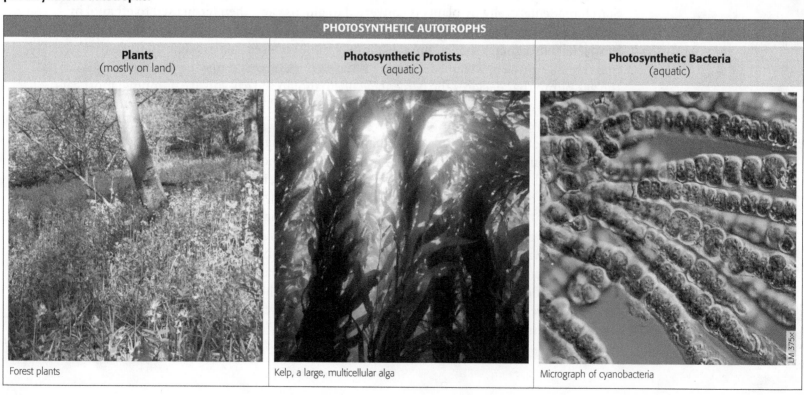

PHOTOSYNTHETIC AUTOTROPHS		
Plants (mostly on land)	**Photosynthetic Protists** (aquatic)	**Photosynthetic Bacteria** (aquatic)

Forest plants

Kelp, a large, multicellular alga

Micrograph of cyanobacteria

LM 375×

▼ Figure 7.2 Journey into a leaf. This series of blowups takes you into a leaf's interior, then into a plant cell, and finally into a chloroplast, the site of photosynthesis.

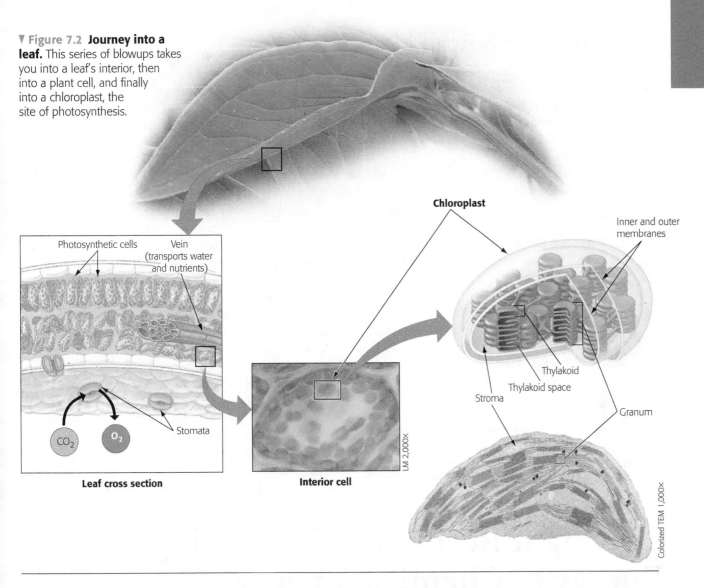

Chloroplast

Inner and outer membranes

Photosynthetic cells

Vein (transports water and nutrients)

CO_2

O_2

Stomata

Leaf cross section

LM 2,000×

Interior cell

Thylakoid

Thylakoid space

Stroma

Granum

Colorized TEM 1,000×

The Simplified Equation for Photosynthesis

The following chemical equation, simplified to highlight the relationship between photosynthesis and cellular respiration, provides a summary of the reactants and products of photosynthesis:

Light energy

$6\ CO_2$ + $6\ H_2O$ → → → $C_6H_{12}O_6$ + $6\ O_2$

Carbon dioxide   Water   **Photosynthesis**   Glucose   Oxygen gas

Notice that the reactants of photosynthesis—carbon dioxide (CO_2) and water (H_2O)—are the same as the waste products of cellular respiration (see Figure 6.2). Also notice that photosynthesis produces what respiration uses—glucose ($C_6H_{12}O_6$) and oxygen (O_2). In other words, photosynthesis recycles the "exhaust" of cellular respiration and rearranges its atoms to produce food and oxygen. Photosynthesis is a chemical transformation that requires a lot of energy, and sunlight absorbed by chlorophyll provides that energy.

You learned in Chapter 6 that cellular respiration is a process of electron transfer. A "fall" of electrons from food molecules to oxygen to form water releases the energy that mitochondria can use to make ATP (see Figure 6.5). The opposite occurs in photosynthesis: Electrons are boosted "uphill" and added to carbon dioxide to produce sugar. Hydrogen is moved along with the electrons being transferred from water to carbon dioxide. This transfer of hydrogen requires the chloroplast to split water molecules into hydrogen and oxygen. The hydrogen is transferred along with electrons to carbon dioxide to form sugar. The oxygen escapes through stomata in leaves into the atmosphere as O_2, a waste product of photosynthesis. ☑

In what sense do photosynthesis and cellular respiration form a complementary cycle?

☑ CHECKPOINT

What molecules are the inputs of photosynthesis? What molecules are the outputs?

Answer: CO_2 and H_2O; glucose and O_2

A Photosynthesis Road Map

The equation for photosynthesis on the previous page is a simple summary of a complex process. Actually, photosynthesis occurs in two multistep stages: the light reactions and the Calvin cycle (Figure 7.3).

In the **light reactions**, chlorophyll in the thylakoid membranes absorbs solar energy (the "photo" part of photosynthesis), which is then converted to the chemical energy of ATP (the molecule that drives most cellular work) and **NADPH** (an electron carrier). In photosynthesis, light drives electrons from water to NADP⁺ (the oxidized form of the carrier) to form NADPH (the reduced form of the carrier). During the light reactions, water is split, providing a source of electrons and giving off O_2 gas as a by-product.

What's the connection between photosynthesis and global climate change?

The **Calvin cycle** uses the products of the light reactions to power the production of sugar from carbon dioxide (the "synthesis" part of photosynthesis). The enzymes that drive the Calvin cycle are dissolved in the stroma, the thick fluid within the chloroplast. ATP generated by the light reactions provides the energy for sugar synthesis. And the NADPH produced by the light reactions provides the high-energy electrons for the reduction of carbon dioxide to glucose. Thus, the Calvin cycle indirectly depends on light to produce sugar because it requires the supply of ATP and NADPH produced by the light reactions. The initial incorporation of carbon from the atmosphere into organic compounds is called **carbon fixation**. This process has important implications for global climate, since the removal of carbon from the air and its incorporation into plant material can help reduce the concentration of carbon dioxide in the atmosphere. Deforestation, which removes a lot of photosynthetic plant life, thereby reduces the ability of the biosphere to absorb carbon.

In the following sections, we'll take a closer look at how these two stages of photosynthesis work: the light reactions first and then the Calvin cycle. ☑

◀ Figure 7.3 **A road map for photosynthesis.** We'll use a smaller version of this road map for orientation as we take a closer look at the light reactions and the Calvin cycle.

The Light Reactions: Converting Solar Energy to Chemical Energy

Chloroplasts are chemical factories powered by the sun. Let's look at how they convert sunlight to chemical energy.

The Nature of Sunlight

Sunlight is a type of energy called radiation or electromagnetic energy. Electromagnetic energy travels through space as rhythmic waves, like the ripples made by a pebble dropped into a pond. The distance between the crests of two adjacent waves is called a **wavelength**. The full range of radiation, from the very short wavelengths of gamma rays to the very long wavelengths of radio signals, is called the **electromagnetic spectrum** (Figure 7.4).

▲ Figure 7.4 **The electromagnetic spectrum.** The middle of the figure expands the thin slice of the spectrum that is visible to us as different colors of light, from about 380 nanometers (nm) to about 750 nm in wavelength. The bottom of the figure shows electromagnetic waves of one particular wavelength of visible light.

☑ **CHECKPOINT**

Name the two stages of photosynthesis in their proper order.

Answer: light reactions, Calvin cycle

Visible light is the fraction of the spectrum that our eyes see as different colors.

When sunlight shines on a pigmented material, certain wavelengths (colors) of the visible light are absorbed and disappear from the light that is reflected by the material. For example, we see a pair of jeans as blue because pigments in the fabric absorb the other colors, leaving only light in the blue part of the spectrum to be reflected from the fabric to our eyes.

The selective absorption of light by leaves explains why they appear green to us; light of that color is poorly absorbed by chloroplasts and is thus reflected or transmitted toward the observer (Figure 7.5). Since energy cannot be destroyed, the absorbed energy must be converted to other forms. Chloroplasts contain pigments that drive the conversion of some of the solar energy they absorb to chemical energy.

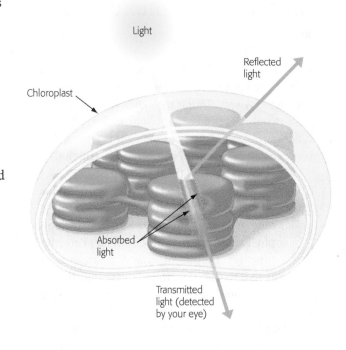

▶ Figure 7.5 **Why are leaves green?** Chlorophyll and other pigments in chloroplasts reflect or transmit green light while absorbing other colors.

Green Energy THE PROCESS OF SCIENCE

What Colors of Light Drive Photosynthesis?

In 1883, German biologist Theodor Engelmann made the **observation** that certain bacteria living in water tend to cluster in areas with higher oxygen concentrations. He already knew that light passed through a prism would separate into the different wavelengths (colors). Engelmann soon began to **question** whether he could use this information to determine which wavelengths of light work best for photosynthesis.

Engelmann's **hypothesis** was that oxygen-seeking bacteria would congregate near regions of algae performing the most photosynthesis (and hence producing the most oxygen). Engelmann began his **experiment** by laying a string of freshwater algal cells within a drop of water on a microscope slide. He then added oxygen-sensitive bacteria to the drop. Next, using a prism, he created a spectrum of light and shined it on the slide. His **results**, summarized in Figure 7.6, showed that most bacteria congregated around algae exposed to red-orange and blue-violet light, with very few bacteria moving to the area of green light. Other experiments have since verified that chloroplasts absorb light mainly in the blue-violet and red-orange part of the spectrum and that those wavelengths of light are the ones mainly responsible for photosynthesis.

▲ Figure 7.6 **Investigating how light wavelength affects photosynthesis.** When algal cells are suspended in water on a microscope slide, oxygen-seeking bacteria migrate toward algae exposed to certain colors of light. These results suggest that blue-violet and orange-red wavelengths best drive photosynthesis, while green wavelengths do so only a little bit.

Chloroplast Pigments

Different pigments absorb light of different wavelengths, and chloroplasts contain several kinds of pigments. **Chlorophyll *a***, the pigment that participates directly in the light reactions, absorbs mainly blue-violet and red light. A very similar molecule, chlorophyll *b*, absorbs mainly blue and orange light. Chlorophyll *b* does not participate directly in the light reactions, but it conveys absorbed energy to chlorophyll *a*, which then puts the energy to work in the light reactions.

Chloroplasts also contain a family of yellow-orange pigments called carotenoids, which absorb mainly blue-green light. Some pass energy to chlorophyll *a*. Other carotenoids have a protective function: They absorb and dissipate excessive light energy that would otherwise damage chlorophyll. (Similar carotenoids, which we obtain from carrots and certain other plants, may help protect our eyes from bright light.) The spectacular colors of fall foliage in some parts of the world are due partly to the yellow-orange light reflected from carotenoids (**Figure 7.7**). The falling autumn temperatures cause a decrease in the levels of chlorophyll, allowing the colors of the longer-lasting carotenoids to be seen in all their fall glory.

Why do some leaves turn color in the fall?

All of these chloroplast pigments are built into the thylakoid membranes (see Figure 7.2). There the pigments are organized into light-harvesting complexes called photosystems. ☑

▲ Figure 7.7 **Photosynthetic pigments.** Falling autumn temperatures cause a decrease in the levels of green chlorophyll within the leaves of leaf-bearing trees. This decrease allows the colors of the carotenoids to be seen.

☑ CHECKPOINT

What is the specific name of the pigment that absorbs energy during the light reactions?

Answer: chlorophyll a

How Photosystems Harvest Light Energy

Thinking about light as waves explains most of light's properties. However, light also behaves as discrete packets of energy called photons. A **photon** is a fixed quantity of light energy. The shorter the wavelength of light, the greater the energy of a photon. A photon of violet light, for example, packs nearly twice as much energy as a photon of red light.

When a pigment molecule absorbs a photon, one of the pigment's electrons gains energy. This electron is now said to be "excited"; that is, the electron has been raised from its starting state (called the ground state) to an excited state. The excited state is highly unstable, so an excited electron usually loses its excess energy and falls back to its ground state almost

▼ Figure 7.8 **Excited electrons in pigments.**

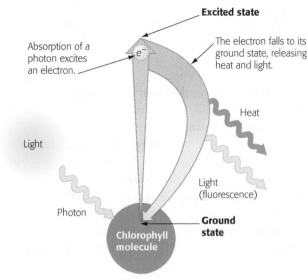

Absorption of a photon excites an electron.

Excited state

The electron falls to its ground state, releasing heat and light.

Light

Heat

Light (fluorescence)

Photon

Chlorophyll molecule

Ground state

(a) Absorption of a photon

(b) Fluorescence of a glow stick. Breaking a vial within a glow stick starts a chemical reaction that excites electrons within a fluorescent dye. As the electrons fall from their excited state to the ground state, the excess energy is emitted as light.

immediately (**Figure 7.8a**). Most pigments merely release heat energy as their light-excited electrons fall back to their ground state. (That's why a surface with a lot of pigment, such as a black driveway, gets so hot on a sunny day.) But some pigments emit light as well as heat after absorbing photons. The fluorescent light emitted by a glow stick is caused by a chemical reaction that excites electrons of a fluorescent dye (**Figure 7.8b**). The excited electrons quickly fall back down to their ground state, releasing energy in the form of fluorescent light.

▲ Figure 7.9 **A photosystem: light-gathering molecules that focus light energy onto a reaction center.**

In the thylakoid membrane, chlorophyll molecules are organized with other molecules into photosystems. Each **photosystem** has a cluster of a few hundred pigment molecules, including chlorophylls *a* and *b* and some carotenoids **(Figure 7.9)**. This cluster of pigment molecules functions as a light-gathering antenna. When a photon strikes one of the pigment molecules, the energy jumps from molecule to molecule until it arrives at the **reaction center** of the photosystem. The reaction center consists of chlorophyll *a* molecules that sit next to another molecule called a **primary electron acceptor**. This primary electron acceptor traps the light-excited electron (⊖) from the chlorophyll *a* in the reaction center. Another team of molecules built into the thylakoid membrane then uses that trapped energy to make ATP and NADPH. ☑

☑ **CHECKPOINT**

What is the role of a reaction center during photosynthesis?

Answer: A reaction center transfers a light-excited photon from pigment molecules to molecules that can use this trapped energy to drive chemical reactions.

How the Light Reactions Generate ATP and NADPH

Two types of photosystems cooperate in the light reactions **(Figure 7.10)**. ❶ Photons excite electrons in the chlorophyll of the water-splitting photosystem. These photons are then trapped by the primary electron acceptor. The water-splitting photosystem replaces its light-excited electrons by extracting electrons from water. This is the step that releases O_2 during photosynthesis. ❷ Energized electrons from the water-splitting photosystem pass down an electron transport chain to the NADPH-producing photosystem. The chloroplast uses the energy released by this electron "fall" to make ATP. ❸ The NADPH-producing photosystem transfers its light-excited electrons to $NADP^+$, reducing it to NADPH.

▶ Figure 7.10 **The light reactions of photosynthesis.** The orange arrows trace a light-driven flow of electrons from H_2O to NADPH. These electrons also produce ATP.

113

☑ CHECKPOINT

1. Why is water required as a reactant in photosynthesis? (*Hint*: Review Figures 7.10 and 7.11.)
2. In addition to conveying electrons from the water-splitting photosystem to the NADPH-producing photosystem, the electron transport chains of chloroplasts provide the energy for the synthesis of _____.

Answers: 1. The splitting of water provides electrons for converting NAD⁺ to NADPH (which will be used in converting CO₂ to sugar in the Calvin cycle). 2. ATP

Figure 7.11 shows the location of the light reactions in the thylakoid membrane. The two photosystems and the electron transport chain that connects them transfer electrons from H_2O to $NADP^+$, reducing it to NADPH. Notice that the mechanism of ATP production during the light reactions is very similar to the mechanism we saw in cellular respiration (see Figure 6.11). In both cases, an electron transport chain pumps hydrogen ions (H^+) across a membrane—the inner mitochondrial membrane in the case of respiration and the thylakoid membrane in photosynthesis. And in both cases, ATP synthases use the energy stored by the H^+ gradient to make ATP. The main difference is that food provides the high-energy electrons in cellular respiration, whereas light-excited electrons flow down the transport chain during photosynthesis. The traffic of electrons shown in Figures 7.10 and 7.11 is analogous to the cartoon in Figure 7.12.

We have seen how the light reactions absorb solar energy and convert it to the chemical energy of ATP and NADPH. Notice again, however, that the light reactions did not produce any sugar. That's the job of the Calvin cycle, as we'll see next. ☑

▼ Figure 7.12 **A hard-hat analogy for the light reactions.**

Water-splitting photosystem **NADPH-producing photosystem**

▼ Figure 7.11 **How the thylakoid membrane converts light energy to the chemical energy of NADPH and ATP.**

The Calvin Cycle: Making Sugar from Carbon Dioxide

The Calvin cycle functions like a sugar factory within a chloroplast. It is called a cycle because, like the citric acid cycle in cellular respiration, the starting material is regenerated. And with each turn of the cycle, there are chemical inputs and outputs. The inputs are CO_2 from the air as well as ATP and NADPH produced by the light reactions. Using carbon from CO_2, energy from ATP, and high-energy electrons from NADPH, the Calvin cycle constructs an energy-rich sugar molecule called glyceraldehyde 3-phosphate (G3P). The plant cell can then use G3P as the raw material to make the glucose and other organic compounds (such as cellulose and starch) that it needs. **Figure 7.13** presents the basics of the Calvin cycle, emphasizing inputs and outputs. Each ● symbol represents a carbon atom, and each Ⓟ symbol represents a phosphate group. ✔

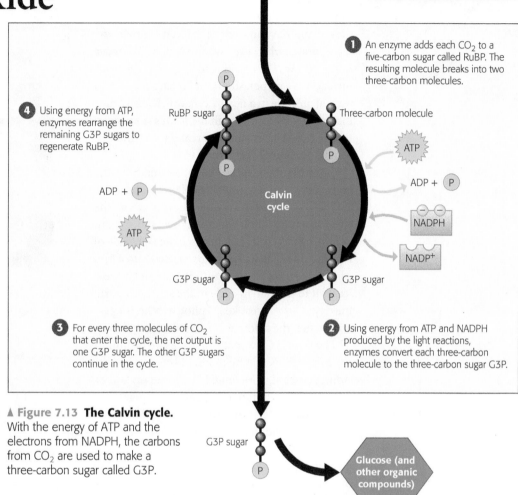

1 An enzyme adds each CO_2 to a five-carbon sugar called RuBP. The resulting molecule breaks into two three-carbon molecules.

2 Using energy from ATP and NADPH produced by the light reactions, enzymes convert each three-carbon molecule to the three-carbon sugar G3P.

3 For every three molecules of CO_2 that enter the cycle, the net output is one G3P sugar. The other G3P sugars continue in the cycle.

4 Using energy from ATP, enzymes rearrange the remaining G3P sugars to regenerate RuBP.

▲ Figure 7.13 **The Calvin cycle.** With the energy of ATP and the electrons from NADPH, the carbons from CO_2 are used to make a three-carbon sugar called G3P.

Green Energy EVOLUTION CONNECTION

Solar-Driven Evolution

Throughout this chapter, you've studied how plants convert solar energy to chemical energy via photosynthesis. Such "green energy" transformations are vital to our welfare and all of Earth's ecosystems.

You probably know that sunlight strikes Earth differently in different geographic regions. Because natural selection promotes the evolution of adaptations that best suit a local environment, it's not surprising that different modes of photosynthesis have evolved in different climates.

So far, we've focused on plants that use CO_2 directly from the air to drive the Calvin cycle. Such plants are called **C₃ plants** because the first organic compound produced in the Calvin cycle is a three-carbon

molecule (see Figure 7.13). C_3 plants are widely distributed and include such common crops as soybeans, oats, wheat, and rice. One problem that farmers face in growing C_3 plants, however, is that plants close their stomata on hot, dry days, helping to prevent dehydration. This adaptation reduces water loss but also prevents CO_2 from entering the leaves. As a result, CO_2 levels get very low in the leaves, and sugar production ceases. Thus, when the weather turns hot, the productivity of C_3 crops is significantly reduced because of their need to save water.

In hot, dry climates, alternative modes of incorporating carbon from CO_2 have evolved in some plants, allowing them to save water without shutting down photosynthesis. These species are categorized as either C_4 plants or CAM plants.

✔ CHECKPOINT

What is the function of NADPH in the Calvin cycle?

Answer: It provides the high-energy electrons that are added to CO_2 to form G3P (a sugar).

C_4 **plants** are so named because they incorporate carbon from CO_2 into a four-carbon compound before proceeding to the Calvin cycle (**Figure 7.14**, left side). When the weather is hot and dry, a C_4 plant keeps its stomata mostly closed, thus conserving water. But these plants have an enzyme that can continue to incorporate carbon even when a leaf's CO_2 concentration is low. The resulting four-carbon compound then acts as a carbon shuttle; it donates the CO_2 to the Calvin cycle in a nearby cell, which keeps on making sugars even though the plant's stomata are mostly closed. Corn and sugarcane are examples of some agriculturally important C_4 plants.

CAM plants include pineapples, many cacti, and succulent (water-storing) plants such as aloe and jade. Adapted to very dry climates, these species conserve water by opening their stomata and admitting CO_2 only at night (see the right side of Figure 7.14). The CO_2 is incorporated into a four-carbon compound that banks it at night and releases it to the Calvin cycle in the same cell during the day. This process keeps photosynthesis operating when the stomata are closed during the day.

The C_4 and CAM pathways are two evolutionary adaptations that maintain photosynthesis with stomata partially or completely closed on hot, dry days. The distribution of C_4 and CAM plants on Earth today reflects this evolutionary history; such plants are found in hot climates where the need to conserve water outweighs the need for continuous sugar production. During the long evolution of plants in diverse environments, natural selection has refined photosynthetic adaptations that enable these plants to continue producing food even in the arid conditions of their local environments. The cultivation of such plants where they thrive is yet another example of this chapter's theme: the ways that humans benefit from the "green energy" process of photosynthesis.

▼ Figure 7.14 **C_4 and CAM photosynthesis.** The C_4 and CAM pathways are two evolutionary adaptations that maintain photosynthesis with stomata partially or completely closed on hot, dry days.

ALTERNATIVE PHOTOSYNTHETIC PATHWAYS

C_4 Pathway
(example: sugarcane)

CAM Pathway
(example: pineapple)

Cell type 1 — CO_2

Four-carbon compound

Cell type 2 — CO_2

Calvin cycle

Sugar

C_4 plant

Carbon incorporation and the Calvin cycle occur in different types of cells.

CO_2 — Night

Four-carbon compound

CO_2

Calvin cycle

Sugar

Day

CAM plant

Carbon incorporation and the Calvin cycle occur in the same cells at different times.

Chapter Review

SUMMARY OF KEY CONCEPTS

 Go to **www.masteringbiology.com** for homework assignments, practice quizzes, Pearson eText, and more.

The Basics of Photosynthesis

Photosynthesis is a process whereby light energy is transformed into chemical energy, which is stored as bonds in sugars made from carbon dioxide and water.

Chloroplasts: Sites of Photosynthesis

Chloroplasts contain a thick fluid called stroma surrounding a network of membranes called thylakoids.

The Simplified Equation for Photosynthesis

A Photosynthesis Road Map

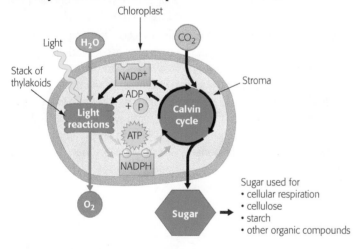

The Light Reactions: Converting Solar Energy to Chemical Energy

The Nature of Sunlight

Visible light is part of the spectrum of electromagnetic energy. It travels through space as waves. Different wavelengths of light appear as different colors; shorter wavelengths carry more energy.

Chloroplast Pigments

Pigment molecules absorb light energy of certain wavelengths and reflect other wavelengths. We see the reflected wavelengths as the color of the pigment. Several chloroplast pigments absorb light of various wavelengths and convey it to other pigments, but it is the green pigment chlorophyll *a* that participates directly in the light reactions.

How Photosystems Harvest Light Energy; How the Light Reactions Generate ATP and NADPH

The Calvin Cycle: Making Sugar from Carbon Dioxide

Within the stroma (fluid) of the chloroplast, carbon dioxide from the air and ATP and NADPH produced during the light reactions are used to produce G3P, an energy-rich sugar molecule that can be used to make glucose and other organic molecules.

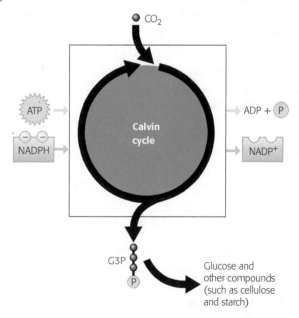

Evolution Connection: Solar-Driven Evolution

The photosynthetic adaptations of C_4 and CAM plants enable sugar production to continue even when stomata are closed, thereby reducing water loss in arid environments.

SELF-QUIZ

1. The light reactions take place in the structures of the chloroplast called the _____, while the Calvin cycle takes place in the _____.

2. In terms of the spatial organization of photosynthesis within the chloroplast, what is the advantage of the light reactions producing NADPH and ATP on the stroma side of the thylakoid membrane?

3. Which of the following are inputs to photosynthesis? Which are outputs?
   a. CO_2
   b. O_2
   c. sugar
   d. H_2O
   e. light

4. What color of light is the least effective in driving photosynthesis? Why?

5. When light strikes chlorophyll molecules, they lose electrons, which are ultimately replaced by splitting molecules of _____.

6. Which of the following are produced by reactions that take place in the thylakoids and are consumed by reactions in the stroma?
   a. CO_2 and H_2O
   b. $NADP^+$ and ADP
   c. ATP and NADPH
   d. glucose and O_2

7. The reactions of the Calvin cycle are not directly dependent on light, and yet they usually do not occur at night. Why?

8. Why is it difficult for most plants to carry out photosynthesis in very hot, dry environments, such as deserts?

9. What is the primary advantage offered by the C_4 and CAM pathways?

10. Of the following metabolic processes, which one is common to photosynthesis and cellular respiration?
    a. reactions that convert light energy to chemical energy
    b. reactions that split H_2O molecules and release O_2
    c. reactions that store energy by pumping H^+ across membranes
    d. reactions that convert CO_2 to sugar

Answers to these questions can be found in Appendix: Self-Quiz Answers.

THE PROCESS OF SCIENCE

11. Tropical rain forests cover only about 3% of Earth's surface, but they are estimated to be responsible for more than 20% of global photosynthesis. For this reason, rain forests are often referred to as the "lungs" of the planet, providing O_2 for life all over Earth. However, most experts believe that rain forests make little or no net contribution to global O_2 production. From your knowledge of photosynthesis and cellular respiration, can you explain why they might think this? (*Hint*: What happens to the energy stored as sugars in the body of a plant when that plant dies or parts of it are eaten by animals?)

12. Suppose you wanted to discover whether the oxygen atoms in the glucose produced by photosynthesis come from H_2O or CO_2. Explain how you could use a radioactive isotope to find out.

BIOLOGY AND SOCIETY

13. There is strong evidence that Earth is getting warmer because of an intensified greenhouse effect resulting from increased CO_2 emissions from industry, vehicles, and the burning of forests. Global climate change could influence agriculture, melt polar ice, and flood coastal regions. In response to these threats, 178 countries have accepted the Kyoto agreement, which calls for mandatory reductions of greenhouse gas emissions in 30 industrialized nations by 2012. As of late 2011, the United States had not signed the agreement, instead proposing a more modest set of voluntary goals allowing businesses to decide whether they wish to participate and providing tax incentives to encourage them to do so. The reasons given for rejecting the agreement are that it might hurt the American economy and that some less industrialized countries (such as India) are exempted from it, even though they produce a lot of pollution. Do you agree with this decision? In what ways might efforts to reduce greenhouse gases hurt the economy? How can those costs be weighed against the costs of global climate change? Should poorer nations carry an equal burden to reduce their emissions?

14. As discussed in the Biology and Society section, burning biomass to produce electricity avoids many of the problems associated with gathering, refining, transporting, and burning fossil fuels. Yet the use of biomass as fuel is not without its own set of problems. What challenges might arise from a large-scale conversion to biomass energy? How do these challenges compare with those encountered with fossil fuels? Which set of challenges do you think is more likely to be overcome? Does one energy source have more benefits and fewer costs than the others? Explain.

Unit 2
Genetics

Chapter 8: **Cellular Reproduction: Cells from Cells**

Chapter Thread: **Life with and without Sex**

Chapter 9: **Patterns of Inheritance**

Chapter Thread: **Dog Breeding**

Chapter 10: **The Structure and Function of DNA**

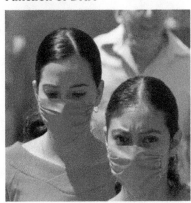

Chapter Thread: **The Deadliest Virus**

Chapter 11: **How Genes Are Controlled**

Chapter Thread: **Cancer**

Chapter 12: **DNA Technology**

Chapter Thread: **DNA Profiling**

8 Cellular Reproduction: Cells from Cells

The Komodo dragon. The Komodo is the world's largest lizard and is found in the wild only on three islands in Indonesia. Komodo dragons can reproduce using two different types of cell division.

Life with and without Sex BIOLOGY AND SOCIETY

Virgin Birth of a Dragon

In 2002, zookeepers at the Chester Zoo in England were startled to discover that Flora, a female Komodo dragon (*Varanus komodoensis*), had laid a clutch of 25 eggs. It wasn't surprising that a captive Komodo dragon would breed. In fact, Flora was at the zoo for that very reason: She was one of two female Komodo dragons taking part in a captive breeding program intended to help repopulate the species.

What made Flora's clutch of eggs so remarkable is that she had not yet been in the company of any male, let alone mated with one. As far as anyone knew at that time, Komodo dragons, like the vast majority of animal species, create offspring through sexual reproduction involving the union of a male's sperm and a female's egg. But despite Flora's virginity, eight of her eggs developed normally and hatched into live, healthy Komodo dragons.

DNA analysis confirmed that Flora's offspring derived their genes solely from her. Her young must have been created by parthenogenesis, the production of offspring by a female without involvement of a male. Parthenogenesis is one form of asexual reproduction, the creation of a new generation without participation of sperm and egg. Although parthenogenesis is known to occur in some animals, it is rare among vertebrates (animals with backbones) and was never before seen in Komodo dragons. Soon, zoologists identified a second European Komodo who had borne young by parthenogenesis. This same Komodo dragon later bore additional offspring via sexual reproduction. Apparently, this species has evolved the potential to produce young through both asexual and sexual reproduction.

The ability of organisms to procreate is the one characteristic that best distinguishes living things from nonliving matter. The same cellular process—cell division—is at the heart of both asexual and sexual reproduction. The perpetuation of life depends on the production of new cells. Lizards born of parthenogenesis are the result of repeated cell divisions, as are eggs and sperm themselves. In this chapter, we'll look at how individual cells are copied and then see how cell reproduction underlies the process of sexual reproduction. During our discussion, we'll consider examples of asexual and sexual reproduction among both plants and animals.

What Cell Reproduction Accomplishes

When you hear the word *reproduction*, you probably think of the birth of new organisms. But reproduction actually occurs much more often at the cellular level. Consider the skin on your arm. Skin cells are constantly reproducing themselves and moving outward toward the surface, replacing dead cells that have rubbed off. This renewal of your skin goes on throughout your life. And when your skin is injured, additional cell reproduction helps heal the wound.

How does a new sea star grow from a lost arm?

When a cell undergoes reproduction, or **cell division**, the two "daughter" cells that result are genetically identical to each other and to the original "parent" cell. (Biologists traditionally use the word *daughter* in this context; it does not imply gender.) Before the parent cell splits into two, it duplicates its **chromosomes**, the structures that contain most of the cell's DNA. Then, during the division process, one set of chromosomes is distributed to each daughter cell. Each daughter cell receives identical sets of chromosomes from the lone, original parent cell.

As summarized in **Figure 8.1**, cell division plays several important roles in the lives of organisms. For example, within your body, millions of cells must divide every second to replace damaged or lost cells. Another function of cell division is growth. All of the trillions of cells in your body are the result of repeated cell divisions that began in your mother's body with a single fertilized egg cell.

Another vital function of cell division is reproduction. Many single-celled organisms, such as amoebas, reproduce by dividing in half, and the offspring are genetic replicas of the parent. Because it does not involve fertilization of an egg by a sperm, this type of reproduction is called **asexual reproduction**. Offspring produced by asexual reproduction inherit all of their chromosomes from a single parent.

Many multicellular organisms can reproduce asexually as well. For example, some sea star species have the ability to grow new individuals from fragmented pieces. And if you've ever grown a houseplant from a clipping, you've observed asexual reproduction in plants. In asexual reproduction, there is one simple principle of inheritance: The lone parent and each of its offspring have identical genes. The type of cell division responsible for asexual reproduction and for the growth and maintenance of multicellular organisms is called mitosis.

Sexual reproduction is different; it requires fertilization of an egg by a sperm. The production of **gametes**—egg and sperm—involves a special type of cell division called meiosis, which occurs only in reproductive organs (such as testes and ovaries in humans). As we'll discuss later, a gamete has only half as many chromosomes as the parent cell that gave rise to it.

In summary, two kinds of cell division are involved in the lives of sexually reproducing organisms: meiosis for reproduction and mitosis for growth and maintenance. The remainder of the chapter is divided into two main sections, one devoted to each type of cell division. ✔

✔ CHECKPOINT

Ordinary cell division produces two daughter cells that are genetically identical. Name three functions of this type of cell division.

Answer: cell replacement, growth of an organism, asexual reproduction of an organism

▶ Figure 8.1 **Three functions of cell division.**

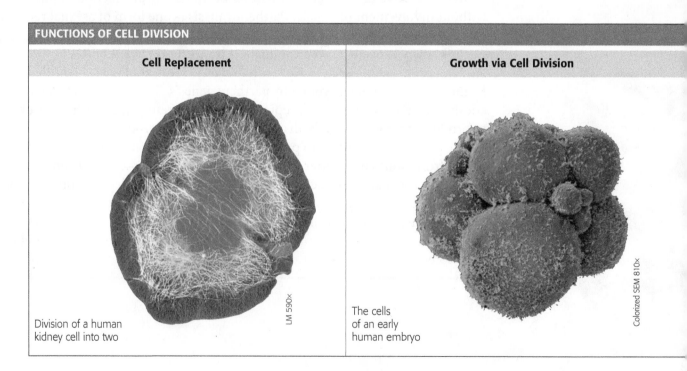

FUNCTIONS OF CELL DIVISION

Cell Replacement	Growth via Cell Division

Division of a human kidney cell into two

LM 590x

The cells of an early human embryo

Colonized SEM 810x

The Cell Cycle and Mitosis

Almost all of the genes of a eukaryotic cell—around 21,000 in humans—are located on chromosomes in the cell nucleus. (The main exceptions are genes on small DNA molecules found in mitochondria and chloroplasts.) Because chromosomes are the lead players in cell division, let's focus on them before turning our attention to the cell as a whole.

Eukaryotic Chromosomes

Each eukaryotic chromosome contains one very long DNA molecule, typically bearing thousands of genes. The number of chromosomes in a eukaryotic cell depends on the species (Figure 8.2). Chromosomes are made up of a material called **chromatin**, fibers composed of roughly equal amounts of DNA and protein molecules. The protein molecules help organize the chromatin and help control the activity of its genes.

Most of the time, the chromosomes exist as thin fibers that are much longer than the nucleus they are stored in. In fact, if stretched out, the DNA in just one of your cells would be taller than you! As a cell prepares to divide, its chromatin

► Figure 8.2 **The number of chromosomes in the cells of selected mammals.** Notice that humans have 46 chromosomes and that the number of chromosomes does not correspond to the size or complexity of an organism.

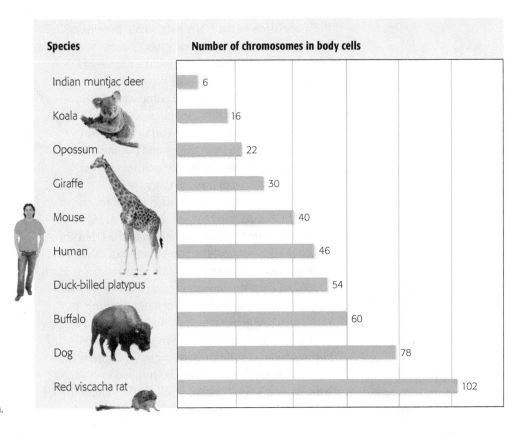

Species	Number of chromosomes in body cells
Indian muntjac deer	6
Koala	16
Opossum	22
Giraffe	30
Mouse	40
Human	46
Duck-billed platypus	54
Buffalo	60
Dog	78
Red viscacha rat	102

Asexual Reproduction

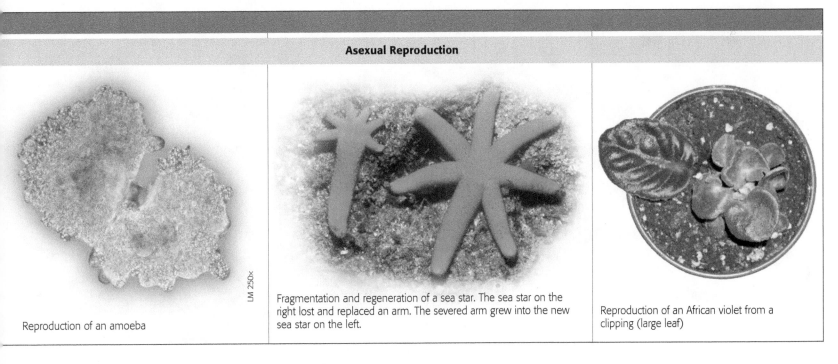

LM 250x

Reproduction of an amoeba

Fragmentation and regeneration of a sea star. The sea star on the right lost and replaced an arm. The severed arm grew into the new sea star on the left.

Reproduction of an African violet from a clipping (large leaf)

fibers coil up, forming compact chromosomes that can be viewed under a light microscope (Figure 8.3). When a cell is not dividing, the chromosomes are too thin to be seen with a light micrograph.

How can yards' worth of DNA fit inside a microscopic nucleus?

Such long molecules of DNA can fit into the tiny nucleus because within each chromosome the DNA is packed into an elaborate, multilevel system of coiling and folding. A crucial aspect of DNA packing is the association of the DNA with small proteins called **histones**, found only in eukaryotes. (Bacteria have similar proteins, but prokaryotes lack the degree of DNA packing found in eukaryotes.) Why is it necessary for a cell's chromosomes to be compacted in this way? Imagine that your belongings are spread out around your room. If you had to move, you would gather up all your things and put them in small containers. Similarly, a cell must compact its DNA before it can move it to a new cell.

Figure 8.4 presents a simplified model for the main levels of DNA packing. At the first level of packing, shown near the top, histones attach to the DNA. In electron micrographs, the combination of DNA and histones has the appearance of beads on a string. Each "bead," called a **nucleosome**, consists of DNA wound around histone molecules. When not dividing, the DNA of active genes takes on this lightly packed, "beads on a string" arrangement. When preparing to divide, chromosomes condense even more. At the next level of packing, the beaded string is wrapped into a tight helical fiber. Then this fiber coils further into a thick

supercoil. Looping and folding can compact the DNA even more still, as you can see in the chromosome at the bottom of the figure. Viewed as a whole, Figure 8.4 gives a sense of how successive levels of coiling and folding enable a huge amount of DNA to fit into a cell's tiny nucleus.

▼ Figure 8.4 **DNA packing in a eukaryotic chromosome.** Successive levels of coiling of DNA and associated proteins ultimately results in highly compacted chromosomes.

DNA double helix

Histones

"Beads on a string"

Nucleosome

TEM 200,000×

Tight helical fiber

Thick supercoil

Duplicated chromosomes (sister chromatids)

Centromere

TEM 14,000×

▼ Figure 8.3 **A plant cell just before division (colored by stains).**

LM 1,400×

Chromosomes

Before a cell begins the division process, it duplicates all of its chromosomes. The DNA molecule of each chromosome is copied through the process of DNA replication (see Chapter 10), and new protein molecules attach as needed. The result is that—at this point—each chromosome consists of two copies called **sister chromatids**, which contain identical genes. At the bottom of Figure 8.4, you can see an electron micrograph of a human chromosome that has duplicated. The fuzzy appearance comes from the intricate twists and folds of the chromatin fibers. The two sister chromatids are joined together tightly at a narrow "waist" called the **centromere**.

When the cell divides, the sister chromatids of a duplicated chromosome separate from each other (Figure 8.5). Once separated from its sister, each chromatid is considered a full-fledged chromosome, and it is identical to the original chromosome. One of the new chromosomes goes to one daughter cell, and the other goes to the other daughter cell. In this way, each daughter cell receives a complete and identical set of chromosomes. A dividing human skin cell, for example, has 46 duplicated chromosomes, and each of the two daughter cells that result from it has 46 single chromosomes.

The Cell Cycle

The rate at which a cell divides depends on its role within the organism's body. Some cells divide once a day, others less often, and highly specialized cells, such as mature muscle cells, do not divide at all.

The ordered sequence of events that extends from the time a cell is first formed from a dividing parent cell until its own division into two cells is called the **cell cycle**. As Figure 8.6 shows, most of the cell cycle is spent in **interphase**. Interphase is a time when a cell performs its normal functions within the organism. For example, a cell in your stomach lining might make and release enzyme molecules that aid in digestion. During interphase, a cell roughly doubles everything in its cytoplasm. It

▲ **Figure 8.5 Duplication and distribution of a single chromosome.** During cell reproduction, the cell duplicates each chromosome and distributes the two copies to the daughter cells.

increases its supply of proteins, increases the number of many of its organelles (such as mitochondria and ribosomes), and grows in size. Typically, interphase lasts for at least 90% of the cell cycle.

From the standpoint of cell reproduction, the most important event of interphase is chromosome duplication, when the DNA in the nucleus is precisely doubled. The period when this occurs is called the S phase (for DNA *synthesis*). The interphase periods before and after the S phase are called the G_1 and G_2 phases, respectively (G stands for *gap*). During G_2, each chromosome in the cell consists of two identical sister chromatids, and the cell during this period is preparing to divide.

The part of the cell cycle when the cell is actually dividing is called the **mitotic (M) phase**. It includes two overlapping stages, mitosis and cytokinesis. In **mitosis**, the nucleus and its contents, most importantly the duplicated chromosomes, divide and are evenly distributed, forming two daughter nuclei. During **cytokinesis**, the cytoplasm is divided in two. The combination of mitosis and cytokinesis produces two genetically identical daughter cells, each with a single nucleus, the surrounding cytoplasm with organelles, and a plasma membrane. ☑

☑ **CHECKPOINT**

1. A duplicated chromosome consists of two sister _____ joined together at the _____.

2. What are the two broadest divisions of the cell cycle? What two processes are involved in the actual duplication of the cell?

Answers: 1. chromatids; centromere 2. interphase and the mitotic phase; mitosis and cytokinesis

▼ **Figure 8.6 The eukaryotic cell cycle.** The cell cycle extends from the "birth" of a cell (just after the dark blue arrow at the bottom of the cycle), resulting from cell reproduction, to the time the cell itself divides in two. (During interphase, the chromosomes are diffuse masses of thin fibers; they do not actually appear in the rodlike form you see here.)

S phase
(DNA synthesis; chromosome duplication)

Interphase: metabolism and growth (90% of time)

G_1

G_2

Mitotic (M) phase: cell division (10% of time)

Cytokinesis (division of cytoplasm)

Mitosis (division of nucleus)

Mitosis and Cytokinesis

Figure 8.7 illustrates the cell cycle for an animal cell using drawings, descriptions, and photos. The micrographs running along the bottom row of the page show dividing cells from a salamander, with chromosomes appearing in blue. The drawings in the top row include details that are not visible in the micrographs. In these cells, we illustrate just four chromosomes to keep the process a bit simpler to follow. The text within the figure describes the events occurring at each stage. Study this figure carefully (it has a lot of

▼ **Figure 8.7** **Cell reproduction: A dance of the chromosomes.** After the chromatin doubles during interphase, the elaborately choreographed stages of mitosis—prophase, metaphase, anaphase, and telophase—distribute the duplicate sets of chromosomes to two separate nuclei. Cytokinesis then divides the cytoplasm, yielding two genetically identical daughter cells.

INTERPHASE

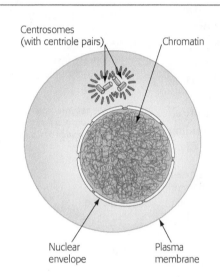

Centrosomes (with centriole pairs)

Chromatin

Nuclear envelope

Plasma membrane

Interphase is the period of cell growth when the cell makes new molecules and organelles. At the point shown here, late interphase (G_2), the cytoplasm contains two centrosomes. Within the nucleus, the chromosomes are duplicated, but they cannot be distinguished individually because they are still in the form of loosely packed chromatin fibers.

PROPHASE

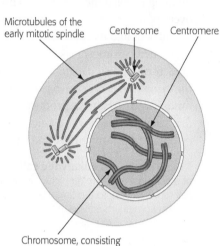

Microtubules of the early mitotic spindle

Centrosome   Centromere

Chromosome, consisting of two sister chromatids

During prophase, changes occur in both nucleus and cytoplasm. In the nucleus, the chromatin fibers coil, so that the chromosomes become thick enough to be seen individually with a light microscope. Each chromosome exists as two identical sister chromatids joined together at the narrow "waist" of the centromere. In the cytoplasm, the mitotic spindle

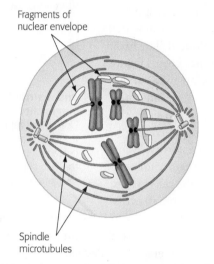

Fragments of nuclear envelope

Spindle microtubules

begins to form as microtubules grow out from the centrosomes, which are moving away from each other. Late in prophase, the nuclear envelope breaks into pieces. The spindle microtubules attach to the centromeres of the chromosomes and move the chromosomes toward the center of the cell.

information and it's important!) and notice the striking changes in the nucleus and other cellular structures.

Biologists distinguish four main stages of mitosis: **prophase**, **metaphase**, **anaphase**, and **telophase**. The chromosomes are the stars of the mitotic drama, and their movements depend on the **mitotic spindle**, a football-shaped structure of microtubules (green in the micrographs) that guides the separation of the two sets of daughter chromosomes. The spindle microtubules grow from structures within the cytoplasm called **centrosomes**.

METAPHASE	ANAPHASE	TELOPHASE AND CYTOKINESIS

Spindle

Daughter chromosomes

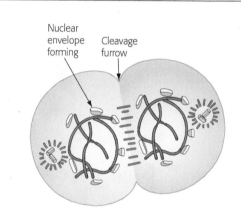

Nuclear envelope forming   Cleavage furrow

The mitotic spindle is now fully formed. The centromeres of all the chromosomes line up between the two poles of the spindle. For each chromosome, the microtubules of the mitotic spindle attached to the two sister chromatids pull toward opposite poles. This tug of war keeps the chromosomes in the middle of the cell.

Anaphase begins suddenly when the sister chromatids of each chromosome separate. Each is now considered a full-fledged (daughter) chromosome. The chromosomes move toward opposite poles of the cell as the spindle microtubules shorten. Simultaneously, the microtubules not attached to chromosomes lengthen, pushing the poles farther apart and elongating the cell.

Telophase begins when the two groups of chromosomes have reached opposite ends of the cell. Telophase is the reverse of prophase: Nuclear envelopes form, the chromosomes uncoil, and the spindle disappears. Mitosis, the division of one nucleus into two genetically identical daughter nuclei, is now finished. Cytokinesis, the division of the cytoplasm, usually occurs with telophase. In animals, a cleavage furrow pinches the cell in two, producing two daughter cells.

▼ Figure 8.8 **Cytokinesis in animal and plant cells.**

(a) Animal cell cytokinesis

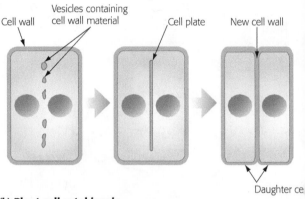

(b) Plant cell cytokinesis

☑ **CHECKPOINT**

An organism called a plasmodial slime mold is one huge cytoplasmic mass with many nuclei. Explain how a variation in the cell cycle could cause this "monster cell" to arise.

Answer: Mitosis occurs repeatedly without cytokinesis

Cytokinesis, the division of the cytoplasm into two cells, usually begins during telophase, overlapping the end of mitosis. In animal cells, the cytokinesis process is known as cleavage. The first sign of cleavage is the appearance of a **cleavage furrow**, an indentation at the equator of the cell. A ring of microfilaments in the cytoplasm just under the plasma membrane contracts, like the pulling of a drawstring on a hooded sweatshirt, deepening the furrow and pinching the parent cell in two **(Figure 8.8a)**.

Cytokinesis in a plant cell occurs differently. Vesicles containing cell wall material collect at the middle of the cell. The vesicles fuse, forming a membranous disk called the **cell plate**. The cell plate grows outward, accumulating more cell wall material as more vesicles join it. Eventually, the membrane of the cell plate fuses with the plasma membrane, and the cell plate's contents join the parental cell wall. The result is two daughter cells **(Figure 8.8b)**. ☑

Cancer Cells: Growing Out of Control

For a plant or animal to grow and maintain its tissues normally, it must be able to control the timing of cell division. The sequential events of the cell cycle are directed by a **cell cycle control system** that consists of specialized proteins within the cell. These proteins integrate information from the environment and from other body cells and send "stop" and "go-ahead" signals at certain key points during the cell cycle using signal transduction pathways (see Figure 5.19). For example, the cell cycle normally halts within the G_1 phase of interphase unless the cell receives a go-ahead signal via certain cell cycle control proteins. If that signal never arrives, the cell will switch into a permanently nondividing state. Some of your nerve and muscle cells, for example, are arrested this way. If the go-ahead signal is received and the G_1 checkpoint is passed, the cell will usually complete the rest of the cycle.

What Is Cancer?

Cancer, which currently claims the lives of one out of every five people in the United States and other industrialized nations, is a disease of the cell cycle. Cancer cells do not respond normally to the cell cycle control system; they divide excessively and may invade other tissues of the body. If unchecked, cancer cells may continue to divide until they kill the host.

The abnormal behavior of cancer cells begins when a single cell undergoes transformation, a process that converts a normal cell to a cancer cell. Transformation occurs after a genetic change (mutation) in one or more genes that encode for proteins in the cell cycle control system. Because a transformed cell grows abnormally, the immune system generally recognizes and destroys it. However, if the cell evades destruction, it may proliferate to form a **tumor**, an abnormally growing mass of body cells. If the abnormal cells remain at the original site, the lump is called a **benign tumor**. Benign tumors can cause problems if they grow large and disrupt certain organs, such as the brain, but often they can be completely removed by surgery.

Why are some tumors worse than others?

In contrast, a **malignant tumor** is one that has begun to spread into neighboring tissues and other parts of the body (Figure 8.9), displacing normal tissue and interrupting organ function. An individual with a malignant tumor is said to have **cancer**. Cancer cells may separate from the original tumor or secrete signal molecules that cause blood vessels to grow toward the tumor. A few tumor cells may then enter the blood or lymph vessels and move to other parts of the body, where they may proliferate and form new tumors. The spread of cancer cells beyond their original site is called **metastasis**. Cancers are named according to where they originate. Liver cancer, for example, always begins in liver tissue and may spread from there.

Cancer Treatment

Once a tumor starts growing in the body, how can it be treated? The three main types of cancer treatment are sometimes referred to as "slash, burn, and poison." Surgery to remove a tumor ("slash") is usually the first step. "Burn" and "poison" refer to treatments that attempt to stop cancer cells from dividing. In **radiation therapy** ("burn"), parts of the body that have cancerous tumors are exposed to concentrated beams of high-energy radiation, which can often harm cancer cells more than the normal cells of the body. However, there is sometimes enough damage to normal body cells to produce side effects, such as nausea and hair loss.

Chemotherapy ("poison"), the use of drugs to disrupt cell division, is used to treat widespread or metastatic tumors. Chemotherapy drugs work in a variety of ways. Some prevent cell division by interfering with the mitotic spindle. For example, paclitaxel (trade name Taxol) freezes the spindle after it forms, keeping it from functioning. Paclitaxel is made from a chemical discovered in the bark of the Pacific yew, a tree found mainly in the northwestern United States. It has fewer side effects than many other anticancer drugs and seems to be effective against some hard-to-treat cancers of the ovary and breast. Another drug, vinblastine, prevents the mitotic spindle from forming in the first place. Vinblastine was first obtained from the periwinkle plant, which is native to the tropical rain forests of Madagascar.

Cancer Prevention and Survival

Although cancer can strike anyone, there are certain lifestyle changes you can make to reduce your chances of developing cancer or increase your chances of surviving it. Not smoking, exercising adequately, avoiding overexposure to the sun, and eating a high-fiber, low-fat diet can all help reduce the likelihood of getting cancer. Seven types of cancer can be easily detected: skin and oral (via physical exam), breast (via self-exams or mammograms for higher-risk women), prostate (via rectal exam), cervical (via Pap smear), testicular (via self-exam), and colon (via colonoscopy). Regular visits to the doctor can help identify tumors early, which is the best way to increase the chance of successful treatment. ☑

▼ Figure 8.9 **Growth and metastasis of a malignant tumor of the breast.**

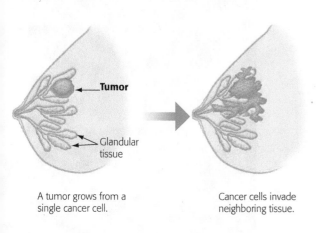

A tumor grows from a single cancer cell.

Cancer cells invade neighboring tissue.

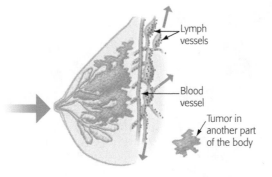

Metastasis: Cancer cells spread through lymph and blood vessels to other parts of the body.

☑ CHECKPOINT

What differentiates a benign tumor from a malignant tumor?

Answer: A benign tumor remains at its point of origin, whereas a malignant tumor spreads.

Meiosis, the Basis of Sexual Reproduction

Only maple trees produce more maple trees, only goldfish make more goldfish, and only people make more people. These simple facts of life have been recognized for thousands of years and are reflected in the age-old saying, "Like begets like." But in a strict sense, "Like begets like" applies only to asexual reproduction, such as the cutting of the African violet in Figure 8.1. Because the offspring of asexual reproduction inherit all their DNA from a single parent, they are exact genetic replicas of that one parent and of each other, and their appearances are very similar.

How do your chromosomes compare with those of the president?

The family photo in **Figure 8.10** makes the point that in a sexually reproducing species, like does not exactly beget like. You probably resemble your parents more closely than you resemble strangers, but—unless you are an identical twin—you do not look exactly like your parents or your siblings. Each offspring of sexual reproduction inherits a unique combination of genes from its two parents, and this combined set of genes programs a unique combination of traits. As a result, sexual reproduction can produce tremendous variety among offspring.

Sexual reproduction depends on the cellular processes of meiosis and fertilization. But before discussing these processes, we need to return to chromosomes and the role they play in the life cycle of sexually reproducing organisms.

Homologous Chromosomes

If we examine cells from different individuals of a single species—sticking to one gender, for now—we find that they have the same number and types of chromosomes. Viewed with a microscope, your chromosomes would look just like those of Angelina Jolie (if you're a woman) or Brad Pitt (if you're a man).

In humans, a typical body cell, called a **somatic cell**, has 46 chromosomes. If you break open a human cell in metaphase of mitosis, stain the chromosomes with dyes, take a picture with the aid of a microscope, and arrange the chromosomes in matching pairs, you produce a display called a **karyotype** (Figure 8.11). Notice in the figure that each chromosome is duplicated, with two sister chromatids joined at the centromere. Notice also that almost every chromosome has a twin that resembles it in length and centromere position. The two chromosomes of such a matching pair, called **homologous chromosomes**, carry genes controlling the same inherited characteristics. For example, if a gene influencing freckles is located at a particular place on one chromosome—within the yellow band in the drawing in Figure 8.11, for instance—then the homologous chromosome has that same gene in the same location. However, the two homologous chromosomes may have different versions of the same gene. Let's restate this concept: A pair of homologous chromosomes has two nearly identical

▼ Figure 8.10 **The varied products of sexual reproduction.** Every child inherits a unique combination of genes from his or her parents and displays a unique combination of traits.

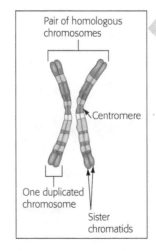

▼ Figure 8.11 **Pairs of homologous chromosomes in a male karyotype.** This karyotype shows 22 completely homologous pairs (autosomes) and a 23rd pair that consists of an X chromosome and a Y chromosome (sex chromosomes). With the exception of X and Y, the homologous chromosomes of each pair match in size, centromere position, and staining pattern.

Pair of homologous chromosomes

Centromere

One duplicated chromosome

Sister chromatids

LM 3,600×

chromosomes, each of which consists of two identical sister chromatids after chromosome duplication (see the drawing in Figure 8.11). Altogether, each human has 23 pairs of homologous chromosomes. Other species have different numbers of chromosomes (see Figure 8.2), but those, too, usually match in pairs.

In human females, the 46 chromosomes fall neatly into 23 homologous pairs, with the members of each pair essentially identical in appearance. For a male, however, the chromosomes in one pair do not look alike. This nonmatching pair, only partly homologous, is the male's sex chromosomes. **Sex chromosomes** determine a person's sex (male versus female). In mammals, males have one X chromosome and one Y chromosome. Females have two X chromosomes. (Other organisms have different systems; in this chapter, we focus on humans.) The remaining chromosomes, found in both males and females, are called **autosomes**. For both autosomes and sex chromosomes, we inherit one chromosome of each pair from our mother and the other from our father.

Gametes and the Life Cycle of a Sexual Organism

The **life cycle** of a multicellular organism is the sequence of stages leading from the adults of one generation to the adults of the next. Having two sets of chromosomes, one inherited from each parent, is a key factor in the life cycle of humans and all other species that reproduce sexually. **Figure 8.12** shows the human life cycle, emphasizing the number of chromosomes.

Humans (as well as most other animals and many plants) are said to be **diploid** organisms because all body cells contain pairs of homologous chromosomes. The total number of chromosomes, 46 in humans, is the diploid number (abbreviated $2n$). The exceptions are the gametes, egg and sperm cells. Made by meiosis in an ovary or testis, each gamete has a single set of chromosomes: 22 autosomes plus a sex chromosome, either X or Y. A cell with a single chromosome set is called a **haploid** cell; it has only one member of each pair of homologous chromosomes. For humans, the haploid number, n, is 23.

In the human life cycle, a haploid sperm cell from the father fuses with a haploid egg cell from the mother in a process called **fertilization**. The resulting fertilized egg, called a **zygote**, is diploid. It has two sets of chromosomes, one set from each parent. The life cycle is completed as a sexually mature adult develops from the zygote. Mitotic cell division ensures that all somatic cells of the human body

receive a copy of all of the zygote's 46 chromosomes. Thus, every one of the trillions of cells in your body can trace its ancestry back through mitotic divisions to the single zygote produced when your father's sperm and your mother's egg fused about nine months before you were born.

All sexual life cycles involve an alternation of diploid and haploid stages. Producing haploid gametes by meiosis keeps the chromosome number from doubling in every generation. To illustrate, **Figure 8.13** tracks one pair of homologous chromosomes.
① Each of the chromosomes is duplicated during interphase (before mitosis).
② The first division, meiosis I, segregates the two chromosomes of the homologous pair, packaging them in separate (haploid) daughter cells. But each chromosome is still doubled. ③ Meiosis II separates the sister chromatids. Each of the four daughter cells is haploid and contains only a single chromosome from the pair of homologous chromosomes.

► Figure 8.12 **The human life cycle.** In each generation, the doubling of chromosome number that results from fertilization is offset by the halving of chromosome number during meiosis.

▼ Figure 8.13 **How meiosis halves chromosome number.**

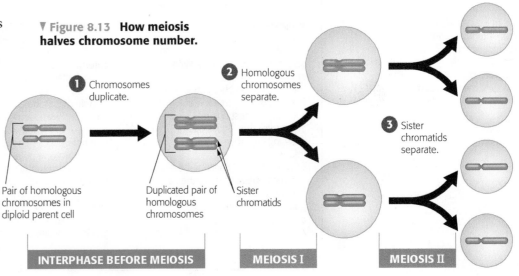

The Process of Meiosis

Meiosis, the process of cell division that produces haploid gametes in diploid organisms, resembles mitosis, but with two special features. The first is that the number of chromosomes is reduced to half. In meiosis, a cell that has duplicated its chromosomes undergoes two consecutive divisions, called meiosis I and meiosis II. Because one duplication of the chromosomes is followed by two divisions, each of the four daughter cells resulting from meiosis has a haploid set of chromosomes—half as many chromosomes as the starting cell.

The second special feature of meiosis is an exchange of genetic material—pieces of chromosomes—between homologous chromosomes. This exchange, called crossing over, occurs during the first prophase of meiosis. We'll look more closely at crossing over later. For now, study Figure 8.14, including the text below it, which describes the stages of meiosis in detail for a hypothetical animal cell containing four chromosomes.

As you go through Figure 8.14, keep in mind the difference between homologous chromosomes and sister chromatids: The two chromosomes of a homologous pair are individual chromosomes that were inherited

▼ Figure 8.14 **The stages of meiosis.**

MEIOSIS I: HOMOLOGOUS CHROMOSOMES SEPARATE

INTERPHASE	PROPHASE I	METAPHASE I	ANAPHASE I
Chromosomes duplicate.	**Homologous chromosomes pair up and exchange segments.**	**Pairs of homologous chromosomes line up.**	**Pairs of homologous chromosomes split up.**

Like mitosis, meiosis is preceded by an interphase during which the chromosomes duplicate. Each chromosome then consists of two identical sister chromatids. The chromosomes consist of uncondensed chromatin fibers.

Prophase I As the chromosomes coil up, special proteins cause the homologous chromosomes to stick together in pairs. The resulting structure has four chromatids. Within each set, chromatids of the homologous chromosomes exchange corresponding segments—they "cross over." Crossing over rearranges genetic information.

As prophase I continues, the chromosomes coil up further, a spindle forms, and the homologous pairs are moved toward the center of the cell.

Metaphase I At metaphase I, the homologous pairs are aligned in the middle of the cell. The sister chromatids of each chromosome are still attached at their centromeres, where they are anchored to spindle microtubules. Notice that for each chromosome pair, the spindle microtubules attached to one homologous chromosome come from one pole of the cell, and the microtubules attached to the other chromosome come from the opposite pole. With this arrangement, the homologous chromosomes are poised to move toward opposite poles of the cell.

Anaphase I The attachment between the homologous chromosomes of each pair breaks, and the chromosomes now migrate toward the poles of the cell. *In contrast to mitosis, the sister chromatids migrate as a pair instead of splitting up.* They are separated not from each other but from their homologous partners.

from different parents, one from the mother and one from the father. The members of a pair of homologous chromosomes in Figure 8.14 (and later figures) are identical in size and shape but colored differently (red versus blue) to remind you that they differ in this way. In the interphase just before meiosis, each chromosome duplicates to form sister chromatids that remain together until anaphase of meiosis II. Before crossing over occurs, sister chromatids are identical and carry the same versions of all their genes. ☑

Meiosis II in a lily cell

LM 900×

☑ CHECKPOINT

If a single diploid somatic cell with 18 chromosomes undergoes meiosis and produces sperm, the result will be _____ sperm, each with _____ chromosomes. (Provide two numbers.)

Answer: four; nine

MEIOSIS II: SISTER CHROMATIDS SEPARATE

TELOPHASE I AND CYTOKINESIS	PROPHASE II	METAPHASE II	ANAPHASE II	TELOPHASE II AND CYTOKINESIS

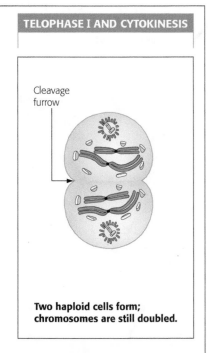

Cleavage furrow

Two haploid cells form; chromosomes are still doubled.

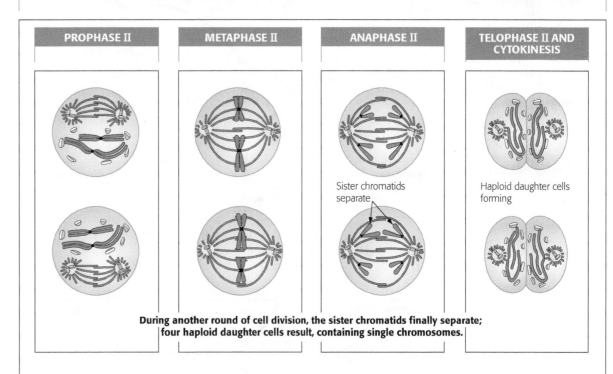

Sister chromatids separate

Haploid daughter cells forming

During another round of cell division, the sister chromatids finally separate; four haploid daughter cells result, containing single chromosomes.

Telophase I and Cytokinesis In telophase I, the chromosomes arrive at the poles of the cell. When they finish their journey, each pole has a haploid chromosome set, although each chromosome is still in duplicate form. Usually, cytokinesis occurs along with telophase I, and two haploid daughter cells are formed.

The Process of Meiosis II Meiosis II is essentially the same as mitosis. The important difference is that meiosis II starts with a haploid cell that has *not* undergone chromosome duplication during the preceding interphase.

During prophase II, a spindle forms and moves the chromosomes toward the middle of the cell. During metaphase II, the chromosomes are aligned as they are in mitosis, with the microtubules attached to the sister chromatids of each chromosome coming from opposite poles. In anaphase II, the centromeres of sister chromatids separate, and the sister chromatids of each pair move toward opposite poles of the cell. In telophase II, nuclei form at the cell poles, and cytokinesis occurs at the same time. There are now four haploid daughter cells, each with single chromosomes.

Review: Comparing Mitosis and Meiosis

You have now learned the two ways that cells of eukaryotic organisms divide. Mitosis, which provides for growth, tissue repair, and asexual reproduction, produces daughter cells that are genetically identical to the parent cell. Meiosis, needed for sexual reproduction, yields genetically unique haploid daughter cells—cells with only one member of each homologous chromosome pair.

For both mitosis and meiosis, the chromosomes duplicate only once, in the preceding interphase. Mitosis involves one division of the nucleus and cytoplasm, producing two diploid cells. Meiosis entails two nuclear and cytoplasmic divisions, yielding four haploid cells.

Figure 8.15 compares mitosis and meiosis, tracing these two processes for a diploid parent cell with four

▶ Figure 8.15 **Comparing mitosis and meiosis.** The events unique to meiosis occur during meiosis I: In prophase I, duplicated homologous chromosomes pair along their lengths, and crossing over occurs between homologous (nonsister) chromatids. In metaphase I, pairs of homologous chromosomes (rather than individual chromosomes) are aligned at the center of the cell. During anaphase I, sister chromatids of each chromosome stay together and go to the same pole of the cell as homologous chromosomes separate. At the end of meiosis I, there are two haploid cells, but each chromosome still has two sister chromatids.

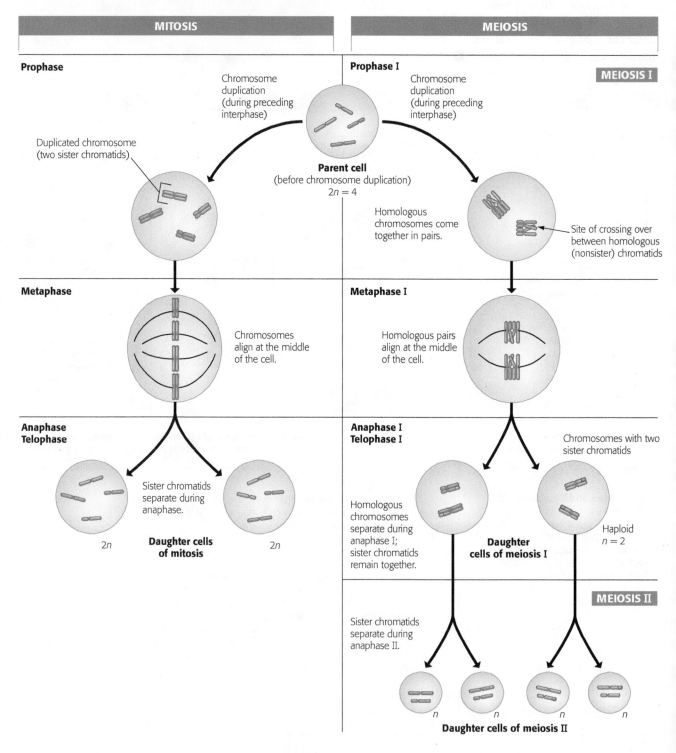

chromosomes. As before, homologous chromosomes are those matching in size. (Imagine that the red chromosomes were inherited from the mother and the blue chromosomes from the father.) Notice that all the events unique to meiosis occur during meiosis I. Meiosis II is virtually identical to mitosis in that it separates sister chromatids. But unlike mitosis, meiosis II yields daughter cells with a haploid set of chromosomes. ☑

The Origins of Genetic Variation

As we discussed earlier, offspring that result from sexual reproduction are genetically different from their parents and from one another. How does meiosis produce such genetic variation?

Independent Assortment of Chromosomes

Figure 8.16 illustrates one way in which meiosis contributes to genetic variety. The figure shows how the arrangement of homologous chromosomes at metaphase of meiosis I affects the resulting gametes. Once again, our example is from a diploid organism with four chromosomes (two pairs of homologous chromosomes), with colors used to differentiate homologous

chromosomes (red for chromosomes inherited from the mother and blue for chromosomes from the father).

When aligned during metaphase I, the side-by-side orientation of each homologous pair of chromosomes (consisting of two sister chromatids) is a matter of chance—either the red or blue chromosome may be on the left or right. Thus, in this example, there are two possible ways that the chromosome pairs can align during metaphase I. In possibility 1, the chromosome pairs are oriented with both red chromosomes on the same side (blue/red and blue/red). In this case, each of the gametes produced at the end of meiosis II has only red or only blue chromosomes (combinations a and b). In possibility 2, the chromosome pairs are oriented differently (blue/red and red/blue). This arrangement produces gametes with one red and one blue chromosome (combinations c and d). Thus, with the two possible arrangements shown in this example, the organism will produce gametes with four different combinations of chromosomes. For a species with more than two pairs of chromosomes, such as humans, every chromosome pair orients independently of all the others at metaphase I. (Chromosomes X and Y behave as a homologous pair in meiosis.)

For any species, the total number of chromosome combinations that can appear in gametes is 2^n, where n is the haploid number. For the hypothetical organism in

☑ **CHECKPOINT**

True or false: Both mitosis and meiosis are preceded by chromosome duplication.

Answer: *true*

◄ **Figure 8.16 Results of alternative arrangements of chromosomes at metaphase of meiosis I.** The arrangement of chromosomes at metaphase I determines which chromosomes will be packaged together in the haploid gametes.

| POSSIBILITY 1 | | POSSIBILITY 2 |

Two equally probable arrangements of chromosomes at metaphase of meiosis I

Metaphase of meiosis II

Gametes

Combination a   Combination b   Combination c   Combination d

Because possibilities 1 and 2 are equally likely, the four possible types of gametes will be made in approximately equal numbers.

135

Figure 8.16, $n = 2$, so the number of chromosome combinations is 2^2, or 4. For a human ($n = 23$), there are 2^{23}, or about 8 million, possible chromosome combinations! This means that every gamete a person produces contains one of about 8 million possible combinations of maternal and paternal chromosomes.

Random Fertilization

How many possibilities are there when a gamete from one individual unites with a gamete from another individual during fertilization **(Figure 8.17)**? A human egg cell, representing one of about 8 million possibilities, is fertilized at random by one sperm cell, representing one of about 8 million other possibilities. By multiplying 8 million by 8 million, we find that a man and a woman can produce a diploid zygote with any of 64 trillion combinations of chromosomes! So we see that the random nature of fertilization adds a huge amount of potential variability to the offspring of sexual reproduction.

In what sense are you 1 in 64,000,000,000,000?

Crossing Over

So far, we have focused on genetic variety in gametes and zygotes at the whole-chromosome level. We'll now take a closer look at **crossing over**, the exchange of corresponding segments between nonsister chromatids of homologous chromosomes, which occurs during prophase I of meiosis. **Figure 8.18** shows crossing over between two homologous chromosomes and the resulting gametes. At the time that crossing over begins, homologous chromosomes are closely paired all along their lengths, with a precise gene-by-gene alignment. The sites of crossing over appear as X-shaped regions; each is called a **chiasma** (plural, *chiasmata*). The homologous chromatids remain attached to each other at chiasmata until anaphase I.

▼ **Figure 8.17 The process of fertilization: a close-up view.** Here you see many human sperm contacting an egg. Only one sperm can add its chromosomes to produce a zygote.

Colorized LM 1320x

▼ **Figure 8.18 The results of crossing over during meiosis for a single pair of homologous chromosomes.** A real cell has multiple pairs of homologous chromosomes that produce a huge variety of recombinant chromosomes in the gametes.

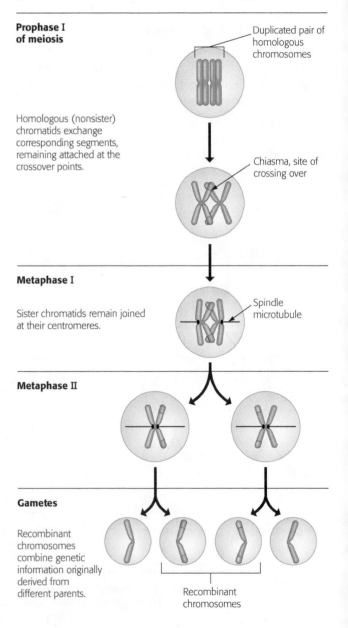

Prophase I of meiosis

Duplicated pair of homologous chromosomes

Homologous (nonsister) chromatids exchange corresponding segments, remaining attached at the crossover points.

Chiasma, site of crossing over

Metaphase I

Sister chromatids remain joined at their centromeres.

Spindle microtubule

Metaphase II

Gametes

Recombinant chromosomes combine genetic information originally derived from different parents.

Recombinant chromosomes

The exchange of segments between nonsister chromatids—one maternal chromatid and one paternal chromatid of a homologous pair—adds to the genetic variety resulting from sexual reproduction. In Figure 8.18, if there were no crossing over, meiosis could produce only two types of gametes. These would be the ones ending up with the "parental" types of chromosomes, either all blue or all red (as in Figure 8.16). With crossing over, gametes arise that have chromosomes that are part red and part blue. These chromosomes are called "recombinant" because they result from **genetic recombination**, the production of gene combinations different from those carried by the parental chromosomes.

Because most chromosomes contain thousands of genes, a single crossover event can affect many genes. When we also consider that multiple crossovers can occur in each pair of homologous chromosomes, it's not surprising that gametes and the offspring that result from them can be so varied. ☑

☑ **CHECKPOINT**

Name two events during meiosis that contribute to genetic variety among gametes. During what stages of meiosis does each occur?

Answer: crossing over between homologous chromosomes during prophase I and independent orientation/assortment of the pairs of homologous chromosomes at metaphase I

Life with and without Sex THE PROCESS OF SCIENCE

Do All Animals Have Sex?

As discussed in the Biology and Society section, some species can reproduce via both sexual and asexual routes. But although some animal species can *also* reproduce asexually, very few animals reproduce *only* asexually. In fact, evolutionary biologists have traditionally considered asexual reproduction an evolutionary dead end (for reasons we'll discuss in the Evolution Connection section at the end of the chapter).

To investigate a case where asexual reproduction seemed to be the norm, researchers from Harvard University studied a group of animals called bdelloid rotifers (Figure 8.19). This class of nearly microscopic freshwater invertebrates includes more than 300 known species. Despite hundreds of years of observations, no one had ever found bdelloid rotifer males or evidence of sexual reproduction. But the possibility remained that bdelloids had sex very infrequently or that the males were impossible to recognize by appearance. Thus, the Harvard research team posed the question, Does this entire class of animals reproduce solely by asexual means?

The researchers formed the hypothesis that bdelloid rotifers have indeed thrived for millions of years despite a lack of sexual reproduction. But how to test it? In most species, the two versions of a gene in a pair of homologous chromosomes are very similar due to the constant trading of genes during sexual reproduction. If a species has survived without sex for millions of years, the researchers reasoned, then changes in the DNA sequences of homologous genes should accumulate independently, and the two versions of the genes should have significantly diverged from each other over time. This led to the prediction that bdelloid rotifers would display much more variation in their pairs of homologous genes than most organisms.

In a simple but elegant experiment, the researchers compared the sequences of a particular gene in bdelloid and non-bdelloid rotifers. Their results were striking. Among non-bdelloid rotifers that reproduce sexually, the two homologous versions of the gene were nearly identical, differing by only 0.5% on average. In contrast, the two versions of the same gene in bdelloid rotifers differed by 3.5–54%. These data provided strong evidence that bdelloid rotifers have evolved for millions of years without any sexual reproduction.

▶ **Figure 8.19**
A bdelloid rotifer.

LM 300×

When Meiosis Goes Awry

So far, our discussion of meiosis has focused on the process as it normally and correctly occurs. But what happens when there is an error in the process? Such a mistake can result in genetic abnormalities that range from mild to severe to fatal.

How Accidents during Meiosis Can Alter Chromosome Number

Within the human body, meiosis occurs repeatedly as the testes or ovaries produce gametes. Almost always, the meiotic spindle distributes chromosomes to daughter cells without error. But occasionally there is a mishap, called a **nondisjunction**, in which the members of a chromosome pair fail to separate at anaphase. Nondisjunction can occur during meiosis I or II (Figure 8.20). In either case, gametes with abnormal numbers of chromosomes are the result.

Figure 8.21 shows what can happen when an abnormal gamete produced by nondisjunction unites with a normal gamete during fertilization. When a normal sperm fertilizes an egg cell with an extra chromosome,

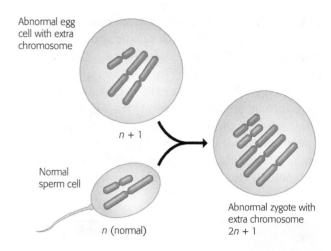

▲ Figure 8.21 **Fertilization after nondisjunction in the mother.**

the result is a zygote with a total of $2n + 1$ chromosomes. Mitosis then transmits the abnormality to all embryonic cells. If the organism survives, it will have an abnormal karyotype and probably a syndrome of disorders caused by the abnormal number of genes. ☑

▼ Figure 8.20 **Two types of nondisjunction.** In both examples in the figure, the cell at the top is diploid (2n), with two pairs of homologous chromosomes.

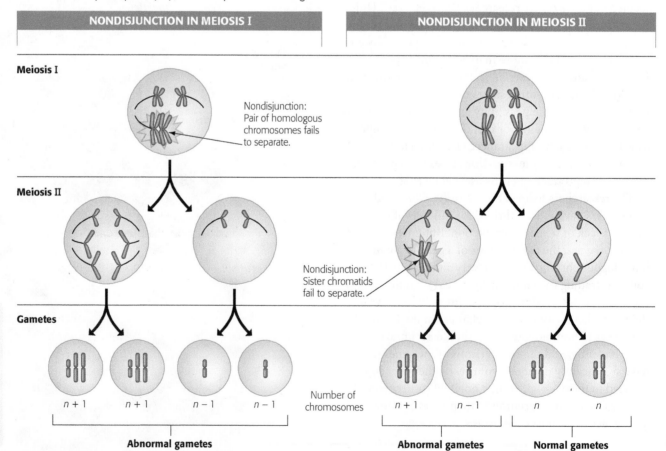

Down Syndrome: An Extra Chromosome 21

Figure 8.11 showed a normal human complement of 23 pairs of chromosomes. Compare it with the karyotype in Figure 8.22; besides having two X chromosomes (because it's from a female), the karyotype in Figure 8.22 has three number 21 chromosomes, making 47 chromosomes in total. This condition is called **trisomy 21**.

In most cases, a human embryo with an atypical number of chromosomes is spontaneously aborted

▼ Figure 8.22 **Trisomy 21 and Down syndrome.** This child displays the characteristic facial features of Down syndrome. The karyotype (bottom) shows trisomy 21; notice the three copies of chromosome 21.

LM 4,000×

Trisomy 21

(miscarried) long before birth. However, some aberrations in chromosome number seem to upset the genetic balance less drastically, and individuals with such abnormalities can survive. These people usually have a characteristic set of symptoms, called a syndrome. A person with trisomy 21 has a condition called **Down syndrome** (named after John Langdon Down, who described it in 1866).

Affecting about 1 out of every 700 children, trisomy 21 is the most common chromosome number abnormality and the most common serious birth defect in the United States. Down syndrome includes characteristic facial features—frequently a fold of skin at the inner corner of the eye, a round face, and a flattened nose—as well as short stature, heart defects, and susceptibility to leukemia and Alzheimer's disease. People with Down syndrome usually have a life span shorter than normal. They also exhibit varying degrees of mental retardation. However, some individuals with the syndrome may live to middle age or beyond, and many are socially adept and can function well within society.

As indicated in Figure 8.23, the incidence of Down syndrome in the offspring of normal parents increases markedly with the age of the mother. Down syndrome affects less than 0.05% of children (fewer than 1 in 2,000) born to women under age 30. The risk climbs to 1% (10 in 1,000) for mothers at age 40 and is even higher (80 per 1,000) for women at age 50. Because of this relatively high risk, the fetuses of pregnant women age 35 and older are candidates for testing for trisomy 21 and other chromosomal abnormalities (see Chapter 9). ☑

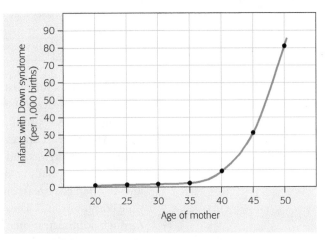

▲ Figure 8.23 **Maternal age and Down syndrome.** The chance of having a baby with Down syndrome rises with the age of the mother.

Abnormal Numbers of Sex Chromosomes

Nondisjunction in meiosis can lead to abnormal numbers of sex chromosomes, X and Y. Unusual numbers of sex chromosomes seem to upset the genetic balance less than unusual numbers of autosomes. This may be because the Y chromosome is very small and carries relatively few genes. Furthermore, mammalian cells normally operate with only one functioning X chromosome because other copies of the chromosome become inactivated in each cell (see Chapter 11).

☑ CHECKPOINT

According to Figure 8.23, how much more likely is a 45-year-old woman to have a child with Down syndrome than a 40-year-old woman?

Answer: three times (30 per 1,000 versus 10 per 1,000)

Table 8.1	Abnormalities of Sex Chromosome Number in Humans		
Sex Chromosomes	**Syndrome**	**Origins of Nondisjunction**	**Frequency in Population**
XXY	Klinefelter syndrome (male)	Meiosis in egg or sperm formation	$\frac{1}{2,000}$
XYY	None (normal male)	Meiosis in sperm formation	$\frac{1}{2,000}$
XXX	None (normal female)	Meiosis in egg or sperm formation	$\frac{1}{1,000}$
XO	Turner syndrome (female)	Meiosis in egg or sperm formation	$\frac{1}{5,000}$

Table 8.1 lists the most common human sex chromosome abnormalities. An extra X chromosome in a male, making him XXY, produces a condition called Klinefelter syndrome. If untreated, men with this disorder have male sex organs and normal intelligence, but the testes are abnormally small, the individual is sterile, and he often has breast enlargement and other feminine body contours. These symptoms can be reduced through administration of the sex hormone testosterone. Klinefelter syndrome is also found in individuals with more than three sex chromosomes, such as XXYY, XXXY, or XXXXY. These abnormal numbers of sex chromosomes result from multiple nondisjunctions.

Human males with a single extra Y chromosome (XYY) do not have any well-defined syndrome, although they tend to be taller than average. Females with an extra X chromosome (XXX) cannot be distinguished from XX females except by karyotype.

Females who are lacking an X chromosome are designated XO; the O indicates the absence of a second sex chromosome. These women have Turner syndrome. They have a characteristic appearance, including short stature and often a web of skin extending between the neck and shoulders. Women with Turner syndrome are of normal intelligence, but are sterile. If left untreated, they have poor development of breasts and other secondary sex characteristics. Administration of estrogen can alleviate those symptoms. The XO condition is the sole known case where having only 45 chromosomes is not fatal in humans.

Notice the crucial role of the Y chromosome in determining a person's sex. In general, a single Y chromosome is enough to produce "maleness," regardless of the number of X chromosomes. The absence of a Y chromosome results in "femaleness." ☑

☑ **CHECKPOINT**

Why is an individual more likely to survive with an abnormal number of sex chromosomes than an abnormal number of autosomes?

Answer: because the Y chromosome is very small and extra X chromosomes are inactivated

▼ Figure 8.24 **Sexual and asexual reproduction.** Many plants, such as this strawberry, have the ability to reproduce both sexually (via flowers that produce fruit) and asexually (via runners).

Runner

Life with and without Sex EVOLUTION CONNECTION

The Advantages of Sex

Throughout this chapter, we've examined cell division within the context of reproduction. Like the Komodo dragon discussed in the Biology and Society section, many species (especially among the plant kingdom) can reproduce both sexually and asexually (Figure 8.24). An important advantage of asexual reproduction is that there is no need for a partner. Asexual reproduction may thus confer an evolutionary advantage when organisms are sparsely distributed (on an isolated island, for example) and unlikely to be able to meet a mate. Furthermore, if an organism is superbly suited to a stable environment, asexual reproduction has the advantage of passing on its entire genetic legacy intact. Asexual reproduction also eliminates the need to expend energy forming gametes and copulating with a partner.

In contrast to plants, the vast majority of animals reproduce by sexual means. There are exceptions, such as the few species that can reproduce via parthenogenesis and the bdelloid rotifers discussed in the Process of Science section. But most animals reproduce only through sex. Therefore, sex must enhance evolutionary fitness. But how? The answer remains elusive. Most hypotheses focus on the unique combinations of genes formed during meiosis and fertilization. By producing offspring of varied genetic makeup, sexual reproduction may enhance survival by speeding adaptation to a changing environment. Another idea is that shuffling genes during sexual reproduction might allow a population to rid itself of harmful genes more rapidly. But for now, one of biology's most basic questions—Why have sex?—remains a hotly debated topic that is the focus of much ongoing research and discussion.

Chapter Review

SUMMARY OF KEY CONCEPTS

Go to **www.masteringbiology.com** for homework assignments, practice quizzes, Pearson eText, and more.

What Cell Reproduction Accomplishes

Cell reproduction, also called cell division, produces genetically identical daughter cells:

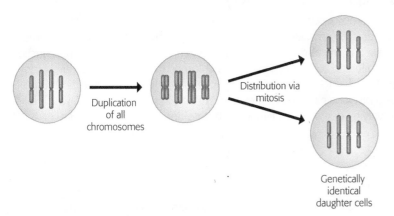

Duplication of all chromosomes

Distribution via mitosis

Genetically identical daughter cells

Some organisms use mitosis (ordinary cell division) to reproduce. This is called asexual reproduction, and it results in offspring that are genetically identical to the lone parent and to each other. Mitosis also enables multicellular organisms to grow and develop and to replace damaged or lost cells. Organisms that reproduce sexually, by the union of a sperm with an egg cell, carry out meiosis, a type of cell division that yields gametes with only half as many chromosomes as body (somatic) cells.

The Cell Cycle and Mitosis

Eukaryotic Chromosomes

The genes of a eukaryotic genome are grouped into multiple chromosomes in the nucleus. Each chromosome contains one very long DNA molecule, with many genes, that is wrapped around histone proteins. Individual chromosomes are coiled up and therefore visible with a light microscope only when the cell is in the process of dividing; otherwise, they are in the form of thin, loosely packed chromatin fibers. Before a cell starts dividing, the chromosomes duplicate, producing sister chromatids (containing identical DNA) joined together at the centromere.

Chromosome (one long piece of DNA)

Centromere

Sister chromatids

Duplicated chromosome

The Cell Cycle

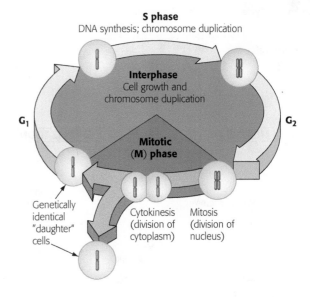

S phase
DNA synthesis; chromosome duplication

Interphase
Cell growth and chromosome duplication

G_1

G_2

Mitotic (M) phase

Genetically identical "daughter" cells

Cytokinesis (division of cytoplasm)

Mitosis (division of nucleus)

Mitosis and Cytokinesis

Mitosis is divided into four phases: prophase, metaphase, anaphase, and telophase. At the start of mitosis, the chromosomes coil up and the nuclear envelope breaks down (prophase). Next, a mitotic spindle made of microtubules moves the chromosomes to the middle of the cell (metaphase). The sister chromatids then separate and are moved to opposite poles of the cell (anaphase), where two new nuclei form (telophase). Cytokinesis overlaps the end of mitosis. In animals, cytokinesis occurs by cleavage, which pinches the cell in two. In plants, a membranous cell plate divides the cell in two. Mitosis and cytokinesis produce genetically identical cells.

Cancer Cells: Growing Out of Control

When the cell cycle control system malfunctions, a cell may divide excessively and form a tumor. Cancer cells may grow to form malignant tumors, invade other tissues (metastasize), and even kill the host. Surgery can remove tumors, and radiation and chemotherapy are effective as treatments because they interfere with cell division. You can increase the likelihood of surviving some forms of cancer through lifestyle changes and regular screenings.

Meiosis, the Basis of Sexual Reproduction

Homologous Chromosomes

The somatic cells (body cells) of each species contain a specific number of chromosomes; human cells have 46, made up of 23 pairs of homologous chromosomes. The chromosomes of a homologous pair carry genes for the same characteristics at the same places. Mammalian males have X and Y sex chromosomes (only partly homologous), while females have two X chromosomes.

Gametes and the Life Cycle of a Sexual Organism

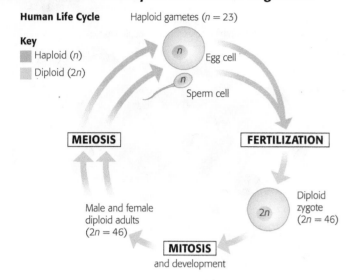

Human Life Cycle

Haploid gametes (*n* = 23)

Key
■ Haploid (*n*)
■ Diploid (2*n*)

n — Egg cell

n — Sperm cell

MEIOSIS

FERTILIZATION

Male and female
diploid adults
(2*n* = 46)

2*n* — Diploid
zygote
(2*n* = 46)

MITOSIS
and development

The Process of Meiosis

Meiosis, like mitosis, is preceded by chromosome duplication. But in meiosis, the cell divides twice to form four daughter cells. The first division, meiosis I, starts with the pairing of homologous chromosomes. In crossing over, homologous chromosomes exchange corresponding segments. Meiosis I separates the members of the homologous pairs and produces two daughter cells, each with one set of (duplicated) chromosomes. Meiosis II is essentially the same as mitosis; in each of the cells, the sister chromatids of each chromosome separate.

Review: Comparing Mitosis and Meiosis

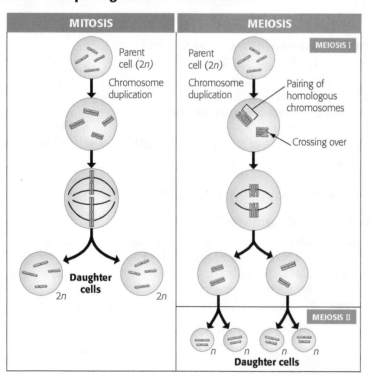

MITOSIS

Parent cell (2*n*)

Chromosome duplication

Daughter cells
2*n*   2*n*

MEIOSIS

MEIOSIS I

Parent cell (2*n*)

Chromosome duplication

Pairing of homologous chromosomes

Crossing over

MEIOSIS II

n   *n*   *n*   *n*

Daughter cells

The Origins of Genetic Variation

Because the chromosomes of a homologous pair come from different parents, they carry different versions of many of their genes. The large number of possible arrangements of chromosome pairs at metaphase of meiosis I leads to many different combinations of chromosomes in eggs and sperm. Random fertilization of eggs by sperm greatly increases the variation. Crossing over during prophase of meiosis I increases variation still further.

When Meiosis Goes Awry

Sometimes a person has an abnormal number of chromosomes, which causes problems. Down syndrome is caused by an extra copy of chromosome 21. The abnormal chromosome count is a product of nondisjunction, the failure of a pair of homologous chromosomes to separate during meiosis I or of sister chromatids to separate during meiosis II. Nondisjunction can also produce gametes with extra or missing sex chromosomes, which lead to varying degrees of malfunction but do not usually affect survival.

SELF-QUIZ

1. Which of the following is not a function of mitosis in humans?
   a. repair of wounds
   b. growth
   c. production of gametes from diploid cells
   d. replacement of lost or damaged cells

2. In what sense are the two daughter cells produced by mitosis identical?

3. Why is it difficult to observe individual chromosomes during interphase?

4. A biochemist measures the amount of DNA in cells growing in the laboratory. The quantity of DNA in a cell would be found to double
   a. between prophase and anaphase of mitosis.
   b. between the G_1 and G_2 phases of the cell cycle.
   c. during the M phase of the cell cycle.
   d. between prophase I and prophase II of meiosis.

5. Which two phases of mitosis are essentially opposites in terms of changes in the nucleus?

6. Complete the following table to compare mitosis and meiosis:

	Mitosis	Meiosis
a. Number of chromosomal duplications		
b. Number of cell divisions		
c. Number of daughter cells produced		
d. Number of chromosomes in daughter cells		
e. How chromosomes line up during metaphase		
f. Genetic relationship of daughter cells to parent cells		
g. Functions performed in the human body		

7. A chemical that disrupts microfilament formation would interfere with
   a. DNA replication.
   b. formation of the mitotic spindle.
   c. cleavage.
   d. crossing over.

8. If an intestinal cell in a dog contains 78 chromosomes, a dog sperm cell would contain _____ chromosomes.

9. A micrograph of a dividing cell from a mouse shows 19 chromosomes, each consisting of two sister chromatids. During which stage of meiosis could this picture have been taken? (Explain your answer.)

10. Tumors that remain at their site of origin are called _____, while tumors from which cells migrate to other body tissues are called _____.

11. A diploid body (somatic) cell from a fruit fly contains eight chromosomes. This means that _____ different combinations of chromosomes are possible in its gametes.

12. Although nondisjunction is a random event, there are many more individuals with an extra chromosome 21, which causes Down syndrome, than individuals with an extra chromosome 3 or chromosome 16. Propose an explanation for this.

Answers to these questions can be found in Appendix: Self-Quiz Answers.

THE PROCESS OF SCIENCE

13. A mule is the offspring of a horse and a donkey. A donkey sperm contains 31 chromosomes and a horse egg 32 chromosomes, so the zygote contains a total of 63 chromosomes. The zygote develops normally. The combined set of chromosomes is not a problem in mitosis, and the mule combines some of the best characteristics of horses and donkeys. However, a mule is sterile; meiosis cannot occur normally in its testes or ovaries. Explain why mitosis is normal in cells containing both horse and donkey chromosomes but the mixed set of chromosomes interferes with meiosis.

14. You prepare a slide with a thin slice of an onion root tip. You see the following view in a light microscope. Identify the stage of mitosis for each of the outlined cells, a–d.

BIOLOGY AND SOCIETY

15. Every year, about a million Americans are diagnosed with cancer. This means that about 75 million Americans now living will eventually have cancer, and one in five will die of the disease. There are many kinds of cancers and many causes of the disease. For example, smoking causes most lung cancers. Overexposure to ultraviolet rays in sunlight causes most skin cancers. There is evidence that a high-fat, low-fiber diet is a factor in breast, colon, and prostate cancers. And agents in the workplace, such as asbestos and vinyl chloride, are also implicated as causes of cancer. Hundreds of millions of dollars are spent each year in the search for effective treatments for cancer, yet far less money is spent on preventing cancer. Why might this be true? What kinds of lifestyle changes can you make to help reduce your risk of cancer? What kinds of prevention programs could be initiated or strengthened to encourage these changes? What factors might impede such changes and programs? Should we devote more of our resources to treating cancer or to preventing it? Defend your position.

16. The practice of buying and selling gametes, particularly eggs from fertile women, is becoming increasingly common in the United States and some other industrialized countries. Do you have any objections to this type of transaction? Would you be willing to sell your gametes? At any price? Whether you are willing to do so or not, do you think that other people should be restricted from doing so?

9 Patterns of Inheritance

Canine genetics.
Dogs, such as these
Labrador retrievers, are
one of humankind's
longest running genetic
experiments.

Dog Breeding BIOLOGY AND SOCIETY

Our Longest-Running Genetic Experiment: Dogs

All of the cute canines shown in the photo on the left are purebred Labrador retrievers. If you were to mate two purebred Labs, you'd expect offspring that look much like these, displaying the traits that distinguish this breed—like a short, water-resistant coat and gentle eyes. This is a reasonable expectation because each purebred dog has a well-documented pedigree that includes several generations of ancestors with similar genetic makeup and appearance. But similarities among purebred Labs extend beyond mere appearance; Labradors are generally sweet tempered, playful, intelligent, and docile—traits that make these dogs the most popular breed in the U.S. and Canada. Such behavioral similarities suggest that dog breeders can select for personality as well as physical traits.

Purebred pooches are living proof that dogs are more than man's best friend: They are also one of our longest-running genetic experiments. Evidence (which we'll explore at the end of this chapter) suggests that people have selected and mated dogs with preferred traits for more than 15,000 years. Nearly every modern Lab, for example, can trace its ancestry back to a single breeding pair—named Avon and Ned—that were raised by the Duke of Buccleuch in England in the 1880s. These original dogs were chosen for their superb ability to retrieve objects from the water, a trait that is very useful to hunters of waterfowl. Similar choices were made for every modern dog breed. Over thousands of years, such genetic tinkering has led to the incredible variety of body types and behaviors we have today, from huge, docile Great Danes to tiny, spunky Chihuahuas.

Although people have been applying genetics for thousands of years—by breeding food crops (such as wheat, rice, and corn) as well as domesticated animals (such as cows, sheep, and goats)—the biological principles underlying genetics have only recently been understood. In this chapter, you will learn the basic rules of how genetic traits are passed from generation to generation and how the behavior of chromosomes (the topic of Chapter 8) accounts for these rules. In the process, you will learn how to predict the ratios of offspring with particular traits. At several points in the chapter, we'll return to the subject of dog breeding to help illustrate genetic principles.

Heritable Variation and Patterns of Inheritance

Heredity is the transmission of traits from one generation to the next. **Genetics**, the scientific study of heredity, began in the 1860s, when an Augustinian monk named Gregor Mendel **(Figure 9.1)** deduced its fundamental principles by breeding garden peas. Mendel lived and worked in an abbey in Brunn, Austria (now Brno, in the Czech Republic). Strongly influenced by his study of physics, mathematics, and chemistry at the University of Vienna, his research was both experimentally and mathematically rigorous, and these qualities were largely responsible for his success.

In a paper published in 1866, Mendel correctly argued that parents pass on to their offspring discrete "heritable factors" that are responsible for inherited traits, such as purple flowers or round seeds in pea plants. (It is interesting to note that Mendel's publication came just seven years after Darwin's 1859 publication of *On the Origin of Species*, making the 1860s a banner decade in the development of modern biology.) In his paper, Mendel stressed that the heritable factors (today called genes) retain their individual identities generation after generation, no matter how they are mixed up or temporarily masked.

▲ Figure 9.1
Gregor Mendel.

reach the carpel. When he wanted cross-fertilization (fertilization of one plant by pollen from a different plant), he pollinated the plants by hand, as shown in **Figure 9.3.** Thus, whether Mendel let a pea plant self-fertilize or cross-fertilized it with a known source of pollen, he could always be sure of the parentage of his new plants.

Each of the characters Mendel chose to study, such as flower color, occurred in two distinct traits. Mendel worked with his plants until he was sure he had purebred varieties—that is, varieties for which self-fertilization produced offspring all identical to the parent. For instance, he identified a purple-flowered

In an Abbey Garden

Mendel probably chose to study garden peas because they were easy to grow and they came in many readily distinguishable varieties. For example, one variety has purple flowers and another variety has white flowers. A heritable feature that varies among individuals, such as flower color, is called a **character**. Each variant of a character, such as purple or white flowers, is called a **trait**.

Perhaps the most important advantage of pea plants as an experimental model was that Mendel could strictly control their reproduction. The petals of a pea flower **(Figure 9.2)** almost completely enclose the egg-producing part (the carpel) and the sperm-producing parts (the stamens). Consequently, in nature, pea plants usually self-fertilize because sperm-carrying pollen grains released from the stamens land on the tip of the egg-containing carpel of the same flower. Mendel could ensure self-fertilization by covering a flower with a small bag so that no pollen from another plant could

▼ Figure 9.2 **The structure of a pea flower.** To reveal the reproductive organs—the stamens and carpel—one of the petals has been removed in this drawing.

Petal

Stamen (makes sperm-producing pollen)

Carpel (produces eggs)

▼ Figure 9.3 **Mendel's technique for cross-fertilizing pea plants.**

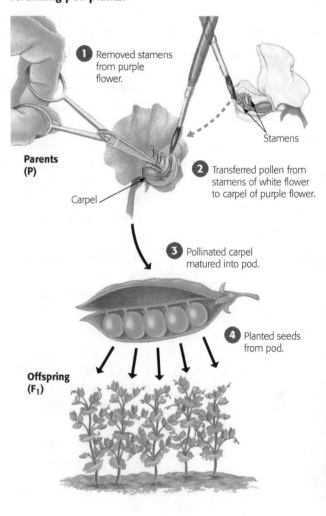

1 Removed stamens from purple flower.

Stamens

Parents (P)

Carpel

2 Transferred pollen from stamens of white flower to carpel of purple flower.

3 Pollinated carpel matured into pod.

4 Planted seeds from pod.

Offspring (F₁)

variety that, when self-fertilized, always produced off-spring plants that had all purple flowers.

Next Mendel was ready to ask what would happen when he crossed different purebred varieties with each other. For example, what offspring would result if plants with purple flowers and plants with white flowers were cross-fertilized as shown in Figure 9.3? The offspring of two different purebred varieties are called **hybrids**, and the cross-fertilization itself is referred to as a genetic **cross**. The parental plants are called the **P generation**, and their hybrid offspring are the **F₁ generation** (F for *filial*, from the Latin for "son" or "daughter"). When F₁ plants self-fertilize or fertilize each other, their offspring are the **F₂ generation**. ☑

Mendel's Law of Segregation

Mendel performed many experiments in which he tracked the inheritance of characters, such as flower color, that occur as two alternative traits (Figure 9.4). The results led him to formulate several hypotheses about inheritance. Let's look at some of his experiments and follow the reasoning that led to his hypotheses.

▼ Figure 9.4 **The seven characters of pea plants studied by Mendel.** Each character comes in the two alternative traits shown here.

	Dominant	Recessive
Flower color	Purple	White
Flower position	Axial	Terminal
Seed color	Yellow	Green
Seed shape	Round	Wrinkled
Pod shape	Inflated	Constricted
Pod color	Green	Yellow
Stem length	Tall	Dwarf

☑ **CHECKPOINT**

Why was the development of purebred pea plant varieties critical to Mendel's work?

Answer: Purebred varieties allowed Mendel to predict the outcome of specific crosses and therefore to run controlled experiments.

Monohybrid Crosses

Figure 9.5 shows a cross between a purebred pea plant with purple flowers and a purebred pea plant with white flowers. This is called a **monohybrid cross** because the parent plants differ in only one character—flower color. Mendel saw that the F_1 plants all had purple flowers. Was the heritable factor for white flowers now lost as a result of the cross? By mating the F_1 plants with each other, Mendel found the answer to be no. Of the 929 F_2 plants, about three-fourths (705) had purple flowers and one-fourth (224) had white flowers; that is, there were about three purple F_2 plants for every white plant, or a 3:1 ratio of purple to white. Mendel figured out that the heritable factor for white flowers did not disappear in the F_1 plants, but was somehow hidden or masked when the purple-flower factor was present. He also deduced that the F_1 plants must have carried two factors for the flower-color character, one for purple and one for white. From these results and others, Mendel developed four hypotheses, listed here using modern terminology (including "gene" instead of "heritable factor"):

1. *There are alternative versions of genes that account for variations in inherited characters.* For example, the gene for flower color in pea plants exists in one form for purple and another for white. The alternative versions of a gene are called **alleles**.

2. *For each inherited character, an organism inherits two alleles, one from each parent.* These alleles may be the same or different. An organism that has two identical alleles for a gene is said to be **homozygous** for that gene (and is called a homozygote). An organism that has two different alleles for a gene is said to be **heterozygous** for that gene (and is called a heterozygote).

3. *If the two alleles of an inherited pair differ, then one determines the organism's appearance and is called the* **dominant allele**; *the other has no noticeable effect on the organism's appearance and is called the* **recessive allele**. Geneticists use uppercase italic letters to represent dominant alleles and lowercase italic letters to represent recessive alleles.

4. *A sperm or egg carries only one allele for each inherited character because the two alleles for a character segregate (separate) from each other during the production of gametes.* This statement is called the **law of segregation**. When sperm and egg unite at fertilization, each contributes its alleles, restoring the paired condition in the offspring.

Do Mendel's hypotheses account for the 3:1 ratio he observed in the F_2 generation? **Figure 9.6** illustrates Mendel's law of segregation, which explains the inheritance pattern shown in Figure 9.5. His hypotheses predict that when alleles segregate during gamete formation in the F_1 plants, half the gametes will receive a purple-flower allele (P) and the other half a white-flower allele (p). During pollination among the F_1 plants, the gametes unite randomly. An egg with a purple-flower allele has an equal chance of being fertilized by a sperm with a purple-flower allele or one with a white-flower allele (that is, a P egg may fuse with a P sperm or a p sperm). Because the same is true for an egg with a white-flower allele (a p egg with a P sperm or p sperm), there are a total of four equally likely combinations of sperm and egg.

The diagram at the bottom of Figure 9.6, called a **Punnett square**, repeats the cross shown in Figure 9.5 in a way that highlights the four possible combinations of gametes and the resulting four possible offspring in the F_2 generation. Each square represents an equally probable product of fertilization. For example, the box in the upper right corner of the Punnett square shows the genetic combination resulting from a p sperm fertilizing a P egg.

According to the Punnett square, what will be the physical appearance of these F_2 offspring? One-fourth of the plants have two alleles specifying purple flowers (PP); clearly, these plants will have purple flowers. One-half (two-fourths) of the F_2 offspring have

▼ **Figure 9.5 Mendel's cross tracking one character (flower color).** Note the 3:1 ratio of purple flowers to white flowers in the F_2 generation.

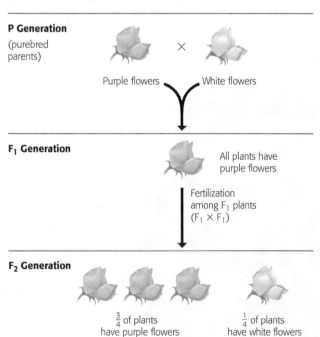

P Generation
(purebred parents)

Purple flowers × White flowers

F₁ Generation

All plants have purple flowers

Fertilization among F₁ plants
($F_1 \times F_1$)

F₂ Generation

$\frac{3}{4}$ of plants have purple flowers

$\frac{1}{4}$ of plants have white flowers

▼ Figure 9.6 **The law of segregation.**

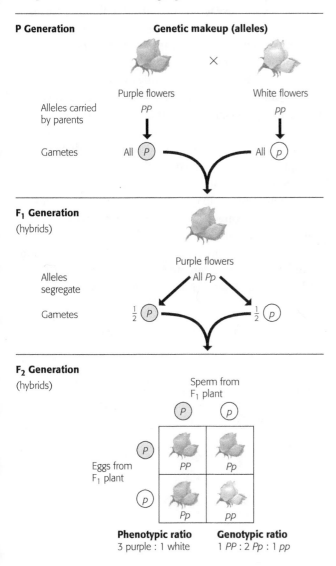

P Generation

Genetic makeup (alleles)

Purple flowers
PP

White flowers
pp

Alleles carried
by parents

Gametes   All ⓟ (P)   All ⓟ (p)

F₁ Generation
(hybrids)

Purple flowers

Alleles
segregate   All *Pp*

Gametes   ½ (P)   ½ (p)

F₂ Generation
(hybrids)

Sperm from
F₁ plant

Eggs from
F₁ plant

Phenotypic ratio | Genotypic ratio
3 purple : 1 white | 1 *PP* : 2 *Pp* : 1 *pp*

Mendel found that each of the seven characters he studied had the same inheritance pattern: A parental trait disappeared in the F₁ generation, only to reappear in one-fourth of the F₂ offspring. The underlying mechanism is stated by Mendel's law of segregation: Pairs of alleles segregate (separate) during gamete formation; the fusion of gametes at fertilization creates allele pairs again. Research since Mendel's day has established that the law of segregation applies to all sexually reproducing organisms, including dogs and people.

Genetic Alleles and Homologous Chromosomes

Before continuing with Mendel's experiments, let's see how some of the concepts we discussed earlier (in Chapter 8) fit with what we've said about genetics so far. The diagram in **Figure 9.7** shows a pair of homologous chromosomes—chromosomes that carry alleles of the same genes. Recall that every diploid cell, whether from a pea plant or a person, has pairs of homologous chromosomes. One member of each pair comes from the organism's female parent and the other member of each pair comes from the male parent. Each labeled band on the chromosomes in the figure represents a gene **locus** (plural, *loci*), a specific location of a gene along the chromosome. You can see the connection between Mendel's law of segregation and homologous chromosomes: Alleles (alternative versions) of a gene reside at the same locus on homologous chromosomes. However, the two chromosomes may bear either identical alleles or different ones at any one locus. In other words, the organisms may be homozygous or heterozygous for the gene at that locus. We will return to the chromosomal basis of Mendel's law later in the chapter. ✓

✓ CHECKPOINT

1. Genes come in different versions called _____. What term describes the condition where the two copies are identical? What term describes the condition where the two copies are different?
2. If two plants have the same genotype, must they have the same phenotype? If two plants have the same phenotype, must they have the same genotype?
3. You carry two alleles for every trait. Where did these alleles come from?

Answers: 1. alleles; homozygous; heterozygous 2. Yes. No, one could be homozygous for the dominant allele, while the other is heterozygous. 3. One is from your father via his sperm and one is from your mother via her egg.

inherited one allele for purple flowers and one allele for white flowers (*Pp*); like the F₁ plants, these plants will also have purple flowers, the dominant trait. (Note that *Pp* and *pP* are equivalent and usually written as *Pp*.) Finally, one-fourth of the F₂ plants have inherited two alleles specifying white flowers (*pp*) and will express this recessive trait. Thus, Mendel's model accounts for the 3:1 ratio that he observed in the F₂ generation.

Geneticists distinguish between an organism's physical appearance, called its **phenotype** (such as purple or white flowers), and its genetic makeup, called its **genotype** (in our example, *PP*, *Pp*, or *pp*). Now we can see that Figure 9.5 shows only the phenotypes and Figure 9.6 both the genotypes and phenotypes in our sample cross. For the F₂ plants, the ratio of plants with purple flowers to those with white flowers (3:1) is called the phenotypic ratio. The genotypic ratio is 1(*PP*):2(*Pp*):1(*pp*).

▼ Figure 9.7 **The relationship between alleles and homologous chromosomes.** The matching colors of corresponding loci highlight the fact that homologous chromosomes carry alleles for the same genes at the same positions along their lengths.

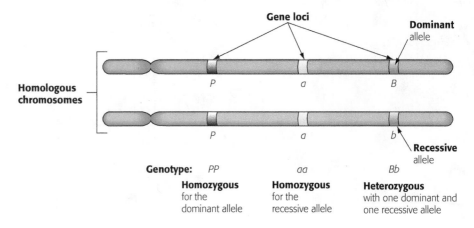

Gene loci

Dominant
allele

Homologous
chromosomes

P   *a*   *B*

P   *a*   *b*

Recessive
allele

Genotype: *PP*   *aa*   *Bb*

Homozygous
for the
dominant allele

Homozygous
for the
recessive allele

Heterozygous
with one dominant and
one recessive allele

Mendel's Law of Independent Assortment

Two other pea plant characters Mendel studied were seed shape and seed color. Mendel's seeds were either round or wrinkled in shape and either yellow or green in color. From tracking these characters one at a time in monohybrid crosses, Mendel knew that the allele for round shape (designated R) was dominant to the allele for wrinkled shape (r) and that the allele for yellow seed color (Y) was dominant to the allele for green seed color (y). What would result from a **dihybrid cross**, the mating of parental varieties differing in two characters? Mendel crossed homozygous plants having round-yellow seeds (genotype $RRYY$) with plants having wrinkled-green seeds ($rryy$). As shown in **Figure 9.8**, the union of RY and ry gametes from the P generation yielded

hybrids heterozygous for both characters ($RrYy$)—that is, dihybrids. As we would expect, all of these offspring, the F_1 generation, had round-yellow seeds (the two dominant traits). But were the two characters transmitted from parents to offspring as a package, or was each character inherited independently of the other?

The question was answered when Mendel allowed fertilization to occur among the F_1 plants. If the genes for the two characters were inherited together (Figure 9.8a), then the F_1 hybrids would produce only the same two kinds of gametes that they received from their parents. In that case, the F_2 generation would show a 3:1 phenotypic ratio (three plants with round-yellow seeds for every one with wrinkled-green seeds), as in the Punnett square in Figure 9.8a. If, however, the two seed characters sorted independently, then the F_1 generation would produce four gamete genotypes—RY, rY, Ry, and ry—in equal quantities. The Punnett square in

▼ **Figure 9.8 Testing alternative hypotheses for gene assortment in a dihybrid cross.**

(a) Hypothesis: Dependent assortment
Leads to prediction that F_2 plants will have seeds that match the parents, either round-yellow or wrinkled-green

(b) Hypothesis: Independent assortment
Leads to prediction that F_2 plants will have four different seed phenotypes

Predicted results
(not actually seen)

Actual results
(support hypothesis)

$\frac{9}{16}$ Yellow round

$\frac{3}{16}$ Green round

$\frac{3}{16}$ Yellow wrinkled

$\frac{1}{16}$ Green wrinkled

Figure 9.8b shows all possible combinations of alleles that can result in the F$_2$ generation from the union of four kinds of sperm with four kinds of eggs. If you study the Punnett square, you'll see that it predicts nine different genotypes in the F$_2$ generation. These nine genotypes will produce four different phenotypes in a ratio of 9:3:3:1.

The Punnett square in Figure 9.8b also reveals that a dihybrid cross is equivalent to two monohybrid crosses occurring simultaneously. From the 9:3:3:1 ratio, we can see that there are 12 plants with round seeds compared to 4 with wrinkled seeds, and 12 yellow-seeded plants compared to four green-seeded ones. These 12:4 ratios each reduce to 3:1, which is the F$_2$ ratio for a monohybrid cross. Mendel tried his seven pea characters in various dihybrid combinations and always observed a 9:3:3:1 ratio (or two simultaneous 3:1 ratios) of phenotypes in the F$_2$ generation. These results supported the hypothesis that *each pair of alleles segregates independently of the other pairs of alleles during gamete formation*. In other words, the inheritance of one

Why are there fewer chocolate Labs than black Labs?

character has no effect on the inheritance of another. This is called Mendel's **law of independent assortment**.

For another application of the law of independent assortment, examine **Figure 9.9**. The inheritance of two hereditary characters in Labrador retrievers is controlled by separate genes: black versus chocolate coat color, and normal vision versus the eye disorder progressive retinal atrophy (PRA). Black Labs have at least one copy of an allele called *B*, which gives their hairs densely packed granules of a dark pigment. The *B* allele is dominant to *b*, which leads to a less tightly packed distribution of pigment granules. As a result, the coats of dogs with genotype *bb* are chocolate in color. The allele that causes PRA, called *n*, is recessive to allele *N*, which is necessary for normal vision. Thus, only dogs of genotype *nn* become blind from PRA. If you mate two doubly heterozygous (*BbNn*) Labs (bottom of Figure 9.9), the phenotypic ratio of the offspring (F$_2$) is 9:3:3:1. These results resemble the F$_2$ results in Figure 9.8, demonstrating that the coat color and PRA genes are inherited independently. ☑

☑ CHECKPOINT

Looking at the Punnett square in Figure 9.9, what is the ratio of black coat to chocolate coat in Labs? Of normal vision to blindness?

Answer: 3:1; 3:1

▼ **Figure 9.9 Independent assortment of genes in Labrador retrievers.**
Blanks in the genotypes indicate alleles that can be either dominant or recessive.

Blind dog   Blind dog

Phenotypes	Black coat, normal vision	Black coat, blind (PRA)	Chocolate coat, normal vision	Chocolate coat, blind (PRA)
Genotypes	*B_N_*	*B_nn*	*bbN_*	*bbnn*

(a) Possible phenotypes of Labrador retrievers

Mating of double heterozygotes
(black coat, normal vision)
BbNn —— X —— *BbNn*

Blind   Blind

Phenotypic ratio of offspring	9 black coat, normal vision	3 black coat, blind (PRA)	3 chocolate coat, normal vision	1 chocolate coat, blind (PRA)

(b) A Labrador dihybrid cross

Using a Testcross to Determine an Unknown Genotype

Suppose you have a Labrador retriever with a chocolate coat. Consulting Figure 9.9, you can tell that its genotype must be *bb*, the only combination of alleles that produces the chocolate-coat phenotype. But what if you have a black Lab? It could have one of two possible genotypes—*BB* or *Bb*—and there is no way to tell which genotype is the correct one by looking at the dog. To determine your dog's genotype, you could perform a **testcross**, a mating between an individual of dominant phenotype but unknown genotype (your black Lab) and a homozygous recessive individual—in this case, a *bb* chocolate Lab.

Figure 9.10 shows the offspring that could result from such a mating. If, as shown on the left, the black Lab parent's genotype is *BB*, we would expect all the offspring to be black, because a cross between genotypes *BB* and *bb* can produce only *Bb* offspring. On the other hand, if the black Lab parent is *Bb*, we would expect both black (*Bb*) and chocolate (*bb*) offspring. Thus, the appearance of the offspring may reveal the original black dog's genotype. ☑

The Rules of Probability

Mendel's strong background in mathematics served him well in his studies of inheritance. For instance, he understood that genetic crosses obey the rules of probability—the same rules that apply to the tossing of coins, the rolling of dice, and the drawing of cards. An important lesson we can learn from coin tossing is that for each and every toss of the coin, the probability of heads is $\frac{1}{2}$. Even if heads has landed five times in a row, the probability of the next toss coming up heads is still $\frac{1}{2}$. In other words, the outcome of any particular toss is unaffected by what has happened on previous attempts. Each toss is an independent event.

If two coins are tossed simultaneously, the outcome for each coin is an independent event, unaffected by the other coin. What is the chance that both coins will land heads-up? The probability of such a dual event is the product of the separate probabilities of the independent events—for the coins, $\frac{1}{2} \times \frac{1}{2} = \frac{1}{4}$. This is called the **rule of multiplication**, and it holds true for independent events that occur in genetics as well as coin tosses, as shown in Figure 9.11. In our dihybrid cross of Labradors (see

▼ Figure 9.11 **Segregation of alleles and fertilization as chance events.** When heterozygotes (*Bb*) form gametes, segregation of alleles during sperm and egg formation is like two separately tossed coins (that is, two independent events).

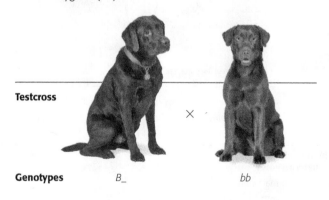

▼ Figure 9.10 **A Labrador retriever testcross.** To determine the genotype of a black Lab, it can be crossed with a chocolate Lab (homozygous recessive, *bb*). If all the offspring are black, the black parent most likely had genotype *BB*. If half the offspring are chocolate, the black parent must be heterozygous (*Bb*).

☑ CHECKPOINT

If you mate a chocolate Lab with a black Lab of unknown genotype and you end up with a litter of three black puppies, do you know for certain the genotype of the black parent?

Answer: No. It could be BB and would always produce black puppies or Bb and just happened to have three black puppies in a row. Producing more puppies would increase confidence in the result.

Figure 9.9), the genotype of the F$_1$ dogs for coat color was *Bb*. What is the probability that a particular F$_2$ dog will have the *bb* genotype? To produce a *bb* offspring, both egg and sperm must carry the *b* allele. The probability that an egg from a *Bb* dog will have the *b* allele is $\frac{1}{2}$, and the probability that a sperm will have the *b* allele is also $\frac{1}{2}$. By the rule of multiplication, the probability that two *b* alleles will come together at fertilization is $\frac{1}{2} \times \frac{1}{2} = \frac{1}{4}$. This is exactly the answer given by the Punnett square in Figure 9.11. If we know the genotypes of the parents, we can predict the probability for any genotype among the offspring. By applying the rules of probability to segregation and independent assortment, we can solve some rather complex genetics problems. ☑

Family Pedigrees

Mendel's laws apply to the inheritance of many human traits. **Figure 9.12** illustrates alternative forms of three human characters that are each thought to be determined by simple dominant-recessive inheritance of one gene. (The genetic basis of many other human characters—such as eye and hair color—are much more complex and poorly understood.) If we call the dominant allele of any such gene *A*, the dominant phenotype results from either the homozygous genotype *AA* or the heterozygous genotype *Aa*. Recessive phenotypes result only from the homozygous genotype *aa*. In genetics, the word *dominant* does not imply that a phenotype is either normal or more common than a recessive phenotype; **wild-type traits** (those seen most often in nature) are not necessarily specified by dominant alleles. In genetics, dominance means that a heterozygote (*Aa*), carrying only a single copy of a dominant allele, displays the dominant phenotype. By contrast, the phenotype of the corresponding recessive allele is seen only in a homozygote (*aa*). Recessive traits may in fact be more common in the population than dominant ones. For example, the absence of freckles is more common than their presence.

How can human genetics be studied? Researchers working with pea plants or Labrador retrievers can perform testcrosses. But geneticists who study people obviously cannot control the mating of their research participants. Instead, they must analyze the results of matings that have already occurred. First, the geneticist collects as much information as possible about a family's history for a trait. Then the researcher assembles this information into a family tree, called a **pedigree**. (You may associate pedigrees with purebred animals such as racehorses and champion dogs, but they

Is your earlobe trait dominant or recessive?

☑ **CHECKPOINT**
Using a standard 52-card deck, what is the probability of being dealt an ace? What about being dealt an ace or a king? What about being dealt an ace and then another ace?

Answer: $\frac{1}{13}$ (4 aces / 52 cards); $\frac{2}{13}$ ($\frac{4}{52} + \frac{4}{52}$); $\frac{3}{52} \times \frac{3}{51}$ (since there are 3 aces left in a deck with 51 cards remaining) = 0.0045, or $\frac{1}{221}$

◄ **Figure 9.12 Examples of inherited human traits thought to be controlled by a single gene.**

DOMINANT TRAITS

Freckles

Widow's peak

Free earlobe

RECESSIVE TRAITS

No freckles

Straight hairline

Attached earlobe

153

can represent human matings just as well.) To analyze a pedigree, the geneticist applies logic and Mendel's laws.

Let's apply this approach to the example in **Figure 9.13**, a pedigree tracing the incidence of free versus attached earlobes. The letter *F* stands for the dominant allele for free earlobes, and *f* symbolizes the recessive allele for attached earlobes. In the pedigree, □ represents a male, ○ represents a female, colored symbols (■ and ●) indicate that the person has the trait being investigated (in this case, attached earlobes), and an unshaded symbol represents a person who does not have the trait (that person has free earlobes). The earliest (oldest) generation is at the top of the pedigree, and the most recent generation is at the bottom.

By applying Mendel's laws, we can deduce that the attached allele is recessive because that is the only way that Kevin can have attached earlobes when neither of his parents (Hal and Ina) do. We can therefore label all the individuals with attached earlobes in the pedigree (that is, all those with colored circles or squares) as homozygous recessive (*ff*).

Mendel's laws enable us to deduce the genotypes for most of the people in the pedigree. For example, Hal and Ina must have carried the *f* allele (which they passed on to Kevin) along with the *F* allele that gave them free earlobes. The same must be true of Aaron and Betty because they both have free earlobes but Fred and Gabe have attached earlobes. For each of these cases, Mendel's laws and simple logic allow us to definitively assign a genotype.

Notice that we cannot deduce the genotype of every member of the pedigree. For example, Lisa must have at least one *F* allele, but she could be *FF* or *Ff*. We cannot distinguish between these two possibilities using the available data. Perhaps future generations will provide the data that solves this mystery. ☑

Human Disorders Controlled by a Single Gene

The human genetic disorders listed in **Table 9.1** are known to be inherited as dominant or recessive traits controlled by a single gene. These disorders therefore show simple inheritance patterns like the ones Mendel studied in pea plants. The genes involved are all located on autosomes, chromosomes other than the sex chromosomes X and Y.

Recessive Disorders

Most human genetic disorders are recessive. They range in severity from harmless to life-threatening. Most people who have recessive disorders are born to normal parents who are both heterozygotes—that is, parents who are **carriers** of the recessive allele for the disorder but appear normal themselves.

Using Mendel's laws, we can predict the fraction of affected offspring that is likely to result from a marriage between two carriers. Consider a form of inherited deafness caused by a recessive allele. Suppose two heterozygous carriers (*Dd*) have a child. What is the probability that the child will be deaf? As the Punnett square in

☑ **CHECKPOINT**

What is a wild-type trait?

Answer: a trait that is the prevailing one in nature

▼ Figure 9.13 **A family pedigree showing inheritance of free versus attached earlobes.**

First generation (grandparents)	Aaron *Ff* — Betty *Ff*	Cletus *ff* — Debra *Ff*
Second generation (parents, aunts, and uncles)	Evelyn *FF* or *Ff* Fred *ff* Gabe *ff* Hal *Ff*	Ina *Ff* Jill *ff*
Third generation (brother and sister)	Kevin *ff*	Lisa *FF* or *Ff*

Female   **Male**
○   ■ Attached
○   □ Free

Table 9.1	Some Autosomal Disorders in People	
Disorder	**Major Symptoms**	**Incidence**
Recessive Disorders		
Albinism	Lack of pigment in skin, hair, and eyes	$\frac{1}{22,000}$
Cystic fibrosis	Excess mucus in lungs, digestive tract, liver; increased susceptibility to infections; death in early childhood unless treated	$\frac{1}{1,800}$ European Americans
Phenylketonuria (PKU)	Accumulation of phenylalanine in blood; lack of normal skin pigment; mental retardation unless treated	$\frac{1}{100,000}$ in U.S. and Europe
Sickle-cell disease	Sickled red blood cells; damage to many tissues	$\frac{1}{500}$ African Americans
Tay Sachs disease	Lipid accumulation in brain cells; mental deficiency; blindness; death in childhood	$\frac{1}{3,500}$ European Jews
Dominant Disorders		
Achondroplasia	Dwarfism	$\frac{1}{25,000}$
Alzheimer's disease (one type)	Mental deterioration; usually strikes late in life	Not known
Huntington's disease	Mental deterioration and uncontrollable movements; strikes in middle age	$\frac{1}{25,000}$
Hypercholesterolemia	Excess cholesterol in blood; heart disease	$\frac{1}{500}$

Figure 9.14 shows, each child of two carriers has a $\frac{1}{4}$ chance of inheriting two recessive alleles. Thus, we can say that about one-fourth of the children of this couple are likely to be deaf. We can also say that a hearing child from such a family has a $\frac{2}{3}$ chance of being a carrier (that is, on average, two out of three of the offspring with the hearing phenotype will be *Dd*). We can apply this same method of pedigree analysis and prediction to any genetic trait controlled by a single gene.

The most common lethal genetic disease in the United States is **cystic fibrosis (CF)**. Affecting about 30,000 Americans and about 70,000 people worldwide, the recessive CF allele is carried by about 1 in 31

▼ **Figure 9.14 Predicted offspring when both parents are carriers for a recessive disorder.**

Americans. A person with two copies of this allele has cystic fibrosis, which is characterized by an excessive secretion of very thick mucus from the lungs, pancreas, and other organs. This mucus can interfere with breathing, digestion, and liver function and makes the person vulnerable to recurrent bacterial infections. Although there is no cure for this fatal disease, a special diet, antibiotics to prevent infection, frequent pounding of the chest and back to clear the lungs, and other treatments can greatly extend life. Once invariably fatal in childhood, advances in CF treatment have raised the median survival age of Americans with CF to 37.

Like cystic fibrosis, most genetic disorders are not evenly distributed across all ethnic groups. Such uneven distribution is the result of prolonged geographic isolation of certain populations. For example, the isolated lives of the early inhabitants of Martha's Vineyard (an island off the coast of Massachusetts) led to frequent marriages between blood relatives. Consequently, the frequency of an allele that caused deafness was high, and the deafness allele was rarely transmitted to outsiders.

With the increased mobility in most societies today, it is relatively unlikely that two carriers of a rare, harmful allele will meet and mate. However, the probability increases greatly if close blood relatives marry and have children. People with recent common ancestors are more likely to carry the same recessive alleles than are unrelated people. Therefore, a mating between close blood relatives, called **inbreeding**, is more likely to produce offspring homozygous for a harmful recessive trait.

Genetically speaking, why is it a bad idea to marry your first cousin?

155

Geneticists have observed an increased incidence of harmful recessive traits among many types of inbred animals. Most lines of purebred dogs have known genetic defects. The Labrador retrievers discussed in the Biology and Society section, for example, are susceptible to hip dysplasia as well as blindness. The detrimental effects of inbreeding are also seen in some endangered species, such as cheetahs (see Chapter 13).

Dominant Disorders

A number of human disorders are caused by dominant alleles. Some are harmless, such as extra fingers and toes or digits that are webbed. A serious but nonlethal disorder caused by a dominant allele is **achondroplasia**, a form of dwarfism in which the head and torso develop normally but the arms and legs are short (Figure 9.15). The homozygous dominant genotype (*AA*) causes death of the embryo, and therefore only heterozygotes (*Aa*), individuals with a single copy of the defective allele, have this disorder. This also means that a person with achondroplasia has a 50% chance of passing the condition on to any children (Figure 9.16). Therefore, all those who do not have achondroplasia, more than 99.99% of the population, are homozygous for the recessive allele (*aa*). This example makes it clear that a dominant allele is not necessarily more common in a population than the corresponding recessive allele.

Dominant alleles that cause lethal disorders are much less common than lethal recessive alleles. One example is the allele that causes **Huntington's disease**, a degeneration of the nervous system that usually does not begin until middle age. Once the deterioration of the nervous system begins, it is irreversible and inevitably fatal. Because the allele for Huntington's disease is dominant, any child born to a parent with the allele has a 50% chance of inheriting the allele and the disorder. This example makes it clear that a dominant allele is not necessarily "better" than the corresponding recessive allele.

One way that geneticists study human traits is to find similar genes in animals, which can then be studied in greater detail through controlled matings and other experiments. Let's return to the chapter thread—dog breeding—to investigate the furry coats of man's best friend.

▼ **Figure 9.15**
Achondroplasia, a dominant trait.
Dr. Michael C. Ain, a pediatric orthopedic surgeon at the Johns Hopkins Children's Center, specializes in the repair of bone defects caused by achondroplasia and related disorders.

▼ **Figure 9.16 A family with and without achondroplasia.** Amy Roloff (who has achondroplasia) and her husband Matt (who has an unrelated form of dwarfism) have four children. Zachary received Amy's achondroplasia allele while twin brother Jeremy, sister Molly Jo, and brother Jacob did not. The hypothetical Punnett square shows the offspring expected from a mating of a wild-type male with a dwarf female.

Parents

Normal (no achondroplasia) × Dwarf (achondroplasia)
dd   *Dd*

	Sperm *d*	*d*
D	*Dd* Dwarf	*Dd* Dwarf
d	*dd* Normal	*dd* Normal

Eggs

Dog Breeding THE PROCESS OF SCIENCE

What Is the Genetic Basis of Coat Variation in Dogs?

You've probably made the **observation** that compared with most mammals, dogs come in a wide variety of physical types. For instance, dog coats can be short or long, straight or curly or wire-haired (having a "moustache" and "eyebrows"). Sometimes a single breed, such as the fox terrier, may display two or more of these variations (**Figure 9.17**).

In 2005, the complete genome of a dog—the sequence of all the DNA of a female boxer named Tasha—was published. Since that time, canine geneticists have added a wealth of data from other breeds. In 2009, an international group of researchers set out to investigate the **question** of the genetic basis for canine coats. They proposed the **hypothesis** that a comparison of genes from a wide variety of dogs with different coats would identify the genes responsible. They made the **prediction** that mutations in just a few genes could account for the coat appearance. Their **experiment** compared DNA sequences in 622 dogs from dozens of breeds. Their **results** identified three genes that in different combinations produced seven different coat appearances, from

◀ Figure 9.17 **Smooth versus wired fox terrier.** The fox terrier, like several other breeds, comes in smooth (left) and wired (right) coats.

very short hair to full, thick, wired hair. The difference between the two dogs in the photo, for example, is due to a change in a single gene that regulates keratin, a protein that is one of the primary structural components of hair.

This experiment shows how the extreme range of phenotypes in dogs combined with the availability of genome sequences can be used to provide insight into interesting genetic questions. Indeed, similar research has uncovered the genetic basis of other dog traits, such as body size, hairlessness, and coat color.

Genetic Testing

Until relatively recently, the onset of symptoms was the only way to know if a person had inherited an allele that might lead to disease. Today, there are many tests that can detect the presence of disease-causing alleles in an individual's genome.

Most genetic tests are performed during pregnancy if the prospective parents are aware that they have an increased risk of having a baby with a genetic disease. Genetic testing before birth usually requires the collection of fetal cells. In amniocentesis, a physician uses a needle to extract about 2 teaspoonfuls of the fluid that bathes the developing fetus. In chorionic villus sampling, a physician inserts a narrow, flexible tube through the mother's vagina and into her uterus, removing some placental tissue. Once cells are obtained, they can be screened for genetic diseases.

Because amniocentesis and chorionic villus sampling have risks of complications, these techniques are usually reserved for situations in which the possibility of a genetic disease is significantly higher than average.

Newer genetic screening procedures involve isolating tiny amounts of fetal cells or DNA released into the mother's bloodstream. Although few reliable tests are yet available using this method, this promising and complication-free technology may soon replace more invasive procedures.

As genetic testing becomes more routine, geneticists are working to make sure that the tests do not cause more problems than they solve. Geneticists stress that patients seeking genetic testing should receive counseling both before and after to explain the test and to help them cope with the results. If fetal tests reveal a serious disorder, the parents must choose between terminating the pregnancy and preparing themselves for a baby with severe problems. Identifying a genetic disease early can give families time to prepare—emotionally, medically, and financially. Advances in biotechnology offer possibilities for reducing human suffering, but not before key ethical issues are resolved. The dilemmas posed by human genetics reinforce one of this book's themes: the immense social implications of biology. ☑

☑ CHECKPOINT

1. A man and a woman who are both carriers of cystic fibrosis have had three children without cystic fibrosis. If the couple has a fourth child, what is the probability that the child will have the disorder?
2. Peter is a 28-year-old man whose father died of Huntington's disease. Peter's mother shows no signs of the disease. What is the probability that Peter has inherited Huntington's disease?

Answers: 1. 1/4 (The genotypes and phenotypes of their other children are irrelevant) 2. 1/2

Variations on Mendel's Laws

Mendel's two laws explain inheritance in terms of discrete factors—genes—that are passed along from generation to generation according to simple rules of probability. These laws are valid for all sexually reproducing organisms, including garden peas, Labrador retrievers, and people. But just as the basic rules of musical harmony cannot account for all the rich sounds of a symphony, Mendel's laws stop short of explaining some patterns of genetic inheritance. In fact, for most sexually reproducing organisms, cases where Mendel's rules can strictly account for the patterns of inheritance are relatively rare. More often, the observed inheritance patterns are more complex. We will now add several extensions to Mendel's laws that help account for this complexity.

Incomplete Dominance in Plants and People

The F_1 offspring of Mendel's pea crosses always looked like one of the two parent plants. In such situations, the dominant allele has the same effect on the phenotype whether present in one or two copies. But for some characters, the appearance of F_1 hybrids falls between the phenotypes of the two parents, an effect called **incomplete dominance**. For instance, when red snapdragons are crossed with white snapdragons, all the F_1 hybrids have pink flowers (Figure 9.18). And in the F_2 generation, the genotypic ratio and the phenotypic ratio are the same: 1:2:1.

We also see examples of incomplete dominance in people. One case involves a recessive allele (h) that causes **hypercholesterolemia**, dangerously high levels of cholesterol in the blood. Normal individuals are homozygous dominant, HH. Heterozygotes (Hh) have blood cholesterol levels about twice what is normal. They are very prone to cholesterol buildup in artery walls and may have heart attacks from blocked heart arteries by their mid-30s. Hypercholesterolemia is even more serious in homozygous individuals (hh). Homozygotes have about five times the normal amount of blood cholesterol and may have heart attacks as early as age 2. If we look at the molecular basis for hypercholesterolemia, we can understand the intermediate phenotype of heterozygotes (Figure 9.19). The H allele specifies a cell-surface receptor protein that liver cells use to mop up excess low-density lipoprotein (LDL, or "bad cholesterol") from the blood. With only half as many receptors as HH individuals, heterozygotes can remove much less excess cholesterol.

▼ Figure 9.18 **Incomplete dominance in snapdragons.** Compare this diagram with Figure 9.6, where one of the alleles displays complete dominance.

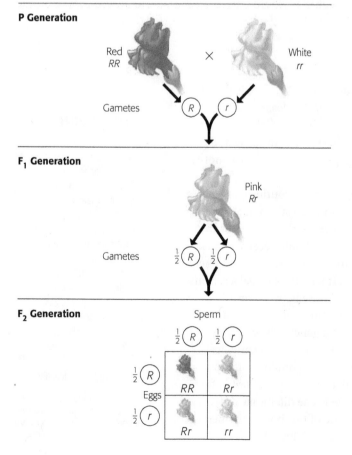

▼ Figure 9.19 **Incomplete dominance in human hypercholesterolemia.** LDL receptors on liver cells promote the breakdown of cholesterol carried in the bloodstream by LDL (low-density lipoproteins). This process helps prevent the accumulation of cholesterol in the arteries. Having too few receptors allows dangerous levels of LDL to build up in the blood.

ABO Blood Groups: An Example of Multiple Alleles and Codominance

So far, we have discussed inheritance patterns involving only two alleles per gene (H versus h, for example). But most genes can be found in populations in more than two forms, known as multiple alleles. Although each individual carries, at most, two different alleles for a particular gene, in cases of multiple alleles, more than two possible alleles exist in the population.

The **ABO blood groups** in humans involve three alleles of a single gene. Various combinations of these three alleles produce four phenotypes: A person's blood type may be A, B, AB, or O. These letters refer to two carbohydrates, designated A and B, that may be found on the surface of red blood cells (**Figure 9.20**). A person's red blood cells may be coated with carbohydrate A (giving them type A blood), carbohydrate B (type B), both (type AB), or neither (type O). (In case you are wondering, the "positive" and "negative" notations associated with blood types—referred to as the Rh blood group system—are due to inheritance of a separate, unrelated gene.)

Matching compatible blood groups is critical for safe blood transfusions. If a donor's blood cells have a carbohydrate (A or B) that is foreign to the recipient, then the recipient's immune system produces blood proteins called antibodies that bind to the foreign carbohydrates and cause the donor blood cells to clump together, potentially killing the recipient. The clumping reaction is also the basis of a blood-typing lab test.

The four blood groups result from various combinations of the three different alleles: I^A (for the ability to make substance A), I^B (for B), and i (for neither A nor B). Each person inherits one of these alleles from each parent. Because there are three alleles, there are six possible genotypes, as listed in Figure 9.20. Both the I^A and I^B alleles are dominant to the i allele. Thus, $I^A I^A$ and $I^A i$ people have type A blood, and $I^B I^B$ and $I^B i$ people have type B. Recessive homozygotes (ii) have type O blood with neither carbohydrate. Finally, people of genotype $I^A I^B$ make *both* carbohydrates. In other words, the I^A and I^B alleles are **codominant**, meaning that both alleles are expressed in heterozygous individuals ($I^A I^B$) who have type AB blood. Be careful to distinguish codominance (the expression of both alleles) from incomplete dominance (the expression of one intermediate trait). ☑

Why must a blood donor be carefully matched to a recipient?

▼ **Figure 9.20 Multiple alleles for the ABO blood groups.** The three versions of the gene responsible for blood type may produce carbohydrate A (allele I^A), carbohydrate B (allele I^B), or neither carbohydrate (allele i). Because each person carries two alleles, six genotypes are possible that result in four different phenotypes. The clumping reaction that occurs between antibodies and foreign blood cells is the basis of blood-typing (shown in the photograph at right) and of the adverse reaction that occurs when someone receives a transfusion of incompatible blood.

Blood Group (Phenotype)	Genotypes	Red Blood Cells	Antibodies Present in Blood	Reactions When Blood from Groups Below Is Mixed with Antibodies from Groups at Left			
				O	A	B	AB
A	$I^A I^A$ or $I^A i$	Carbohydrate A	Anti-B				
B	$I^B I^B$ or $I^B i$	Carbohydrate B	Anti-A				
AB	$I^A I^B$		—				
O	ii		Anti-A Anti-B				

☑ **CHECKPOINT**

1. Why is a testcross unnecessary to determine whether a snapdragon with red flowers is homozygous or heterozygous?
2. Maria has type O blood and her sister has type AB blood. What are the genotypes of the girls' parents?

Answers: 1. Only plants homozygous for the dominant allele have red flowers; heterozygotes have pink flowers; 2. One parent is $I^A i$, and the other parent is $I^B i$.

Pleiotropy and Sickle-Cell Disease

Our genetic examples to this point have been cases in which each gene specifies only one hereditary character. But in many cases, one gene influences several characters, a property called **pleiotropy**.

An example of pleiotropy in humans that may be familiar to you is **sickle-cell disease** (sometimes called sickle-cell anemia), a disorder characterized by a diverse set of symptoms. The direct effect of the sickle-cell allele is to make red blood cells produce abnormal hemoglobin proteins (see Figure 3.19). These abnormal molecules tend to link together and crystallize, especially when the oxygen content of the blood is lower than usual because of high altitude, overexertion, or respiratory ailments. As the hemoglobin crystallizes, the normally disk-shaped red blood cells deform to a sickle shape with jagged edges **(Figure 9.21)**. Sickled cells are destroyed rapidly by the body, and their destruction may cause anemia and general weakening of the body. Also, because of their shape, sickled cells do not flow smoothly in the blood and tend to accumulate and clog tiny blood vessels. Blood flow to body parts is reduced,

resulting in periodic fever, severe pain, and damage to the heart, brain, and kidneys. Blood transfusions and drugs may relieve some of the symptoms, but there is no cure, and sickle-cell disease kills about 100,000 people in the world annually.

In most cases, only people who are homozygous for the sickle-cell allele have sickle-cell disease. Heterozygotes, who have one sickle-cell allele and one normal allele, are usually healthy; hence, the disease is considered recessive. However, at the molecular level, the two alleles are actually codominant: Both alleles are expressed in heterozygous individuals, and their red blood cells contain both normal and abnormal hemoglobin. A simple blood test can distinguish homozygotes from heterozygotes. ☑

Polygenic Inheritance

Mendel studied genetic characters that could be classified on an either–or basis, such as purple or white flower color. However, many characters, such as human skin color and height, vary along a continuum in a population. Many such features result from **polygenic inheritance**, the additive effects of two or more genes on a single phenotypic character. (This is the logical opposite of pleiotropy, in which one gene affects several characters.)

There is evidence that height in people is controlled by several genes that are inherited separately. In actuality, human height is probably affected by a great number of genes, but we will simplify here. Let's consider three genes, with a tall allele for each (*A*, *B*, and *C*) contributing one "unit" of tallness to the phenotype and being incompletely dominant to the other alleles (*a*, *b*, and *c*). A person who is *AABBCC* would be very tall, while an *aabbcc* individual would be very short. An

▼ **Figure 9.21 Sickle-cell disease: multiple effects of a single human gene.**

Individual homozygous
for sickle-cell allele

Sickle-cell (abnormal) hemoglobin

Abnormal hemoglobin crystallizes into long flexible chains, causing red blood cells to become sickle-shaped.

Colorized SEM
4,000×

Sickled cells can lead to a cascade of symptoms, such as weakness, pain, organ damage, and paralysis.

AaBbCc person would be of intermediate height. Because the alleles have an additive effect, the genotype *AaBbCc* would produce the same height as any other genotype with just three tallness alleles, such as *AABbcc*. The Punnett square in **Figure 9.22** shows all possible genotypes from a mating of two triple heterozygotes (*AaBbCd*). The row of figures below the Punnett square shows the seven height phenotypes that would theoretically result. This hypothetical example shows how inheritance of three genes could lead to seven different versions of a trait at the frequencies indicated by the bars in the graph. ☑

☑ CHECKPOINT

Based on the height model in Figure 9.22, put the following individuals in order by height, from shortest to tallest: *AAbbCC, aaBBcc, AabBCc, Aabbcc, AaBBCC.*

Answer: Aabbcc, aaBBcc, AabBCc, AAbbCC, AaBBCC.

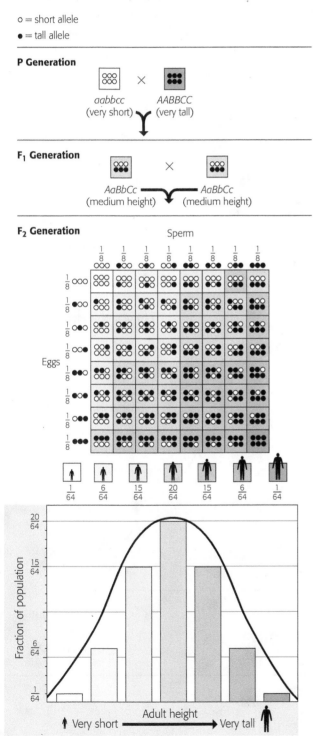

▼ **Figure 9.22 A model for polygenic inheritance of height.** The seven bars in the graph at the bottom of the figure depict the relative numbers of each of the phenotypes in the F₂ generation. The bell-shaped curve indicates the distribution of an even greater variety of height phenotypes in the population that might result from the combination of heredity and environmental effects, such as diet and exercise.

The Role of Environment

If we examine a real human population for height, we would see more height phenotypes than just seven. The true range might be similar to the entire distribution of height under the bell-shaped curve in Figure 9.22. In fact, no matter how carefully we characterize the genes for height, a purely genetic description will always be incomplete. This is because height is also influenced by environmental factors, such as nutrition and exercise.

Many phenotypic characters result from a combination of heredity and environment. For example, the leaves of a tree all have the same genotype, but they vary in size, shape, and color, depending on exposure to wind and sun and the tree's nutritional state. For people, exercise alters build; experience improves performance on intelligence tests; and social and cultural factors can greatly affect appearance. As geneticists learn more and more about our genes, it's becoming clear that many human characters—such as risk of heart disease, cancer, alcoholism, and schizophrenia—are influenced by both genes *and* environment.

Whether human characters are more influenced by genes or by the environment—nature or nurture—is a very old and hotly contested issue. For some characters, such as the ABO blood group, a given genotype mandates an exact phenotype, and the environment plays no role whatsoever. In contrast, the number of blood cells in a drop of your blood varies quite a bit, depending on such factors as the altitude, your physical activity, and whether or not you have a cold.

Simply spending time with identical twins will convince anyone that environment, and not just genes, affects a person's traits (**Figure 9.23**). However, there is an important difference between these two sources of variation: Only genetic influences are inherited. Any effects of the environment are not passed to the next generation.

▼ **Figure 9.23 As a result of environmental influences, even identical twins can look different.**

The Chromosomal Basis of Inheritance

It was not until many years after Mendel's death that biologists understood the significance of his work. Cell biologists worked out the processes of mitosis and meiosis in the late 1800s (see Chapter 8). Then, around 1900, researchers began to notice parallels between the behavior of chromosomes and the behavior of Mendel's "heritable factors" (what we now call genes). One of biology's most important concepts began to emerge.

The **chromosome theory of inheritance** states that genes are located at specific positions (loci) on chromosomes and that the behavior of chromosomes during meiosis and fertilization accounts for inheritance patterns. Indeed, it is chromosomes that undergo segregation and independent assortment during meiosis and thus account for Mendel's laws. **Figure 9.24** correlates the results of the dihybrid cross in Figure 9.8b with the movement of chromosomes through meiosis. Starting with two purebred parental plants, the diagram follows two genes on different chromosomes—one for seed shape (alleles *R* and *r*) and one for seed color (alleles *Y* and *y*)—through the F_1 and F_2 generations. ✔

► Figure 9.24 **The chromosomal basis of Mendel's laws.**

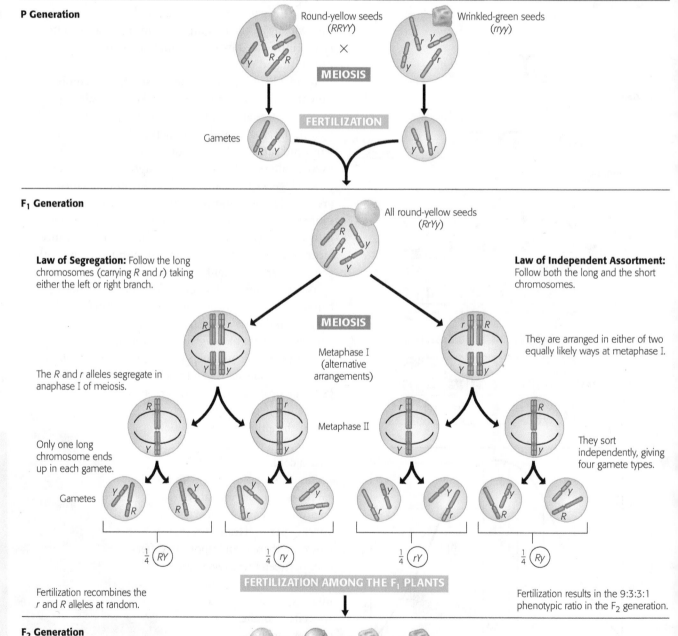

P Generation

Round-yellow seeds (*RRYY*) ✕ Wrinkled-green seeds (*rryy*)

MEIOSIS

FERTILIZATION

Gametes

F₁ Generation

All round-yellow seeds (*RrYy*)

Law of Segregation: Follow the long chromosomes (carrying *R* and *r*) taking either the left or right branch.

Law of Independent Assortment: Follow both the long and the short chromosomes.

MEIOSIS

Metaphase I (alternative arrangements)

They are arranged in either of two equally likely ways at metaphase I.

The *R* and *r* alleles segregate in anaphase I of meiosis.

Metaphase II

Only one long chromosome ends up in each gamete.

They sort independently, giving four gamete types.

Gametes

¼ (*RY*)   ¼ (*ry*)   ¼ (*rY*)   ¼ (*Ry*)

FERTILIZATION AMONG THE F₁ PLANTS

Fertilization recombines the *r* and *R* alleles at random.

Fertilization results in the 9:3:3:1 phenotypic ratio in the F_2 generation.

F₂ Generation

9 : 3 : 3 : 1

✔ **CHECKPOINT**

Which of Mendel's laws have their physical basis in the following phases of meiosis?

a. the orientation of pairs of homologous chromosomes in metaphase I

b. the separation of pairs of homologous chromosomes in anaphase I

*Answer: **a.** the law of independent assortment **b.** the law of segregation*

Linked Genes

Realizing that genes are on chromosomes when they segregate enables us to extend Mendel's work in several important ways. For example, alleles that start out together on the same chromosome would be expected to travel together during meiosis and fertilization. In general, genes that are located close together on a chromosome, called **linked genes**, tend to be inherited as a set and therefore do not follow Mendel's law of independent assortment.

The most important early studies into linked genes took place in the New York City laboratory of American biologist Thomas Hunt Morgan. In the early 1900s, Morgan and his colleagues studied the fruit fly *Drosophila melanogaster* (**Figure 9.25**). Often seen flying around overripe fruit, *Drosophila* is a good research animal for studies of inheritance because it is easily and inexpensively grown and can produce several generations in a matter of months.

Wild-type *Drosophila* flies have gray bodies (genotype *GG*) and long wings (*LL*). Morgan cultivated purebred mutant (non–wild-type) fruit flies that had black bodies (*gg*) and short, underdeveloped wings (*ll*). He then performed a dihybrid testcross, crossing doubly heterozygous flies (*GgLl*) with double mutants (*ggll*). Morgan expected that the offspring would show equal numbers of all four possible phenotypes ($\frac{1}{4}$ gray-long, $\frac{1}{4}$ gray-short, $\frac{1}{4}$ black-long, $\frac{1}{4}$ black-short).

In fact, Morgan's testcross produced equal numbers of two of the four expected phenotypes but far smaller numbers of the other two phenotypes. He found that 83% of the flies displayed the phenotypes of the parents (gray-long and black-short), while only 17% showed nonparental phenotypes (gray-short and black-long). Morgan reasoned that the genes for body color and wing shape were linked—in this case, *G* with *L* and *g* with *l*—causing them to be inherited together. Such linkage would mean that meiosis in the heterozygous fruit flies would yield gametes with only two genotypes (*GL* and *gl* but not *Gl* or *gL*). The large numbers of flies with gray-long and black-short traits in the experiment resulted from fertilization among the *GL* and *gl* gametes. ☑

Genetic Recombination: Crossing Over

But what of the smaller numbers of Morgan's gray-short and black-long flies? How could they be produced if the two genes involved are linked? We saw in Chapter 8 that during meiosis, crossing over between homologous chromosomes results in shuffled chromosome segments in the haploid daughter cells (see Figure 8.18), thereby producing new combinations of alleles. **Figure 9.26** reviews crossing over, showing how two linked genes can give rise to four different gamete genotypes. Two of the gamete genotypes reflect the presence of parental-type chromosomes, which have not been altered by crossing

Dihybrid testcross

Gray body, long wings (wild-type)

GgLl

Female

×

Black body, short wings (mutant)

ggll

Male

Results

Offspring

Gray-long *GgLl*	Black-short *ggll*	Gray-short *Ggll*	Black-long *ggLl*

965	944	206	185

Parental phenotypes 83% (more than expected)

Recombinant phenotypes 17% (less than expected)

$$\text{Recombination frequency} = \frac{391 \text{ recombinants}}{2{,}300 \text{ total offspring}} = 0.17, \text{ or } 17\%$$

◄ **Figure 9.25 Thomas Morgan's experiment and results.** Among the 2,300 offspring of this dihybrid testcross, Morgan observed more than the expected parental phenotypes (gray-long and black-short) and fewer than expected nonparental phenotypes (gray-short and black-long).

▼ **Figure 9.26 Review: Crossing over can produce recombinant gametes.**

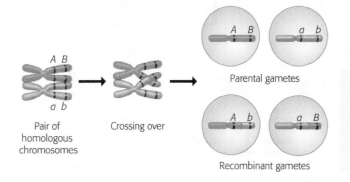

A B

a b

Pair of homologous chromosomes

Crossing over

A B   *a b*

Parental gametes

A b   *a B*

Recombinant gametes

over. In contrast, the other two gamete genotypes are recombinant (nonparental). The chromosomes of these gametes carry new combinations of alleles that result from the exchange of chromosome segments during crossing over.

Morgan hypothesized that crossing over accounted for the observed nonparental offspring, those with the recombinant phenotypes (gray-short and black-long). Furthermore, the 17% of offspring with recombinant phenotypes must have resulted from fertilization involving recombinant gametes (Figure 9.27). The percentage of recombinant offspring among the total is called the **recombination frequency** (see bottom of Figure 9.25).

Linkage Maps

While working with *Drosophila*, Alfred H. Sturtevant, one of Morgan's students, developed a way to use crossover data to map gene loci. This technique is based on the assumption that the chance of crossing over is approximately equal at all points along a chromosome. Sturtevant hypothesized that the farther apart two genes are on a chromosome, the higher the probability that a crossover will occur between them. His reasoning was elegantly simple: The greater the distance between two genes, the more points there are between them where crossing over can occur. (This assumption is not entirely accurate, but it is good enough to provide useful data.)

By applying Sturtevant's reasoning, geneticists can use recombination data to assign genes to relative positions on chromosomes—that is, to map genes. Figure 9.28 shows some of the data used to map three linked genes (*g*, *c*, and *l*) that reside on one of the *Drosophila* chromosomes. Under the chromosome are the actual recombination frequencies (crossover frequencies) between these genes, taken two at a time: 17% between *g* and *l*, 9% between *g* and *c*, and 9.5% between *l* and *c*. Geneticists reasoned that these values represent the relative distances between the genes. Because the recombination frequencies between *g* and *c* and between *l* and *c* are approximately half the frequency between *g* and *l*, gene *c* must lie roughly midway between *g* and *l*. Thus, the sequence of these genes on their chromosome must be *g-c-l* (or the equivalent *l-c-g*). Such a diagram of relative gene locations is called a **linkage map**.

The linkage-mapping method has proved extremely valuable in establishing the relative positions of many genes in many organisms. The real beauty of the technique is that a wealth of information about genes can be learned simply by breeding and observing the organisms; no fancy equipment is required. ☑

▼ Figure 9.27 **Explaining the unexpected results from the dihybrid testcross in Figure 9.25.** The disproportionately large numbers of the parental phenotypes among the offspring is explained by gene linkage, the fact that the gene loci for the two characters are located nearby on the same chromosome and tend to remain together during meiosis and fertilization (*G* with *L* and *g* with *l*). As a result of crossing over, some of the gametes end up with recombinant chromosomes, carrying new combinations of alleles, either *Gl* or *gL*. When the recombinant gametes participate in fertilization, recombinant offspring can result.

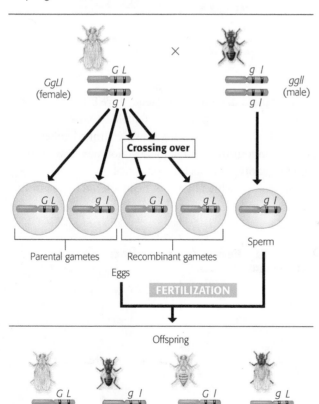

☑ **CHECKPOINT**

If the order of three genes on a chromosome is *A-B-C*, which two genes will have the highest recombination frequency?

Answer: A and C

▼ Figure 9.28 **Using crossover data to map genes.** The three recessive alleles specify black body (*g*), cinnabar eyes (*c*), and short wings (*l*). The corresponding dominant alleles specify the wild-type traits of gray body, red eyes, and long wings.

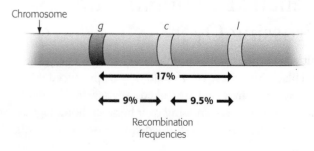

Sex Chromosomes and Sex-Linked Genes

The patterns of genetic inheritance we've discussed so far have always involved genes located on autosomes, not on the sex chromosomes. We're now ready to look at the role of sex chromosomes and the inheritance patterns exhibited by the characters they control. As you'll see, genes located on sex chromosomes produce some unusual patterns of inheritance.

Sex Determination in Humans

Many animals, including all mammals, have a pair of sex chromosomes—designated X and Y—that determine an individual's sex (Figure 9.29). Individuals with one X chromosome and one Y chromosome are males; XX individuals are females. Human males and females both have 44 autosomes (chromosomes other than sex chromosomes). As a result of chromosome segregation during meiosis, each gamete contains one sex chromosome and a haploid set of autosomes (22 in humans). All eggs contain a single X chromosome. Of the sperm cells, half contain an X chromosome and half contain a Y chromosome. An offspring's sex depends on whether the sperm cell that fertilizes the egg bears an X or a Y. ☑

Why was Henry VIII wrong to blame his wives for always producing daughters?

Sex-Linked Genes

Besides bearing genes that determine sex, the sex chromosomes also contain genes for characters unrelated to maleness or femaleness. A gene located on a sex chromosome is called a **sex-linked gene**. The human X chromosome contains more than a thousand genes, whereas the Y chromosome contains only about a dozen (and none of them are vital); therefore, most sex-linked genes are found on the X chromosome.

A number of human conditions, including red-green colorblindness, hemophilia, and a type of muscular dystrophy, result from sex-linked recessive alleles. **Red-green colorblindness** is a common sex-linked disorder that is caused by a malfunction of light-sensitive cells in the eyes. (Colorblindness is actually a large class of disorders involving several sex-linked genes, but we will focus on just one specific type of colorblindness here.) A person with normal color vision can see more than 150 colors. In contrast, someone with red-green colorblindness can see fewer than 25. Figure 9.30 shows a simple test for red-green colorblindness. Mostly males are affected, but heterozygous females have some defects.

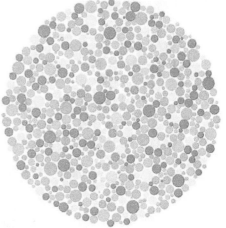

▲ Figure 9.30 **A test for red-green colorblindness.** Can you see a green numeral 7 against the reddish background? If not, you probably have some form of red-green colorblindness, a sex-linked trait.

▼ Figure 9.29 **The chromosomal basis of sex determination in humans.** The micrograph at right shows human X and Y chromosomes in a duplicated state.

Colorized SEM 41,500×

☑ CHECKPOINT

At the moment of fertilization in humans, what determines the sex of the offspring?

Answer: whether the egg is fertilized by a sperm bearing an X chromosome (producing a female offspring) or a Y chromosome (producing a male)

▼ **Figure 9.31 Inheritance of colorblindness, a sex-linked recessive trait.** We use an uppercase N for the dominant, normal color-vision allele and n for the recessive, colorblind allele. To indicate that these alleles are on the X chromosome, we show them as superscripts to the letter X. The Y chromosome does not have a gene locus for vision; therefore, the male's phenotype results entirely from the sex-linked gene on his single X chromosome.

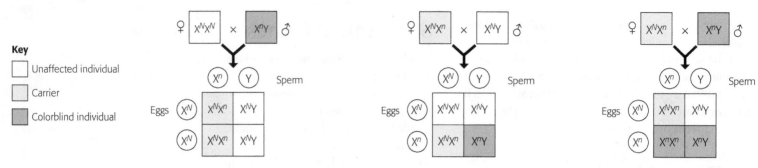

Key
☐ Unaffected individual
▨ Carrier
▨ Colorblind individual

(a) Normal female × colorblind male

(b) Carrier female × normal male

(c) Carrier female × colorblind male

Why are there so few colorblind women?

Because they are located on the sex chromosomes, sex-linked genes exhibit unusual inheritance patterns. Figure 9.31a illustrates what happens when a colorblind male has offspring with a homozygous female with normal color vision. All the children have normal color vision, suggesting that the allele for wild-type (normal) color vision is dominant. If a female carrier mates with a male who has normal color vision, the classic 3:1 phenotypic ratio of normal color vision to colorblindness appears among the children (Figure 9.31b). However, there is a surprising twist: The colorblind trait shows up only in males. All the females have normal vision, while half the males are colorblind and half are normal. This is because the gene involved in this inheritance pattern is located exclusively on the X chromosome; there is no corresponding locus on the Y. Thus, females (XX) carry two copies of the gene for this character, while males (XY) carry only one. Because the colorblindness allele is recessive, a female will be colorblind only if she receives that allele on both X chromosomes (Figure 9.31c). For a male, however, a single copy of the recessive allele confers colorblindness. For this reason, recessive sex-linked traits are expressed much more frequently in men than in women. For example, colorblindness is about 20-fold more common among males than among females. This inheritance pattern is why people often say that certain genes "skip a generation"—because they are passed from a

male to a female carrier (who does not express it) back to a male.

Hemophilia is a sex-linked recessive trait with a long, well-documented history. Hemophiliacs bleed excessively when injured because they have inherited an abnormal allele for a factor involved in blood clotting. The most seriously affected individuals may bleed to death after relatively minor bruises or cuts. A high incidence of hemophilia plagued the royal families of Europe. Queen Victoria (1819–1901) of England was a carrier of the hemophilia allele. She passed it on to one of her sons and two of her daughters. Through marriage, her daughters then introduced the disease into the royal families of Prussia, Russia, and Spain. In this way, the age-old practice of strengthening international alliances by marriage effectively spread hemophilia through the royal families of several nations (Figure 9.32). ☑

▼ **Figure 9.32 Hemophilia in the royal family of Russia.** The photograph shows Queen Victoria's granddaughter Alexandra, her husband Nicholas, who was the last czar of Russia, their son Alexis, and their daughters. In the pedigree, half-colored symbols represent heterozygous carriers of the hemophilia allele and fully colored symbols represent a person with hemophilia.

Queen Victoria — Albert

Alice — Louis

Alexandra — Czar Nicholas II of Russia

Alexis

Barking Up the Evolutionary Tree

As we've seen throughout this chapter, dogs are more than man's best friend: They are also one of our longest-running genetic experiments. About 15,000 years ago, in East Asia, people began to cohabit with ancestral canines that were predecessors of both modern wolves and dogs. As people moved into permanent, geographically isolated settlements, populations of canines were separated from one another and eventually became inbred.

Different groups of people chose dogs with different traits, depending on their needs. Herders selected dogs that were good at controlling flocks. Hunters chose dogs that were good at retrieving prey. A 2010 study indicated that small dogs were first bred within early agricultural settlements of the Middle East around 12,000 years ago. Continued over millennia, such genetic tinkering has resulted in a diverse array of dog body types and behaviors. In each breed, a distinct genetic makeup results in a distinct set of physical and behavioral traits.

As discussed in the Process of Science section, our understanding of canine evolution took a big leap forward when researchers sequenced the complete genome of a dog. Using the genome sequence and a wealth of other data, canine geneticists produced an evolutionary tree based on a genetic analysis of 85 breeds (Figure 9.33). The analysis shows that the canine family tree includes a series of well-defined branch points. Each fork represents a purposeful selection by people that produced a genetically distinct subpopulation with specific desired traits.

The genetic tree shows that the most ancient breeds, those most closely related to the wolf, are Asian species such as the shar-pei and Akita. Subsequent genetic splits created distinct breeds in Africa (basenji), the Arctic (Alaskan malamute and Siberian husky), and the Middle East (Afghan hound and saluki). The remaining breeds, primarily of European ancestry, were developed most recently and can be grouped by genetic makeup into those bred for guarding (for example, the rottweiler), herding (such as sheepdogs), and hunting (including the Labrador retriever and beagle). The formulation of an evolutionary tree for the domestic dog shows that new technologies can provide important insights into genetic and evolutionary questions about life on Earth.

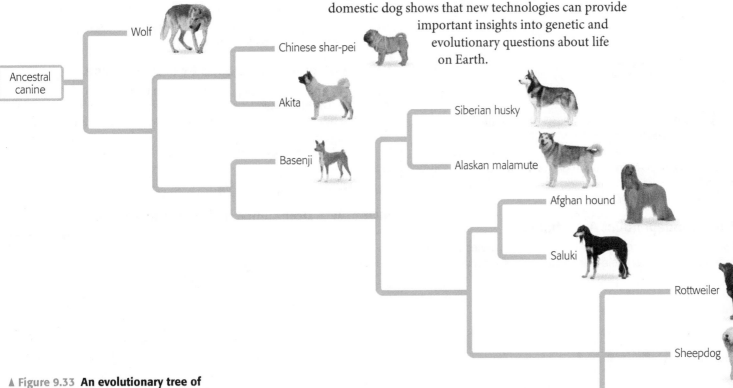

▲ Figure 9.33 **An evolutionary tree of dog breeds.** Genetic analysis has revealed the ancestral history of various dog breeds.

Chapter Review

SUMMARY OF KEY CONCEPTS

Heritable Variation and Patterns of Inheritance

Gregor Mendel was the first to study genetics, the science of heredity, by analyzing patterns of inheritance. He emphasized that heritable factors (genes) retain permanent identities.

In an Abbey Garden

Mendel started with purebred varieties of pea plants representing two alternative variants of a hereditary character, such as flower color. He then crossed the different varieties and traced the inheritance of traits from generation to generation.

Mendel's Law of Segregation

Pairs of alleles separate during gamete formation; fertilization restores the pairs.

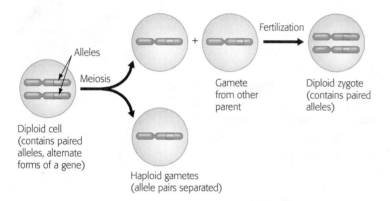

If an individual's genotype (genetic makeup) has two different alleles for a gene and only one influences the organism's phenotype (appearance), that allele is said to be dominant and the other allele recessive. Alleles of a gene reside at the same locus, or position, on homologous chromosomes. When the allele pair matches, the organism is homozygous; when the alleles are different, the organism is heterozygous.

Mendel's Law of Independent Assortment

By following two characters at once, Mendel found that the alleles of a pair segregate independently of other allele pairs during gamete formation.

Using a Testcross to Determine an Unknown Genotype

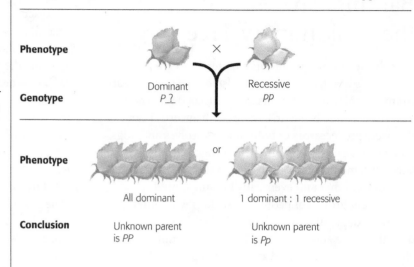

The Rules of Probability

Inheritance follows the rules of probability. The chance of inheriting a recessive allele from a heterozygous parent is $\frac{1}{2}$. The chance of inheriting it from both of two heterozygous parents is $\frac{1}{2} \times \frac{1}{2} = \frac{1}{4}$, illustrating the rule of multiplication for calculating the probability of two independent events.

Family Pedigrees

The inheritance of many human traits, from freckles to genetic diseases, follows Mendel's laws and the rules of probability. Geneticists can use family pedigrees to determine patterns of inheritance and individual genotypes.

Human Disorders Controlled by a Single Gene

For traits that vary within a population, the one most commonly found in nature is called the wild type. Many inherited disorders in humans are controlled by a single gene with two alleles. Most of these disorders, such as cystic fibrosis, are caused by autosomal recessive alleles. A few, such as Huntington's disease, are caused by dominant alleles.

Variations on Mendel's Laws

Incomplete Dominance in Plants and People

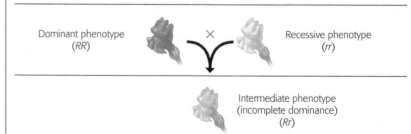

ABO Blood Groups: An Example of Multiple Alleles and Codominance

Within a population, there are often multiple kinds of alleles for a character, such as the three alleles for the ABO blood groups. The alleles determining the A and B blood factors are codominant; that is, both are expressed in a heterozygote.

Pleiotropy and Sickle-Cell Disease

The presence of two copies of the sickle-cell allele at a single gene locus brings about the many symptoms of sickle-cell disease.

Polygenic Inheritance

The Role of Environment

Many phenotypic characters result from a combination of genetic and environmental effects, but only genetic influences are biologically heritable.

The Chromosomal Basis of Inheritance

Genes are located on chromosomes. The behavior of chromosomes during meiosis and fertilization accounts for inheritance patterns.

Linked Genes

Certain genes are linked: They tend to be inherited as a set because they lie close together on the same chromosome.

Genetic Recombination: Crossing Over

Crossing over can separate linked genes producing gametes with recombinant chromosomes and offspring with recombinant phenotypes.

Linkage Maps

The fact that crossing over between linked genes is more likely to occur between genes that are farther apart enables geneticists to map the relative positions of genes on chromosomes.

Sex Chromosomes and Sex-Linked Genes
Sex Determination in Humans

In humans, sex is determined by whether a Y chromosome is present. A person who inherits two X chromosomes develops as a female. A person who inherits one X and one Y chromosome develops as a male.

Sex-Linked Genes

Genes on the sex chromosomes (most often the X) are said to be sex-linked. Their inheritance pattern reflects the fact that females have two homologous X chromosomes, but males have only one X chromosome. Most sex-linked human disorders, such as red-green colorblindness and hemophilia, are due to recessive alleles and are seen mostly in males. A male receiving a single sex-linked recessive allele from his mother will have the disorder; a female has to receive the allele from both parents to be affected.

Sex-Linked Traits				
Female: Two alleles	Genotype	$X^N X^N$	$X^N X^n$	$X^n X^n$
	Phenotype	Normal female	Carrier female	Affected female (rare)
Male: One allele	Genotype	$X^N Y$		$X^n Y$
	Phenotype	Normal male		Affected male

SELF-QUIZ

1. The genetic makeup of an organism is called its _____, and the physical traits of an organism are called its _____.

2. Which of Mendel's laws is represented by each statement?
   a. Alleles of each homologous pair separate independently during gamete formation.
   b. Alleles segregate during gamete formation; fertilization creates pairs of alleles once again.

3. Edward was found to be heterozygous (Ss) for the sickle-cell trait. The alleles represented by the letters S and s are
   a. on the X and Y chromosomes.
   b. linked.
   c. on homologous chromosomes.
   d. both present in each of Edward's sperm cells.

4. Whether an allele is dominant or recessive depends on
   a. how common the allele is, relative to other alleles.
   b. whether it is inherited from the mother or the father.
   c. whether it or another allele determines the phenotype when both are present.
   d. whether or not it is linked to other genes.

5. Two fruit flies with eyes of the usual red color are crossed, and their offspring are as follows: 77 red-eyed males, 71 ruby-eyed males, 152 red-eyed females. The gene that controls whether eyes are red or ruby is _____, and the allele for ruby eyes is _____.
   a. autosomal (carried on an autosome); dominant
   b. autosomal; recessive
   c. sex-linked; dominant
   d. sex-linked; recessive

6. All the offspring of a white hen and a black rooster are gray. The simplest explanation for this pattern of inheritance is
   a. pleiotropy.
   b. sex linkage.
   c. codominance.
   d. incomplete dominance.

7. A man who has type B blood and a woman who has type A blood could have children of which of the following phenotypes? (*Hint*: Review Figure 9.20.)
   a. A, B, or O
   b. AB only
   c. AB or O
   d. A, B, AB, or O

8. Duchenne muscular dystrophy is a sex-linked recessive disorder characterized by a progressive loss of muscle tissue. Neither Rudy nor Carla has Duchenne muscular dystrophy, but their first son does have it. If the couple has a second child, what is the probability that he or she will also have the disease?

9. In fruit flies, the genes for wing shape and body stripes are linked. In a fly whose genotype is WwSs, W is linked to S, and w is linked to s. But this fly produces gametes with four different combinations of gametes. What process is responsible for this? Of the four types of gametes, which are parental-type gametes? Which are recombinant gametes?

10. Adult height in people is at least partially hereditary; tall parents tend to have tall children. But people come in a range of sizes, not just tall or short. What extension of Mendel's model could produce this variation in height?

11. A purebred brown mouse is repeatedly mated with a purebred white mouse, and all their offspring are brown. If two of these brown offspring are mated, what fraction of the F$_2$ mice will be brown?

12. How could you determine the genotype of one of the brown F$_2$ mice in problem 11? How would you know whether a brown mouse is homozygous? Heterozygous?

13. Tim and Jan both have freckles (a dominant trait), but their son Michael does not. Show with a Punnett square how this is possible. If Tim and Jan have two more children, what is the probability that *both* of them will have freckles?

14. Incomplete dominance is seen in the inheritance of hypercholesterolemia. Mack and Toni are both heterozygous for this character, and both have elevated levels of cholesterol. Their daughter Katerina has a cholesterol level six times normal; she is apparently homozygous, *hh*. What fraction of Mack and Toni's children are likely to have elevated but not extreme levels of cholesterol, like their parents? If Mack and Toni have one more child, what is the probability that the child will suffer from the more serious form of hypercholesterolemia seen in Katerina?

15. A female fruit fly with forked bristles on her body is mated with a male fly with normal bristles. Their offspring are 121 females with normal bristles and 138 males with forked bristles. Explain the inheritance pattern for this trait.

16. Both parents of a boy are phenotypically normal, but their son suffers from hemophilia, a sex-linked recessive disorder. Draw a pedigree that shows the genotypes of the three individuals. What fraction of the couple's children are likely to suffer from hemophilia? What fraction are likely to be carriers?

17. Heather was surprised to discover that she suffered from red-green colorblindness. She told her biology professor, who said, "Your father is colorblind too, right?" How did her professor know this? Why did her professor not say the same thing to the colorblind males in the class?

Answers to these questions can be found in Appendix: Self-Quiz Answers.

THE PROCESS OF SCIENCE

18. In 1981, a stray cat with unusual curled-back ears was adopted by a family in Lakewood, California. Hundreds of descendants of this cat have since been born, and cat fanciers hope to develop the "curl" cat into a show breed. The curl allele is apparently dominant and carried on an autosome. Suppose you owned the first curl cat and wanted to develop a purebred variety. Describe tests that would determine whether the curl gene is dominant or recessive and whether it is auto-somal or sex-linked.

19. Imagine that you have a large collection of fruit flies divided into ten different strains. Each strain is purebred (homozygous) and differs from wild-type flies in just one character. The only special equipment available is a magnifying glass that lets you determine the sex and readily observable traits of a fly, a large number of bottles to perform controlled matings, and an anesthetic liquid that enables you to examine and sort live flies. Using only this equipment, how much could you learn about the genetic makeup of the flies? Describe a series of experiments that would give you knowledge about fruit fly genetics.

BIOLOGY AND SOCIETY

20. Gregor Mendel never saw a gene, yet he concluded that "heritable factors" were responsible for the patterns of inheritance he observed in peas. Similarly, maps of *Drosophila* chromosomes (and the very idea that genes are carried on chromosomes) were conceived by observing the patterns of inheritance of linked genes, not by observing the genes directly. Is it legitimate for biologists to claim the existence of objects and processes they cannot actually see? How do scientists know whether an explanation is correct?

21. Many infertile couples turn to in vitro fertilization to try to have a baby. In this technique, sperm and ova are collected and used to create eight-cell embryos for implantation into a woman's uterus. At the eight-cell stage, one of the fetal cells can be removed without causing harm to the developing fetus. Once removed, the cell can be genetically tested. Some couples may know that a particular genetic disease runs in their family. They might wish to avoid implanting any embryos with the disease-causing genes. Do you think this is an acceptable use of genetic testing? What if a couple wanted to use genetic testing to select embryos for traits unrelated to disease, such as freckles? Do you think that couples undergoing in vitro fertilization should be allowed to perform whatever genetic tests they wish? Or do you think that there should be limits on what tests can be performed? How do you draw the line between genetic tests that are acceptable and those that are not?

10 The Structure and Function of DNA

The Deadliest Virus BIOLOGY AND SOCIETY

Mix-and-Match Viruses

In 2009, a cluster of unusual flu cases broke out around Mexico City. Despite a near total shutdown of the city, the new viral strain, called 2009 H1N1, quickly spread to California and Texas. This strain was originally misnamed the "swine flu"; in fact, pigs had little impact on the spread of this virus, which, like most flu viruses, is passed from person to person through respiratory fluids. Nonetheless, the new strain received nearly constant media attention and caused considerable worry among the general public. In June 2009, the World Health Organization (WHO) declared H1N1 a pandemic (global epidemic) and unveiled a massive effort to contain it.

Scientists soon determined that H1N1 was a hybrid flu strain, made when a previously known flu virus (which itself originated through a combination of viruses from birds, swine, and people) mixed with an Asian swine flu virus. This novel combination of genes produced some unusual features in the H1N1 strain. Most significantly, it infected young, healthy people, whereas the flu usually affects the elderly or people who are already sick. Many countries participated in coordinated response, including widespread distribution of a new vaccine. As a result, the virus was contained, and WHO declared the pandemic over in August 2010. Although exact numbers are difficult to produce, WHO estimates that this virus killed about 18,000 people.

You may wonder, What's the big deal about the flu? Don't we all get the flu from time to time? While you may think of the flu as merely a seasonal inconvenience, the influenza virus may be the deadliest pathogen known to science. Each year in the United States, over 20,000 people die from influenza infection. And that is in a good year. Once every few decades, a new strain explodes on the scene, causing pandemics and widespread death. H1N1 pales in comparison to the deadliest outbreak: the pandemic of 1918–1919, which in just 18 months killed about 40 million people worldwide—that's more people than have died of AIDS since it was discovered over 30 years ago.

The flu virus, like all viruses, consists of a relatively simple structure of nucleic acid (RNA in this case) and protein. Therefore, combating any virus requires a detailed understanding of life at the molecular level. In this chapter, we will explore the structure of DNA, how it replicates and mutates, and how it controls the cell by directing the synthesis of RNA and protein.

DNA: Structure and Replication

DNA was known to be a chemical in cells by the late 1800s, but Mendel and other early geneticists did all their work without any knowledge of DNA's role in heredity. By the late 1930s, experimental studies had convinced most biologists that one specific kind of molecule, rather than a complex chemical mixture, is the basis of inheritance. Attention focused on chromosomes, which were already known to carry genes. By the 1940s, scientists knew that chromosomes consist of two types of chemicals: DNA and protein. And by the early 1950s, a series of discoveries had convinced the scientific world that DNA was the molecule that acts as the hereditary material. This breakthrough ushered in the field of **molecular biology**, the study of heredity at the molecular level.

What came next was one of the most celebrated quests in the history of science: the effort to figure out the structure of DNA. A good deal was already known about DNA. Scientists had identified all its atoms and knew how they were bonded to one another. What was not understood was the specific three-dimensional arrangement of atoms that gives DNA its unique properties—the capacity to store genetic information, copy it, and pass it

from generation to generation. A race was on to discover how the structure of this molecule could account for its role in heredity. We will describe that momentous discovery shortly. First, let's review the underlying chemical structure of DNA and its chemical cousin RNA.

DNA and RNA Structure

Both DNA and RNA are nucleic acids, which consist of long chains (polymers) of chemical units (monomers) called **nucleotides**. (For an in-depth refresher, see the information on nucleic acids in Chapter 3, particularly Figures 3.22–3.26.) A diagram of a nucleotide polymer, or **polynucleotide**, is shown in Figure 10.1. This sample polynucleotide chain shows only one of many possible arrangements of the four different types of nucleotides (abbreviated A, C, T, and G) that make up DNA. Polynucleotides can be very long and may have any sequence of nucleotides, so a large number of polynucleotide chains are possible.

Nucleotides are joined together by covalent bonds between the sugar of one nucleotide and the phosphate of the next. This results in a **sugar-phosphate backbone**, a repeating pattern of sugar-phosphate-sugar-phosphate.

DNA double helix

► Figure 10.1 **The chemical structure of a DNA polynucleotide.** A molecule of DNA contains two polynucleotides, each a chain of nucleotides. Each nucleotide consists of a nitrogenous base, a sugar (blue), and a phosphate group (gold).

Polynucleotide

Sugar-phosphate backbone

Phosphate group

Nitrogenous base

Sugar

DNA nucleotide

Nitrogenous base
(can be A, G, C, or T)

H₃C

Thymine (T)

Phosphate group

Sugar
(deoxyribose)

DNA nucleotide

The nitrogenous bases are arranged like ribs that project from this backbone. Moving from left to right across Figure 10.1, we can zoom in to see that each nucleotide consists of three components: a nitrogenous base, a sugar (blue), and a phosphate group (gold). Examining a single nucleotide even more closely, we see the chemical structure of its three components. The phosphate group, with a phosphorus atom (P) at its center, is the source of the *acid* in nucleic acid. The phosphate has given up a hydrogen ion, H^+, leaving a negative charge on one of its oxygen atoms. The sugar has five carbon atoms (shown in red): four in its ring and one extending above the ring. The ring also includes an oxygen atom. The sugar is called *deoxyribose* because, compared with the sugar ribose, it is missing an oxygen atom. The full name for **DNA** is *deoxyribonucleic acid*, with *nucleic* referring to DNA's location in the nuclei of eukaryotic cells. The nitrogenous base (thymine, in our example) has a ring of nitrogen and carbon atoms with various chemical groups attached. In contrast to the acidic phosphate group, nitrogenous bases are basic; hence their name.

The four nucleotides found in DNA differ only in their nitrogenous bases (see Figure 3.24 for a review). The bases can be divided into two types. **Thymine (T)** and **cytosine (C)** are single-ring structures. **Adenine (A)** and **guanine (G)** are larger, double-ring structures. Instead of thymine, RNA has a similar base called **uracil (U)**. And RNA contains a slightly different sugar than DNA (ribose instead of deoxyribose). Other than that, RNA and DNA polynucleotides have the same chemical structure. **Figure 10.2** is a computer graphic of a piece of RNA polynucleotide about 20 nucleotides long. ✓

▶ **Figure 10.2 An RNA polynucleotide.** The yellow used for the phosphorus atoms and the blue of the sugar atoms make it easy to spot the sugar-phosphate backbone.

☑ CHECKPOINT

Compare and contrast the chemical components of DNA and RNA.

Answer: Both are polymers of nucleotides (a sugar + a nitrogenous base + a phosphate group). In RNA, the sugar is ribose; in DNA, it is deoxyribose. Both RNA and DNA have the bases A, G, and C, but DNA has T and RNA has U.

Watson and Crick's Discovery of the Double Helix

The celebrated partnership that solved the puzzle of DNA structure began soon after a 23-year-old newly minted American Ph.D. named James D. Watson journeyed to Cambridge University in England. There, a more senior scientist named Francis Crick was studying protein structure with a technique called X-ray crystallography. While visiting the laboratory of Maurice Wilkins at King's College in London, Watson saw an X-ray image of DNA produced by Wilkins's colleague Rosalind Franklin. A careful study of the image enabled Watson to figure out that the basic shape of DNA is a helix (spiral) with a uniform diameter. The thickness of the helix suggested that it was made up of two polynucleotide strands—in other words, a **double helix**. But how were the nucleotides arranged in the double helix?

Using wire models, Watson and Crick began trying to construct a double helix that would conform both to Franklin's data and to what was then known about the chemistry of DNA (**Figure 10.3**). Watson placed the backbones on the outside of the model, forcing the nitrogenous bases to swivel to the interior of the molecule. It then occurred to him that the four kinds of bases might pair in a specific way. This idea of *specific base pairing* was a flash of inspiration that enabled Watson and Crick to solve the DNA puzzle.

▼ **Figure 10.3 Discoverers of the double helix.**

James Watson (left) and **Francis Crick.** The discoverers of the structure of DNA are shown in 1953 with their model of the double helix.

Rosalind Franklin (top). By generating X-ray images of DNA (bottom), Franklin provided Watson and Crick with some key data about the structure of DNA.

175

At first, Watson imagined that the bases paired like with like—for example, A with A, C with C. But that kind of pairing did not fit with the fact that the DNA molecule has a uniform diameter. An AA pair (made of two double-ringed bases) would be almost twice as wide as a CC pair (made of two single-ringed bases), resulting in an uneven molecule. It soon became apparent that a double-ringed base on one strand must always be paired with a single-ringed base on the opposite strand.

Moreover, Watson and Crick realized that the chemical structure of each kind of base dictated the pairings even more specifically. Each base has chemical groups that can best form hydrogen bonds with just one appropriate partner. Adenine can best form hydrogen bonds with thymine, and guanine with cytosine. In the biologist's shorthand: A pairs with T, and G pairs with C. A is also said to be "complementary" to T, and G to C.

You can picture the model of the DNA double helix proposed by Watson and Crick as a rope ladder having rigid, wooden rungs, with the ladder twisted into a spiral (Figure 10.4). Figure 10.5 shows three more detailed representations of the double helix. The ribbonlike diagram in Figure 10.5a symbolizes the bases with shapes that emphasize their complementarity. Figure 10.5b is a more chemically precise version showing only four base pairs, with the helix untwisted and the individual hydrogen bonds specified by dashed lines. Figure 10.5c is a computer model showing part of a double helix in atomic detail.

Although the base-pairing rules dictate the side-by-side combinations of nitrogenous bases that form the rungs of the double helix, they place no restrictions on the sequence of nucleotides along the length of a DNA strand. In fact, the sequence of bases can vary in countless ways.

▶ **Figure 10.4 A rope-ladder model of a double helix.** The ropes at the sides represent the sugar-phosphate backbones. Each wooden rung stands for a pair of bases connected by hydrogen bonds.

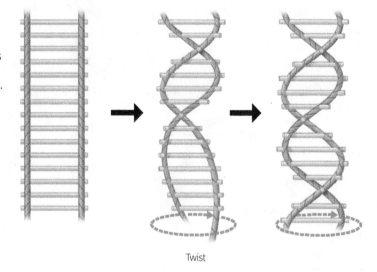

Twist

▼ Figure 10.5 **Three representations of DNA.**

Hydrogen bond

(a) Ribbon model. The sugar-phosphate backbones are blue ribbons, and the bases are complementary shapes in shades of green and orange.

(b) Atomic model. In this more chemically detailed structure, you can see the individual hydrogen bonds (dashed lines). You can also see that the strands run in opposite directions: Notice that the sugars on the two strands are upside down with respect to each other.

(c) Computer model. Each atom is shown as a sphere, creating a space-filling model.

In April 1953, Watson and Crick rocked the scientific world with a succinct paper proposing their molecular model for DNA in the British scientific journal *Nature*. Few milestones in the history of biology have had as broad an impact as their double helix, with its AT and CG base pairing. In 1962, Watson, Crick, and Wilkins received the Nobel Prize for their work. (Franklin deserved the prize as well, but she had died from cancer in 1958; Nobel prizes are never awarded posthumously.)

In their 1953 paper, Watson and Crick wrote that the structure they proposed "immediately suggests a possible copying mechanism for the genetic material." In other words, the structure of DNA also points toward a molecular explanation for life's unique properties of reproduction and inheritance, as we see next.

DNA Replication

When a cell or a whole organism reproduces, a complete set of genetic instructions must pass from one generation to the next. For this to occur, there must be a means of copying the instructions. Watson and Crick's model for DNA structure immediately suggested to them that each DNA strand serves as a mold, or template, to guide reproduction of the other strand. The logic behind the Watson-Crick proposal for how DNA is copied is quite simple. If you know the sequence of bases in one strand of the double helix, you can very easily determine the sequence of bases in the other strand by applying the base-pairing rules: A pairs with T (and T with A), and G pairs with C (and C with G). For example, if one polynucleotide has the sequence AGTC, then the complementary polynucleotide in that DNA molecule must have the sequence TCAG.

Figure 10.6 shows how this model can account for the direct copying of a piece of DNA. The two strands of parental DNA separate, and each becomes a template for the assembly of a complementary strand from a supply of free nucleotides. The nucleotides are lined up one at a time along the template strand in accordance with the base-pairing rules. Enzymes link the nucleotides to form the new DNA strands. The completed new molecules, identical to the parental molecule, are known as daughter DNA molecules (no gender should be inferred from this name).

Although the general mechanism of DNA replication is conceptually simple, the actual process is complex and requires the cooperation of more than a dozen enzymes and other proteins. The enzymes that make the covalent bonds between the nucleotides of a new DNA strand are called **DNA polymerases**. As an incoming nucleotide base-pairs with its complement on the template strand, a DNA polymerase adds it to the end of the growing daughter strand (polymer). The process is both fast and amazingly accurate; typically, DNA replication proceeds at a rate of 50 nucleotides per second, with fewer than one in a billion incorrectly paired. In addition to their roles in DNA replication, DNA polymerases and some of the associated proteins are also involved in repairing damaged DNA. DNA can be harmed by toxic chemicals in the environment or by high-energy radiation, such as X-rays and ultraviolet light.

DNA replication begins at specific sites on a double helix, called origins of replication. It then proceeds in both directions, creating what are called replication "bubbles" (Figure 10.7). The parental DNA strands open up as daughter strands elongate on both sides of each bubble. The DNA molecule of a typical eukaryotic chromosome has many origins where replication can start simultaneously, shortening the total time needed for the process. Eventually, all the bubbles merge, yielding two completed double-stranded daughter DNA molecules.

DNA replication ensures that all the body cells in a multicellular organism carry the same genetic information. It is also the means by which genetic information is passed along to offspring. ☑

▲ Figure 10.6 **DNA replication.** Replication results in two daughter DNA molecules, each consisting of one old strand and one new strand. The parental DNA untwists as its strands separate, and the daughter DNA rewinds as it forms.

Parental (old) DNA molecule

Daughter (new) strand

Parental (old) strand

Daughter DNA molecules (double helices)

▼ Figure 10.7 **Multiple "bubbles" in replicating DNA.**

Origin of replication

Origin of replication

Parental strands

Origin of replication

Parental strand

Daughter strand

Bubble

Two daughter DNA molecules

☑ CHECKPOINT

1. How does complementary base pairing make DNA replication possible?
2. What enzymes connect nucleotides together during DNA replication?

Answers: 1. When the two strands of the double helix separate, each serves as a template on which nucleotides can be arranged by specific base pairing into new complementary strands. 2. DNA polymerases

177

The Flow of Genetic Information from DNA to RNA to Protein

Now that we've seen how the structure of DNA allows it to be copied, we can explore how DNA provides instructions to a cell and to an organism as a whole.

How an Organism's Genotype Determines Its Phenotype

We can now define genotype and phenotype in terms of the structure and function of DNA. An organism's *genotype*, its genetic makeup, is the heritable information contained in the sequence of nucleotide bases in its DNA. The *phenotype*, the organism's physical traits, arises from the actions of a wide variety of proteins. For example, structural proteins help make up the body of an organism, and enzymes catalyze the chemical reactions that are necessary for life.

Your genes determine who you are—but how?

What is the connection between the genotype and the protein molecules that more directly determine the phenotype? DNA specifies the synthesis of proteins. However, a gene does not build a protein directly, but rather dispatches instructions in the form of RNA, which in turn programs protein synthesis. This fundamental concept in biology (termed the "central dogma" by Francis Crick) is summarized in Figure 10.8. The

molecular "chain of command" is from DNA in the nucleus (purple area in the figure) to RNA to protein synthesis in the cytoplasm (blue-green). The two main stages are **transcription**, the transfer of genetic information from DNA into an RNA molecule, and **translation**, the transfer of the information from RNA into a protein.

The relationship between genes and proteins was first proposed in 1909, when English physician Archibald Garrod suggested that genes dictate phenotypes through enzymes, the proteins that speed chemical reactions. Garrod hypothesized that inherited diseases reflect a person's inability to make a particular enzyme. He gave as one example the hereditary condition called alkaptonuria, in which the urine appears dark red because it contains a chemical called alkapton. Garrod reasoned that normal individuals have an enzyme that breaks down alkapton, whereas alkaptonuric individuals lack the enzyme. Research conducted decades later proved him right.

The major breakthrough in demonstrating the relationship between genes and enzymes came in the 1940s from the work of American geneticists George Beadle and Edward Tatum with the bread mold *Neurospora crassa* (Figure 10.9). Beadle and Tatum studied strains of the mold that were unable to grow on the usual growth medium. Each of these strains turned out to lack an enzyme in a metabolic pathway that synthesized an amino acid called arginine. Beadle and Tatum also showed that each mutant was defective in a single gene. Accordingly, they hypothesized that the function of an individual gene is to dictate the production of a specific enzyme.

▲ **Figure 10.9 The bread mold *Neurospora crassa* has a fuzzy appearance.**

The "one gene–one enzyme" hypothesis has since been modified. First it was extended beyond enzymes to include all types of proteins. For example, keratin (the structural protein of your hair) is the product of a gene. Then it was discovered that many proteins have two or more different polypeptide chains (see Figure 3.20d); in such cases, each polypeptide is specified by its own gene. Thus, Beadle and Tatum's hypothesis is now stated as follows: the function of a gene is to dictate the production of a polypeptide. ✓

▶ **Figure 10.8 The flow of genetic information in a eukaryotic cell.** A sequence of nucleotides in the DNA is transcribed into a molecule of RNA in the cell's nucleus. The RNA travels to the cytoplasm, where it is translated into the specific amino acid sequence of a protein.

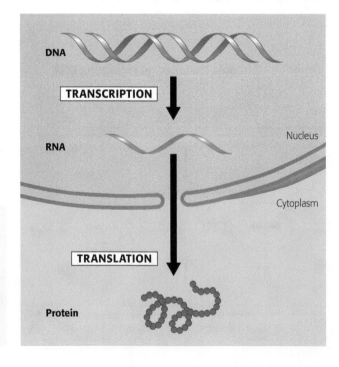

DNA

TRANSCRIPTION

RNA   Nucleus

Cytoplasm

TRANSLATION

Protein

✓ **CHECKPOINT**

What are transcription and translation?

Answer: Transcription is the transfer of genetic information from DNA to RNA. Translation is the use of the information in an RNA molecule for the synthesis of a polypeptide.

From Nucleotides to Amino Acids: An Overview

Genetic information in DNA is transcribed into RNA and then translated into polypeptides, which then fold into proteins. But how do these processes occur? Transcription and translation are linguistic terms, and it is useful to think of nucleic acids and proteins as having languages. To understand how genetic information passes from genotype to phenotype, we need to see how the chemical language of DNA is translated into the different chemical language of proteins.

What exactly is the language of nucleic acids? Both DNA and RNA are polymers made of nucleotide monomers strung together in specific sequences that convey information, much as specific sequences of letters convey information in English. In DNA, the monomers are the four types of nucleotides, which differ in their nitrogenous bases (A, T, C, and G). The same is true for RNA, although it has the base U instead of T.

The language of DNA is written as a linear sequence of nucleotide bases, a sequence such as the blue sequence you see on the enlarged DNA strand in Figure 10.10. Specific sequences of bases, each with a beginning and an end, make up the genes on a DNA strand. A typical gene consists of thousands of nucleotides in a specific sequence.

When a segment of DNA is transcribed, the result is an RNA molecule. The process is called transcription because the nucleic acid language of DNA has simply been rewritten (transcribed) as a sequence of bases of RNA; the language is still that of nucleic acids. The nucleotide bases of the RNA molecule are complementary to those on the DNA strand. As you will soon see, this is because the RNA was synthesized using the DNA as a template.

Translation is the conversion of the nucleic acid language to the polypeptide language. Like nucleic acids, polypeptides are polymers, but the monomers that make them up—the letters of the polypeptide alphabet—are the 20 amino acids common to all organisms (represented as purple shapes in Figure 10.10). Again, the language is written in a linear sequence. In this case, the sequence of nucleotides of the RNA molecule dictates the sequence of amino acids of the polypeptide. But remember, RNA is only a messenger; the genetic information that dictates the amino acid sequence originates in DNA.

What are the rules for translating the RNA message into a polypeptide? In other words, what is the correspondence between the nucleotides of an RNA molecule and the amino acids of a polypeptide? Keep in mind that there are only four different kinds of nucleotides in DNA (A, G, C, T) and RNA (A, G, C, U). In translation, these four must somehow specify 20 amino acids. If each nucleotide base coded for one amino acid, only 4 of the 20 amino acids could be accounted for. In fact, triplets of bases are the smallest "words" of uniform length that can specify all the amino acids. There can be 64 (that is, 4^3) possible code words of this type—more than enough to specify the 20 amino acids. Indeed, there are enough triplets to allow more than one coding for each amino acid. For example, the base triplets AAA and AAG both code for the same amino acid.

Experiments have verified that the flow of information from gene to protein is based on a triplet code. The genetic instructions for the amino acid sequence of a polypeptide chain are written in DNA and RNA as a series of three-base words called **codons**. Three-base codons in the DNA are transcribed into complementary three-base codons in the RNA, and then the RNA codons are translated into amino acids that form a polypeptide. As summarized in Figure 10.10, one DNA codon (three nucleotides) → one RNA codon (three nucleotides) → one amino acid. Next we turn to the codons themselves. ☑

▼ Figure 10.10 **Transcription of DNA and translation of codons.** This figure focuses on a small region of one of the genes carried by a DNA molecule. The enlarged segment from one strand of gene 3 shows its specific sequence of bases. The red strand and purple chain represent the results of transcription and translation, respectively.

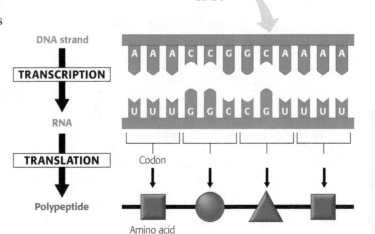

☑ CHECKPOINT

How many nucleotides are necessary to code for a polypeptide that is 100 amino acids long?

Answer: 300

The Genetic Code

During the 1960s, scientists cracked the **genetic code**, the set of rules that convert a nucleotide sequence in RNA to an amino acid sequence. As **Figure 10.11** shows, 61 of the 64 triplets code for amino acids. The triplet AUG has a dual function: It codes for the amino acid methionine (Met) and can also provide a signal for the start of a polypeptide chain. Three codons (UAA, UGA, and UAG) do not designate amino acids. They are the stop codons that instruct the ribosomes to end the polypeptide.

Notice in Figure 10.11 that a given RNA triplet always specifies a given amino acid. For example, although codons UUU and UUC both specify phenylalanine, neither of them ever represents any other amino acid. The codons in the figure are the triplets found in RNA. They have a straightforward, complementary relationship to the codons in DNA.

The nucleotides making up the codons occur in a linear order along the DNA and RNA, with no gaps separating the codons.

The genetic code is nearly universal, shared by organisms from the simplest bacteria to the most complex plants and animals. The universality of the genetic vocabulary suggests that it arose very early in evolution and was passed on over the eons to all the organisms living on Earth today. In fact, such universality is the key to modern DNA technologies. Because diverse organisms share a common genetic code, it is possible to program one species to produce a protein from another species by transplanting DNA (**Figure 10.12**). This allows scientists to mix and match genes from various species—a procedure with many useful applications. Besides having practical purposes, a shared genetic vocabulary also reminds us of the evolutionary kinship that connects all life on Earth. ☑

How is it that genetic engineers can mix and match DNA from different species?

CHECKPOINT

An RNA molecule contains the nucleotide sequence CCAUUUACG. Using Figure 10.11, translate this sequence into the corresponding amino acid sequence.

Answer: Pro-Phe-Thr

Second base of RNA codon

	U	C	A	G	
U	UUU UUC Phenylalanine (Phe) UUA UUG Leucine (Leu)	UCU UCC UCA UCG Serine (Ser)	UAU UAC Tyrosine (Tyr) UAA Stop UAG Stop	UGU UGC Cysteine (Cys) UGA Stop UGG Tryptophan (Trp)	U C A G
C	CUU CUC CUA CUG Leucine (Leu)	CCU CCC CCA CCG Proline (Pro)	CAU CAC Histidine (His) CAA CAG Glutamine (Gln)	CGU CGC CGA CGG Arginine (Arg)	U C A G
A	AUU AUC Isoleucine (Ile) AUA AUG Met or start	ACU ACC ACA ACG Threonine (Thr)	AAU AAC Asparagine (Asn) AAA AAG Lysine (Lys)	AGU AGC Serine (Ser) AGA AGG Arginine (Arg)	U C A G
G	GUU GUC GUA GUG Valine (Val)	GCU GCC GCA GCG Alanine (Ala)	GAU GAC Aspartic acid (Asp) GAA GAG Glutamic acid (Glu)	GGU GGC GGA GGG Glycine (Gly)	U C A G

First base of RNA codon (left side)

Third base of RNA codon (right side)

▲ Figure 10.11 **The dictionary of the genetic code, listed by RNA codons.** Practice using this dictionary by finding the codon UGG. (It is the only codon for the amino acid tryptophan, Trp.) Notice that the codon AUG (highlighted in green) not only stands for the amino acid methionine (Met), but also functions as a signal to "start" translating the RNA at that place. Three of the 64 codons (highlighted in red) function as "stop" signals that mark the end of a genetic message, but do not encode any amino acids.

▲ Figure 10.12 **Mice expressing a foreign gene.** This photo shows the results of an experiment in which researchers incorporated a jelly (jellyfish) gene for a protein called green fluorescent protein (GFP) into the DNA of mice. The mouse in the middle lacks the gene for GFP; the other mice have it.

Transcription: From DNA to RNA

Let's look more closely at transcription, the transfer of genetic information from DNA to RNA. An RNA molecule is transcribed from a DNA template by a process that resembles the synthesis of a DNA strand during DNA replication. **Figure 10.13a** is a close-up view of this process. As with replication, the two DNA strands must first separate at the place where the process will start. In transcription, however, only one of the DNA strands serves as a template for the newly forming RNA molecule; the other strand is unused. The nucleotides that make up the new RNA molecule take their place one at a time along the DNA template strand by forming hydrogen bonds with the nucleotide bases there. Notice that the RNA nucleotides follow the usual base-pairing rules, except that U, rather than T, pairs with A. The RNA nucleotides are linked by the transcription enzyme **RNA polymerase**.

Figure 10.13b is an overview of the transcription of an entire gene. Special sequences of DNA nucleotides tell the RNA polymerase where to start and where to stop the transcribing process.

❶ Initiation of Transcription

The "start transcribing" signal is a nucleotide sequence called a **promoter**, which is located in the DNA at the beginning of the gene. A promoter is a specific place where RNA polymerase attaches. The first phase of transcription, called initiation, is the attachment of RNA polymerase to the promoter and the start of RNA

synthesis. For any gene, the promoter dictates which of the two DNA strands is to be transcribed (the particular strand varies from gene to gene).

❷ RNA Elongation

During the second phase of transcription, elongation, the RNA grows longer. As RNA synthesis continues, the RNA strand peels away from its DNA template, allowing the two separated DNA strands to come back together in the region already transcribed.

❸ Termination of Transcription

In the third phase, termination, the RNA polymerase reaches a special sequence of bases in the DNA template called a **terminator**. This sequence signals the end of the gene. At this point, the polymerase molecule detaches from the RNA molecule and the gene, and the DNA strands rejoin.

In addition to producing RNA that encodes amino acid sequences, transcription makes two other kinds of RNA that are involved in building polypeptides. We discuss these kinds of RNA a little later. ☑

☑ CHECKPOINT

How does RNA polymerase "know" where to start transcribing a gene?

Answer: It recognizes the gene's promoter, a specific nucleotide sequence.

▼ Figure 10.13 **Transcription.**

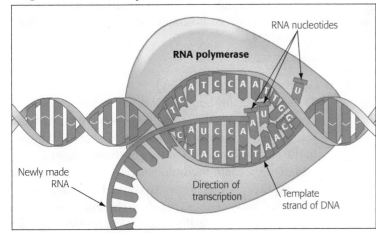

(a) A close-up view of transcription. As RNA nucleotides base-pair one by one with DNA bases on one DNA strand (called the template strand), the enzyme RNA polymerase (orange) links the RNA nucleotides into an RNA chain.

(b) Transcription of a gene. The transcription of an entire gene occurs in three phases: initiation, elongation, and termination of the RNA. The section of DNA where the RNA polymerase starts is called the promoter; the place where it stops is called the terminator.

The Processing of Eukaryotic RNA

In the cells of prokaryotes, which lack nuclei, the RNA transcribed from a gene immediately functions as **messenger RNA (mRNA)**, the molecule that is translated into protein. But this is not the case in eukaryotic cells. The eukaryotic cell not only localizes transcription in the nucleus but also modifies, or processes, the RNA transcripts there before they move to the cytoplasm for translation by the ribosomes.

One kind of RNA processing is the addition of extra nucleotides to the ends of the RNA transcript. These additions, called the **cap** and **tail**, protect the RNA from attack by cellular enzymes and help ribosomes recognize the RNA as mRNA.

Another type of RNA processing is made necessary in eukaryotes by noncoding stretches of nucleotides that interrupt the nucleotides that actually code for amino acids. It is as if nonsense words were randomly interspersed in a story. Most genes of plants and animals, it turns out, include such internal noncoding regions, which are called **introns**. The coding regions—the parts of a gene that are expressed—are called **exons**. As Figure 10.14 illustrates, both exons and introns are transcribed from DNA into RNA. However, before the RNA leaves the nucleus, the introns are removed, and the exons are joined to produce an mRNA molecule with a continuous coding sequence. This process is called **RNA splicing**. RNA splicing is believed to play a significant role in humans in allowing our approximately 21,000 genes to produce many thousands

Do your genes contain gobbledygook?

☑ **CHECKPOINT**

Why is a final mRNA often shorter than the DNA gene that coded for it?

Answer: because introns are removed from the RNA

▲ Figure 10.14 **The production of messenger RNA (mRNA) in a eukaryotic cell.** Note that the molecule of mRNA that leaves the nucleus is substantially different from the molecule of RNA that was first transcribed from the gene. In the cytoplasm, the coding sequence of the final mRNA will be translated.

more polypeptides. This is accomplished by varying the exons that are included in the final mRNA.

With capping, tailing, and splicing completed, the "final draft" of eukaryotic mRNA is ready for translation. ☑

Translation: The Players

As we have already discussed, translation is a conversion between different languages—from the nucleic acid language to the protein language—and it involves more elaborate machinery than transcription.

Messenger RNA (mRNA)

The first important ingredient required for translation is the mRNA produced by transcription. Once it is present, the machinery used to translate mRNA requires enzymes and sources of chemical energy, such

as ATP. In addition, translation requires two heavy-duty components: ribosomes and a kind of RNA called transfer RNA.

Transfer RNA (tRNA)

Translation of any language into another language requires an interpreter, someone or something that can recognize the words of one language and convert them to the other. Translation of the genetic message carried in mRNA into the amino acid language of proteins also requires an interpreter. To convert the three-letter words (codons) of nucleic acids to the amino acid words of proteins, a cell uses a molecular interpreter, a type of RNA called **transfer RNA (tRNA)**, depicted in Figure 10.15.

▼ Figure 10.15 **The structure of tRNA.** At one end of the tRNA is the site where an amino acid will attach (purple), and at the other end is the three-nucleotide anticodon where the mRNA will attach (light green).

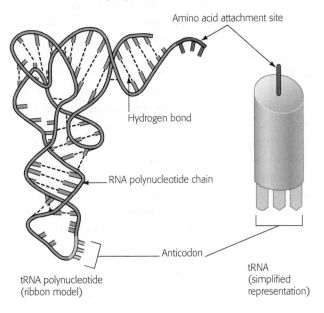

Amino acid attachment site

Hydrogen bond

RNA polynucleotide chain

Anticodon

tRNA polynucleotide (ribbon model)

tRNA (simplified representation)

A cell that is producing proteins has in its cytoplasm a supply of amino acids. But amino acids themselves cannot recognize the codons arranged in sequence along messenger RNA. It is up to the cell's molecular interpreters, tRNA molecules, to match amino acids to the appropriate codons to form the new polypeptide. To perform this task, tRNA molecules must carry out two distinct functions: (1) pick up the appropriate amino acids and (2) recognize the appropriate codons in the mRNA. The unique structure of tRNA molecules enables them to perform both tasks.

As shown on the left in Figure 10.15, a tRNA molecule is made of a single strand of RNA—one polynucleotide chain—consisting of about 80 nucleotides. The chain twists and folds upon itself, forming several double-stranded regions in which short stretches of RNA base-pair with other stretches. At one end of the folded molecule is a special triplet of bases called an **anticodon**. The anticodon triplet is complementary to a codon triplet on mRNA. During translation, the anticodon on the tRNA recognizes a particular codon on the mRNA by using base-pairing rules. At the other end of the tRNA molecule is a site where one specific kind of amino acid attaches. Although all tRNA molecules are similar, there are slightly different versions of tRNA for each amino acid.

Ribosomes

Ribosomes are the organelles that coordinate the functioning of the mRNA and tRNA and actually make polypeptides. As you can see in **Figure 10.16a**, a ribosome consists of two subunits. Each subunit is made up of proteins and a considerable amount of yet another kind of RNA, **ribosomal RNA (rRNA)**. A fully assembled ribosome has a binding site for mRNA on its small subunit and binding sites for tRNA on its large subunit. **Figure 10.16b** shows how two tRNA molecules get together with an mRNA molecule on a ribosome. One of the tRNA binding sites, the P site, holds the tRNA carrying the growing polypeptide chain, while another, the A site, holds a tRNA carrying the next amino acid to be added to the chain. The anticodon on each tRNA base-pairs with a codon on the mRNA. The subunits of the ribosome act like a vise, holding the tRNA and mRNA molecules close together. The ribosome can then connect the amino acid from the tRNA in the A site to the growing polypeptide. ✓

▼ Figure 10.16 **The ribosome.**

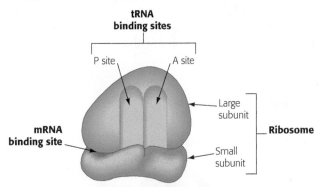

tRNA binding sites

P site   A site

mRNA binding site

Large subunit

Ribosome

Small subunit

(a) A simplified diagram of a ribosome. Notice the two subunits and sites where mRNA and tRNA molecules bind.

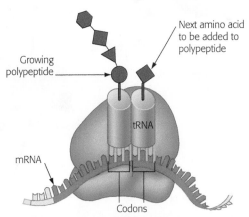

Growing polypeptide

Next amino acid to be added to polypeptide

tRNA

mRNA

Codons

(b) The "players" of translation. When functioning in polypeptide synthesis, a ribosome holds one molecule of mRNA and two molecules of tRNA. The growing polypeptide is attached to one of the tRNAs.

☑ CHECKPOINT

What is an anticodon?

Answer: An anticodon is the base triplet of a tRNA molecule that couples the tRNA to a complementary codon in the mRNA. The base pairing of anticodon to codon is a key step in translating mRNA to a polypeptide.

Translation: The Process

Translation is divided into the same three phases as transcription: initiation, elongation, and termination.

Initiation

This first phase brings together the mRNA, the first amino acid with its attached tRNA, and the two subunits of a ribosome. An mRNA molecule, even after splicing, is longer than the genetic message it carries (Figure 10.17). Nucleotide sequences at either end of the molecule (pink) are not part of the message, but along with the cap and tail in eukaryotes, they help the mRNA bind to the ribosome. The initiation process determines exactly where translation will begin so that the mRNA codons will be translated into the correct sequence of amino acids. Initiation occurs in two steps, as shown in Figure 10.18. **1** An mRNA molecule binds to a small ribosomal subunit. A special initiator tRNA then binds to the **start codon**, where translation is to begin on the mRNA. The initiator tRNA carries the amino acid methionine (Met); its anticodon, UAC, binds to the start codon, AUG. **2** A large ribosomal subunit binds to the small one, creating a functional ribosome. The initiator tRNA fits into the P site on the ribosome.

Elongation

Once initiation is complete, amino acids are added one by one to the first amino acid. Each addition occurs in the three-step elongation process shown in Figure 10.19. **1** **Codon recognition**. The anticodon of an incoming tRNA molecule, carrying its amino acid, pairs with the mRNA codon in the A site of the ribosome. **2** **Peptide bond formation**. The polypeptide leaves the tRNA in the P site and attaches to the amino acid on the tRNA in the A site. The ribosome catalyzes bond formation. Now the chain has one more amino acid. **3** **Translocation**. The P site tRNA now leaves the ribosome, and the ribosome moves the remaining tRNA, carrying the growing polypeptide, to the P site. The mRNA and tRNA move as a unit. This movement brings into the A site the next mRNA codon to be translated, and the process can start again with step 1.

Termination

Elongation continues until a **stop codon** reaches the ribosome's A site. Stop codons—UAA, UAG, and UGA—do not code for amino acids but instead tell translation to stop. The completed polypeptide, typically several hundred amino acids long, is freed, and the ribosome splits back into its subunits. ☑

▼ Figure 10.17 **A molecule of mRNA.**

▼ Figure 10.18 **The initiation of translation.**

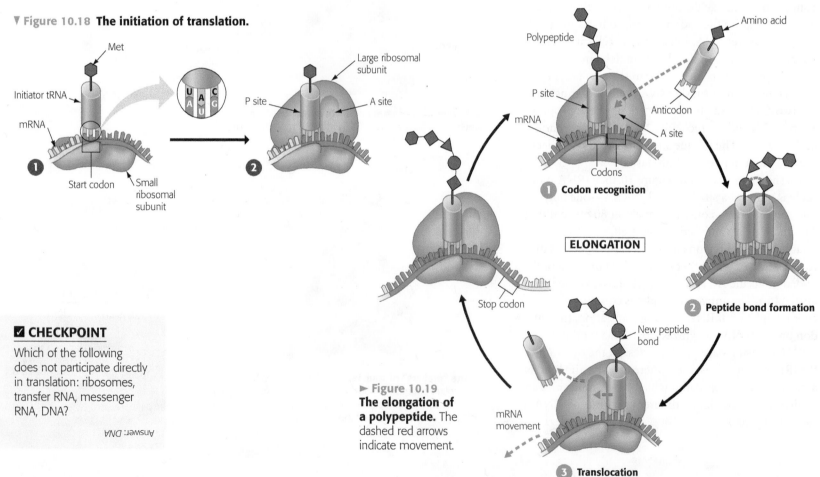

► Figure 10.19
The elongation of a polypeptide. The dashed red arrows indicate movement.

Review:
DNA → RNA → Protein

Figure 10.20 reviews the flow of genetic information in the cell, from DNA to RNA to protein. In eukaryotic cells, transcription (DNA → RNA) occurs in the nucleus, and the RNA is processed before it enters the cytoplasm. Translation (RNA → protein) is rapid; a single ribosome can make an average-sized polypeptide in less than a minute. As it is made, a polypeptide coils and folds, assuming a three-dimensional shape, its tertiary structure.

What is the overall significance of transcription and translation? These are the processes whereby genes control the structures and activities of cells—or, more broadly, the way the genotype produces the phenotype. The chain of command originates with the information in a gene, a specific sequence of nucleotides in DNA. The gene dictates the transcription of a complementary sequence of nucleotides in mRNA. In turn, mRNA specifies the sequence of amino acids in a polypeptide. Finally, the proteins that form from the polypeptides determine the appearance and capabilities of the cell and organism.

For decades, the DNA → RNA → protein pathway was believed to be the sole means by which genetic information controls traits. In recent years, however, this notion has been challenged by discoveries that point to more complex roles for RNA. We will explore some of these special properties of RNA in Chapter 11. ☑

☑ CHECKPOINT

1. Transcription is the synthesis of _____, using _____ as a template.
2. Translation is the synthesis of _____, with one _____ determining each amino acid in the sequence.
3. Which organelle coordinates translation?

Answers: 1. mRNA; DNA 2. protein (polypeptides); codon 3. ribosomes

▼ **Figure 10.20 A summary of transcription and translation.** This figure summarizes the main stages in the flow of genetic information from DNA to protein in a eukaryotic cell.

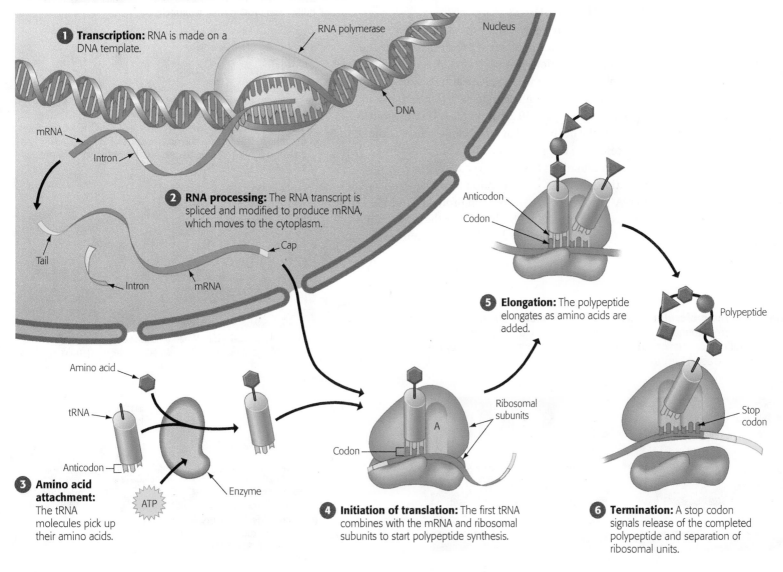

① **Transcription:** RNA is made on a DNA template.

RNA polymerase

Nucleus

DNA

mRNA

Intron

② **RNA processing:** The RNA transcript is spliced and modified to produce mRNA, which moves to the cytoplasm.

Cap

Tail

Intron

mRNA

Amino acid

tRNA

Anticodon

③ **Amino acid attachment:** The tRNA molecules pick up their amino acids.

ATP

Enzyme

Codon

④ **Initiation of translation:** The first tRNA combines with the mRNA and ribosomal subunits to start polypeptide synthesis.

A

Ribosomal subunits

Anticodon

Codon

⑤ **Elongation:** The polypeptide elongates as amino acids are added.

Polypeptide

Stop codon

⑥ **Termination:** A stop codon signals release of the completed polypeptide and separation of ribosomal units.

Mutations

Since discovering how genes are translated into proteins, scientists have been able to describe many heritable differences in molecular terms. For instance, sickle-cell

How can a molecular "typo" make you sick?

disease can be traced to a change in a single amino acid in one of the polypeptides in the hemoglobin protein (see Figure 3.19). This difference is caused by a single nucleotide difference in the DNA coding for that polypeptide (Figure 10.21).

Any change in the nucleotide sequence of DNA is called a **mutation**. Mutations can involve large regions of a chromosome or just a single nucleotide pair, as in sickle-cell disease. Occasionally, a base substitution leads to an improved protein or one with new capabilities that enhance the success of the mutant organism and its descendants. Much more often, though, mutations are harmful. Let's consider how mutations involving only one or a few nucleotide pairs can affect gene translation.

Types of Mutations

Mutations within a gene can be divided into two general categories: nucleotide substitutions and nucleotide insertions or deletions (Figure 10.22). A substitution is the replacement of one nucleotide and its base-pairing partner with another nucleotide pair. For example, in the second row in Figure 10.22, A replaces G in the fourth codon of the mRNA. What effect can a substitution have? Because the genetic code is redundant, some substitution mutations have no effect at all. For example, if a mutation causes an mRNA codon to change from GAA to GAG, no change in the protein product would result because GAA and GAG both code for the same amino acid (Glu). Such a change is called a silent mutation.

Other substitutions involving a single nucleotide do change the amino acid coding. Such mutations are called missense mutations. For example, if a mutation causes an mRNA codon to change from GGC to AGC, the resulting protein will have a serine (Ser) instead of a glycine (Gly) at this position. Some missense mutations have little or no effect on the shape or function of the resulting protein, but others, as we saw in the sickle-cell case, cause changes in the protein that prevent it from performing normally.

▼ Figure 10.22 **Three types of mutations and their effects.** Mutations are changes in DNA, but they are shown here in mRNA and the polypeptide product.

mRNA and protein from a normal gene

(a) Base substitution. Here, an A replaces a G in the fourth codon of the mRNA. The result in the polypeptide is a serine (Ser) instead of a glycine (Gly). This amino acid substitution may or may not affect the protein's function.

(b) Nucleotide deletion. When a nucleotide is deleted, all the codons from that point on are misread. The resulting polypeptide is likely to be completely nonfunctional.

(c) Nucleotide insertion. As with a deletion, inserting one nucleotide disrupts all codons that follow, most likely producing a nonfunctional polypeptide.

▼ Figure 10.21 **The molecular basis of sickle-cell disease.** The sickle-cell allele differs from its normal counterpart, a gene for hemoglobin, by only one nucleotide (orange). This difference changes the mRNA codon from one that codes for the amino acid glutamic acid (Glu) to one that codes for valine (Val).

Some substitutions, called nonsense mutations, change an amino acid codon into a stop codon. For example, if an AGA (Arg) codon is mutated to a UGA (stop) codon, the result will be a prematurely terminated protein, which probably will not function properly.

Mutations involving the deletion or insertion of one or more nucleotides in a gene often have disastrous effects (see Figure 10.22b and c). Because mRNA is read as a series of nucleotide triplets during translation, adding or subtracting nucleotides may alter the triplet grouping of the genetic message. All the nucleotides that are "downstream" of the insertion or deletion will be regrouped into different codons. For example, consider an mRNA molecule containing the sequence AAG-UUU-GGC-GCA; this codes for Lys-Phe-Gly-Ala. If a U is missing in the second codon (as a result of a deletion in the DNA), the resulting sequence will be AAG-UUG-GCG-CA, which codes for Lys-Leu-Ala (see Figure 10.22b). The altered polypeptide is likely to be nonfunctional. Inserting one or two nucleotides would have a similarly profound effect.

Mutagens

What causes mutations? Mutagenesis, the creation of mutations, can occur in a number of ways. Spontaneous mutations result from errors during DNA replication or recombination. Other sources of mutation are physical and chemical agents called **mutagens**. The most common physical mutagen is high-energy radiation, such as X-rays and ultraviolet (UV) light. Chemical mutagens are of various types. One type, for example, consists of chemicals that are similar to normal DNA bases but that base-pair incorrectly when incorporated into DNA. For example, the anti-AIDS drug AZT works because its structure is similar enough to thymine that viral polymerases incorporate it into newly synthesized DNA, but different enough that the drug blocks further replication.

Many mutagens can act as carcinogens, agents that cause cancer. What can you do to avoid exposure to mutagens? Several lifestyle practices can help, including not smoking and wearing protective clothing and sunscreen to minimize direct exposure to the sun's UV rays. But such precautions are not foolproof, and it is not possible to avoid mutagens (such as UV radiation and secondhand smoke) entirely.

Although mutations are often harmful, they can also be extremely useful, both in nature and in the laboratory. Mutations are one source of the rich diversity of genes in the living world, a diversity that makes evolution by natural selection possible (Figure 10.23). Mutations are also essential tools for geneticists. Whether naturally occurring or created in the laboratory, mutations are responsible for the different alleles needed for genetic research. ☑

▼ Figure 10.23 **Mutations and diversity.** Mutations are one source of the diversity of life visible in this scene from the big island of Hawaii.

☑ CHECKPOINT

1. What would happen if a mutation changed a start codon to some other codon?
2. What happens when one nucleotide is lost from the middle of a gene?

Answers: 1. mRNA transcribed from the mutated gene would be nonfunctional because ribosomes would not initiate translation. 2. In the mRNA, the reading of the triplets downstream from the deletion is shifted, leading to a long string of incorrect amino acids in the polypeptide.

Viruses and Other Noncellular Infectious Agents

Viruses share some of the characteristics of living organisms, such as having genetic material in the form of nucleic acid packaged within a highly organized structure. A virus is generally not considered alive, however, because it is not cellular and cannot reproduce on its own. In a sense, a **virus** is nothing more than "genes in a box": a bit of nucleic acid wrapped in a protein coat (Figure 10.24). A virus can

Is a virus a living creature?

survive only by infecting a living cell and directing the cell's molecular machinery to make more viruses. In this section, we'll look at viruses that infect different types of host organisms, starting with bacteria.

Bacteriophages

Viruses that attack bacteria are called **bacteriophages** ("bacteria-eaters"), or **phages** for short. Figure 10.25 shows a micrograph of a bacteriophage called T4 infecting an *E. coli* bacterium. The phage consists of a molecule of DNA enclosed within an elaborate structure made of proteins. The "legs" of the phage (called tail fibers) bend when they touch the cell surface. The tail is a hollow rod enclosed in a springlike sheath. As the legs bend, the spring compresses, the bottom of the rod punctures the cell membrane, and the viral DNA passes from inside the head of the virus into the cell.

Once they infect a bacterium, most phages enter a reproductive cycle called the **lytic cycle**. The lytic cycle gets its name from the fact that after many copies of the phage are produced within the bacterial cell, the bacterium lyses (breaks open). Some viruses can also reproduce by an alternative route—the **lysogenic cycle**.

▼ Figure 10.24 **Adenovirus.** A virus that infects the human respiratory system, an adenovirus consists of DNA enclosed in a protein coat shaped like a 20-sided polyhedron, shown here in a computer-generated model that is magnified approximately 500,000 times the actual size. At each corner of the polyhedron is a protein spike, which helps the virus attach to a susceptible cell.

Protein coat

DNA

▼ Figure 10.25 **Bacteriophages (viruses) infecting a bacterial cell.**

Head

Bacteriophage
(200 nm tall)

Tail

Tail
fiber

Bacterial cell

DNA
of virus

Colorized TEM 225,000×

During a lysogenic cycle, viral DNA replication occurs without phage production or the death of the cell.

Figure 10.26 illustrates the two kinds of cycles for a phage named lambda that can infect *E. coli* bacteria. Lambda has a head (containing DNA) and a tail. At the start of infection, ❶ lambda binds to the outside of a bacterium and injects its DNA inside. ❷ The injected lambda DNA forms a circle. In the lytic cycle, this DNA immediately turns the cell into a virus-producing factory. ❸ The cell's own machinery for DNA replication,

transcription, and translation is hijacked by the virus and used to produce copies of the virus. ❹ The cell lyses, releasing the new phages.

In the lysogenic cycle, ❺ the viral DNA is inserted into the bacterial chromosome. Once there, the phage DNA is referred to as a **prophage**, and most of its genes are inactive. Survival of the prophage depends on the reproduction of the cell where it resides. ❻ The host cell replicates the prophage DNA along with its cellular DNA and then, upon dividing, passes on both the prophage and the cellular DNA to its two daughter cells. A single infected bacterium can quickly give rise to a large population of bacteria that all carry prophages. The prophages may remain in the bacterial cells indefinitely. ❼ Occasionally, however, a prophage leaves its chromosome; this event may be triggered by environmental conditions such as exposure to a mutagen. Once separate, the lambda DNA usually switches to the lytic cycle, which results in the production of many copies of the virus and lysing of the host cell.

Sometimes the few prophage genes active in a lysogenic bacterial cell can cause medical problems. For example, the bacteria that cause diphtheria, botulism, and scarlet fever would be harmless to people if it were not for the prophage genes they carry. Certain of these genes direct the bacteria to produce toxins that make people ill. ☑

☑ CHECKPOINT

Describe one way some viruses can perpetuate their genes without destroying the cells they infect.

Answer: Some viruses can insert their DNA into the DNA of the cell they infect. The viral DNA is replicated along with the cell's DNA every time the cell divides.

▼ Figure 10.26 **Alternative phage reproductive cycles.** Certain phages can undergo alternative reproductive cycles. After entering the bacterial cell, the phage DNA can either integrate into the bacterial chromosome (lysogenic cycle) or immediately start the production of progeny phages (lytic cycle), destroying the cell. Once it enters a lysogenic cycle, the phage's DNA may be carried in the host cell's chromosome for many generations.

Phage lambda

E. coli

Phage

❶ Phage attaches to cell.

Phage DNA

Bacterial chromosome (DNA)

Phage injects DNA

❹ Cell lyses, releasing phages.

LYTIC CYCLE

Phages assemble

❸ New phage DNA and proteins are synthesized.

❷ Phage DNA circularizes.

OR

❼ Occasionally a prophage may leave the bacterial chromosome.

LYSOGENIC CYCLE

Many cell divisions

Prophage

❺ Phage DNA is inserted into the bacterial chromosome.

❻ Lysogenic bacterium reproduces normally, replicating the prophage at each cell division.

189

Plant Viruses

Viruses that infect plant cells can stunt plant growth and diminish crop yields. Most known plant viruses have RNA rather than DNA as their genetic material. Many of them, like the tobacco mosaic virus shown in Figure 10.27, are rod-shaped with a spiral arrangement of proteins surrounding the nucleic acid.

To infect a plant, a virus must first get past the plant's outer protective layer of cells (the epidermis). For this reason, a plant damaged by wind, chilling, injury, or insects is more susceptible to infection than a healthy plant. Some insects carry and transmit plant viruses, and farmers and gardeners may spread plant viruses through the use of pruning shears and other tools. Also, infected plants may pass viruses to their offspring.

There is no cure for most viral plant diseases, and agricultural scientists focus on preventing infection and on breeding or genetically engineering varieties of crop plants that resist viral infection. In Hawaii, for example, the spread of papaya ringspot potyvirus (PRSV) by aphids wiped out the papaya (Hawaii's second largest crop) in certain island regions. But since 1998, farmers have been able to plant a genetically engineered PRSV-resistant strain of papaya, and papayas have been reintroduced into their old habitats. ☑

▼ Figure 10.27 **Tobacco mosaic virus.** The photo shows the mottling of leaves in tobacco mosaic disease. The rod-shaped virus causing the disease has RNA as its genetic material.

RNA

Protein

Tobacco mosaic virus

Animal Viruses

Viruses that infect animal cells are common causes of disease. As discussed in the Biology and Society section, no virus is a greater human health threat than the influenza (flu) virus (Figure 10.28). Like many animal viruses, this one has an outer envelope made of phospholipid membrane, with projecting spikes of protein. The envelope enables the virus to enter and leave a host cell. Many viruses, including those that cause the flu, common cold, measles, mumps, AIDS, and polio, have RNA as their genetic material. Diseases caused by DNA viruses include hepatitis, chicken pox, and herpes infections.

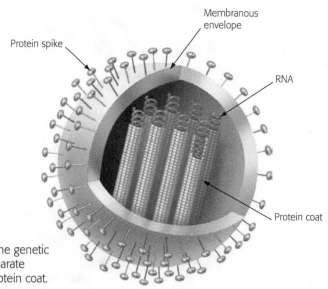

Membranous envelope

Protein spike

RNA

Protein coat

► Figure 10.28 **An influenza virus.** The genetic material of this virus consists of eight separate molecules of RNA, each wrapped in a protein coat.

Figure 10.29 shows the reproductive cycle of a typical enveloped RNA virus: the mumps virus. Once a common childhood disease characterized by fever and swelling of the salivary glands, mumps has become quite rare in industrialized nations due to widespread vaccination. When the virus contacts a susceptible cell, protein spikes on its outer surface attach to receptor proteins on the cell's plasma membrane. ❶ The viral envelope fuses with the cell's membrane, allowing the protein-coated RNA to enter the cytoplasm. ❷ Enzymes then remove the protein coat. ❸ An enzyme that entered the cell as part of the virus uses the virus's RNA genome as a template for making complementary strands of RNA. The new strands have two functions: ❹ They serve as

mRNA for the synthesis of new viral proteins, and ❺ they serve as templates for synthesizing new viral genome RNA. ❻ The new coat proteins assemble around the new viral RNA. ❼ Finally, the viruses leave the cell by cloaking themselves in plasma membrane. In other words, the virus obtains its envelope from the cell, leaving the cell without necessarily lysing it.

Not all animal viruses reproduce in the cytoplasm. For example, herpesviruses—which cause chicken pox, shingles, cold sores, and genital herpes—are enveloped DNA viruses that reproduce in a host cell's nucleus, and they get their envelopes from the cell's nuclear membrane. Copies of the herpesvirus DNA usually remain behind in the nuclei of certain nerve cells. There they remain dormant until some sort of stress, such as a cold, sunburn, or emotional stress, triggers virus production, resulting in unpleasant symptoms. Once acquired, herpes infections may flare up repeatedly throughout a person's life. Over 75% of American adults are thought to carry herpes simplex 1 (which causes cold sores), and over 20% carry herpes simplex 2 (which causes genital herpes).

Why does a herpes infection last forever?

The amount of damage a virus causes the body depends partly on how quickly the immune system responds to fight the infection and partly on the ability of the infected tissue to repair itself. We usually recover completely from colds because our respiratory tract tissue can efficiently replace damaged cells by mitosis. In contrast, the poliovirus attacks nerve cells, which are not usually replaceable. The damage to such cells by polio is permanent. In such cases, the only medical option is to prevent the disease with vaccines.

How effective are vaccines? We'll examine this question next using the example of the flu vaccine. ✓

✓ **CHECKPOINT**

Why is infection by herpesvirus permanent?

Answer: because herpesvirus leaves viral DNA in the nuclei of nerve cells

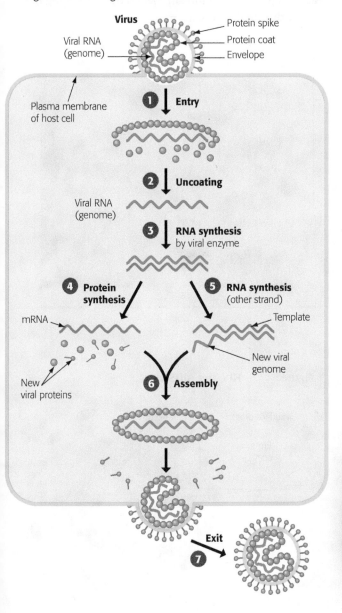

▼ Figure 10.29 **The reproductive cycle of an enveloped virus.** This virus is the one that causes mumps. Like the flu virus, it has a membranous envelope with protein spikes, but its genome is a single molecule of RNA.

Virus
Protein spike
Viral RNA (genome)
Protein coat
Envelope
Plasma membrane of host cell
❶ Entry
❷ Uncoating
Viral RNA (genome)
❸ RNA synthesis by viral enzyme
❹ Protein synthesis
❺ RNA synthesis (other strand)
mRNA
Template
New viral genome
New viral proteins
❻ Assembly
Exit
❼

Mumps virus
Protein spike
Envelope

Colorized TEM 294,000×

The Deadliest Virus THE PROCESS OF SCIENCE

Do Flu Vaccines Protect the Elderly?

Yearly flu vaccinations are recommended for nearly all people over the age of six months. But how can we be sure they are effective? Epidemiologists (who study the distribution, causes, and control of diseases in populations) have made the **observation** that vaccination rates among the elderly rose from 15% in 1980 to 65% in 1996. This observation has led them to ask the **question:** Do flu vaccines decrease the mortality rate among those elderly people who receive them? To find out, researchers investigated data from the general population. Their main **hypothesis** was that elderly people who were immunized would have fewer hospital stays and deaths during the winter after vaccination. Their **experiment** followed tens of thousands of people over the age of 65 during the ten flu seasons of the 1990s. The **results** are summarized in **Figure 10.30**. People who were vaccinated had a 27% less chance of being hospitalized during the next flu season and a 48% less chance of dying. But could some factor other than flu shots be at play? For example, maybe people who choose to be vaccinated are healthier for other reasons. As a control, the researchers examined health data for the summer (when flu is not a factor). During these months, there was no difference in the hospitalization rates and only 16% fewer deaths for the immunized, suggesting that flu vaccines provide a significant health benefit among the elderly during the flu season.

► **Figure 10.30 The effect of flu vaccines on the elderly.** Receiving a flu vaccine greatly reduced the risk of hospitalization and death in the flu season following the shot. The reduction was much smaller or nonexistent in later summer months.

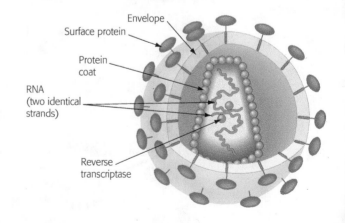

HIV, the AIDS Virus

The devastating disease **AIDS** (acquired immunodeficiency syndrome) is caused by **HIV** (human immunodeficiency virus), an RNA virus with some special twists. In outward appearance, HIV (**Figure 10.31**) resembles the flu or mumps virus. Its envelope enables HIV to enter and leave a cell much the way the mumps virus does. But HIV has a different mode of reproduction. It is a **retrovirus**, an RNA virus that reproduces by means of a DNA molecule. Retroviruses are so named because they reverse the usual DNA → RNA flow of genetic information. These viruses carry molecules of an enzyme called **reverse transcriptase**, which catalyzes reverse transcription: the synthesis of DNA on an RNA template.

▼ **Figure 10.31 HIV, the AIDS virus.**

Figure 10.32 illustrates what happens after HIV RNA is uncoated in the cytoplasm of a cell. The reverse transcriptase (green) **1** uses the RNA as a template to make a DNA strand and then **2** adds a second, complementary DNA strand. **3** The resulting double-stranded viral DNA then enters the cell nucleus and inserts itself into the chromosomal DNA, becoming a **provirus**. Occasionally, the provirus is **4** transcribed into RNA and **5** translated into viral proteins. **6** New viruses assembled from these components eventually leave the cell and can then infect other cells. This is the standard reproductive cycle for retroviruses.

HIV infects and eventually kills several kinds of white blood cells that are important in the body's immune system. The loss of such cells causes the body to become susceptible to other infections that it would normally be able to fight off. Such secondary

Why is HIV so deadly?

infections cause the syndrome (a collection of symptoms) that eventually kills AIDS patients. Since it was first recognized in 1981, HIV has infected tens of millions of people worldwide, resulting in millions of deaths.

While there is no cure for AIDS, its progression can be slowed by two categories of anti-HIV drugs. Both types of medicine interfere with the reproduction of the virus. The first type inhibits the action of enzymes called proteases, which help produce the final versions of HIV proteins. The second type, which includes the drug AZT, inhibits the action of the HIV enzyme reverse transcriptase. The key to AZT's effectiveness is its shape. The shape of a molecule of AZT is very similar to the shape of part of the T (thymine) nucleotide (Figure 10.33). In fact, AZT's shape is so similar to the T nucleotide that AZT can bind to reverse transcriptase, essentially taking the place of T. But unlike thymine, AZT cannot be incorporated into a growing DNA chain. Thus, AZT "gums up the works," interfering with the synthesis of HIV DNA. Because this synthesis is an essential step in the reproductive cycle of HIV, AZT may block the spread of the virus within the body.

Many HIV-infected people in the United States and other industrialized countries take a "drug cocktail" that contains both reverse transcriptase inhibitors and protease inhibitors, and the combination seems to be much more effective than the individual drugs in keeping the virus at bay and extending patients' lives. However, even in combination, the drugs do not completely rid the body of the virus. Typically, HIV reproduction and the symptoms of AIDS return if a patient discontinues the medications. Because AIDS has no cure yet, prevention (namely, the avoidance of unprotected sex and needle sharing) is the only healthy option. ✔

▼ **Figure 10.32 The behavior of HIV nucleic acid in an infected cell.**

HIV (red dots) infecting a white blood cell

SEM 5,500×

✔ **CHECKPOINT**

Why is HIV called a retrovirus?

Answer: Because it synthesizes DNA from its RNA genome. This is the reverse ("retro") of the usual DNA ⟶ RNA information flow.

▼ **Figure 10.33 AZT and the T nucleotide.** The anti-HIV drug AZT (right) has a chemical shape very similar to part of the T (thymine) nucleotide of DNA.

Part of a T nucleotide **AZT**

Viroids and Prions

Viruses may be small and simple, but they dwarf two other classes of pathogens: viroids and prions. Viroids are small circular RNA molecules that infect plants. Viroids do not encode proteins but can nonetheless replicate in host plant cells, apparently using cellular enzymes. These small RNA molecules seem to cause disease by interfering with the regulatory systems that control plant growth.

Even stranger are infectious proteins called **prions**. Prions cause a number of brain diseases in various animal species, including scrapie in sheep and goats, chronic wasting disease in deer and elk, and mad cow disease (formally called bovine spongiform encephalopathy or BSE), which infected over 2 million cattle in the United Kingdom in the 1980s **(Figure 10.34)**. In humans, prions cause an extremely rare disease called Creutzfeldt-Jakob disease. A prion is thought to be a misfolded form of a protein normally present in brain cells. When the prion enters a cell containing the normal form of protein, the prion somehow converts the normal protein molecules to the misfolded prion version. To date, there is no known cure for prion diseases, so the only hope for avoiding future illnesses lies in understanding and preventing the process of infection. ☑

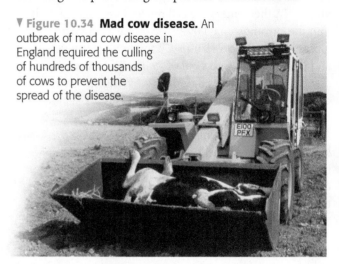

▼ **Figure 10.34 Mad cow disease.** An outbreak of mad cow disease in England required the culling of hundreds of thousands of cows to prevent the spread of the disease.

☑ CHECKPOINT

What makes prions so unusual as pathogens?

Answer: Prions, unlike any other infectious agent, have no nucleic acid (DNA or RNA).

The Deadliest Virus EVOLUTION CONNECTION

Emerging Viruses

Viruses that suddenly come to the attention of medical scientists are called **emerging viruses**. H1N1 (discussed in the Biology and Society section) is one example; another is avian flu. In 1997, at least 18 people in Hong Kong were infected with a strain of flu virus previously seen only in birds. A mass culling of all of Hong Kong's 1.5 million domestic birds appeared to stop that outbreak. Beginning in 2002, however, new cases of human infection by this bird strain spread to Europe and Africa, infecting over 400 people and killing over 250 of them. Over 100 million birds have either died from the disease or been killed to prevent the spread of infection **(Figure 10.35)**. If this virus evolves so that it can spread easily from person to person, a major human outbreak could occur.

How do such viruses burst on the human scene, giving rise to new diseases? One way is by the mutation of existing viruses. RNA viruses tend to have unusually high rates of mutation because errors in replicating their RNA genomes are not subject to proofreading mechanisms that help reduce errors during DNA replication. Some mutations enable existing viruses to evolve into new strains that can cause disease in individuals who have developed resistance to the ancestral virus. This is why we need yearly flu vaccines: Mutations create new influenza virus strains to which people have no immunity.

New viral diseases also arise from the spread of existing viruses from one host species to another. Scientists estimate that about three-quarters of new human diseases have originated in other animals. The avian flu is a prime example. The spread of a viral disease from a small, isolated population can also lead to widespread epidemics. For instance, AIDS went unnamed and virtually unnoticed for decades before it began to spread around the world. In this case, technological and social factors, including affordable international travel, blood transfusions, sexual promiscuity, and the abuse of intravenous drugs, allowed a previously rare human disease to become a global scourge.

Acknowledging the persistent threat that viruses pose to human health, geneticist and Nobel Prize winner Joshua Lederberg once warned: "We live in evolutionary competition with microbes. There is no guarantee that we will be the survivors." If we ever do manage to control HIV, influenza, and other emerging viruses, this success will likely arise from our understanding of molecular biology.

▼ **Figure 10.35 Rounding up ducks in India to help prevent the spread of the Avian flu virus.**

Chapter Review

SUMMARY OF KEY CONCEPTS

(MB) Go to **www.masteringbiology.com** for homework assignments, practice quizzes, Pearson eText, and more.

DNA: Structure and Replication

DNA and RNA Structure

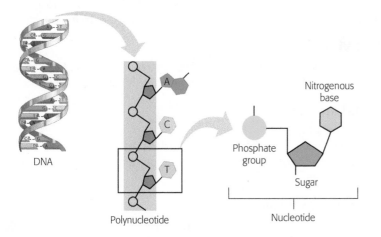

	DNA	RNA
Nitrogenous base	C G A T	C G A U
Sugar	Deoxy-ribose	Ribose
Number of strands	2	1

Watson and Crick's Discovery of the Double Helix

Watson and Crick worked out the three-dimensional structure of DNA: two polynucleotide strands wrapped around each other in a double helix. Hydrogen bonds between bases hold the strands together. Each base pairs with a complementary partner: A with T, and G with C.

DNA Replication

The Flow of Genetic Information from DNA to RNA to Protein

How an Organism's Genotype Determines Its Phenotype

The information constituting an organism's genotype is carried in the sequence of its DNA bases. Studies of inherited metabolic defects first suggested that phenotype is expressed through proteins.

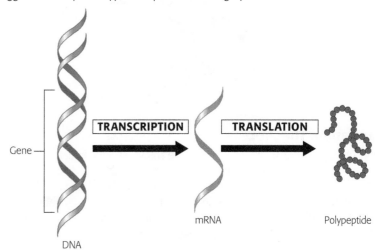

From Nucleotides to Amino Acids: An Overview

The DNA of a gene is transcribed into RNA using the usual base-pairing rules, except that an A in DNA pairs with U in RNA. In the translation of a genetic message, each triplet of nucleotide bases in the RNA, called a codon, specifies one amino acid in the polypeptide.

The Genetic Code

In addition to codons that specify amino acids, the genetic code has one codon that is a start signal and three that are stop signals for translation. The genetic code is redundant: There is more than one codon for most amino acids.

Transcription: From DNA to RNA

In transcription, RNA polymerase binds to the promoter of a gene, opens the DNA double helix there, and catalyzes the synthesis of an RNA molecule using one DNA strand as a template. As the single-stranded RNA transcript peels away from the gene, the DNA strands rejoin.

The Processing of Eukaryotic RNA

The RNA transcribed from a eukaryotic gene is processed before leaving the nucleus to serve as messenger RNA (mRNA). Introns are spliced out, and a cap and tail are added.

Translation: The Players

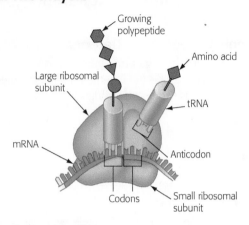

Translation: The Process

In initiation, a ribosome assembles with the mRNA and the initiator tRNA bearing the first amino acid. Beginning at the start codon, the codons of the mRNA are recognized one by one by tRNAs bearing succeeding amino acids. The ribosome bonds the amino acids together. With each addition, the mRNA translocates by one codon through the ribosome. When a stop codon is reached, the completed polypeptide is released.

Review: DNA → RNA → Protein

Figure 10.20 summarizes transcription, RNA processing, and translation. The sequence of codons in DNA, via the sequence of codons in mRNA, spells out the primary structure of a polypeptide.

Mutations

Mutations are changes in the DNA base sequence, caused by errors in DNA replication or recombination or by mutagens. Substituting, deleting, or inserting nucleotides in a gene has varying effects on the polypeptide and organism.

Type of Mutation	Effect
Substitution of one DNA base for another	**Silent** mutations result in no change to amino acids.
	Missense mutations swap one amino acid for another.
	Nonsense mutations change an amino acid codon to a stop codon.
Insertions or **deletions** of DNA nucleotides	These mutations can alter the triplet grouping of codons and greatly change the amino acid sequence.

Viruses and Other Noncellular Infectious Agents

Viruses can be regarded as genes packaged in protein.

Bacteriophages

When phage DNA enters a lytic cycle inside a bacterium, it is replicated, transcribed, and translated. The new viral DNA and protein molecules then assemble into new phages, which burst from the cell. In the lysogenic cycle, phage DNA inserts into the cell's chromosome and is passed on to generations of daughter cells. Much later, it may initiate phage production.

Plant Viruses

Viruses that infect plants can be a serious agricultural problem. Most have RNA genomes. Viruses enter plants via breaks in the plant's outer layers.

Animal Viruses

Many animal viruses, such as flu viruses, have RNA genomes; others, such as hepatitis viruses, have DNA. Some animal viruses "steal" a bit of cell membrane as a protective envelope. Some, such as the herpesvirus, can remain latent inside cells for long periods.

HIV, the AIDS Virus

HIV is a retrovirus. Inside a cell it uses its RNA as a template for making DNA, which is then inserted into a chromosome.

Viroids and Prions

Even smaller than viruses, viroids are small molecules of RNA that can infect plants. Prions are infectious proteins that cause a number of degenerative brain diseases in humans and other animals.

SELF-QUIZ

1. A molecule of DNA contains two polymer strands called _____, made by bonding together many monomers called _____. Each monomer contains three parts: a _____, a _____, and a _____.

2. Which of the following correctly ranks nucleic acid structures in order of size, from largest to smallest?
   a. gene, chromosome, nucleotide, codon
   b. chromosome, gene, codon, nucleotide
   c. nucleotide, chromosome, gene, codon
   d. chromosome, nucleotide, gene, codon

3. A scientist inserts a radioactively labeled DNA molecule into a bacterium. The bacterium replicates this DNA molecule and distributes one daughter molecule (double helix) to each of two daughter cells. How much radioactivity will the DNA in each of the two daughter cells contain? Why?

4. The nucleotide sequence of a DNA codon is GTA. In an mRNA molecule transcribed from this DNA, the codon has the sequence _____. In the process of protein synthesis, a tRNA pairs with the mRNA codon. The nucleotide sequence of the tRNA anticodon is _____. The amino acid attached to the tRNA is _____. (See Figure 10.11.)

5. Describe the process by which the information in a gene is transcribed and translated into a protein. Correctly use these terms in your description: tRNA, amino acid, start codon, transcription, mRNA, gene, codon, RNA polymerase, ribosome, translation, anticodon, peptide bond, stop codon.

6. Match the following molecules with the cellular process or processes in which they are primarily involved.

   a. ribosomes   **1.** DNA replication
   b. tRNA   **2.** transcription
   c. DNA polymerases **3.** translation
   d. RNA polymerase
   e. mRNA

7. A geneticist finds that a particular mutation has no effect on the polypeptide encoded by the gene. This mutation probably involves
   a. deletion of one nucleotide.
   b. alteration of the start codon.
   c. insertion of one nucleotide.
   d. substitution of one nucleotide.

8. Scientists have discovered how to put together a bacteriophage with the protein coat of phage A and the DNA of phage B. If this composite phage were allowed to infect a bacterium, the phages produced in the cell would have
   a. the protein of A and the DNA of B.
   b. the protein of B and the DNA of A.
   c. the protein and DNA of A.
   d. the protein and DNA of B.

9. How do some viruses reproduce without ever having DNA?

10. HIV requires an enzyme called _____ to convert its RNA genome to a DNA version.

11. Why is reverse transcriptase a particularly good target for anti-AIDS drugs? (*Hint*: Would you expect such a drug to harm the human host?)

Answers to these questions can be found in Appendix: Self-Quiz Answers.

THE PROCESS OF SCIENCE

12. A cell containing a single chromosome is placed in a medium containing radioactive phosphate, making any new DNA strands formed by DNA replication radioactive. The cell replicates its DNA and divides. Then the daughter cells (still in the radioactive medium) replicate their DNA and divide, resulting in a total of four cells. Sketch the DNA molecules in all four cells, showing a normal (nonradioactive) DNA strand as a solid line and a radioactive DNA strand as a dashed line.

13. In a classic 1952 experiment, biologists Alfred Hershey and Martha Chase labeled two batches of bacteriophages, one with radioactive sulfur (which only tags protein) and the other with radioactive phosphorus (which only tags DNA). In separate test tubes, they allowed each batch of phages to bind to nonradioactive bacteria and inject its DNA. After a few minutes, they separated the bacterial cells from the viral parts that remained outside the bacterial cells and measured the radioactivity of both portions. What results do you think they obtained? How would these results help them to determine which viral component—DNA or protein—was the infectious portion?

BIOLOGY AND SOCIETY

14. Scientists at the National Institutes of Health (NIH) have worked out thousands of sequences of genes and the proteins they encode, and similar analysis is being carried out at universities and private companies. Knowledge of the nucleotide sequences of genes might be used to treat genetic defects or produce lifesaving medicines. NIH and some U.S. biotechnology companies have applied for patents on their discoveries. In Britain, the courts have ruled that a naturally occurring gene cannot be patented. Do you think individuals and companies should be able to patent genes and gene products? Before answering, consider the following: What are the purposes of a patent? How might the discoverer of a gene benefit from a patent? How might the public benefit? What negative effects might result from patenting genes?

15. Your college roommate seeks to improve her appearance by visiting a tanning salon. How would you explain the dangers of this to her?

11 How Genes Are Controlled

A lung tumor.
In this micrograph, you can see a mass of cancer cells filling an air sac in a human lung.

Cancer BIOLOGY AND SOCIETY

Tobacco's Smoking Gun

When European explorers returned from their first voyages to the Americas, they brought back tobacco, a common trade item among Native Americans. The novelty of smoking quickly spread through Europe, and the southern United States soon became a major tobacco producer. By the 1950s, about half of all Americans smoked over a pack of cigarettes each day. Little credence was paid to health risks; in fact, cigarette advertising often touted the "health benefits" of tobacco. Smoking was pervasive in American society.

But doctors began to notice a disturbing trend: As tobacco use increased, so did the rate of lung cancer. This disease was rare in 1930, but by 1955 it had become the deadliest form of cancer among American men. In fact, by 1990, lung cancer was killing more than twice as many men each year as any other type of cancer. But a few vocal skeptics, mostly supported by the tobacco industry, doubted the link between smoking and cancer. They pointed out that the evidence was purely statistical or based on animal studies; no direct proof had been found that tobacco smoke causes cancer in humans.

The "smoking gun" of proof was found in 1996 when researchers added one component of tobacco smoke, called BPDE, to human lung cells growing in the lab. In these cells, the researchers showed, BPDE binds to DNA within a gene called *p53*, which codes for a protein that normally helps suppress the formation of tumors. The researchers proved that BPDE causes mutations in the *p53* gene that deactivate the protein and lead to tumors. This work directly linked a chemical in tobacco smoke to the formation of human lung tumors. This evidence linking cigarettes to cancer was impossible to ignore.

How can a mutation in a gene lead to cancer? It turns out that many cancer-associated genes encode proteins that turn other genes on or off. When these proteins malfunction, the cell may become cancerous. In fact, the ability to properly control which genes are active at any given time is crucial to normal cell function. How genes are controlled and how the regulation of genes affects cells and organisms are the subjects of this chapter. You'll soon find out that these topics deeply affect your life.

How and Why Genes Are Regulated

In a multicellular organism, every somatic (body) cell is produced by repeated rounds of mitosis, starting from a zygote, the original cell that formed after fusion of sperm and egg. Since a cell's genes are duplicated with each round of the cell cycle, every body cell has the same DNA as the zygote. To put it simply: Every somatic cell contains every gene.

If every cell contains identical genetic instructions, how do cells become different from one another? Cells with the same genetic information can develop into cells with different structures and functions only if gene activity is regulated. Control mechanisms must turn *on* certain genes while other genes remain turned *off* in a particular cell. In other words, individual cells must undergo **cellular differentiation**—that is, they must become specialized in structure and function. It is **gene regulation**, the turning on and off of genes, that leads to this specialization.

Patterns of Gene Expression in Differentiated Cells

What does it mean to say that genes are active or inactive, turned on or off? Genes determine the nucleotide sequence of specific mRNA molecules, and mRNA in turn determines the sequence of amino acids in proteins (DNA→RNA→protein; see Chapter 10). A gene that is turned on is being transcribed into mRNA, and that message is being translated into specific proteins. The overall process by which genetic information

flows from genes to proteins—that is, from genotype to phenotype—is called **gene expression**.

Because all the differentiated cells in an individual organism contain the same genes, the differences among the cells must result from the selective expression of genes—that is, from the pattern of genes turned on in a given cell at a given time. Such regulation of gene expression plays a central role in the development of a unicellular zygote into a multicellular organism. During embryonic growth, groups of cells follow diverging pathways, and each group becomes a particular kind of tissue. In the mature organism, each cell type—nerve or pancreas, for instance—has a different pattern of turned-on genes. This is like a company-wide book of procedures; every worker has the complete manual, but each worker reads only those few sections that are relevant to his or her job.

Figure 11.1 shows the patterns of gene expression for four genes in three different specialized cells of an adult human. Note that the genes for "housekeeping" enzymes, such as those that provide energy via glycolysis, are "on" in all the cells. In contrast, the genes for some proteins, such as insulin and hemoglobin, are expressed only by particular kinds of cells. One protein, hemoglobin, is not expressed in any of the cell types shown in the figure. ☑

Gene Regulation in Bacteria

To understand how a cell can regulate gene expression, consider the relatively simple case of bacteria. In the course of their lives, bacteria must regulate their genes in response to environmental changes. For example,

☑ **CHECKPOINT**

If your nerve cells and skin cells have the same genes, how can they be so different?

Answer: Each cell type expresses different genes than the other cell type.

▶ Figure 11.1 **Patterns of gene expression in three types of human cells.** Different types of cells express different combinations of genes. The specialized proteins whose genes are represented here are an enzyme involved in glucose digestion; an antibody, which aids in fighting infection; insulin, a hormone made in the pancreas; and the oxygen transport protein hemoglobin, which is expressed only in red blood cells.

Key

Active gene

	Pancreas cell	White blood cell	Nerve cell
Gene for a glycolysis enzyme	✓	✓	✓
Antibody gene		✓	
Insulin gene	✓		
Hemoglobin gene			

when a nutrient is plentiful, bacteria do not squander valuable resources to make it from scratch. Bacterial cells that can conserve resources and energy have a survival advantage over cells that are unable to do so. Thus, natural selection has favored bacteria that express only the genes whose products are needed by the cell.

Imagine an *Escherichia coli* bacterium living in your intestines. It will be bathed in various nutrients, depending on what you eat. If you drink a milk shake, for example, there will be a sudden rush of the sugar lactose. In response, *E. coli* will express three genes for enzymes that enable the bacterium to absorb and digest this sugar. After the lactose is gone, *E. coli* turns the genes off; it does not waste its energy continuing to produce these enzymes when they are not needed. Thus, a bacterium can adjust its gene expression to changes in the environment.

How does the presence or absence of lactose influence the activity of the genes that code for the lactose enzymes? The key is the way the three genes are organized: They are adjacent in the DNA and turned on and off as a single unit. This regulation is achieved through short stretches of DNA that help turn all three genes on and off at once, coordinating their expression. Such a cluster of genes with related functions, along with the DNA control sequences, is called an **operon** (Figure 11.2). The operon considered here, the *lac* (short for lactose) operon, was first described in the 1960s by French biologists François Jacob and Jacques Monod. The *lac* operon illustrates principles of gene regulation that apply to a wide variety of prokaryotic genes.

How do DNA control sequences turn genes on or off? One control sequence, called a **promoter** (green in the figure), is the site where the enzyme RNA polymerase attaches and initiates transcription—in our example, transcription of the genes for lactose enzymes. Between the promoter and the enzyme genes, a DNA segment called an **operator** (yellow) acts as a switch that is turned on or off, depending on whether a specific protein is bound there. The operator and protein together determine whether RNA polymerase can attach to the promoter and start transcribing the genes (light blue). In the *lac* operon, when the operator switch is turned on, all the enzymes needed to metabolize lactose are made at once.

The top half of Figure 11.2 shows the *lac* operon in "off" mode, its status when there is no lactose around. Transcription is turned off because ❶ a protein called a **repressor** (🥄) binds to the operator (〰) and ❷ physically blocks the attachment of RNA polymerase (🦠) to the promoter (▱).

The bottom half of Figure 11.2 shows the operon in "on" mode, when lactose is present. The lactose (◯)

interferes with attachment of the *lac* repressor to the operator by ❶ binding to the repressor and ❷ changing the repressor's shape. In its new shape (🥄), the repressor cannot bind to the operator, and the operator switch remains on. ❸ RNA polymerase is no longer blocked, so it can now bind to the promoter and from there ❹ transcribe the genes for the lactose enzymes into mRNA. ❺ Translation produces all three lactose enzymes (purple).

Many operons have been identified in bacteria. Some are quite similar to the *lac* operon, while others have somewhat different mechanisms of control. For example, operons that control amino acid synthesis cause bacteria to stop making these molecules when they are already present in the environment, saving materials and energy for the cells. In these cases, the amino acid *activates* the repressor. Armed with a variety of operons, *E. coli* and other prokaryotes can thrive in frequently changing environments. ☑

▼ Figure 11.2 **The *lac* operon of *E. coli*.**

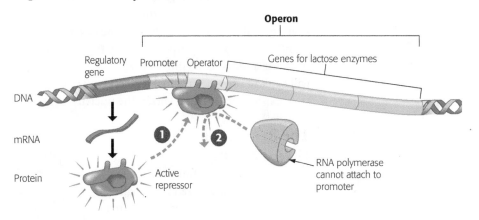

Operon turned off (lactose absent)

Operon turned on (lactose inactivates repressor)

Gene Regulation in Eukaryotic Cells

Eukaryotes, especially multicellular ones, have more sophisticated mechanisms than bacteria for regulating the expression of their genes. This is not surprising because a prokaryote, being a single cell, does not require the elaborate regulation of gene expression that leads to cell specialization in multicellular eukaryotic organisms. A bacterium does not have blood cells that need to be different from muscle cells, for example.

The pathway from gene to protein in eukaryotic cells is a long one, providing a number of points where the process can be turned on or off, speeded up or slowed down. Picture the series of pipes that carry water from your local reservoir to a faucet in your home. At various points, valves control the flow of water. We use this analogy in **Figure 11.3** to illustrate the flow of genetic information from a eukaryotic chromosome—a reservoir of genetic information— to an active protein that has been made in the cell's cytoplasm. The multiple mechanisms that control gene expression are analogous to the control valves in your water pipes. In the figure, each control knob indicates a gene expression "valve." All these knobs represent possible control points, although only one or a few control points are likely to be important for a typical protein.

How is gene expression like plumbing?

Using a reduced version of Figure 11.3 as a guide, we will explore several ways that eukaryotes can control gene expression, starting within the nucleus.

The Regulation of DNA Packing

Eukaryotic chromosomes may be in a more or less condensed state, with the DNA and accompanying proteins more or less tightly wrapped together (see Chapter 8). DNA packing tends to prevent gene expression by preventing RNA polymerase and other transcription proteins from binding to the DNA.

Cells may use DNA packing for the long-term inactivation of genes. One intriguing case is seen in female mammals, where one X chromosome in each somatic cell is highly compacted and almost entirely inactive. This **X chromosome inactivation** first takes place early in embryonic development, when one of the two X chromosomes in each cell is inactivated at random. After one X chromosome is inactivated in each embryonic cell, all of that cell's descendants will have the same X chromosome turned off. Consequently, if a female is heterozygous for a gene on the X chromosome (a sex-linked gene; see Chapter 9), about half of her cells will express one allele, while the other half will express the alternate allele (Figure 11.4). ☑

☑ CHECKPOINT

Would an X-linked gene be expressed more in human females (who have two copies of the X chromosome) than in human males (who have one copy)?

Answer: No, because in females one of the X chromosomes in each cell is inactivated.

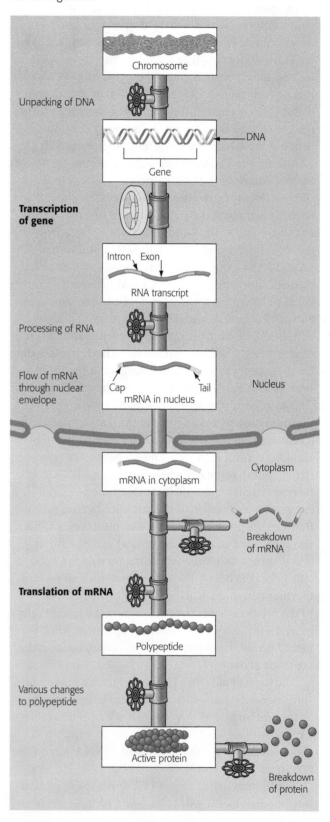

▼ **Figure 11.3 The gene expression "pipeline" in a eukaryotic cell.** Each valve in the pipeline represents a stage at which the pathway from chromosome to functioning protein can be regulated.

Chromosome

Unpacking of DNA

DNA

Gene

Transcription of gene

Intron Exon

RNA transcript

Processing of RNA

Flow of mRNA through nuclear envelope

Cap   Tail

mRNA in nucleus

Nucleus

Cytoplasm

mRNA in cytoplasm

Breakdown of mRNA

Translation of mRNA

Polypeptide

Various changes to polypeptide

Active protein

Breakdown of protein

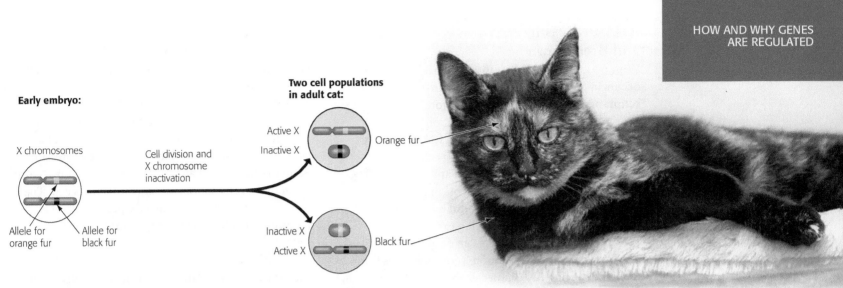

Early embryo:

X chromosomes

Allele for orange fur

Allele for black fur

Cell division and X chromosome inactivation

Two cell populations in adult cat:

Active X

Inactive X

Orange fur

Inactive X

Active X

Black fur

▲ **Figure 11.4 X chromosome inactivation: the tortoiseshell pattern on a cat.** The tortoiseshell gene is on the X chromosome, and the tortoiseshell phenotype requires the presence of two different alleles, one for orange fur and one for non-orange (black) fur. If a female is heterozygous for the tortoiseshell gene, orange patches are formed by populations of cells in which the X chromosome with the orange allele is active; black patches have cells in which the X chromosome with the non-orange allele is active.

The Initiation of Transcription

The initiation of transcription (whether transcription starts or not) is the most important stage for regulating gene expression. In both prokaryotes and eukaryotes, regulatory proteins bind to DNA and turn the transcription of genes on and off. Unlike prokaryotic genes, however, most eukaryotic genes have individual promoters and other control sequences. That is, eukaryotic genes are generally not organized into groups as operons.

As seen in **Figure 11.5**, transcriptional regulation in eukaryotes is complex, typically involving many proteins (collectively called **transcription factors**, purple in the figure) acting in concert to bind to DNA sequences called **enhancers** (yellow) and to the promoter (green). The DNA-protein assembly promotes the binding of RNA polymerase (orange) to the promoter. Genes coding for related enzymes, such as those in a metabolic pathway, may share a specific kind of enhancer (or collection of enhancers), allowing these genes to be activated at the same time. Not shown in the figure are repressor proteins, which may bind to DNA sequences called **silencers**, inhibiting the start of transcription.

In fact, repressor proteins that turn genes off are less common in eukaryotes than **activators**, proteins that turn genes on by binding to DNA. Activators act by making it easier for RNA polymerase to bind to the promoter. The use of activators is efficient because a typical animal or plant cell needs to turn on (transcribe) only a small percentage of its genes, those required for the cell's specialized structure and function. The "default" state for most genes in multicellular eukaryotes seems to be off, with the exception of "housekeeping" genes for routine activities such as glucose metabolism. ☑

▼ **Figure 11.5 A model for turning on a eukaryotic gene.** A large assembly of proteins and several control sequences in the DNA are involved in initiating the transcription of a eukaryotic gene.

Enhancers (DNA control sequences)

Bend in the DNA

RNA polymerase

Transcription factor

Promoter

Gene

Transcription

203

RNA Processing and Breakdown

Within a eukaryotic cell, transcription occurs in the nucleus, where RNA transcripts are processed into mRNA before moving to the cytoplasm for translation by the ribosomes (see Figure 10.20). RNA processing includes the addition of a cap and a tail, as well as the removal of any introns—noncoding DNA segments that interrupt the genetic message—and the splicing together of the remaining exons.

Within a cell, exon splicing can occur in more than one way, generating different mRNA molecules from the same starting RNA molecule. Notice in **Figure 11.6**, for example, that one mRNA ends up with the green exon and the other with the brown exon. With this sort of **alternative RNA splicing**, an organism can produce more than one type of polypeptide from a single gene. A typical human gene contains about ten exons; nearly all genes are spliced in at least two different ways, and some are spliced hundreds of different ways.

After an mRNA is produced in its final form, its "lifetime" can be highly variable, from hours to weeks to months. Controlling the timing of mRNA breakdown provides another opportunity for regulation. But all mRNAs are eventually broken down and their parts recycled.

How can your 20,000 genes produce more than 100,000 kinds of protein?

CHECKPOINT

After a gene is transcribed in the nucleus, how is the transcript converted to mRNA? After the mRNA reaches the cytoplasm, what are four control mechanisms that can regulate the amount of active protein in the cell?

Answer: by RNA processing, including the addition of cap and tail and RNA splicing; control by microRNAs, initiation of translation, activation of the protein, and breakdown of the protein

microRNAs

Recent research has established an important role for a variety of small single-stranded RNA molecules, called microRNAs (miRNAs), that can bind to complementary sequences on mRNA molecules in the cytoplasm. After binding, some miRNAs trigger breakdown of their target mRNA, whereas others block translation. It has been estimated that miRNAs may regulate the expression of up to one-third of all human genes, a striking figure given that miRNAs were unknown 20 years ago. These discoveries hint at a large, diverse population of RNA molecules that help regulate gene expression.

The Initiation of Translation

The process of translation—in which an mRNA is used to make a protein—offers additional opportunities for control by regulatory molecules. Red blood cells, for instance, have a protein that prevents the translation of hemoglobin mRNA unless the cell has a supply of heme, an iron-containing chemical group essential for hemoglobin function.

Protein Activation and Breakdown

The final opportunities for regulating gene expression occur after translation. Post-translational control mechanisms in eukaryotes often involve cutting polypeptides into smaller, active final products. The hormone insulin, for example, is synthesized as one long, inactive polypeptide **(Figure 11.7)**. After translation, an enzyme removes an interior section, leaving two shorter chains that make up the active insulin molecule.

Another control mechanism operating after translation is the selective breakdown of proteins. Some proteins that trigger metabolic changes in cells are broken down within a few minutes or hours. This regulation allows a cell to adjust the kinds and amounts of its proteins in response to changes in its environment. ☑

▼ Figure 11.7 **The formation of an active insulin molecule.** Only in its final form does insulin act as a hormone.

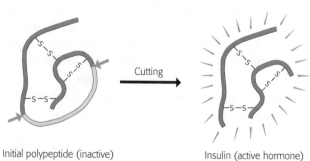

Initial polypeptide (inactive)   Cutting   Insulin (active hormone)

▼ Figure 11.6 **Alternative RNA splicing: producing multiple mRNAs from the same gene.** Two different cells can use the same DNA gene to synthesize different mRNAs and proteins. The cells might be from different tissues or the same type of cell at different times in the organism's life. In this example, one mRNA has ended up with exon 3 (brown) and the other with exon 4 (green). These mRNAs, which are just two of many possible outcomes, can then be translated into different proteins.

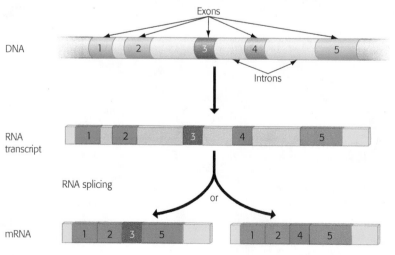

Cell Signaling

So far, we have considered gene regulation only within a single cell. In a multicellular organism, the process can cross cell boundaries. A cell can produce and secrete chemicals, such as hormones, that affect gene regulation in another cell.

A signal molecule can act by binding to a receptor protein and initiating a **signal transduction pathway**, a series of molecular changes that converts a signal received outside a cell to a specific response inside the target cell (as you saw in Figure 5.19). **Figure 11.8** shows an example of cell-to-cell signaling in which the target cell's response is the transcription (turning on) of a gene. **①** First, the signaling cell secretes the signal molecule (⬠). **②** This molecule binds to a specific receptor protein (⬠) embedded in the target cell's plasma membrane. **③** The binding activates a signal transduction pathway consisting of a series of relay proteins (green) within the target cell. Each relay molecule activates the next. **④** The last relay molecule in the series activates a transcription factor (⬠) that **⑤** triggers the transcription of a specific gene. **⑥** Translation of the mRNA produces a protein that can then perform the function originally called for by the signal. ☑

HOW AND WHY GENES
ARE REGULATED

☑ CHECKPOINT

How can a signal molecule from one cell alter gene expression in a target cell without entering the target cell?

Answer: by binding to a receptor protein in the membrane of the target cell and triggering a signal transduction pathway that activates transcription factors

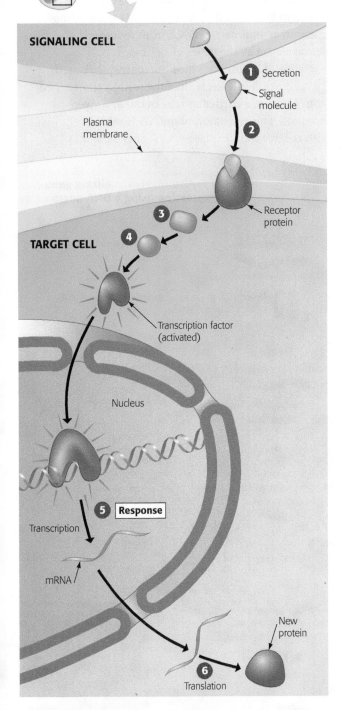

▲ Figure 11.8 **A cell-signaling pathway that turns on a gene.** The coordination of cellular activities in a multicellular organism depends on cell-to-cell signaling that helps regulate genes.

Homeotic Genes

Cell-to-cell signaling and the control of gene expression are most important during early embryonic development, when a single-celled zygote develops into a multicellular organism. Master control genes called **homeotic genes** regulate groups of other genes that determine what body parts will develop in which locations. For example, one set of homeotic genes in fruit flies instructs cells in the midbody to form legs. Elsewhere, these homeotic genes remain turned off, while others are turned on. Mutations in homeotic genes can produce bizarre effects. For example, fruit flies with mutations in homeotic genes may have extra sets of legs growing from their head **(Figure 11.9)**.

► Figure 11.9 **The effect of homeotic genes.** The strange mutant fruit fly shown at the bottom results from a mutation in a homeotic (master control) gene.

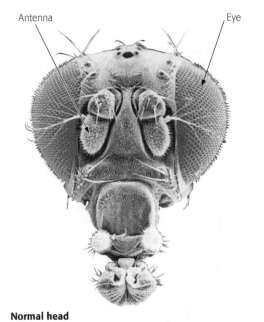

Antenna Eye

Normal head

Mutant fly with extra legs growing from head

Extra pair of legs

One of the most significant biological discoveries in recent years is that similar homeotic genes help direct embryonic development in nearly every eukaryotic organism examined so far, including yeasts, plants, earthworms, frogs, chickens, mice, and humans. **Figure 11.10** highlights some striking similarities in the chromosomal locations and developmental roles of homeotic genes in two quite different animals: a fruit fly and a mouse. The colored segments represent homeotic genes that are very similar in both animals. Notice that the fruit fly and mouse chromosomes have the same order of homeotic genes, corresponding to analogous body regions in both animals. These similarities suggest that these homeotic genes arose very early in the history of life and that the genes have remained remarkably unchanged over eons of animal evolution. The evolution and role of homeotic genes is a very active and exciting area of research. ☑

☑ **CHECKPOINT**

How can a mutation in just one homeotic gene drastically affect an organism's physical appearance?

Answer: Because homeotic genes control many other genes, a single change can affect the expression of many of the proteins that control appearance.

DNA Microarrays: Visualizing Gene Expression

Scientists who study gene regulation often want to determine which genes are on or off in a particular cell. A **DNA microarray** is a glass slide with thousands of different kinds of single-stranded DNA fragments attached to wells in a tightly spaced array (grid). Each DNA fragment is obtained from a particular gene; a single microarray thus carries DNA from thousands of genes, perhaps even all the genes of an organism.

Figure 11.11 outlines how microarrays are used. ❶ A researcher collects all of the mRNA transcribed from genes in a particular type of cell at a given moment. This collection of mRNA is mixed with reverse transcriptase, a viral enzyme that

▼ Figure 11.10 **Homeotic genes in two different animals.** At the top of the figure are portions of chromosomes that carry homeotic genes. The colored boxes represent homeotic genes that have especially close DNA sequences in fruit flies and mice. The same color coding identifies the parts of the animals affected by these genes.

Fruit fly chromosome   Mouse chromosomes

Fruit fly embryo (10 hours)   Mouse embryo (12 days)

Adult fruit fly   Adult mouse

▼ Figure 11.11 **Visualizing gene expression using a DNA microarray.**

❶ mRNA isolated

Reverse transcriptase combined with fluorescently labeled DNA nucleotides

❷ cDNA made from mRNA

Fluorescent cDNA

❸ cDNA mixture added to wells

DNA microarray (each well contains DNA from a particular gene)

❹ Unbound cDNA rinsed away

Nonfluorescent spot

Fluorescent spot

Fluorescent cDNA

DNA of an expressed gene

DNA of an unexpressed gene

DNA microarray, actual size (6,400 genes)

② produces DNA that is complementary to each mRNA sequence. This **complementary DNA (cDNA)** is synthesized using nucleotides that have been modified to fluoresce (glow). The fluorescent cDNA collection thus represents all of the genes being actively transcribed in the cell. ③ A small amount of the fluorescently labeled cDNA mixture is added to the DNA fragment in each well of the microarray. If a molecule in the cDNA mixture is complementary to a DNA fragment at a particular location on the grid, the cDNA molecule binds to it, becoming fixed there. ④ After unbound cDNA is rinsed away, the remaining cDNA glows in the microarray. The pattern of glowing spots enables the researcher to determine which genes were being transcribed in the starting cells. Researchers can thus learn which genes are active in different tissues, at different times, or in tissues from individuals in different states of health. ✓

Cloning Plants and Animals

The Genetic Potential of Cells

Now that we have examined how gene expression is regulated, we will devote the rest of this chapter to how gene regulation affects two important processes: cloning and cancer.

One of the most important take-home lessons from this chapter is that most cells express only a small percentage of their genes. So how do we know that all the genes are still present? And if all the genes are still there, do differentiated cells retain the potential to express them?

One way to approach these questions is to see if a differentiated cell can be stimulated to generate a whole new organism. In plants, this ability is common. For example, if you have ever grown a plant from a small cutting, you've seen evidence that a differentiated plant cell can undergo cell division and give rise to all the tissues of an adult plant. On a larger scale, the technique described in **Figure 11.12** can be used to produce hundreds or thousands of genetically identical organisms—clones—from the cells of a single plant.

Plant cloning is now used extensively in agriculture. For some plants, such as orchids, cloning is the only commercially practical means of reproducing plants. In other cases, cloning has been used to reproduce a plant with specific desirable traits, such as high fruit yield or resistance to disease. Seedless plants (such as seedless grapes) cannot reproduce sexually, leaving cloning as the sole means of mass-producing these common foods.

A similar, naturally occurring process in animals is **regeneration**, the regrowth of lost body parts. When a salamander loses a leg, for example, certain cells in the leg stump reverse their differentiated state, divide, and then differentiate again to give rise to a new leg. Many other animals, especially among the invertebrates, can regenerate lost parts, and isolated pieces of a few relatively simple animals can dedifferentiate and then develop into an entirely new organism (see Figure 8.1).

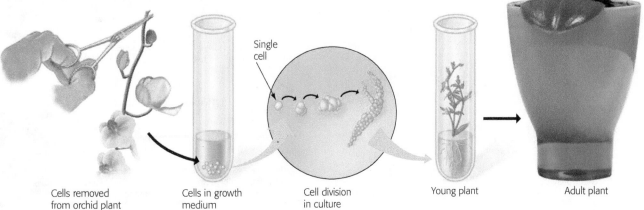

▶ **Figure 11.12 Test-tube cloning of an orchid.** Tissue removed from the stem of an orchid plant and placed in growth medium may begin dividing and eventually grow into an adult plant. The new plant is a genetic duplicate of the parent plant. This process proves that mature plant cells can reverse their differentiation and develop into all the specialized cells of an adult plant.

Cells removed from orchid plant

Cells in growth medium

Single cell

Cell division in culture

Young plant

Adult plant

Reproductive Cloning of Animals

Animal cloning is achieved through a procedure called **nuclear transplantation** (Figure 11.13). First performed in the 1950s on frog embryos, nuclear transplantation involves replacing the nucleus of an egg cell or a zygote with a nucleus removed from an adult body cell. The recipient cell may then begin to divide. Repeated cell divisions form a blastocyst, a hollow ball of about 100 cells that is an early stage in normal animal development. At this point, the blastocyst may be used for different purposes, as indicated by the two branches in Figure 11.13.

If the animal to be cloned is a mammal, further development requires implanting the blastocyst into the uterus of a surrogate mother (Figure 11.13, upper branch). The resulting animal will be a "clone" (genetic copy) of the donor. This type of cloning is called **reproductive cloning** because it results in the birth of a new animal.

In 1996, Scottish researcher Ian Wilmut and his colleagues used reproductive cloning to produce the first mammal cloned from an adult cell, a sheep named Dolly. The researchers used an electric shock to fuse specially treated adult sheep udder cells with 277 eggs from which they had removed the nuclei. After several days of growth, 29 of the resulting embryos were implanted in the uteruses of surrogate mothers. One of the embryos developed into Dolly. As expected, Dolly resembled her genetic parent, the nucleus donor, not the egg donor or the surrogate mother.

Practical Applications of Reproductive Cloning

In the years since Dolly's landmark birth, researchers have cloned many species of mammals, including mice, horses, dogs, mules, cows, pigs, rabbits, ferrets, and cats (Figure 11.14a). Why would anyone want to do this? In agriculture, farm animals with specific sets of desirable traits might be cloned to produce herds with these traits. In research, genetically identical animals can provide perfect "control animals" for experiments. The pharmaceutical industry is experimenting with cloning animals for potential medical use. For example, the pigs in Figure 11.14b are clones that lack a gene for a protein that can cause immune system rejection in humans. Organs from such pigs may one day be used in human patients who need transplants.

Perhaps the most intriguing use of reproductive cloning is to restock populations of endangered animals. Among the rare animals that have been cloned are a wild mouflon (a small European sheep), a banteng (a Javanese cow), a gaur (an Asian ox), and gray wolves (Figure 11.14c). The 2003 cloning of a banteng, whose numbers have dwindled to just a few in the wild, is a remarkable case. Using frozen cells from a zoo-raised banteng that had died 23 years prior, scientists transplanted nuclei from the frozen cells

▼ Figure 11.13 **Cloning by nuclear transplantation.** In nuclear transplantation, a nucleus from an adult body cell is injected into a nucleus-free egg cell. The resulting embryo may then be used to produce a new organism (reproductive cloning, shown in the upper branch) or to provide stem cells (therapeutic cloning, lower branch). The lamb in the photograph is the famous Dolly, shown with her surrogate mother.

Remove nucleus from egg cell

Add somatic cell from adult donor

Donor cell

Nucleus from donor cell

Grow in culture to produce a blastocyst (early embryo)

Reproductive cloning

Implant embryo in surrogate mother

Clone of donor is born

Therapeutic cloning

Remove embryonic stem cells from embryo and grow in culture

Induce stem cells to form specialized cells for therapeutic use into nucleus-free eggs from dairy cows. The resulting embryos were implanted into surrogate cows, leading to the birth of a healthy baby banteng. This success shows that it is possible to produce a baby even when a female of the donor species is unavailable. Scientists may someday be able to use similar cross-species methods to clone an animal from a recently extinct species.

in cloning reverse extinction?

The use of cloning to repopulate endangered species holds tremendous promise. However, cloning may also create new problems. Conservationists object that cloning may detract from efforts to preserve natural habitats. They correctly point out that cloning does not increase genetic diversity and is therefore not as beneficial to endangered species as natural reproduction. Cloned animals may be less healthy than those arising from a fertilized egg. In 2003, Dolly was euthanized after suffering complications from a lung disease that is normally seen only in much older sheep, although no one is sure whether her illness was related to her unusual birth. Other cloned animals have exhibited defects such as susceptibility to obesity, pneumonia, liver failure, and premature death.

Human Cloning

The cloning of various mammals has heightened speculation that humans could be cloned. Critics point out the many practical and ethical objections to human cloning. Practically, cloning of mammals is extremely difficult and inefficient. Only a small percentage of cloned embryos develop normally, and they appear less healthy than naturally born kin. Ethically, the discussion about whether or not people should be cloned—and if so, under what circumstances—is far from settled. Consensus on this topic is unlikely anytime soon. Meanwhile, the research and the debate continue. ☑

▼ Figure 11.14 **Reproductive cloning of mammals.**

(a) **The first cloned cat.** CC ("Copy Cat") and her lone parent (left).

(b) **Cloning for medical use.** These piglets are clones of a pig that was genetically modified to lack a protein that causes transplant rejection in humans.

(c) **Clones of endangered animals**

Mouflon lamb with mother   Banteng   Gaur   Gray wolf

209

Therapeutic Cloning and Stem Cells

The lower branch of Figure 11.13 shows the process of **therapeutic cloning**. The purpose of this procedure is not to produce a living organism but rather to produce embryonic stem cells.

Embryonic Stem Cells

In mammals, **embryonic stem cells (ES cells)** are derived from blastocysts. During development in the uterus, embryonic stem cells differentiate, giving rise to all the specialized cells in the body. When removed from an early embryo and grown in laboratory culture, embryonic stem cells can divide indefinitely. The right conditions—such as the presence of certain growth-stimulating proteins—can (hypothetically) induce changes in gene expression that cause the cells to develop into a particular cell type (Figure 11.15). If scientists can discover the right conditions, they may be able to grow cells for the repair of injured or diseased organs. Some people speculate, for example, that ES cells may one day be used to replace cells damaged by spinal cord injuries or heart attacks. The use of embryonic stem cells in therapeutic cloning is controversial, however, because the removal of ES cells destroys the embryo.

Adult Stem Cells

Embryonic stem cells are not the only stem cells available to researchers. **Adult stem cells** can also generate replacements for some of the body's cells. Unlike ES cells, adult stem cells are partway along the road to differentiation. In the body, adult stem cells usually give rise to only a few related types of specialized cells. For example, stem cells in bone marrow generate different kinds of blood cells. Because no embryonic tissue is involved in their harvest, adult stem cells may provide an ethically less problematic therapy than ES cells. However, some researchers think that only the more versatile ES cells are likely to lead to groundbreaking advances in human health.

Umbilical Cord Blood Banking

Another source of stem cells is blood collected from the umbilical cord and placenta at birth. Such stem cells appear to be partially differentiated, less so than adult stem cells, more so than embryonic stem cells. To obtain these cells, a physician inserts a needle into the umbilical cord and extracts 1/4 to 1/2 cup of blood (Figure 11.16). The cells are then frozen and kept in a blood bank, where they are available if needed for medical treatment. In 2005, doctors reported that an infusion of umbilical cord blood stem cells from a compatible (but unrelated) donor appeared to cure some babies of Krabbe's disease, a usually fatal inherited disorder of the nervous system. Other people have received cord blood as a treatment for leukemia. To date, however, most attempts at umbilical cord blood therapy have not been successful. At present, the American Academy of Pediatrics recommends cord blood banking only for babies born into families with a known genetic risk. So far, the promise of cord blood banking vastly exceeds the accomplishments. ✓

Why do some parents save their baby's umbilical cord blood?

☑ CHECKPOINT

How do the results of reproductive cloning and therapeutic cloning differ?

Answer: Reproductive cloning results in the production of a live individual; therapeutic cloning produces stem cells.

▼ Figure 11.15 **Differentiation of embryonic stem cells in culture.** Scientists hope to someday discover growth conditions that will stimulate cultured stem cells to differentiate into specialized cells.

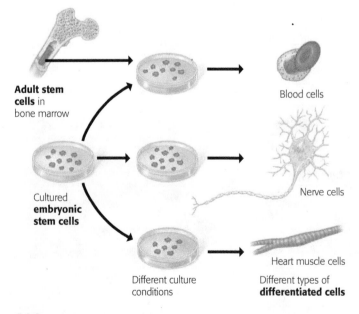

Adult stem cells in bone marrow

Cultured embryonic stem cells

Blood cells

Nerve cells

Heart muscle cells

Different culture conditions

Different types of **differentiated cells**

▼ Figure 11.16 **Umbilical cord blood banking.** Just after birth, a doctor may collect blood from a newborn's umbilical cord. The umbilical cord blood (inset), rich in stem cells, is stored for possible future use.

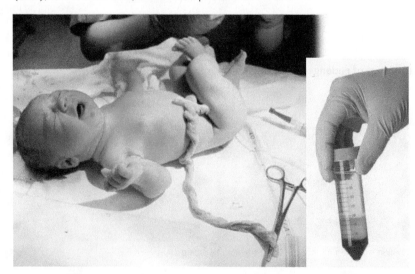

The Genetic Basis of Cancer

Cancer is a variety of diseases in which cells escape from the control mechanisms that normally limit their growth and division (as introduced in Chapter 8). This escape involves changes in gene expression.

Genes That Cause Cancer

One of the earliest clues to the role of genes in cancer was the discovery in 1911 of a virus that causes cancer in chickens. Recall that viruses are simply "genes in a box," molecules of DNA or RNA surrounded by protein. Viruses that cause cancer can become permanent residents in host cells by inserting their nucleic acid into the DNA of host chromosomes. Researchers have identified a number of viruses that harbor genes that if inserted into a host cell can make the cell cancerous. A gene that causes cancer is called an **oncogene** ("tumor gene").

Oncogenes and Tumor-Suppressor Genes

In 1976, American molecular biologists J. Michael Bishop, Harold Varmus, and their colleagues made a startling discovery. They found that a cancer-causing chicken virus contains an oncogene that is an altered version of a normal chicken gene. Subsequent research has shown that the chromosomes of many animals, including humans, contain genes that can be converted to oncogenes. A normal gene with the potential to become an oncogene is called a **proto-oncogene**. (These terms can be confusing, so let's repeat them: A *proto-oncogene* is a normal, healthy gene that, if changed, can become a cancer-causing *oncogene*.) A cell can acquire an oncogene from a virus or from the mutation of one of its own proto-oncogenes.

How can a change in a gene cause cancer? Searching for the normal roles of proto-oncogenes in the cell, researchers found that many of these genes code for **growth factors**—proteins that stimulate cell division—or for other proteins that affect the cell cycle. When all these proteins are functioning normally, in the right amounts at the right times, they help keep the rate of cell division at an appropriate level. When they malfunction—if a growth factor becomes hyperactive, for example—cancer (uncontrolled cell growth) may result.

For a proto-oncogene to become an oncogene, a mutation must occur in the cell's DNA. **Figure 11.17** illustrates three kinds of changes in DNA that can produce active oncogenes. In all three cases, abnormal gene expression stimulates the cell to divide excessively.

Changes in genes whose products inhibit cell division are also involved in cancer. These genes are called **tumor-suppressor genes** because the proteins they encode normally help prevent uncontrolled cell growth (**Figure 11.18**). Any mutation that keeps a growth-inhibiting protein from being made or from functioning may contribute to the development of cancer. Researchers have identified many mutations in both tumor-suppressor and growth factor genes that are associated with cancer, as we'll discuss next.

▼ **Figure 11.17 How a proto-oncogene can become an oncogene.**

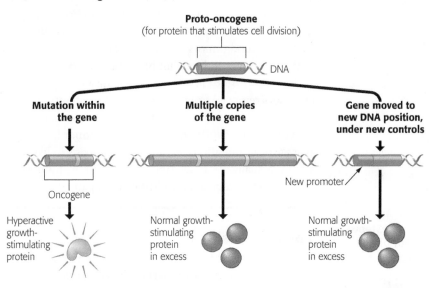

Proto-oncogene
(for protein that stimulates cell division)

DNA

| Mutation within the gene | Multiple copies of the gene | Gene moved to new DNA position, under new controls |

New promoter

Oncogene

Hyperactive growth-stimulating protein

Normal growth-stimulating protein in excess

Normal growth-stimulating protein in excess

▼ **Figure 11.18 Tumor-suppressor genes.**

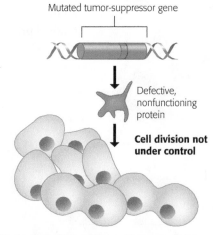

Tumor-suppressor gene

Normal growth-inhibiting protein

Cell division under control

Mutated tumor-suppressor gene

Defective, nonfunctioning protein

Cell division not under control

(a) Normal cell growth. A tumor-suppressor gene normally codes for a protein that inhibits cell growth and division. In this way, the gene helps prevent cancerous tumors from arising.

(b) Uncontrolled cell growth (cancer). When a mutation in a tumor-suppressor gene makes its protein defective, cells that are usually under the control of the normal protein may divide excessively, forming a tumor.

Cancer THE PROCESS OF SCIENCE

Are Childhood Tumors Special?

Medical researchers have made many **observations** of specific mutations that can lead to cancer. They therefore **question** whether different kinds of cancers are associated with specific mutations. A large research team led by the Johns Hopkins Kimmel Cancer Center in Baltimore formed the **hypothesis** that young patients with medulloblastoma (MB)—the most common pediatric brain cancer and the deadliest form of childhood cancer (Figure 11.19)—harbor unique mutations. They made the **prediction** that a genetic map of MB cells from childhood tumors would have cancer-associated mutations not found in adult brain cancer tissue.

The **experiment** involved sequencing all the genes in tumors removed from 22 pediatric MB patients and comparing them with normal tissue from these same patients. Their **results** showed that each tumor had an average of 11 mutations. Although this may seem like a lot, it is actually five to ten times fewer than the number of mutations associated with MB in adult patients. Young

MB patients therefore seem to have fewer, but deadlier, mutations. When they investigated the role that the mutated genes play, the research team found that some help control DNA packing, whereas others play a role in the development of organs. The researchers hope that this new knowledge about the genetic basis of MB may be used to develop new therapies for this often fatal disease.

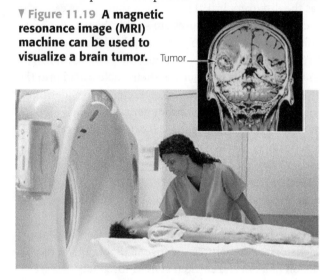

▼ Figure 11.19 **A magnetic resonance image (MRI) machine can be used to visualize a brain tumor.** Tumor

The Progression of a Cancer

Nearly 150,000 Americans will be stricken by cancer of the colon (the main part of the large intestine) this year. One of the best-understood types of human cancer, colon cancer illustrates an important principle about how cancer develops: More than one mutation is needed to produce a full-fledged cancer cell. As in many cancers, the development of colon cancer is a gradual process.

As shown in Figure 11.20, **1** colon cancer begins when an oncogene arises through mutation, causing unusually frequent division of normal-looking cells in the colon lining. **2** Later, additional DNA mutations (such as the inactivation of a tumor-suppressor gene) cause the growth of a small benign tumor (called a polyp) in the colon wall. **3** Further mutations eventually lead to formation of a malignant tumor—a tumor that has the potential to metastasize (spread).

▼ Figure 11.20 **Stepwise development of a typical colon cancer.**

Colon wall

Colon wall

Cellular changes: Increased cell division Growth of benign tumor Growth of malignant tumor

DNA changes: Oncogene activated Tumor-suppressor gene inactivated Second tumor-suppressor gene inactivated

The development of a malignant tumor is accompanied by a gradual accumulation of mutations that convert proto-oncogenes to oncogenes and knock out tumor-suppressor genes (Figure 11.21). The requirement for several DNA mutations—usually four or more—explains why cancers can take a long time to develop. This requirement may also help explain why the incidence of cancer increases with age; the longer we live, the more likely we are to accumulate mutations that cause cancer.

"Inherited" Cancer

Most mutations that lead to cancer arise in the organ where the cancer starts—the colon, for example. Because these mutations do not affect the cells that give rise to eggs or sperm, they are not passed from parent to child. Sometimes, however, a cancer-causing mutation occurs in a cell that gives rise to gametes and is therefore passed on from generation to generation. Such mutations predispose the people who inherit them to developing cancer. Such cancer is said to be familial or inherited. But even familial cancers don't appear unless the person acquires additional mutations in the susceptible tissue.

One well-studied inherited cancer gene is *BRCA1* (pronounced "braca-1"), the normal allele of which encodes a tumor-suppressor protein. Certain alleles of *BRCA1* are associated with breast cancer, a disease that strikes one out of every ten American women (Figure 11.22). Some *BRCA1* mutations give a woman an 80% risk of developing breast or ovarian cancer during

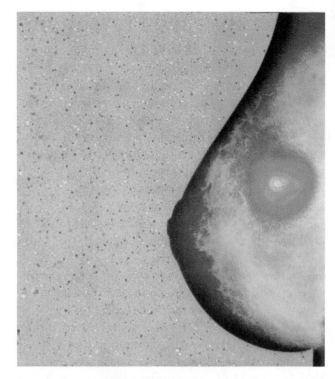

▲ Figure 11.22 **Breast cancer.** In this mammogram, normal breast tissue appears as greenish-blue, while the tumor is highlighted in yellow and red.

her lifetime. In recent years, tests for *BRCA1* mutations have become available. Unfortunately, these tests are of limited use because surgical removal of the breasts and/or ovaries is the only preventive option currently available to women who carry the mutant genes. ☑

▼ Figure 11.21 **Accumulation of mutations in the development of a cancer cell.** Mutations leading to cancer accumulate in a lineage of cells. In this figure, colors distinguish the normal cells from cells with one or more mutations, leading to increased cell division and cancer. Once a cancer-promoting mutation occurs (orange band on chromosome), it is passed to all the descendants of the cell carrying it.

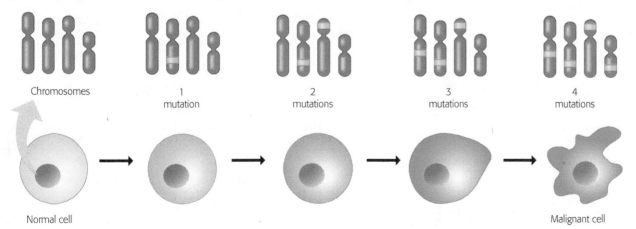

Chromosomes · 1 mutation · 2 mutations · 3 mutations · 4 mutations

Normal cell · Malignant cell

☑ CHECKPOINT

How can a mutation in a tumor-suppressor gene contribute to the development of cancer?

Answer: A mutated tumor-suppressor gene may produce a defective protein unable to function in a pathway that normally inhibits cell division and therefore normally suppresses tumors.

Cancer Risk and Prevention

Cancer is the second-leading cause of death (after heart disease) in most industrialized countries. Death rates due to certain forms of cancer have decreased in recent years, but the overall cancer death rate is still on the rise, currently increasing at about 1% per decade.

Most cancers arise from mutations that are caused by **carcinogens**, cancer-causing agents found in the environment. Mutations often result from decades of exposure to carcinogens. One of the most potent carcinogens is ultraviolet (UV) radiation. Excessive exposure to UV radiation from the sun can cause skin cancer, including a deadly type called melanoma.

What can you do to lower your risk of cancer?

The one substance known to cause more cases and types of cancer than any other is tobacco. By a wide margin, more people die from lung cancer (nearly 160,000 Americans in 2011) than from any other form of cancer. Most tobacco-related cancers are due to smoking, but inhaling secondhand smoke also poses a risk. As Table 11.1 indicates, tobacco use, sometimes in combination with alcohol consumption, causes several types of cancer. In nearly all cases, cigarettes are the main culprit, but smokeless tobacco products (chewing tobacco, or "dip") are linked to cancer of the mouth and throat. Exposure to some of the most lethal carcinogens is often a matter of individual choice: Tobacco use, the consumption of alcohol, and excessive time spent in the sun are all avoidable behaviors that affect cancer risk.

Some food choices significantly reduce a person's cancer risk. For instance, eating 20–30 g of plant fiber daily (about the amount found in 7 apples, which is twice the amount the average American consumes) while eating less animal fat may help prevent colon cancer. There is also evidence that certain substances in fruits and vegetables, including vitamins C and E and certain compounds related to vitamin A, may help protect against a variety of cancers. Cabbage and its relatives, such as broccoli and cauliflower, are thought to be especially rich in substances that help prevent cancer, although some of the specific substances have not yet been identified. Determining how diet influences cancer has become an important focus of nutrition research.

The battle against cancer is being waged on many fronts, and there is reason for optimism in the progress being made. It is especially encouraging that we can help reduce our risk of acquiring some of the most common forms of cancer by the choices we make in our daily lives. ☑

Table 11.1	Cancer in the United States (Ranked by Number of Cases)		
Cancer	**Known or Likely Carcinogens or Factors**	**Estimated Cases (2011)**	**Estimated Deaths (2011)**
Prostate	Testosterone; possibly dietary fat	241,000	33,700
Breast	Estrogen; possibly dietary fat	233,000	40,000
Lung	Cigarette smoke	221,000	157,000
Colon and rectum	High dietary fat; low dietary fiber	141,000	49,400
Skin	Ultraviolet light	76,300	12,000
Lymphomas	Viruses (for some types)	75,200	20,600
Bladder	Cigarette smoke	69,300	15,000
Kidney	Cigarette smoke	60,900	13,100
Uterus	Estrogen	46,500	8,100
Leukemias	X-rays; benzene; viruses (for some types)	44,600	21,800
Pancreas	Cigarette smoke	44,000	37,700
Liver	Alcohol; hepatitis viruses	26,200	19,600
Brain and nerve	Trauma; X-rays	22,300	13,100
Ovary	Large number of ovulation cycles	22,000	15,500
Stomach	Table salt; cigarette smoke	21,500	10,300
Cervix	Viruses; cigarette smoke	12,700	4,300
All other types		239,200	100,800
Total		1,596,700	572,000

Source: *Cancer Facts and Figures 2011* (American Cancer Society Inc.).

☑ **CHECKPOINT**

Of all known behavioral factors, which one causes the most cancer cases and deaths?

Answer: tobacco use

Cancer EVOLUTION CONNECTION

The Evolution of Cancer in the Body

The theory of evolution describes natural selection acting on populations of organisms. Recently, medical researchers have been using an evolutionary perspective to gain insight into the development of tumors, such as the bone tumor shown in **Figure 11.23**. Evolution drives the growth of a tumor—which can be thought of as a population of cancer cells—and also affects how those cells respond to cancer treatments.

Recall that there are several assumptions behind Darwin's theory of natural selection (see Chapter 1). Let's consider how each one can be applied to cancer. First, all evolving populations have the potential to produce more offspring than can be supported by the environment. Cancer cells, with their uncontrolled growth, clearly demonstrate such overproduction. Second, there must be variation among individuals of the population. Studies of tumor cell DNA, like the one described in the Process of Science section, show genetic variability within tumors. Finally, variations in the population must affect survival and reproductive success. Indeed, the accumulation of mutations in cancer cells renders them less susceptible to normal mechanisms of reproductive control. Mutations that enhance survival of malignant cancer cells are passed on to that cell's descendants. In short, a tumor evolves.

Viewing the progression of cancer through the lens of evolution helps explain why there is no easy "cure" for cancer but may also pave the way for novel therapies. For example, some researchers are attempting to "prime" tumors for treatment by increasing the reproductive success of only those cells that will be susceptible to a chemotherapy drug. Our understanding of cancer, like all other aspects of biology, benefits from an evolutionary perspective.

▼ Figure 11.23 **X-ray of shoulder and upper arm, revealing a large bone tumor.**

Chapter Review

SUMMARY OF KEY CONCEPTS

 Go to **www.masteringbiology.com** for homework assignments, practice quizzes, Pearson eText, and more.

How and Why Genes Are Regulated

Patterns of Gene Expression in Differentiated Cells

The various types of cells in a multicellular organism arise due to different combinations of genes being turned on and off via gene regulation in each cell type.

Gene Regulation in Bacteria

An operon is a cluster of genes with related functions together with their promoter and other DNA sequences that control their transcription. The *lac* operon allows *E. coli* to produce enzymes for lactose use only when the sugar is present.

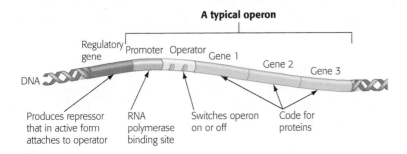

A typical operon

Regulatory gene | Promoter | Operator | Gene 1 | Gene 2 | Gene 3

DNA

Produces repressor that in active form attaches to operator | RNA polymerase binding site | Switches operon on or off | Code for proteins

Gene Regulation in Eukaryotic Cells

In the nucleus of eukaryotic cells, there are several possible control points in the pathway of gene expression.

- DNA packing tends to block gene expression, presumably by preventing access of transcription proteins to the DNA. An extreme example is X chromosome inactivation in the cells of female mammals.

- The most important control point in both eukaryotes and prokaryotes is at gene transcription. Various regulatory proteins interact with DNA and with each other to turn the transcription of eukaryotic genes on or off.

- There are also opportunities for the control of eukaryotic gene expression after transcription, when introns are cut out of the RNA and a cap and tail are added to process RNA transcripts into mRNA.

- In the cytoplasm, presence of microRNAs may block the translation of an mRNA, and various proteins may regulate the start of translation.

- Finally, the cell may activate the finished protein in various ways (for instance, by cutting out portions). Eventually, the protein may be selectively broken down.

DNA unpacking

Transcription

RNA processing

RNA transport

mRNA breakdown

Translation

Protein activation

Protein breakdown

Cell Signaling

Cell-to-cell signaling is key to the development and functioning of multicellular organisms. Signal transduction pathways convert molecular messages to cell responses, such as the transcription of particular genes.

Homeotic Genes

Evidence for the evolutionary importance of gene regulation is apparent in homeotic genes, master genes that regulate other genes that in turn control embryonic development.

DNA Microarrays: Visualizing Gene Expression

DNA microarrays can be used to determine which genes are turned on in a particular cell type.

Cloning Plants and Animals

The Genetic Potential of Cells

Most differentiated cells retain a complete set of genes, so an orchid plant, for example, can be made to grow from a single orchid cell. Under special conditions, animals can also be cloned.

Reproductive Cloning of Animals

Nuclear transplantation is a procedure whereby a donor cell nucleus is inserted into a nucleus-free egg. First demonstrated in frogs in the 1950s, reproductive cloning was used in 1996 to clone a sheep from an adult mammary cell and has since been used to create many other cloned animals.

Nucleus from donor cell → Early embryo resulting from nuclear transplantation → Embryo implanted in surrogate mother → Clone of nucleus donor

Therapeutic Cloning and Stem Cells

The purpose of therapeutic cloning is to produce embryonic stem cells for medical uses. Both embryonic and adult stem cells show promise for future therapeutic uses.

Nucleus from donor cell → Early embryo resulting from nuclear transplantation → Embryonic stem cells in culture → Specialized cells

The Genetic Basis of Cancer

Genes That Cause Cancer

Cancer cells, which divide uncontrollably, can result from mutations in genes whose protein products regulate the cell cycle.

Many proto-oncogenes and tumor-suppressor genes code for proteins active in signal transduction pathways regulating cell division. Mutations of these genes cause malfunction of the pathways. Cancers result from a series of genetic changes in a cell lineage. Researchers have gained insight into the genetic basis of breast cancer by studying families in which a disease-predisposing mutation is inherited.

Cancer Risk and Prevention

Reducing exposure to carcinogens (which induce cancer-causing mutations) and making other healthful lifestyle choices can help reduce cancer risk.

SELF-QUIZ

1. Your bone cells, muscle cells, and skin cells look different because
   a. different kinds of genes are present in each kind of cell.
   b. they are present in different organs.
   c. different genes are active in each kind of cell.
   d. different mutations have occurred in each kind of cell.

2. A group of prokaryotic genes with related functions that are regulated as a single unit, along with the control sequences that perform this regulation, is called a(n) _____.

3. The regulation of gene expression must be more complex in multicellular eukaryotes than in prokaryotes because
   a. eukaryotic cells are much larger.
   b. in a multicellular eukaryote, different cells are specialized for different functions.
   c. prokaryotes are restricted to stable environments.
   d. eukaryotes have fewer genes, so each gene must do several jobs.

4. A eukaryotic gene was inserted into the DNA of a bacterium. The bacterium then transcribed this gene into mRNA and translated the mRNA into protein. The protein produced was useless and contained many more amino acids than the protein made by the eukaryotic cell. Why?
   a. The mRNA was not spliced as it is in eukaryotes.
   b. Eukaryotes and prokaryotes use different genetic codes.
   c. Repressor proteins interfered with transcription and translation.
   d. Ribosomes were not able to bind to tRNA.

5. How does dense packing of DNA in chromosomes prevent gene expression?

6. What evidence demonstrates that differentiated cells in a plant or animal retain their full genetic potential?

7. The most common procedure for cloning an animal is _____.

8. What is learned from a DNA microarray?

9. Which of the following is a valid difference between embryonic stem cells and the stem cells found in adult tissues?
   a. In laboratory culture, only adult stem cells are immortal.
   b. In nature, only embryonic stem cells give rise to all the different types of cells in the organism.
   c. Only adult stem cells can be made to differentiate in the laboratory.
   d. Only embryonic stem cells are in every tissue of the adult body.

10. Name three potential sources of stem cells.

11. What is the difference between oncogenes and proto-oncogenes? How can one turn into the other? What function do proto-oncogenes serve?

12. A mutation in a single gene may cause a major change in the body of a fruit fly, such as an extra pair of legs or wings. Yet it takes many genes to produce a wing or leg. How can a change in just one gene cause such a big change in the body? What are such genes called?

Answers to these questions can be found in Appendix: Self-Quiz Answers.

THE PROCESS OF SCIENCE

13. Study the depiction of the *lac* operon in Figure 11.2. Normally, the genes are turned off when lactose is not present. Lactose activates the genes, which code for enzymes that enable the cell to use lactose. Mutations can alter the function of this operon; in fact, the effects of various mutations enabled Jacob and Monod to figure out how the operon works. Predict how the following mutations would affect the function of the operon in the presence and absence of lactose:
   a. mutation of regulatory gene; repressor will not bind to lactose
   b. mutation of operator; repressor will not bind to operator
   c. mutation of regulatory gene; repressor will not bind to operator
   d. mutation of promoter; RNA polymerase will not attach to promoter

14. The human body has a far greater variety of proteins than genes, a fact that seems to highlight the importance of alternative RNA splicing, which allows several different mRNAs to be made from a single gene. Suppose you have samples of two types of adult cells from one person. Design an experiment using microarrays to determine whether or not the different gene expression is due to alternative RNA splicing.

15. Because a cat must have both orange and non-orange alleles to be tortoiseshell (see Figure 11.4), we would expect only female cats, which have two X chromosomes, to be tortoiseshell. Normal male cats (XY) can carry only one of the two alleles. Male tortoiseshell cats are rare and usually sterile. What might you guess their genotype to be?

16. Design a DNA microarray experiment that measures the difference in gene expression between normal colon cells and cells from a colon tumor.

BIOLOGY AND SOCIETY

17. A chemical called dioxin is produced as a by-product of certain chemical manufacturing processes. Trace amounts of this substance were present in Agent Orange, a defoliant sprayed on vegetation during the Vietnam War. There has been a continuing controversy over its effects on soldiers exposed to Agent Orange during the war. Animal tests have suggested that dioxin can cause cancer, liver and thymus damage, immune system suppression, and birth defects; at high dosage it can be lethal. But such animal tests are inconclusive; a hamster is not affected by a dose that can kill a much larger guinea pig, for example. Researchers have discovered that dioxin enters a cell and binds to a protein that in turn attaches to the cell's DNA. How might this mechanism help explain the variety of dioxin's effects on different body systems and in different animals? How might you determine whether a particular individual became ill as a result of exposure to dioxin? Do you think this information is relevant in the lawsuits of soldiers suing over exposure to Agent Orange? Why or why not?

18. There are genetic tests available for several types of "inherited cancer." The results from these tests cannot usually predict that someone will get cancer within a particular amount of time. Rather, they indicate only that a person has an increased risk of developing cancer. For many of these cancers, lifestyle changes cannot decrease a person's risk. Therefore, some people consider the tests useless. If your close family had a history of cancer and a test were available, would you want to get screened? Why or why not? What would you do with this information? If a sibling decided to get screened, explain whether you would want to know the results.

12 DNA Technology

A DNA profile.
Even minuscule bits of
evidence can provide a
DNA profile.

DNA Profiling BIOLOGY AND SOCIETY

DNA, Guilt, and Innocence

It was a horrific crime: Early in the morning of May 3, 1992, a 3-year-old girl sleeping in her Mississippi home was abducted, raped, murdered, and thrown into a creek. A tiny semen sample was recovered at the crime scene. Police arrested the mother's boyfriend, who had been babysitting the girl that night. Although police could not conclusively match the crime scene sample to the suspect, the jury found the circumstantial evidence compelling. He was convicted of the crime and sentenced to death.

How can a biological sample be used to provide evidence of guilt? Modern forensic investigations hinge on a simple fact: The cells of every person (except identical twins) contain unique DNA. DNA profiling is the analysis of DNA samples to determine whether they come from the same individual. Although the semen sample from the 1992 crime scene was insufficient for DNA profiling at the time, new methods allowed a DNA profile to be determined in 2001. The results this time were conclusive: The semen at the crime scene did *not* match the man originally convicted of the crime.

Several years later, the DNA profile obtained from the crime scene was matched to a different man. The second man soon confessed to the crime and to the nearly identical 1990 murder of another 3-year-old girl, for which a third man was serving jail time. After years of legal maneuvering, the two wrongly convicted men were freed in 2008, exonerated based on the DNA evidence.

A steady stream of stories such as the one told here demonstrates the relevance of DNA technology to forensic science. Even beyond the courtroom, DNA technology has led to some of the most remarkable scientific advances in recent years: Corn and other crops, such as soybeans and tomatoes, have been genetically modified to produce their own insecticides; human genes are being compared with those of other animals to help shed light on what makes us distinctly human; and significant advances have been made toward detecting and curing fatal genetic diseases. This chapter will describe these and other uses of DNA technology and explain how various DNA techniques are performed. Along the way, we'll also examine some of the social, legal, and ethical issues that lie at the intersection of biology and society.

Recombinant DNA Technology

You may think of **biotechnology**, the manipulation of organisms or their components to make useful products, as a modern phenomenon, but it actually dates back to the dawn of civilization. Consider such ancient practices as using yeast to make bread and the selective breeding of livestock. But when people use the term *biotechnology* today, they are usually referring to **DNA technology**, modern laboratory techniques for studying and manipulating genetic material. Using these methods, scientists can modify specific genes and move them between organisms as different as bacteria, plants, and animals.

Are there any products of biotechnology in your lunch?

In the 1970s, the field of biotechnology exploded with the invention of methods for making recombinant DNA in the laboratory. **Recombinant DNA** is constructed when scientists combine pieces of DNA from two different sources—often from different species—to form a single DNA molecule. Recombinant DNA technology is widely used in **genetic engineering**, the direct manipulation of genes for practical purposes. Scientists have genetically engineered bacteria to mass-produce a variety of useful chemicals, from cancer drugs to pesticides. Scientists have also transferred genes from bacteria to plants and from one animal species to another (**Figure 12.1**). Such engineering can serve a variety of purposes, from basic research (What does this gene do?) to medical applications (Can we create animal models for this human disease?). ☑

☑ CHECKPOINT

What is biotechnology? What is recombinant DNA?

Answer: the manipulation of organisms or their parts to produce a useful product; a molecule containing DNA from two different sources, often different species

▼ **Figure 12.1** **Glowing fish.** Genetic engineers produced glowing fish by transferring a gene for a fluorescent protein originally obtained from jellies ("jellyfish").

Applications: From Humulin to Foods to "Pharm" Animals

By transferring the gene for a desired protein into a bacterium, yeast, or other kind of cell that is easy to grow in culture, scientists can produce large quantities of useful proteins that are present naturally only in small amounts. In this section, you'll learn about some applications of recombinant DNA technology.

Making Humulin

Humulin is human insulin produced by genetically modified bacteria (**Figure 12.2**). In humans, insulin is a protein normally made by the pancreas. Insulin functions as a hormone and helps regulate the level of glucose in the blood. If the body fails to produce enough insulin, the result is type 1 diabetes. There is no cure, so people with this disease must inject themselves daily with doses of insulin for the rest of their lives.

Because human insulin is not readily available, diabetes was historically treated using insulin from cows and pigs. This treatment was problematic, however. Pig and cow insulins can cause allergic reactions in people because their chemical structures differ slightly from that of human insulin. In addition, by the 1970s, the supply of beef and pork pancreas available for insulin extraction could not keep up with the demand.

In 1978, scientists working at the biotechnology company Genentech chemically synthesized two genes, one for each of the polypeptides of the active form of human insulin (see Figure 11.7). Because the amino acid sequences of the two insulin polypeptides were already known, it was easy to use the genetic code (see Figure 10.11) to determine nucleotide sequences that would encode for them. Researchers synthesized DNA fragments and linked them

► **Figure 12.2**
Humulin, human insulin produced by genetically modified bacteria.

to form the insulin genes. In 1979, they succeeded in inserting these artificial genes into *Escherichia coli* host cells. Under proper growing conditions, these bacteria cranked out large quantities of the human protein.

In 1982, Humulin hit the market as the world's first genetically engineered pharmaceutical product. Today, it is produced around the clock in gigantic fermentation vats filled with a liquid culture of bacteria. Each day, more than 4 million people with diabetes use the insulin collected, purified, and packaged at such facilities (Figure 12.3).

Insulin is just one of many human proteins produced by genetically modified bacteria. Another example is human growth hormone (HGH). Abnormally low levels of this hormone during childhood and adolescence can cause dwarfism. Because growth hormones from other animals are not effective in people, HGH was an early target of genetic engineers. Before genetically engineered HGH became available in 1985, children with an HGH deficiency could only be treated with scarce and expensive supplies of HGH obtained from human cadavers.

Besides bacteria, yeast and mammalian cells can also be used to produce medically valuable human proteins. For example, genetically modified mammalian cells growing in laboratory cultures are currently used to produce a hormone called erythropoietin (EPO) that stimulates production of red blood cells. EPO is used to treat anemia; unfortunately, some athletes abuse the drug to seek the advantage of artificially high levels of oxygen-carrying red blood cells (a practice called "blood doping").

DNA technology is also helping medical researchers develop vaccines. A **vaccine** is a harmless variant or derivative of a disease-causing microbe—such as a bacterium or virus—that is used to prevent an infectious disease. When a person is inoculated, the vaccine stimulates the immune system to develop lasting defenses against the microbe. For many viral diseases, the only

way to prevent serious harm from the illness is to use vaccination to prevent the illness in the first place. One approach to vaccine production is to use genetically engineered yeast cells to make large amounts of a protein found on the microbe's outer surface. The vaccine against hepatitis B, a disabling and sometimes fatal liver disease, is made in this way.

Genetically Modified (GM) Foods

Since ancient times, people have selectively bred agricultural crops to make them more useful (see Figure 1.13a). Today, DNA technology is quickly replacing traditional breeding programs as scientists work to improve the productivity of agriculturally important plants and animals. Scientists have produced many varieties of **genetically modified (GM) organisms**, organisms that have acquired one or more genes by artificial means. If the newly acquired gene is from another organism, typically of another species, the recombinant organism is called a **transgenic organism**.

In the United States today, roughly half the corn crop and more than three-quarters of the soybean and cotton crops are genetically modified. Figure 12.4 shows corn that has been genetically engineered to resist attack by an insect called the European corn borer (shown in the inset). Growing insect-resistant plants reduces the need for chemical insecticides. In another example, modified strawberry plants produce bacterial proteins that act as a natural antifreeze, protecting the plants from cold weather, which can harm the delicate crop. Potatoes and rice have been experimentally modified to produce harmless proteins derived from the cholera bacterium; researchers hope that these modified foods will one day serve as an edible vaccine against cholera, a disease that kills thousands of children in developing nations every year. In India, the insertion of a natural but rare saltwater-resistance gene has enabled new varieties of rice to thrive in water three times as salty as seawater, allowing food to be grown in drought-stricken or flooded regions.

▼ Figure 12.4 **Genetically modified corn.** The corn plants in this field carry a bacterial gene that helps prevent infestation by the European corn borer (inset).

▼ Figure 12.3 **A factory that produces genetically engineered insulin.**

▲ Figure 12.5 **Genetically modified rice.** "Golden rice 2," the yellow grains shown here alongside ordinary rice, has been genetically modified to produce high levels of beta-carotene, a molecule that the body converts to vitamin A.

Scientists are also using genetic engineering to improve the nutritional value of crop plants. One example is "golden rice 2," a transgenic variety of rice that carries genes from daffodils and corn (Figure 12.5). This rice could help prevent vitamin A deficiency and resulting blindness, especially in developing nations that depend on rice as a staple crop. However, controversy surrounds the use of GM foods, as we'll discuss at the end of the chapter. ☑

"Pharm" Animals

Figure 12.6 shows a transgenic pig that carries a gene for human hemoglobin. The pig-produced hemoglobin can be isolated and used in human blood transfusions. Because transgenic animals are difficult to produce, researchers may create a single transgenic animal and then breed or clone it. The resulting herd of transgenic animals could then serve as a grazing pharmaceutical factory—"pharm" animals.

DNA technology may eventually replace traditional animal breeding. Scientists might, for example, identify a gene that causes the development of larger muscles (which make up most of the meat we eat) in one variety of cattle and transfer it to other cattle or even to chickens. In 2006, University of Pittsburgh researchers genetically modified pigs to carry a roundworm gene whose protein converts less healthy fatty acids to omega-3 fatty acids. Meat from the modified pigs contains four to five times as much healthy omega-3 fat as regular pork. Unlike transgenic plants, however, transgenic animals are currently used only to produce potentially useful proteins; as of 2011, no transgenic animals are sold as food, although the Food and Drug Administration has issued regulatory guidelines for their eventual introduction.

Recombinant DNA technology serves many roles today and will certainly play an even larger part in our future. In the next section, you'll learn how scientists create and manipulate recombinant DNA.

☑ **CHECKPOINT**

What is a genetically modified organism?

Answer: one that carries DNA introduced through artificial means

Recombinant DNA Techniques

Although recombinant DNA techniques can be performed using many types of cells, bacteria are the workhorses of modern biotechnology. To manipulate genes in the laboratory, biologists often use bacterial **plasmids**, which are small, circular DNA molecules that replicate (duplicate) separately from the larger bacterial chromosome (Figure 12.7). Because plasmids can carry virtually any gene and are passed from one generation of bacteria to the next, they are key tools for **gene cloning**, the production of multiple identical copies of a gene-carrying piece of DNA. Gene-cloning methods are central to the production of useful products from genetically engineered organisms.

Consider a typical genetic engineering challenge: A molecular biologist at a pharmaceutical company identifies a gene of interest that codes for a valuable protein, such as a potential new drug. The biologist wants to manufacture the protein on a large scale. Figure 12.8 illustrates a way to accomplish this by using recombinant DNA techniques.

To start, the biologist isolates two kinds of DNA: ❶ bacterial plasmids that will serve as **vectors** (gene carriers) and ❷ DNA from another organism that includes the gene of interest (along with other unwanted genes). This other DNA may be from any type of organism, even a human. ❸ The researcher uses an enzyme to cut the two kinds of DNA. Each plasmid is cut in only one place; the other DNA is cut into many fragments, one of which carries the gene of interest. The figure shows the processing of just three of these DNA fragments and three plasmids, but actually millions of

▼ Figure 12.7 **Bacterial plasmids.** The micrograph shows a bacterial cell that has been ruptured, revealing one long chromosome and several smaller plasmids. The inset is an enlarged view of a single plasmid.

◄ Figure 12.6 **A genetically modified swine.**

Plasmids

Bacterial chromosome

Remnant of bacterium

Colorized TEM 2,700x

▼ Figure 12.8 **Using recombinant DNA technology to produce useful products.**

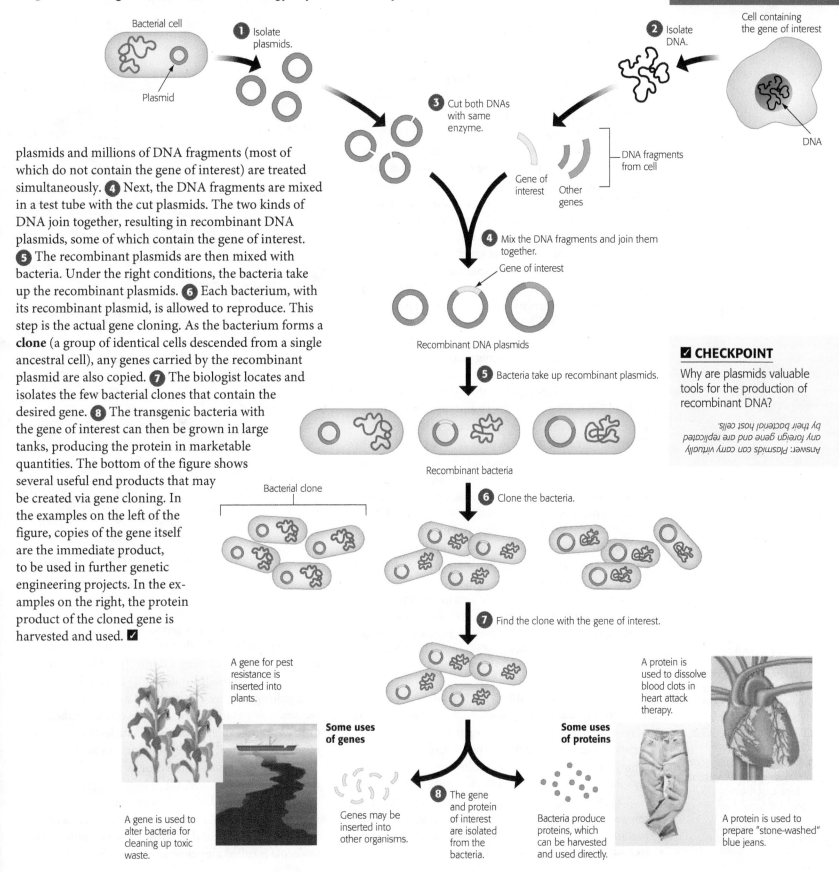

Bacterial cell

1 Isolate plasmids.

Plasmid

2 Isolate DNA.

Cell containing the gene of interest

DNA

3 Cut both DNAs with same enzyme.

Gene of interest

Other genes

DNA fragments from cell

4 Mix the DNA fragments and join them together.

Gene of interest

Recombinant DNA plasmids

5 Bacteria take up recombinant plasmids.

Recombinant bacteria

Bacterial clone

6 Clone the bacteria.

7 Find the clone with the gene of interest.

plasmids and millions of DNA fragments (most of which do not contain the gene of interest) are treated simultaneously. **4** Next, the DNA fragments are mixed in a test tube with the cut plasmids. The two kinds of DNA join together, resulting in recombinant DNA plasmids, some of which contain the gene of interest. **5** The recombinant plasmids are then mixed with bacteria. Under the right conditions, the bacteria take up the recombinant plasmids. **6** Each bacterium, with its recombinant plasmid, is allowed to reproduce. This step is the actual gene cloning. As the bacterium forms a **clone** (a group of identical cells descended from a single ancestral cell), any genes carried by the recombinant plasmid are also copied. **7** The biologist locates and isolates the few bacterial clones that contain the desired gene. **8** The transgenic bacteria with the gene of interest can then be grown in large tanks, producing the protein in marketable quantities. The bottom of the figure shows several useful end products that may be created via gene cloning. In the examples on the left of the figure, copies of the gene itself are the immediate product, to be used in further genetic engineering projects. In the examples on the right, the protein product of the cloned gene is harvested and used. ✔

✔ CHECKPOINT

Why are plasmids valuable tools for the production of recombinant DNA?

Answer: Plasmids can carry virtually any foreign gene and are replicated by their bacterial host cells.

A gene for pest resistance is inserted into plants.

Some uses of genes

A gene is used to alter bacteria for cleaning up toxic waste.

Genes may be inserted into other organisms.

8 The gene and protein of interest are isolated from the bacteria.

Some uses of proteins

Bacteria produce proteins, which can be harvested and used directly.

A protein is used to dissolve blood clots in heart attack therapy.

A protein is used to prepare "stone-washed" blue jeans.

A Closer Look: Cutting and Pasting DNA with Restriction Enzymes

As you saw in Figure 12.8, recombinant DNA is created by combining two ingredients: a bacterial plasmid and the gene of interest. To understand how these DNA molecules are spliced together, you need to learn how enzymes cut and paste DNA.

The cutting tools used for making recombinant DNA are bacterial enzymes called **restriction enzymes**. Biologists have identified hundreds of restriction enzymes, each recognizing a particular short DNA sequence (usually four to eight nucleotides long). For example, one restriction enzyme only recognizes the DNA sequence GAATTC, whereas another recognizes GGATCC. The DNA sequence recognized by a particular restriction enzyme is called a **restriction site**. After a restriction enzyme binds to its restriction site, it cuts the two strands of the DNA at specific points within the sequence, like a pair of highly specific molecular scissors.

The top of Figure 12.9 shows a piece of DNA (blue) that contains one recognition sequence for a particular restriction enzyme. ❶ The restriction enzyme cuts the DNA strands between the bases A and G within the recognition sequence, producing pieces of DNA called **restriction fragments**. The staggered cuts yield two double-stranded DNA fragments with single-stranded ends, called "sticky ends." Sticky ends are the key to joining DNA restriction fragments originating from different sources. ❷ Next, a piece of DNA from another source (green) is added. Notice that the green DNA has single-stranded ends identical in base sequence to the sticky ends on the blue DNA because the same restriction enzyme was used to cut both types of DNA. ❸ The complementary ends on the blue and green fragments stick together by base pairing. ❹ The union between the blue and green fragments is then made permanent by the "pasting" enzyme **DNA ligase**. This enzyme, which is one of the proteins the cell normally uses in DNA replication, connects the DNA pieces into continuous strands by forming bonds between adjacent nucleotides. The final outcome is a single molecule of recombinant DNA. ✓

A Closer Look: Obtaining the Gene of Interest

The procedure shown in Figure 12.8 can yield millions of recombinant plasmids carrying many different segments of foreign DNA. Such a procedure is called a "shotgun" approach to gene cloning because it "hits" an enormous number of different pieces of DNA. A typical cloned DNA fragment is big enough to carry one or a few genes. A collection of cloned DNA fragments that includes an organism's entire genome (a complete set of its genes) is called a **genomic library**.

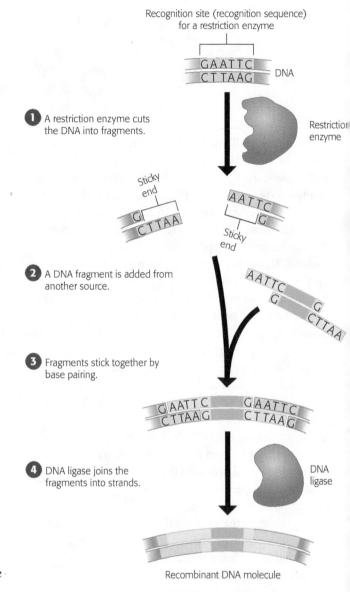

▼ Figure 12.9 **Cutting and pasting DNA.** The production of recombinant DNA requires two enzymes: a restriction enzyme, which cuts the original DNA molecules into pieces, and DNA ligase, which pastes the pieces together.

Recognition site (recognition sequence) for a restriction enzyme

GAATTC
CTTAAG DNA

❶ A restriction enzyme cuts the DNA into fragments.

Restriction enzyme

Sticky end

G   AATTC
CTTAA   G

Sticky end

❷ A DNA fragment is added from another source.

AATTC
G   G
CTTAA

❸ Fragments stick together by base pairing.

G AATTC   G AATTC
CTTAA G   CTTAA G

❹ DNA ligase joins the fragments into strands.

DNA ligase

Recombinant DNA molecule

After you've created a genomic library, you have to find the right "book"—that is, you must identify the bacterial clone containing a desired gene (step 7 in Figure 12.8). Methods for detecting a gene depend on base pairing between the gene and a complementary sequence on another nucleic acid molecule, either DNA or RNA. When at least part of the nucleotide sequence of a gene is known, this information can be used to advantage. For example, if we know that a gene contains the sequence TAGGCT, a biologist can synthesize a short single strand of DNA with a complementary sequence (ATCCGA) and label it with a radioactive isotope or fluorescent dye. This labeled complementary molecule is called a **nucleic acid probe** because it is used to find a specific gene or other nucleotide sequence within a mass of DNA. (In actual practice, probe molecules are considerably longer than six nucleotides.) When a radioactive DNA probe is added to the DNA of various clones, it tags the correct molecule—finds the right book in the library—by base-pairing to the complementary sequence in the gene of interest (Figure 12.10). After a probe detects the desired clone within a library, more of the tagged cells can be grown, resulting in the production of large quantities of the gene of interest.

Another approach to obtaining a gene of interest is to synthesize it. One method uses reverse transcriptase, a viral enzyme that can synthesize DNA by using an mRNA template (see Chapter 10). Figure 12.11 shows the steps involved. A eukaryotic cell ❶ transcribes the gene of interest and ❷ processes the transcript, removing introns and splicing exons together to produce mRNA. A researcher then ❸ isolates the mRNA in a test tube and ❹ makes single-stranded DNA from it using reverse transcriptase. ❺ DNA polymerase is then used to synthesize a second DNA strand.

When the researcher starts with an mRNA mixture from a particular cell type, the DNA that results from this procedure, called complementary DNA (cDNA), represents only those genes that were actually transcribed in the starting cells. Because cDNA molecules lack introns, they are shorter than the full version of the genes and therefore easier to work with.

A final approach is to synthesize a gene of interest from scratch. Automated DNA-synthesizing machines can accurately and rapidly produce customized DNA molecules of any sequence up to lengths of a few hundred nucleotides (Figure 12.12). ☑

▼ Figure 12.11 **Making a gene from eukaryotic mRNA.** Using the enzyme reverse transcriptase (shown in green), a researcher can produce an artificial DNA gene (cDNA, in blue) from a molecule of messenger RNA (mRNA, in red).

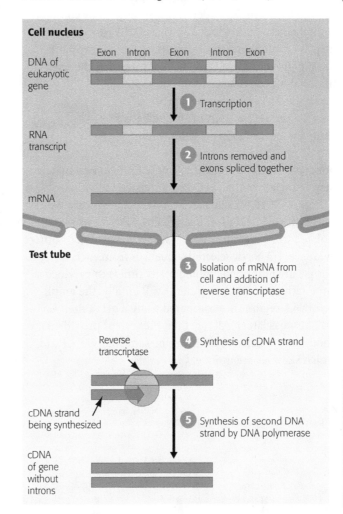

CHECKPOINT
Name three ways a gene of interest can be obtained.

Answer: The gene can be isolated from a genomic library, produced from mRNA using reverse transcriptase, or synthesized from scratch.

▼ Figure 12.10 **How a DNA probe tags a gene.** The probe is a short, radioactive, single-stranded molecule of DNA or RNA. When it is mixed with single-stranded DNA from a gene with a complementary sequence, it attaches by hydrogen bonds (shown by the small red dots), "labeling" the gene.

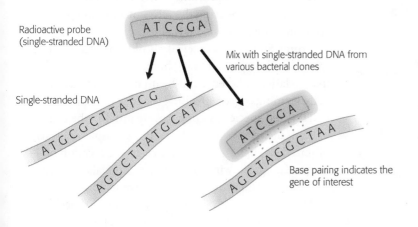

► Figure 12.12 **A DNA synthesizer.** This synthesizer constructs molecules of DNA from a programmed sequence, using solutions of the four DNA nucleotides (stored in the bottles beneath the machine).

DNA Profiling and Forensic Science

As discussed in the Biology and Society section, the analysis of DNA samples to determine whether they come from the same individual, known as **DNA profiling**, can help in criminal investigations. Indeed, DNA profiling has rapidly transformed the field of **forensics**, the scientific analysis of evidence for crime scene investigations and other legal proceedings. To produce a DNA profile, scientists compare sequences in the genome that vary from person to person. Like a gene, a noncoding genetic sequence is more likely to be a match between relatives than between unrelated individuals.

How have the techniques of DNA technology revolutionized forensics?

Figure 12.13 presents an overview of a typical investigation using DNA profiling. ❶ First, DNA samples are isolated from the crime scene, suspects, victims, or other evidence. ❷ Next, selected sequences from each DNA sample are amplified (copied many times) to produce a large sample of DNA fragments. ❸ Finally, the amplified DNA regions are compared using a gel (a method we'll discuss later). All together, these steps provide data about which samples are from the same individual and which samples are unique. ☑

CHECKPOINT

DNA profiling depends on analyzing genetic markers. What is a genetic marker?

Answer: A genetic marker is any sequence in the genome that varies from person to person.

▶ Figure 12.13 **Overview of DNA profiling.** In this example, DNA from suspect 1 does not match DNA found at the crime scene, but DNA from suspect 2 does match.

Crime scene   Suspect 1   Suspect 2

❶ DNA isolated

❷ DNA amplified

❸ DNA compared

Investigating Murder, Paternity, and Ancient DNA

Since its introduction in 1986, DNA profiling has become a standard tool of forensics and has provided crucial evidence in many famous cases. DNA profiling first came to widespread attention during the O. J. Simpson murder trial. In this case, DNA analysis proved that blood in Simpson's car belonged to the victims and that blood at the crime scene belonged to Simpson. (The jury did not find the DNA evidence alone to be sufficient to convict the suspect, and Simpson was found not guilty.) And during the investigation that led up to his impeachment, President Bill Clinton repeatedly denied that he had sexual relations with Monica Lewinsky—until DNA profiling proved that his semen was on her dress. Of course, DNA evidence can prove innocence as well as guilt. As of 2011, lawyers at the Innocence Project, a nonprofit legal organization located in New York City, have helped to exonerate more than 270 convicted criminals in 34 states, including 17 who were on death row. In more than a third of these cases, DNA profiling has also identified the true perpetrators.

DNA profiling can also be used to identify murder victims. The largest such effort in history took place after the World Trade Center attack on September 11, 2001. Forensic scientists in New York City worked for years to identify more than 20,000 samples of victims' remains. DNA profiles of tissue samples from the disaster site were matched to DNA profiles from tissue known to be from the victims. If no sample of a victim's DNA was available, blood samples from close relatives were used to confirm identity through near matches. More than half of the victims identified at the World Trade Center site were recognized solely by DNA evidence, providing closure to many grieving families.

The use of DNA profiling extends beyond crimes. For instance, comparing the DNA of a mother, her child, and the purported father can settle a question of paternity. Sometimes paternity is of historical interest: DNA profiling proved that Thomas Jefferson or a close male relative fathered a child with one of his slaves, Sally Hemings. DNA profiling can also help protect endangered species by conclusively proving the origin of contraband animal products. For example, analysis of seized elephant tusks can pinpoint the location of the poaching, allowing enforcement officials to increase surveillance and prosecute those responsible.

Modern methods of DNA profiling are so specific and powerful that the DNA samples can be in a partially degraded state. This allows DNA analysis to be applied in a great number of ways. In evolution research, the technique has been used to study DNA recovered from an ancient mummified human and from a 30-million-year-old plant fossil. A 2005 study determined that DNA extracted from a 27,000-year-old Siberian mammoth was 98.6% identical to DNA from modern African elephants. One of the strangest cases of DNA profiling is that of Cheddar Man, a 9,000-year-old skeleton found in a cave near Cheddar, England (Figure 12.14). DNA was extracted from his tooth and used to construct a DNA profile. The results suggested that Cheddar Man was a direct ancestor (through approximately 300 generations) of a present-day schoolteacher who lived only half a mile from the cave!

▶ **Figure 12.14 Cheddar Man.** Analysis of DNA extracted from "Cheddar Man"—a 9,000-year-old skeleton found in an English cave—suggested that he was a direct ancestor of a local schoolteacher (shown in the inset).

DNA Profiling Techniques

In this section, you'll learn about techniques for making a DNA profile (steps 2 and 3 in Figure 12.13).

The Polymerase Chain Reaction (PCR)

The **polymerase chain reaction (PCR)** is a technique by which a specific segment of DNA can be targeted and copied quickly and precisely. Through PCR, a scientist can obtain enough DNA from even minute amounts of blood or other tissue to allow a DNA profile to be constructed.

In principle, PCR is simple. A DNA sample is mixed with nucleotides, the DNA replication enzyme DNA polymerase, and a few other ingredients. The solution is then exposed to cycles of heating (to separate the DNA strands) and cooling (to allow double-stranded DNA to re-form). During these cycles, specific regions of each molecule of DNA are replicated, doubling the amount of that DNA (Figure 12.15). The key to automated PCR is an unusually heat-stable DNA polymerase, first isolated from prokaryotes living in hot springs. Unlike most proteins, this enzyme can withstand the heat at the start of each cycle. Beginning with a single DNA molecule, automated PCR can generate hundreds of billions of copies in a few hours. ☑

Initial DNA segment

| 1 | 2 | 4 | 8 |

Number of DNA molecules

◀ **Figure 12.15 DNA amplification by PCR.** The polymerase chain reaction (PCR) is a method for making many copies of a specific segment of DNA. Each round of PCR, performed on a table-top thermal cycler (shown at top), doubles the total quantity of DNA.

☑ CHECKPOINT

Why is only the slightest trace of DNA at a crime scene often sufficient for forensic analysis?

Answer: because PCR can be used to produce enough molecules for analysis

Short Tandem Repeat (STR) Analysis

How do you prove that two samples of DNA come from the same person? You could compare the entire genomes found in the two samples. But such an approach would be extremely impractical, requiring a lot of time and money. Instead, forensic scientists typically compare about a dozen short segments of noncoding repetitive DNA. **Repetitive DNA**, which makes up much of the DNA that lies between genes in humans, consists of nucleotide sequences that are present in multiple copies in the genome. Some of this DNA consists of short sequences repeated many times tandemly (one after another); such a series of repeats is called a **short tandem repeat (STR)**. For example, one person might have the sequence AGAT repeated 12 times in a row at one place in the genome, the sequence GATA repeated 35 times at a second place, and so on; another person is likely to have the same sequences at the same places

but with a different number of repeats. These stretches of repetitive DNA are more likely to be an exact match between relatives than between unrelated individuals.

STR analysis is a method of DNA profiling that compares the lengths of STR sequences at specific sites in the genome. Most commonly, STR analysis compares the number of repeats of specific four-nucleotide DNA sequences at 13 sites scattered throughout the genome. Each repeat site, which typically contains from 3 to 50 four-nucleotide repeats in a row, varies widely from person to person. In fact, some STRs used in the standard procedure have up to 80 variations in the number of repeats. In the United States, the number of repeats at each site is entered into a database called CODIS (Combined DNA Index System) administered by the Federal Bureau of Investigation. Law enforcement agencies around the world can access CODIS to search for matches to DNA samples they have obtained from crime scenes or suspects.

Consider the two samples of DNA shown in Figure 12.16. Imagine that the top DNA segment was obtained at a crime scene and the bottom from a suspect's blood. The two segments have the same number of repeats at the first site: 7 repeats of the four-nucleotide DNA sequence AGAT (in orange). Notice, however, that they differ in the number of repeats at the second site: 8 repeats of GATA (in purple) in the crime scene DNA, compared with 13 repeats in the suspect's DNA. To create a DNA profile, a scientist uses PCR to specifically amplify the regions of DNA that include these STR sites. The resulting fragments are then compared. Next we'll look at how this comparison is made. ☑

▼ **Figure 12.16 Short tandem repeat (STR) sites.** Scattered throughout the genome, STR sites contain tandem repeats of four-nucleotide sequences. The number of repetitions at each site can vary from individual to individual. In this figure, both DNA samples have the same number of repeats (7) at the first STR site, but different numbers (8 versus 13) at the second.

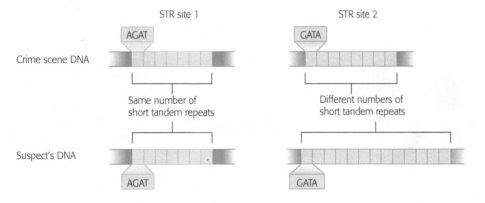

Gel Electrophoresis

The lengths of DNA fragments can be compared using **gel electrophoresis**, a method for sorting macromolecules—usually proteins or nucleic acids—primarily by their electrical charge and size. Figure 12.17 shows how gel electrophoresis separates DNA fragments obtained from

▼ **Figure 12.17 Gel electrophoresis of DNA molecules.**

☑ **CHECKPOINT**

What are STRs, and why are they useful for DNA profiling?

Answer: STRs (short tandem repeats) are nucleotide sequences repeated many times in a row within the human genome. STRs are valuable for DNA profiling because different people have different numbers of repeats at the various STR sites.

different sources. A DNA sample from each source is placed in a separate well (hole) at one end of a flat, rectangular gel, a thin slab of jellylike material that acts as a molecular sieve. A negatively charged electrode is then attached to the DNA-containing end of the gel and a positive electrode to the other end. Because the phosphate (PO_4^-) groups of nucleotides give DNA fragments a negative charge, the fragments move through the gel toward the positive pole. However, longer DNA fragments move more slowly through the thicket of polymer fibers in the gel than do shorter DNA fragments. Over time, shorter molecules move farther through the gel than longer molecules. Gel electrophoresis thus separates DNA fragments by length. When the current is turned off, a series of bands is left in each "lane" of the gel. Each band is a collection of DNA fragments of the same length. The bands can be made visible by staining, by exposure onto photographic film (if the DNA is radioactively labeled), or by measuring fluorescence (if the DNA is labeled with a fluorescent dye).

Figure 12.18 shows the gel that would result from using gel electrophoresis to separate the DNA fragments from the example in Figure 12.16. The differences in the locations of the bands reflect the different lengths of the DNA fragments. This gel would provide evidence that the crime scene DNA did not come from the suspect. Because gel electrophoresis reveals similarities and differences between DNA samples, DNA profiling can provide evidence of either guilt or innocence. ✔

▼ Figure 12.18 **Visualizing STR fragment patterns.** This figure shows the bands that would result from gel electrophoresis of the STR sites illustrated in Figure 12.16. Notice that one of the bands from the crime scene DNA does not match one of the bands from the suspect's DNA. (A gel from an actual DNA profile would typically contain more than just two bands in each lane.)

RFLP Analysis

Gel electrophoresis has many uses besides STR analysis. One application is RFLP analysis. RFLP (pronounced "rif-lip") stands for restriction fragment length polymorphism. In this method, the DNA molecules to be compared are exposed to a restriction enzyme (Figure 12.19). The resulting restriction fragments are separated and made visible on a gel. In this case, both the number and location of bands indicate whether the original DNA samples had identical nucleotide sequences at the sites shown.

▼ Figure 12.19 **RFLP analysis.** The DNA segments shown have nucleotide sequences that differ at one base pair (orange boxes). A particular restriction enzyme may therefore cut the segments at different places. In this case, the difference in DNA sequence results in three restriction fragments from the first DNA sample and two from the second. This difference, revealed by gel electrophoresis, indicates that the two DNA samples come from different individuals.

☑ CHECKPOINT

You use a restriction enzyme to cut a DNA molecule that has three copies of the enzyme's recognition sequence clustered near one end. When you separate the restriction fragments by gel electrophoresis, how do you expect the bands to appear?

Answer: three bands near the positive pole at the bottom of the gel (small fragments) and one band near the negative pole at the top of the gel (large fragment)

Genomics and Proteomics

In 1995, a team of scientists announced that it had determined the nucleotide sequence of the entire genome of *Haemophilus influenzae*, a bacterium that can cause several human diseases, including pneumonia and meningitis. **Genomics**, the study of complete sets of genes (genomes), was born.

The first targets of genomics research were bacteria, which have relatively little DNA. The *H. influenzae* genome, for example, contains 1.8 million nucleotides and 1,709 genes. But soon the attention of genomics researchers turned toward more complex organisms with much larger genomes (Table 12.1). As of 2011, the genomes of more than 1,700 species have been published, and more than 8,000 are in progress. The majority of organisms sequenced to date are prokaryotes, including *E. coli* and more than 1,000 other bacteria (some of medical importance) and more than 100 archaea. Over 100 eukaryotic genomes have also been completed.

Baker's yeast (*Saccharomyces cerevisiae*) was the first eukaryote to have its full sequence determined, and the roundworm *Caenorhabditis elegans* was the first multi-cellular organism. Other sequenced animals include the fruit fly (*Drosophila melanogaster*) and lab rat (*Ratus norvegicus*), both model organisms for genetics research. Among the sequenced plants are *Arabidopsis thaliana*, a type of mustard plant used as a model organism, and rice (*Oryza sativa*) and potato (*Solanum tuberosum*), two of the world's most economically important crops. Next we'll discuss a particularly notable example of a sequenced animal genome—our own.

The Human Genome Project

The **Human Genome Project** was a massive scientific endeavor to determine the nucleotide sequence of all the DNA in the human genome and to identify the location and sequence of every gene. The project began in 1990 as an effort by government-funded researchers from six countries. Several years into the project, private companies, chiefly Celera Genomics, joined the effort. At the completion of the project, more than 99% of the genome had been determined to 99.999% accuracy. (There remain a few hundred gaps of unknown sequence that will require special methods to figure out.) This ambitious project has provided a wealth of data that may illuminate the genetic basis of what it means to be human.

The chromosomes in the human genome (22 autosomes plus the X and Y sex chromosomes) contain approximately 3 billion nucleotide pairs of DNA. To try to get a sense of this quantity of DNA, imagine that its nucleotide sequence is printed in letters (A, T, C, and G) in books the size of this textbook. The sequence would fill a stack of books 18 stories high! However, the biggest surprise from the Human Genome Project is the relatively small number of human genes—currently estimated to be about 21,000—very close to the number found in a roundworm! This number of genes is well below estimates made before the results of the project were known. In fact, a friendly betting pool set up in the year 2000 by the world's leading genome researchers included a wide range of guesses—from 26,000 to 150,000. Every single genome expert overestimated!

Our genome was a major challenge to sequence because, like the genomes of most complex eukaryotes, only a small amount of our total DNA consists of genes that code for proteins, tRNAs, or rRNAs. Most complex eukaryotes have a huge amount of noncoding DNA—about 98% of human DNA is of this type. Some of this

Table 12.1	Some Important Sequenced Genomes		
Organism	**Year Completed**	**Size of Genome (in base pairs)**	**Approximate Number of Genes**
Haemophilus influenzae (bacterium)	1995	1.8 million	1,700
Saccharomyces cerevisiae (yeast)	1996	12 million	5,800
Escherichia coli (bacterium)	1997	4.6 million	4,400
Caenorhabditis elegans (roundworm)	1998	97 million	19,100
Drosophila melanogaster (fruit fly)	2000	180 million	13,700
Arabidopsis thaliana (mustard plant)	2000	120 million	25,500
Oryza sativa (rice)	2002	430 million	40,000
Homo sapiens (human)	2003	3.0 billion	21,000
Rattus norvegicus (lab rat)	2004	2.8 billion	20,000
Pan troglodytes (chimpanzee)	2005	3.1 billion	20,000
Macaca mulatta (macaque)	2007	2.9 billion	22,000
Ornithorhynchus anatinus (duck-billed platypus)	2008	1.8 billion	18,500
Solanum tuberosum (potato)	2011	844 million	39,000

noncoding DNA is made up of gene control sequences such as promoters, enhancers, and microRNAs (see Chapter 11). Other noncoding regions include introns and repetitive DNA (some of which is used in DNA profiling). Some noncoding DNA is important to our health, with certain regions known to carry disease-causing mutations. But the function (if there is any) of most noncoding DNA remains unknown. Biologists used to refer to noncoding DNA as "junk DNA," but it is now generally accepted that much of this DNA plays some (still mysterious) role.

The potential benefits of having a complete map of the human genome are enormous. Already, hundreds of disease-associated genes have been identified. One example is the gene that is mutated in an inherited type of Parkinson's disease, a debilitating brain disorder that causes tremors of increasing severity (Figure 12.20). Data from the Human Genome Project mapped some cases of Parkinson's disease to a specific gene. Interestingly, an altered version of the protein encoded by this gene has also been tied to Alzheimer's disease, suggesting a link between these two brain disorders. Moreover, the same gene is also found in rats, where it plays a role in the sense of smell, and in zebra finches, where it is thought to be involved in song learning. Cross-species comparisons such as these may uncover clues about the role played by the normal version of the protein in the human brain. And such knowledge could eventually lead to treatment for Parkinson's disease. ☑

Tracking the Anthrax Killer

In October 2001, a 63-year-old Florida man died from inhalation anthrax, a disease caused by breathing spores of the bacterium *Bacillus anthracis*. As the first victim of this disease in the United States since 1976 (and coming so soon after the 9/11 terrorist attacks the month before), his death was immediately suspicious. By the end of the year, four more people had died from anthrax. Law enforcement officials realized that someone was sending anthrax spores through the mail (Figure 12.21). The United States was facing an unprecedented bioterrorist attack.

In the investigation that followed, one of the most helpful clues turned out to be the anthrax spores themselves. Investigators compared the genomes of the mailed anthrax spores with several laboratory strains. They quickly established that all of the mailed spores were genetically identical, suggesting that a single perpetrator was behind all the attacks. Furthermore, they were able to match the deadly spores with a laboratory subtype isolated at the U.S. Army Medical Research Institute of Infectious Diseases in Fort Detrick, Maryland. A second, more comprehensive analysis of the spores used in the attack was completed in 2008. This analysis found four unique mutations in the mailed anthrax and traced the mutations to a single flask at the army facility. Based in part on this evidence, the FBI named an army research scientist as a suspect in the case. Although never charged, that suspect committed suicide in 2008; the case remains officially unsolved.

How did the FBI track down the anthrax killer?

☑ CHECKPOINT

1. Approximately how many nucleotides and genes are contained in the human genome?
2. Name three types of DNA that do not code for another molecule.

Answers: 1. about 3 billion nucleotides and 21,000 genes 2. introns, repetitive DNA, and gene control sequences

▼ Figure 12.20 **The fight against Parkinson's disease.** Boxer Muhammad Ali and actor Michael J. Fox—both of whom have Parkinson's disease—testify before the Senate on the status of federal funding for Parkinson's research.

▼ Figure 12.21 **The 2001 anthrax attacks.** In 2001, envelopes containing anthrax spores caused five deaths.

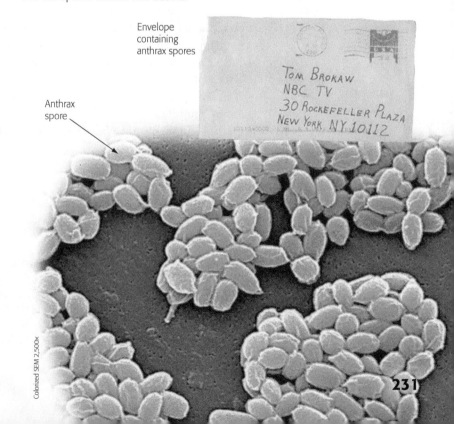

Envelope containing anthrax spores

Anthrax spore

Tom Brokaw
NBC TV
30 Rockefeller Plaza
New York NY 10112

Colonized SEM 2,500x

The anthrax investigation is just one example of the new field of bioinformatics, the application of computational tools to molecular biology. In 1991, sequence data provided strong evidence that a Florida dentist transmitted HIV to several patients. In 1993, after a cult released anthrax spores in downtown Tokyo, genomic analysis showed why their attack didn't kill anyone: They had used a harmless veterinary vaccine strain. And investigation of the West Nile virus outbreak in 1999 proved that a single natural strain of virus was infecting both birds and people. Bioinformatics has even allowed geneticists to produce a family tree of dog breeds (see the Evolution Connection section in Chapter 9).

Bioinformatics can also reveal similarities and differences in organisms more closely related to humans. In 2005, researchers completed the genome sequence for our closest living relative on the evolutionary tree of life, the chimpanzee (*Pan troglodytes*). Comparisons with human DNA revealed that we share 96% of our genome with our closest animal relative. Genomic scientists are currently finding and studying the important differences, shedding scientific light on the age-old question of what makes us human.

How similar is your DNA to the DNA of a chimp?

Genome-Mapping Techniques

Today, entire genomes are most often sequenced using the **whole-genome shotgun method**. The first step in this method is to chop the entire genome into fragments using restriction enzymes. Next, all the fragments are cloned and sequenced. Finally, computers running specialized mapping software reassemble the millions of overlapping short sequences into a single continuous sequence for every chromosome—an entire genome (Figure 12.22).

The DNA sequences determined by the Human Genome Project have been deposited in a database that is available on the World Wide Web. (You can browse it yourself at the website for the National Center for Biotechnology Information.) Scientists use software to scan and analyze the sequences for genes, control elements, and other features. The result is a genetic map containing all the genes and their locations on chromosomes. Next comes the most exciting challenge: figuring out the functions of the genes and other sequences and how they work together to direct the structure and function of a living organism. This challenge and the applications of the new knowledge should keep scientists busy well into the twenty-first century.

The human genome sequenced by government-funded scientists was actually a reference genome compiled from a group of individuals. The genome sequenced by Celera consisted primarily of DNA from scientist

▼ **Figure 12.22 Genome sequencing.** In the photo at the bottom, a technician performs a step in the whole-genome shotgun method (depicted in the diagram).

Chromosome

Chop up with restriction enzyme

DNA fragments

Sequence fragments

AATC
TTAATGTA
TCGGAC
GACGATTA

Align fragments

AATC GACGATTA
TCGGAC TTAATGTA

Reassemble full sequence

AATCGGACGATTAATGTA

Craig Venter, the company's president. As of 2011, the complete genomes of a handful of other individuals—including James Watson, codiscoverer of the structure of DNA—have also been sequenced. Scientists have even begun to gather sequence data from our extinct relatives, such as a nearly complete genome, published in 2010, from a Neanderthal. The more human genomes we have, the more insight we can gain into what makes each person unique. We may soon enter an age of "personal genomics," where individual genetic differences among people will be put to routine medical use. Some of these seemingly minuscule differences can actually be a matter of life and death, as we'll see next.

DNA Profiling THE PROCESS OF SCIENCE

Can Genomics Cure Cancer?

Lung cancer, which kills more Americans every year than any other type of cancer, has long been the target of searches for effective chemotherapy drugs. One drug used to treat lung cancer, called gefitinib, targets the protein encoded by the *EGFR* gene. This protein is found on the surface of cells that line the lungs and is also found in lung cancer tumors.

Unfortunately, treatment with gefitinib is ineffective for many patients. While studying the effectiveness of gefitinib, researchers at the Dana-Farber Cancer Institute in Boston made the **observation** that a few patients actually responded quite positively to the drug. This posed a **question:** Are genetic differences among lung cancer patients responsible for the differences in gefitinib's effectiveness? The researchers' **hypothesis** was that mutations in the *EGFR* gene were causing the different responses to gefitinib. The team made the **prediction** that DNA profiles focusing on the *EGFR* gene would reveal different DNA sequences in the tumors of responsive patients compared with the tumors of unresponsive patients. The researchers' **experiment** involved sequencing the *EGFR* gene in cells extracted from the tumors of five patients who responded to the drug and four who did not.

The **results** were quite striking: All five tumors from gefitinib-responsive patients had mutations in *EGFR*, whereas none of the other four tumors did (**Figure 12.23**). These results suggest that doctors can use DNA profiling techniques to screen lung cancer patients for those who are most likely to benefit from treatment with this drug. In broader terms, this work suggests that genomics may bring about a revolution in the treatment of disease by allowing therapies to be custom-tailored to the genetic makeup of each patient.

▲ Figure 12.23 **The *EGFR* protein: Fighting cancer with genomics.** Mutations (located at sites indicated by black arrows) in the *EGFR* protein can affect the ability of a cancer-fighting drug to destroy lung tumors. Here, the amino acid backbone of the protein is shown in green, with some important regions highlighted in orange, blue, and red.

Proteomics

The successes in the field of genomics have encouraged scientists to begin similar systematic studies of the full protein sets (proteomes) that genomes encode, an approach called **proteomics**. The number of different proteins in humans far exceeds the number of different genes (about 100,000 proteins versus about 21,000 genes). And since proteins, not genes, actually carry out the activities of the cell, scientists must study when and where proteins are produced and how they interact to understand the functioning of cells and organisms.

Genomics and proteomics are enabling biologists to approach the study of life from an increasingly holistic (whole-system) perspective. Biologists are now compiling catalogs of genes and proteins—that is, listings of all the "parts" that contribute to the operation of cells, tissues, and organisms. As such catalogs become complete, researchers are shifting their attention from the individual parts to how these parts function as a whole in biological systems. Such analyses may have many practical applications. For example, proteins associated with specific diseases may be used to aid diagnosis (by developing tests that search for a particular combination of proteins) and treatment (by designing drugs that interact with the proteins involved). ✔

✔ CHECKPOINT

What is the difference between genomics and proteomics?

Answer: Genomics concerns the complete set of an organism's genes, whereas proteomics concerns the complete set of an organism's proteins.

Human Gene Therapy

Human gene therapy is a recombinant DNA procedure intended to treat disease by altering an afflicted person's genes. In some cases, a mutant version of a gene may be replaced or supplemented with the normal allele. This could potentially correct a genetic disorder, perhaps permanently. In other cases, genes are inserted and expressed only long enough to treat a medical problem.

Figure 12.24 summarizes one approach to human gene therapy. ❶ A gene from a normal individual is cloned, converted to an RNA version, and then inserted into the RNA genome of a harmless virus. ❷ Bone marrow cells are taken from the patient and infected with the recombinant virus. ❸ The virus inserts a DNA copy of its genome, including the normal human gene, into the DNA of the patient's cells. ❹ The engineered cells are then injected back into the patient. The normal gene is transcribed and translated within the patient's body, producing the desired protein. Ideally, the non-mutant version of the gene would be inserted into cells that multiply throughout a person's life. Bone marrow cells, which include the stem cells that give rise to all the types of blood cells, are prime candidates. If the procedure succeeds, the cells will multiply permanently and produce a steady supply of the missing protein, curing the patient.

The promise of gene therapy thus far exceeds actual results, but there have been some successes. In 2009, an international research team conducted a trial that focused on a form of progressive blindness linked to a defect in a gene responsible for producing light-detecting pigments in the eye. The researchers found that a single injection of a virus carrying the normal gene into one eye of affected children improved vision in that eye, sometimes enough to allow normal functioning. The other eye was left untreated as a control.

From 2000 to 2011, gene therapy also cured 22 children with severe combined immunodeficiency (SCID), a fatal inherited disease caused by a defective gene that prevents development of the immune system, requiring patients to remain isolated within protective "bubbles." Unless treated with a bone marrow transplant, which is effective only 60% of the time, SCID patients quickly die from infections by microbes that most of us easily fend off. In these cases, researchers periodically removed immune system cells from the patients' blood, infected them with a virus engineered to carry the normal allele of the defective gene, then reinjected the blood into the patient. The treatment cured the patients of SCID, but there have been some serious side effects: Four of the treated patients developed leukemia, and one

died after the inserted gene activated an oncogene (see Chapter 11), creating cancerous blood cells. Gene therapy remains promising, but there is very little evidence to date of safe and effective application. Active research continues, with new, tougher safety guidelines in place that are meant to prevent the problems of the past. ☑

▼ Figure 12.24 **One approach to human gene therapy.**

Healthy person

Normal human gene

❶ An RNA version of a normal human gene is inserted into a harmless RNA virus.

RNA genome of virus

Inserted human RNA

❷ Bone marrow cells of the patient are infected with the virus.

❸ Viral DNA carrying the human gene inserts into the cell's chromosome

Bone marrow cell from the patient

Bone of person with disease

Bone marrow

❹ The engineered cells are injected into the patient.

Safety and Ethical Issues

As soon as scientists realized the power of DNA technology, they began to worry about potential dangers. Early concerns focused on the possibility of creating hazardous new disease-causing organisms. What might happen, for instance, if cancer-causing genes were transferred into infectious bacteria or viruses? To address such concerns, scientists developed a set of guidelines that have become formal government regulations in the United States and some other countries.

One safety measure is a set of strict laboratory procedures to protect researchers from infection by engineered microbes and to prevent microbes from accidentally leaving the laboratory (Figure 12.25). In addition, strains of microbes to be used in recombinant DNA experiments are genetically crippled to ensure that they cannot survive outside the laboratory. Finally, certain obviously dangerous experiments have been banned. Today, most public concern about possible hazards centers not on recombinant microbes but on genetically modified (GM) foods.

What steps are being taken by scientists to prevent the release of a "super germ"?

The Controversy over Genetically Modified Foods

GM strains account for a significant percentage of several staple crops. Controversy about the safety of these foods is an important political issue (Figure 12.26). For example, the European Union has suspended the introduction of new GM crops and considered banning the import of all GM foodstuffs. In the United States and other countries where the GM revolution has proceeded more quietly than in Europe, the labeling of GM foods is now being debated but has not yet become law.

Advocates of a cautious approach fear that crops carrying genes from other species might harm the environment or be hazardous to human health (by, for example, introducing new allergens, molecules that can cause allergic reactions, into foods). A major concern is that transgenic plants might pass their new genes to close relatives in nearby wild areas. We know that lawn and

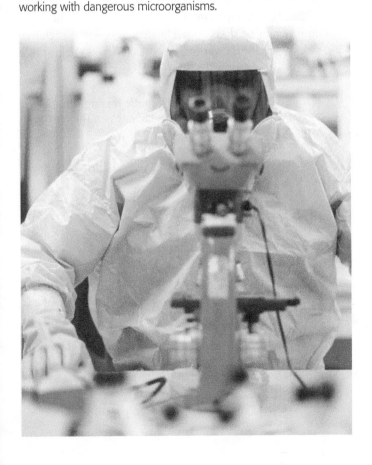

▼ Figure 12.25 **Maximum-security laboratory.** A scientist in a high-containment laboratory wears a biohazard suit, used for working with dangerous microorganisms.

▶ Figure 12.26 **Opposition to genetically modified organisms (GMOs).**
This photo shows tractors destroying a Belgian field of genetically modified crop. The Belgian Minister for Consumer Protection ordered the destruction as part of a widespread opposition to GM crops. The sign translates to "GMO, no thanks! Yes to biodiversity."

OGM non merci ! oui à la biodiversité

crop grasses, for example, commonly exchange genes with wild relatives via pollen transfer. If domestic plants carrying genes for resistance to herbicides, diseases, or insect pests pollinated wild plants, the offspring might become "superweeds" that would be very difficult to control. However, researchers may be able to prevent the escape of such plant genes in various ways—for example, by engineering plants so that they cannot breed. Concern has also been raised that the widespread use of GM seeds may reduce natural genetic diversity, leaving crops susceptible to catastrophic die-offs in the event of a sudden change to the environment or introduction of a new pest.

The U.S. National Academy of Sciences released a study finding no scientific evidence that transgenic crops pose any special health or environmental risks. But the authors of the study also recommended more stringent long-term monitoring to watch for unanticipated environmental impacts.

Negotiators from 130 countries (including the United States) agreed on a Biosafety Protocol that requires exporters to identify GM organisms present in bulk food shipments and allows importing countries to decide whether the shipments pose environmental or health risks. This agreement has been hailed as a breakthrough by environmentalists.

Today, governments and regulatory agencies throughout the world are grappling with how to facilitate the use of biotechnology in agriculture, industry, and medicine while ensuring that new products and procedures are safe. In the United States, all genetic engineering projects are evaluated for potential risks by a number of regulatory agencies, including the Food and Drug Administration, the Environmental Protection Agency, the National Institutes of Health, and the Department of Agriculture. ☑

Ethical Questions Raised by DNA Technology

DNA technology raises legal and ethical questions—few of which have clear answers. Consider, for example, the treatment of dwarfism with injections of human growth hormone (HGH) produced by genetically engineered cells. Should parents of short but hormonally normal children be able to seek HGH treatment to make their kids taller? If not, who decides which children are "tall enough" to be excluded from treatment?

Genetic engineering of gametes (sperm or ova) and zygotes has been accomplished in lab animals. It has not been attempted in humans because such a procedure

would raise very difficult ethical questions. Should we try to eliminate genetic defects in our children and their descendants? Should we interfere with evolution in this way? From a long-term perspective, the elimination of unwanted versions of genes from the gene pool could backfire. Genetic variety is a necessary ingredient for the adaptation of a species as environmental conditions change with time. Genes that are damaging under some conditions may be advantageous under others (one example is the sickle-cell allele—see the Evolution Connection section at the end of Chapter 13). Are we willing to risk making genetic changes that could be detrimental to our species in the future? We may have to face such questions soon.

Similarly, advances in genetic profiling raise privacy issues. If we were to create a DNA profile of every person at birth, then theoretically we could match nearly every violent crime to a perpetrator because it is virtually impossible for someone to commit a violent crime without leaving behind DNA evidence. Furthermore, having a complete profile database could help with the identification of crime victims or remains. But are we, as a society, prepared to sacrifice our genetic privacy, even for such worthwhile goals?

Should widespread DNA profiling be used to try to end violent crime?

As more information becomes available about our personal genetic makeup, many people question whether greater access to this information is always beneficial. For example, mail-in kits (Figure 12.27) have become available that can tell healthy people their relative risk of developing various diseases (such as Parkinson's

▼ **Figure 12.27 Personalized genetic testing.** This kit can be used to send saliva for genetic analysis. The results can indicate a person's risk of developing certain diseases.

☑ **CHECKPOINT**

What is the main concern about adding genes for herbicide resistance to crop plants?

Answer: the possibility that the genes could escape, via cross-pollination, to wild plants that are closely related to the crop species

and Crohn's) later in life. Some argue that such information helps families to prepare. Others say that the tests prey on our fears without offering any real benefit because certain diseases, such as Parkinson's, are not currently preventable or treatable. Other tests, however, such as for breast cancer risk, may help a person make changes that can prevent disease. How can we identify truly useful tests?

There is also a danger that information about disease-associated genes could be abused. One issue is the possibility of discrimination and stigmatization. In response, Congress passed the Genetic Information Nondiscrimination Act of 2008. Title I of the act prohibits insurance companies from requesting or requiring genetic information during an application for health insurance. Title II provides similar protections in employment. But even with such safeguards in place, can we fully prevent genetic information from being used in a discriminatory manner?

A much broader ethical question is how do we really feel about wielding one of nature's powers—the evolution of new organisms? Some might ask if we have any right to alter an organism's genes—or to create new organisms.

The benefits to people and the environment must also be considered. For example, bacteria are being engineered to clean up mining wastes and other pollutants that threaten the soil, water, and air. Since these organisms may be the only feasible solutions to some of our most pressing environmental problems, many people think this type of genetic engineering should be encouraged.

DNA technologies raise many complex issues that have no easy answers. It is up to you, as a "citizen scientist," to make informed choices. ☑

DNA Profiling EVOLUTION CONNECTION

The Y Chromosome as a Window on History

Barring mutations, the human Y chromosome passes essentially intact from father to son. By comparing Y DNA, researchers can learn about the ancestry of human males. DNA profiling can thus provide data about recent human evolution.

In 2003, geneticists discovered that about 8% of males currently living in central Asia have Y chromosomes of striking genetic similarity. Further analysis traced their common genetic heritage to a single man living about 1,000 years ago. In combination with historical records, the data led to the speculation that the Mongolian ruler Genghis Khan (Figure 12.28) may have been responsible for the spread of the chromosome to nearly 16 million men living today. A similar study of Irish men in 2006 suggested that nearly 10% of them were descendants of Niall of the Nine Hostages, a warlord who lived during the 1400s. Another study of Y DNA seemed to confirm the claim by the Lemba people of southern Africa that they are descended from ancient Jews. Sequences of Y DNA distinctive of the Jewish priestly caste called Kohanim are found at high frequencies among the Lemba.

Comparison of Y chromosome DNA profiles is part of a larger effort to learn more about the human genome. Other research efforts are extending genomic studies to many more species. These studies will advance our understanding of all aspects of biology, including health and ecology, as well as evolution. In fact, comparisons of the completed genome sequences of bacteria, archaea, and eukaryotes first supported the theory that these are the three fundamental domains of life—a topic we discuss further in the next unit, "Evolution and Diversity."

▲ Figure 12.28 **Genghis Khan.**

Chapter Review

■ SUMMARY OF KEY CONCEPTS

Go to **www.masteringbiology.com** for homework assignments, practice quizzes, Pearson eText, and more.

Recombinant DNA Technology

DNA technology, the manipulation of genetic material, is a relatively new branch of biotechnology, the use of organisms to make helpful products. DNA technology often involves the use of recombinant DNA, the combination of nucleotide sequences from two different sources.

Applications: From Humulin to Foods to "Pharm" Animals

Recombinant DNA techniques have been used to create genetically modified organisms, organisms that carry artificially introduced genes. Nonhuman cells have been engineered to produce human proteins, genetically modified food crops, and transgenic farm animals. A transgenic organism is one that carries artificially introduced genes, typically from a different species.

Recombinant DNA Techniques

DNA isolated from two sources and cut by same restriction enzyme

Plasmid (vector)

Gene of interest (could be obtained from a library or synthesized)

Recombinant DNA

Transgenic organisms

Useful products

DNA Profiling and Forensic Science

Forensics, the scientific analysis of legal evidence, has been revolutionized by DNA technology. DNA profiling is used to determine whether two DNA samples come from the same individual.

Investigating Murder, Paternity, and Ancient DNA

DNA profiling can be used to establish innocence or guilt of a criminal suspect, identify victims, determine paternity, and contribute to basic research.

DNA Profiling Techniques

Short tandem repeat (STR) analysis compares DNA fragments using the polymerase chain reaction (PCR) and gel electrophoresis.

Crime scene | Suspect 1 | Suspect 2

DNA

Polymerase chain reaction (PCR) amplifies STR sites

Longer DNA fragments

Shorter DNA fragments

Gel

DNA fragments compared by gel electrophoresis
(Bands of shorter fragments move faster toward the positive pole.)

Genomics and Proteomics

The Human Genome Project

The nucleotide sequence of the human genome is providing a wealth of useful data. The 24 different chromosomes of the human genome contain about 3 billion nucleotide pairs and 21,000 genes. The majority of the genome consists of noncoding DNA.

Tracking the Anthrax Killer

Comparing genomes can aid criminal investigations and basic research.

Genome-Mapping Techniques

The whole-genome shotgun method involves sequencing DNA fragments from an entire genome and then assembling the sequences.

Proteomics

Success in genomics has given rise to proteomics, the systematic study of the full set of proteins found in organisms.

Human Gene Therapy

RNA version of a normal human gene

Virus with RNA genome

Bone marrow

A normal human gene is transcribed and translated in a patient, potentially curing the genetic disease permanently

Gene therapy trials have focused on a number of inherited diseases, with both success and failures achieved to date.

Safety and Ethical Issues

The Controversy over Genetically Modified Foods

The debate about genetically modified crops centers on whether they might harm humans or damage the environment by transferring genes through cross-pollination with other species.

Ethical Questions Raised by DNA Technology

We as a society and as individuals must become educated about DNA technologies to address the ethical questions raised by their use.

SELF-QUIZ

1. Suppose you wish to create a large batch of the protein lactase using recombinant DNA. Place the following steps in the order you would have to perform them.
   a. Find the clone with the gene for lactase.
   b. Insert the plasmids into bacteria and grow the bacteria into clones.
   c. Isolate the gene for lactase.
   d. Create recombinant plasmids, including one that carries the gene for lactase.

2. Why is an artificial gene that is made using reverse transcriptase often shorter than the natural form of the gene?

3. A carrier that moves DNA from one cell to another, such as a plasmid, is called a _____.

4. In making recombinant DNA, what is the benefit of using a restriction enzyme that cuts DNA in a staggered fashion?

5. A paleontologist has recovered a bit of organic material from the 400-year-old preserved skin of an extinct dodo. She would like to compare DNA from the sample with DNA from living birds. The most useful method for initially increasing the amount of dodo DNA available for testing is _____.

6. Why do DNA fragments containing STR sites from different people tend to migrate to different locations during gel electrophoresis?

7. What feature of a DNA fragment causes it to move through a gel during electrophoresis?
   a. the electrical charges of its phosphate groups
   b. its nucleotide sequence
   c. the hydrogen bonds between its base pairs
   d. its double helix shape

8. After a gel electrophoresis procedure is run, the pattern of bars in the gel shows
   a. the order of bases in a particular gene.
   b. the presence of various-sized fragments of DNA.
   c. the order of genes along particular chromosomes.
   d. the exact location of a specific gene in a genomic library.

9. Name the steps of the whole-genome shotgun method.

10. Put the following steps of human gene therapy in the correct order.
   a. Virus is injected into patient.
   b. Human gene is inserted into a virus.
   c. Normal human gene is isolated and cloned.
   d. Normal human gene is transcribed and translated in the patient.

Answers to these questions can be found in Appendix: Self-Quiz Answers.

THE PROCESS OF SCIENCE

11. A biochemist hopes to find a gene in human liver cells that codes for a blood-clotting protein. The nucleotide sequence of a small part of the gene is CTGGACTGACA. Briefly explain how to obtain the desired gene.

12. Some scientists once joked that when the DNA sequence of the human genome was complete, "we can all go home" because there would be nothing left for genetic researchers to discover. Why haven't they all "gone home"?

BIOLOGY AND SOCIETY

13. In the not-too-distant future, gene therapy may be used to treat many inherited disorders. What do you think are the most serious ethical issues to face before human gene therapy is used on a large scale? Explain.

14. Today, it is fairly easy to make transgenic plants and animals. What are some safety and ethical issues raised by this use of recombinant DNA technology? What are some dangers of introducing genetically engineered organisms into the environment? What are some reasons for and against leaving such decisions to scientists? Who should make these decisions?

15. In October 2002, the government of the African nation of Zambia announced that it was refusing to distribute 15,000 tons of corn donated by the United States, enough corn to feed 2.5 million Zambians for three weeks. The government rejected the corn because it was likely to contain genetically modified kernels. The government made the decision after its scientific advisers concluded that the studies of the health risks posed by GM crops "are inconclusive." Do you agree with this assessment? Do you think that it is a good justification for refusing the donated corn? At the time of the government's decision, Zambia was facing food shortages, and 35,000 Zambians were expected to die from starvation over the next six months. In light of this, do you think it was morally acceptable for the government to refuse the food? How do the relative risks posed by GM crops compare with the relative risks posed by starvation?

16. In 1983, a 10-year-old girl was kidnapped from her home, raped, and murdered. A jury convicted a local teenager of the crimes and sentenced him to death for the brutal killing. In 1995, DNA analysis proved that semen found near the scene could not have come from the man accused. After 12 years on death row, he was exonerated and released from prison. His case, which took place in Illinois, was far from unique. From 1977 to 2000, 12 convicts were executed and 13 exonerated. In 2000, the governor of Illinois declared a moratorium on all executions in his state because the death penalty system was "fraught with errors." Do you support the Illinois governor's decision? What rights should death penalty inmates have with regard to DNA testing of old evidence? Who should pay for this additional testing?

Unit 3
Evolution and Diversity

13 How Populations Evolve

Malaria.
These children in Uganda are being tested for malaria.

Evolution in Action BIOLOGY AND SOCIETY

Mosquitoes, Microbes, and Malaria

What does actor George Clooney have in common with George Washington, Ernest Hemingway, Christopher Columbus, and Mother Teresa? They all survived bouts with malaria, a disease caused by a protozoan parasite that is one of the worst killers in human history. In the 1960s, the World Health Organization (WHO) launched a campaign to eradicate malaria. It was defeated by the microbe's secret weapon: evolution. Today, malaria causes more than a million deaths and 250 million cases of miserable illness each year.

The campaign against malaria focused on killing the mosquitoes that carry the protozoan from person to person. DDT, a widely used pesticide, was deployed in massive spraying operations. But in one location after another, early success was followed by rebounding mosquito populations. Although the lethal chemical killed most of the mosquitoes immediately, survivors gave rise to new populations. Many of the survivors, it turned out, carried an allele (alternate form of a gene) that coded for an enzyme that destroys DDT. The enzyme gave those mosquitoes a huge advantage wherever DDT was applied, and they passed the allele on to their offspring. In each generation, the proportion of DDT-resistant insects in the population increased, making subsequent sprayings less effective. This is an example of evolution in action, a change in allele frequency in response to environmental changes.

Evolution has also hindered our efforts to alleviate the suffering of malaria victims. At the same time that DDT was being celebrated as a miracle pesticide, a drug called chloroquine was hailed as the miracle cure for malaria. Through a similar process of adaptation to environmental change—in this case, the chloroquine encountered in the human body—the malaria parasite evolved resistance to the drug. At present, the most effective drug is artemisinin, a compound extracted from a plant used in traditional Chinese medicine. As you might expect, though, artemisinin-resistant malaria has already been detected.

An understanding of evolution informs all of biology, from exploring life's molecules to analyzing ecosystems. And applications of evolutionary biology are transforming medicine, agriculture, biotechnology, and conservation biology. In this chapter, you'll read about evolution in action: verifiable, measurable examples of evolution that affect our world.

Charles Darwin and *The Origin of Species*

Biology came of age on November 24, 1859, the day Charles Darwin published *On the Origin of Species by Means of Natural Selection*. In one respect, Darwin's book was similar to volumes written by other naturalists—an assemblage of facts about the natural world, including the characteristics, habitats, behaviors, and geographic distributions of diverse species of plants and animals. Three broad observations emerged from these facts (Figure 13.1):

- the rich diversity of life
- the similarities that allow the classification of organisms into groups nested within broader groups
- the striking ways in which organisms are suited to their environments

Unlike other authors, Darwin proposed a hypothesis, a scientific explanation for his observations. Among the hundreds of pages devoted to the evidence supporting his hypothesis, Darwin also made testable predictions and reported the results of numerous experiments he had performed. Darwin hypothesized that present-day species are the descendants of ancient ancestors that they still resemble in some ways. Over time, differences accumulated by a process that Darwin called "descent with modification," his phrase for evolution (Figure 13.2). He also proposed a mechanism for how life evolves: natural selection.

Natural selection is a process in which organisms with certain inherited traits are more likely to survive and reproduce than are individuals with other traits (see Figure 1.12). As a result of natural selection, a **population**—a group of individuals of the same species living in the same place at the same time—can change over generations. Natural selection leads to **evolutionary adaptation**, a population's increase in the frequency of traits suited to the environment. (The term *adaptation* can also refer to the trait itself; for example, the flower mantid's camouflage is an adaptation that helps it ambush prey.) In modern terms, we would

► Figure 13.2 **A sketch made by Darwin as he pondered the origin of species.**

▼ Figure 13.1 **Key observations about life.**

(a) The diversity of life. The 70 square miles of this rain forest in Madagascar is home to 77 species of birds, 25 species of mammals, nearly 100 species of reptiles and amphibians, more than a thousand species of plants, and countless species of insects, fungi, and microbes.

(b) Patterns of similarities. All species of flowers have the same basic parts, but the shapes and numbers of the parts differ and can be used to classify flowers into narrower groups.

(c) An insect suited to its environment. Camouflage helps this Malaysian flower mantid ambush prey.

say that the genetic composition of the population has changed over time, and that is one way of defining **evolution**. But we can also use the term *evolution* on a much grander scale to mean all of biological history, from the earliest microbes to the enormous diversity of organisms that live on the Earth today. ☑

Darwin's Cultural and Scientific Context

The view of life developed by Darwin in *The Origin of Species* was fundamentally different from the prevailing scientific and cultural views of his time. To help you appreciate the radical nature of Darwin's ideas, let's place them in their historical context.

The Idea of Fixed Species

The Greek philosopher Aristotle, whose ideas had an enormous impact on Western culture, generally held the view that species are fixed, permanent forms that do not evolve. Judeo-Christian culture fortified this idea with a literal interpretation of the biblical book of Genesis, which tells the story of each form of life being individually created in its present-day form. In the 1600s, religious scholars used biblical accounts to estimate the age of Earth at 6,000 years. Thus, the idea that all living species came into being relatively recently and are unchanging in form dominated the intellectual climate of the Western world for centuries.

At the same time, however, naturalists were also grappling with the interpretation of **fossils**—imprints or remains of organisms that lived in the past. Although fossils were thought to be the remains of living creatures, many were puzzling. For example, if "snakestones" (Figure 13.3a) were the coiled bodies of snakes, then why were none ever found with an intact head? Could some fossils represent species that had become extinct? Stunning discoveries in the early 1800s, including fossilized skeletons of a gigantic sea creature dubbed an ichthyosaur, or fish-lizard (Figure 13.3b), convinced many naturalists that extinctions had indeed occurred.

Lamarck and Evolutionary Adaptations

Fossils told of other changes in the history of life, too. Naturalists compared fossil forms with living species and noted patterns of similarities and differences. In the early 1800s, French naturalist Jean-Baptiste de Lamarck suggested that the best explanation for these observations is that life evolves. Lamarck explained evolution as the refinement of traits that equip organisms to perform successfully in their environments. He proposed that by using or not using its body parts, an individual may develop certain traits that it passes on to its offspring. For example, some birds have powerful beaks that enable them to crack tough seeds. Lamarck suggested that these strong beaks are the cumulative result of ancestors exercising their beaks during feeding and passing that acquired beak power on to offspring. However, simple observations provide evidence against the inheritance of acquired traits: A carpenter who builds up strength and stamina through a lifetime of pounding nails with a heavy hammer will not pass enhanced biceps on to children. Although Lamarck's idea of *how* species evolve was mistaken, his proposal that species evolve as a result of interactions between organisms and their environments helped set the stage for Darwin.

☑ **CHECKPOINT**

How did Darwin's *The Origin of Species* differ from other books that described the natural world?

Answer: Darwin proposed a scientific explanation for his observations.

▼ Figure 13.3 **Perplexing fossils.**

(a) **"Snakestone."** This fossil is actually a mollusc called an ammonite, an extinct relative of the present-day nautilus (see Figure 17.13). Ammonites of this type ranged in size from about several inches to more than 7 feet in diameter.

(b) **Ichthyosaur skull and paddle-like forelimb.** These marine reptiles—some more than 50 feet long—ruled the oceans for 155 million years before becoming extinct about 90 million years ago. The enormous eye is thought to be an adaptation to the dim light of the deep sea.

The Voyage of the *Beagle*

Charles Darwin was born in 1809, on the same day as Abraham Lincoln. Even as a boy, Darwin's consuming interest in nature was evident. When he was not reading nature books, he was in the fields and forests fishing, hunting, and collecting insects. His father, an eminent physician, could see no future for a naturalist and sent Charles to the University of Edinburgh to study medi-

How did Charles Darwin go from being an average student to being the most famous person in the history of biology?

cine. But Charles, who was only 16 years old at the time, found medical school boring and distasteful. He left Edinburgh without a degree and then enrolled at Christ College at Cambridge University, intending to become a minister. Darwin received his B.A. degree—which included courses in biology—in 1831. Soon after, his botany professor recommended him to Captain Robert FitzRoy, who was preparing the survey ship HMS *Beagle* for a voyage around the world. It was a tour that would have a profound effect on Darwin's thinking and eventually on the thinking of the entire world.

Darwin was 22 years old when he sailed from Great Britain on the *Beagle* in December 1831 (Figure 13.4). The main mission of the voyage was to chart poorly known stretches of the South American coastline. Darwin spent most of his time on shore collecting thousands of specimens of fossils and living plants and animals. He noted the unique adaptations of organisms that inhabited such diverse environments as the Brazilian jungles, the grasslands of the Argentine pampas, and the desolate and frigid lands at the southern tip of South America.

In spite of their unique adaptations, the plants and animals throughout the continent all had a definite South American stamp, very distinct from the life-forms of Europe. That in itself may not have surprised Darwin. But the plants and animals living in temperate regions of South America seemed more closely related to species living in tropical regions of that continent than to species living in temperate regions of Europe. And the South American fossils Darwin found, though clearly different species from living ones, were distinctly South American in their resemblance to the living plants and animals of that continent. These observations led Darwin to wonder if contemporary South American species owed their features to descent from ancestral species on that continent.

Darwin was particularly intrigued by the geographic distribution of organisms on the Galápagos Islands. The Galápagos are relatively young volcanic islands about 900 km (540 miles) off the Pacific coast of South America. Most of the animals that inhabit these remote

▼ Figure 13.4 **The voyage of the *Beagle*.**

Darwin in 1840

HMS *Beagle*

Galápagos Islands

PACIFIC OCEAN

Pinta
Genovesa
Marchena
Equator
Santiago
Daphne Islands
Fernandina
Pinzón
Isabela
Santa Cruz
Sánta Fe
San Cristobal
Florenza
Española

0   40 km
0   40 miles

North America
ATLANTIC OCEAN
Great Britain
Europe
Asia
Africa
South America
Andes
PACIFIC OCEAN
Equator
Cape of Good Hope
Australia
Cape Horn
Tierra del Fuego
Tasmania
New Zealand

islands are found nowhere else in the world, but they resemble species living on the South American mainland (Figure 13.5).

While on his voyage, Darwin was strongly influenced by the newly published *Principles of Geology*, by Scottish geologist Charles Lyell. The book presented the case for an ancient Earth sculpted by gradual geologic processes that continue today. Having witnessed an earthquake that raised part of the coastline of Chile almost a meter, Darwin realized that natural forces gradually changed Earth's surface and that these forces still operate. Thus, the growth of mountains as a result of earthquakes could account for the presence of marine snail fossils he collected on mountaintops in the Andes.

By the time Darwin returned to Great Britain five years after the *Beagle* set sail, his experiences and reading had led him to seriously doubt that Earth and all its living organisms had been specially created only a few thousand years earlier. The evidence assembled by Lyell and other geologists implied that Earth must be very old—on the order of millions, rather than thousands, of years old—and constantly changing. (Modern scientists have determined that Earth is roughly 4.6 *billion* years old.) The extended time scale, Darwin reasoned, would allow for gradual changes to occur in species as well as in geologic features. Darwin began to analyze his collections and to discuss them with colleagues. He continued to read, correspond with other scientists, and maintain extensive journals of his observations, studies, and thoughts.

Descent with Modification

By the early 1840s, Darwin had composed a long essay describing the major features of his theory of evolution. He realized that his ideas would cause a social furor, however, and therefore delayed publishing his essay. Then, in the mid-1850s, Alfred Wallace, a British naturalist doing fieldwork in Indonesia, developed ideas almost identical to Darwin's. When Wallace sent Darwin a manuscript describing his own concept of natural selection, Darwin wrote, "All my originality . . . will be smashed." To resolve Darwin's dilemma, two of his colleagues presented Wallace's paper and excerpts from Darwin's earlier essay together to the scientific community. With the publication in 1859 of *The Origin of Species*, Darwin presented the world with an avalanche of evidence and a strong, logical argument for evolution.

As noted earlier, Darwin made two main points in *The Origin of Species*. First, he presented evidence that each living species descended from a succession of ancestral species. In the first edition of his book, he did not use the word *evolution*, referring instead to "descent with modification." Darwin hypothesized that as the descendants of the earliest organisms spread into various habitats over millions of years, they were modified (changed) by accumulating adaptations to diverse ways of life. Darwin's second main point was that natural selection is the mechanism for descent with modification. Before we look more closely at Darwin's theory of natural selection, let's examine the evidence for evolution. ☑

☑ **CHECKPOINT**

Darwin's phrase for evolution, _____ with _____, captured the idea that an ancestral species could diversify into many descendant species by the accumulation of different _____ to various environments.

Answer: *descent; modification; adaptations*

▼ Figure 13.5 **A marine iguana (right), an example of the unique species inhabiting the Galápagos.** Darwin noticed that Galápagos marine iguanas—with a flattened tail that aids in swimming—are similar to, but distinct from, land-dwelling iguanas on the islands and on the South American mainland (left).

Evidence of Evolution

Evolution leaves observable signs. Such clues to the past are essential to any historical science. Historians of human civilization can study written records from earlier times. But they can also piece together the evolution of societies by recognizing vestiges of the past in modern cultures. Even if we did not know from written documents that Spaniards colonized the Americas, we would deduce this from the Hispanic stamp on Latin American culture. Similarly, biological evolution has left evidence in today's organisms, as well as in fossils.

In this section, we will examine five of the many lines of evidence in support of evolution. One of them—fossils—is a historical record. The other four—biogeography, comparative anatomy, comparative embryology, and molecular biology—encompass historical vestiges of evolution evident in modern life.

The Fossil Record

Over millions of years, sand and silt that eroded from the land were carried by rivers and deposited in the oceans, piling up and compressing older deposits below into rock. Some dead organisms that settled along with the sediments left imprints in the rocks. Thus, each rock layer, or stratum (plural, *strata*), bears a unique set of fossils representing a local sampling of the organisms that lived and died when that sediment was deposited. Younger strata are on top of older ones, so the positions of fossils in the strata reveal their relative age. (The ages of fossils can be confirmed using radiometric dating— see Figure 14.15.) The **fossil record** is this ordered sequence of fossils as they appear in the rock layers, marking the passage of geologic time (Figure 13.6).

The fossil record reveals the appearance of organisms in a historical sequence. The oldest known fossils, dating from about 3.5 billion years ago, are prokaryotes. This fossil evidence fits with the molecular and cellular evidence that prokaryotes are the ancestors of all life. Fossils in younger layers of rock reveal the evolution of various groups of eukaryotic organisms.

In *The Origin of Species*, Darwin predicted that the fossil record would include transitional forms that link past and present. Paleontologists (scientists who study fossils) have indeed discovered many such fossils. For example, a series of transitional fossils provides evidence that birds descended from one branch of dinosaurs. Another example is a series of transitional whale fossils connecting these aquatic mammals to four-legged land mammals. Whales living today have forelegs in the form of flippers but lack hind legs. The hypothesis that whales evolved from terrestrial (land-dwelling) ancestors predicts a four-limbed beginning for whales. Paleontologists digging in Egypt, Pakistan, and North America have uncovered a series of remarkable fossils of extinct mammals that document the transition from life on land to life in the sea (Figure 13.7). Some whale ancestors had a type of anklebone that is otherwise unique to the group of land mammals that includes pigs, hippos, cows, camels, and deer. The anklebone similarity strongly suggests that whales (as well as dolphins and porpoises) are most closely related to this group of land mammals. ☑

▼ Figure 13.6 **Strata of sedimentary rock at the Grand Canyon.** The Colorado River has cut through more than a mile of rock, exposing sedimentary strata that are like huge pages from the book of life. Each stratum entombs fossils that represent some of the organisms from that period of Earth's history.

▼ Figure 13.7 **A transitional fossil linking past and present.** Shown here are fossilized leg bones of *Basilosaurus*, an ancient whale. Like other extinct whales, *Basilosaurus* was already aquatic and no longer used its legs to support its weight.

Biogeography

It was **biogeography**, the geographic distribution of species, that first suggested to Darwin that today's organisms evolved from ancestral forms. Consider, for example, Darwin's visit to the Galápagos Islands. Darwin noted that the Galápagos animals resembled species of the South American mainland more than they resembled animals on similar but distant islands. He hypothesized that the Galápagos species evolved from animals that migrated from South America. These immigrants eventually gave rise to new species as they became adapted to their new environment.

Many other examples from biogeography seem baffling without an evolutionary perspective. Consider the diversity of marsupials in Australia (Figure 13.8). Australia is home to many kinds of marsupials (mammals that complete embryonic

development outside the uterus, typically in a mother's pouch) but relatively few placental mammals (mammals that complete embryonic development in the uterus). This is not because Australia is inhospitable to placental mammals. Humans have introduced rabbits, foxes, and many other placental mammals to Australia, and these introduced species have thrived to the point of becoming ecological and economic nuisances. The prevailing hypothesis is that the unique Australian wildlife evolved on that island continent in isolation from regions where early placental mammals diversified.

The geographic distribution of species makes little sense if we imagine that species were individually placed in suitable environments. In the Darwinian view, we find species where they are because they evolved from ancestors that inhabited those regions.

Why are marsupial mammals so common in Australia and so uncommon everywhere else?

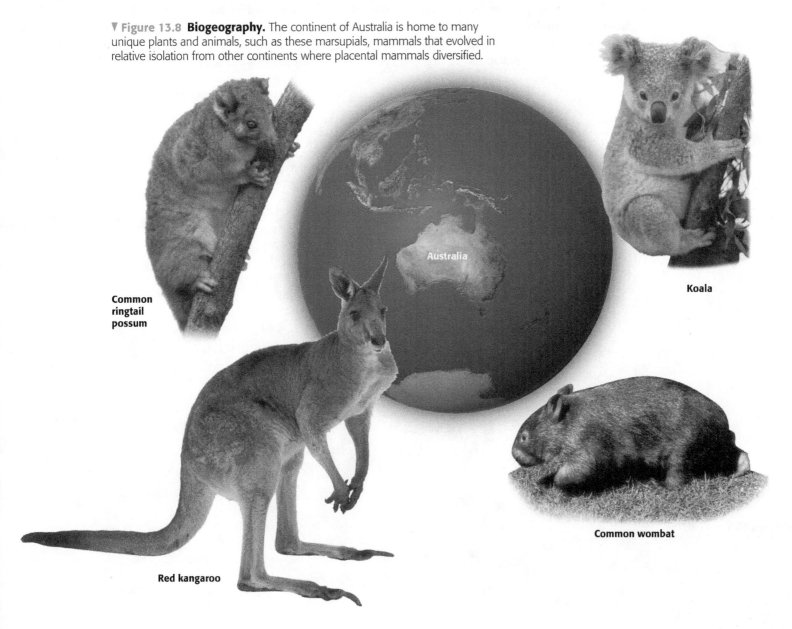

▼ Figure 13.8 **Biogeography.** The continent of Australia is home to many unique plants and animals, such as these marsupials, mammals that evolved in relative isolation from other continents where placental mammals diversified.

Common ringtail possum

Australia

Koala

Common wombat

Red kangaroo

Comparative Anatomy

The comparison of body structures in different species is called **comparative anatomy**. Biologists have observed many anatomical similarities among species. For example, the same skeletal elements make up the forelimbs of humans, cats, whales, and bats, even though the functions of these forelimbs differ greatly; clearly, a whale's flipper does not do the same job as a bat's wing. Scientists interpret these similarities as an indication of common ancestry. The arms, forelegs, flippers, and wings of these different mammals are variations on anatomical structures of an ancestral organism, structures that over millions of years have become adapted to different functions. These adaptations account for the observed similarities in structures despite different uses. Such similarity in structure due to common ancestry is called **homology**. The forelimbs of diverse mammals are therefore known as homologous structures (Figure 13.9).

How is your arm similar to a whale's flipper?

Comparative anatomy attests that evolution is a remodeling process in which ancestral structures become modified as they take on new functions—the kind of process that Darwin referred to as descent with modification. The historical constraints of this modification are evident in anatomical imperfections. For example, the human spine and knee joint were derived from ancestral structures that supported four-legged mammals. Consequently, almost none of us will reach old age without experiencing knee or back problems. If these structures had first taken form specifically to support our bipedal posture, we would expect them to be less subject to sprains, spasms, and other common injuries.

Some of the most interesting homologous structures are "leftover" structures of marginal, if any, importance to the organism. These **vestigial structures** are remnants of features that served important functions in the organism's ancestors, such as the rear leg bones evident in ancient whale fossils (see Figure 13.7). In another example, the skeletons of some snakes retain vestiges of the pelvis and leg bones of walking ancestors. If limbs were a hindrance to ancient snakes' way of life, natural selection would favor snake descendants with successively smaller limbs. ☑

▼ Figure 13.9 **Homologous structures: anatomical signs of descent with modification.** The forelimbs of all mammals are constructed from the same skeletal elements. (Homologous bones in each of these four mammals are colored the same.) The hypothesis that all mammals descended from a common ancestor predicts that their forelimbs, though diversely adapted, would be variations on a common anatomical theme.

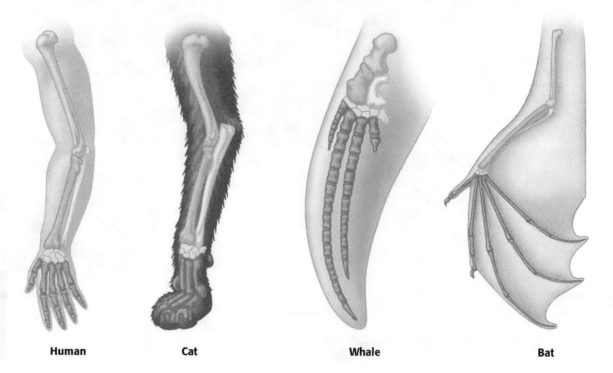

Human **Cat** **Whale** **Bat**

☑ **CHECKPOINT**

What is homology?

Answer: *similarity between species that is due to shared ancestry*

Comparative Embryology

Comparing early stages of development in different animal species reveals additional homologies not visible in adult organisms. For example, all vertebrate embryos have a developmental stage in which structures called pharyngeal pouches appear on the sides of the throat. At this stage, the embryos of fishes, frogs, snakes, birds, and apes—indeed, all vertebrates—look more alike than different (Figure 13.10). The different classes of vertebrates take on more distinctive features as development progresses. For example, pharyngeal pouches develop into gills in fishes but into parts of the ear and throat in humans.

Molecular Biology

The hereditary background of an organism is documented in its DNA and in the proteins encoded by the DNA (see Chapter 10). If two species have genes with nucleotide sequences that match closely, biologists conclude that these sequences are homologous and must have been inherited from a relatively recent common ancestor (Figure 13.11). In contrast, the greater the number of sequence differences between species, the less likely they share a close common ancestor. Molecular comparisons between diverse organisms have allowed biologists to develop hypotheses about the evolutionary divergence of branches on the tree of life. For example, genetic analyses first suggested that the domain Archaea is more closely related to the eukaryotes than it is to the domain Bacteria.

Darwin's boldest hypothesis was that *all* forms of life are related to some extent through branching evolution from the earliest organisms. About 100 years after Darwin made his claim, molecular biology began providing strong evidence for evolution: All forms of life use the same genetic language of DNA and RNA, and the genetic code (how RNA triplets are translated into amino acids) is nearly universal. This genetic language has been passed along through all the branches of evolution since its beginnings in an early form of life. ✓

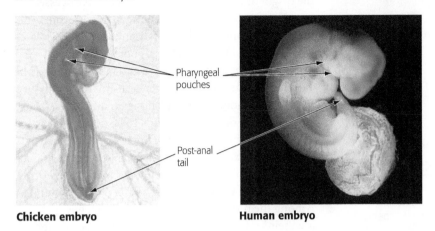

▼ Figure 13.10 **Evolutionary signs from comparative embryology.** At the early stage of development shown here, the kinship of vertebrates is unmistakable. Notice, for example, the pharyngeal pouches and tails in both the chicken embryo and the human embryo.

Pharyngeal pouches

Post-anal tail

Chicken embryo　　　　**Human embryo**

▼ Figure 13.11 **Genetic relationships among some primates.** The bars in this diagram show the percent of selected DNA sequences that match between a chimpanzee and other primates, the animal group that includes monkeys, apes, and humans. For example, note that the selected DNA sequences of chimps and humans are better than a 98% match. In contrast, the DNA sequences of chimps and Old World monkeys (such as macaques, mandrills, baboons, and rhesus monkeys) have less than a 93% match.

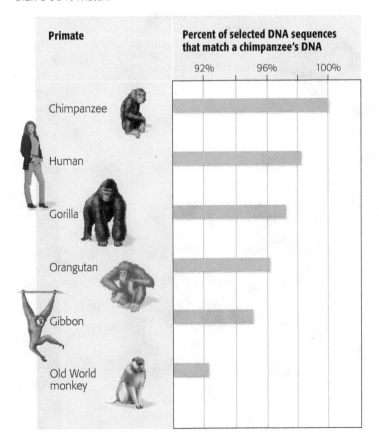

Primate	Percent of selected DNA sequences that match a chimpanzee's DNA
Chimpanzee	
Human	
Gorilla	
Orangutan	
Gibbon	
Old World monkey	

92%　　96%　　100%

☑ CHECKPOINT

Name the five lines of evidence for evolution presented in this section.

Answer: the fossil record, biogeography, comparative anatomy, comparative embryology, molecular biology.

Natural Selection

Darwin perceived adaptation to the environment and the origin of new species as closely related processes. Imagine, for example, that an animal species from a mainland colonizes a chain of distant, relatively isolated islands. In the Darwinian view, populations on the different islands may diverge more and more in appearance as each population adapts to its local environment. Over many generations, the populations on different islands could become dissimilar enough to be designated as separate species. Evolution of the finches on the Galápagos Islands is an example. It is a reasonable hypothesis that the islands were colonized by finches that strayed from elsewhere and then diversified on the different islands. Among the differences between the Galápagos finches are their beaks, which are adapted to the specific foods available on each species' home island (Figure 13.12). Darwin anticipated that explaining how such adaptations arise is the key to understanding evolution. And his theory of natural selection remains our best explanation for the formation of new adaptations. ☑

☑ CHECKPOINT

How did Darwin hypothesize that adaptation is related to the origin of new species?

Answer: Populations in different environments adapt to local conditions. Over time, the populations might become dissimilar enough to be designated as separate species.

Darwin's Theory of Natural Selection

Darwin based his theory of natural selection on two key observations, both of which had already been noted by scientists. First, he recognized that all species tend to produce excessive numbers of offspring (Figure 13.13). Darwin deduced that because natural resources are limited, the production of more individuals than the environment can support leads to a "struggle for existence" (competition) among the individuals of a population. In most cases, only a small percentage of offspring will survive in each generation. Many eggs are laid, young born, and seeds spread, but only a tiny fraction complete their development and leave offspring of their own. The rest are starved, eaten, frozen, diseased, unmated, or unable to reproduce for other reasons.

The second key observation that led Darwin to natural selection was his awareness of variation among individuals of a population. Just as no two people in a human population are alike, individual variation abounds in all species (Figure 13.14). Much of this variation is heritable. Siblings share more traits with

▼ Figure 13.12 **Galápagos finches with beaks adapted for specific diets.**

(a) The large ground finch. This species of Galápagos finch has a large beak specialized for cracking seeds that fall from plants to the ground.

(b) The warbler finch. The smaller beak of the warbler finch is used to grasp insects.

(c) The woodpecker finch. The long, narrow beak of the woodpecker finch allows it to hold tools such as cactus spines to probe for wood-boring insects.

▼ Figure 13.13 **Overproduction of offspring.** This sea slug, a mollusc related to snails (see Figure 17.13), is laying thousands of eggs embedded in the pink ribbon around its body. Only a tiny fraction of the eggs will actually give rise to offspring that survive and reproduce.

▲ Figure 13.14 **Color variation within a population of Asian lady beetles.**

each other and with their parents than they do with less closely related members of the population.

From these two observations, Darwin arrived at the conclusion that defines natural selection: Individuals whose inherited traits are better suited to the local environment are more likely than other individuals to survive and reproduce. In other words, the individuals that function best should leave the most surviving offspring. Darwin's genius was in connecting two observations that anyone could make and drawing a conclusion that could explain how adaptations evolve.

Does evolution produce perfect organisms?

> **Observation 1: Overproduction and competition.** Populations of all species have the potential to produce many more offspring than the environment can possibly support with food, space, and other resources. This overproduction makes competition among individuals inevitable.

> **Observation 2: Individual variation.** Individuals in a population vary in many heritable traits.

> **Conclusion: Unequal reproductive success.** Those individuals with heritable traits best suited to the local environment generally leave a larger share of surviving, fertile offspring.

Darwin's insight was both simple and profound. The environment screens a population's inherent variability. Unequal success in reproduction (natural selection) leads to an accumulation of the favored traits in the population over generations (evolution). In other words, natural selection promotes evolutionary adaptations.

It is important to emphasize three key but subtle points about evolution by natural selection. The first point is that individuals do not evolve, even though natural selection occurs through interactions between individual organisms and their environment. Evolution refers to generation-to-generation changes in populations (as you'll see in the next section).

The second key point is that natural selection can amplify or diminish only traits that are heritable. An organism may become modified through interactions with the environment during its lifetime, and those acquired traits may help it survive. But unless these traits are coded for in the genes of the organism's gametes (sperm or egg), they cannot be passed on to offspring and therefore will not affect the reproductive success of the next generation.

The third key point is that evolution is not goal directed; it does not lead to perfectly adapted organisms. Natural selection is the result of environmental factors that vary from place to place and from time to time. A trait that is favorable in one situation may be useless—or even detrimental—in different circumstances. For example, some genetic mutations that happen to endow mosquitoes with resistance to the pesticide DDT also reduce a mosquito's growth rate. Before DDT was introduced, the resistance allele was a handicap. But after DDT became part of the environment, the mutant alleles were advantageous, and natural selection increased their frequency in mosquito populations. This example also shows that significant evolutionary change can occur in a short time—something we'll stress again in the next section. ✓

Natural Selection in Action

Natural selection and evolution are observable. You learned about one unsettling example in the Biology and Society section: the evolution of pesticide resistance within insect species. Pesticides control insects and prevent them from eating crops, transmitting diseases such as malaria, or just annoying us. But widespread use has led to the evolution of pesticide-resistant insect populations **(Figure 13.15)**. The evolution of antibiotic-resistant bacteria is another example of natural selection in action (see Chapter 1). More recently, doctors have documented an increase in drug-resistant strains of HIV, the virus that causes AIDS. The unifying thread woven throughout this chapter is that evolution and natural selection did not operate only in the distant past, but are observable today. Let's look at another example of evolution in action.

▼ Figure 13.15 **Evolution of pesticide resistance in insect populations.** By spraying crops with poisons to kill insect pests, people have unwittingly favored the reproductive success of insects with inherent resistance to the poisons.

Insecticide application

Chromosome with gene conferring resistance to pesticide

Survivors

Reproduction

Additional applications of the same pesticide will be less effective, and the frequency of resistant insects in the population will grow.

Evolution in Action THE PROCESS OF SCIENCE

Does Predation Drive the Evolution of Lizard Horn Length?

One recent and particularly elegant demonstration of evolution in action involved the flat-tailed horned lizard *Phrynosoma mcalli*, a desert inhabitant of the American Southwest. The lizard's main predator, a bird called the shrike, attacks by biting a lizard's neck just behind the skull, severing the spine. The shrike then carries the dead prey to a convenient place, such as a fence or branch, impales it, and eats it (Figure 13.16).

Evolutionary biologists at Utah State University and Indiana University made the observation that the flat-tailed horned lizard defends against attack by thrusting its head backward, stabbing the shrike with the spiked horns that protrude from the rear and sides of the skull. This led the researchers to question whether longer horn length and spread represented a survival advantage. Their hypothesis was that it did, so they formed the prediction that live horned lizards would have longer and more widely spread horns than killed ones.

The experiment to test this hypothesis was simple: The researchers measured the length of rear horns and the tip-to-tip spread distance of side horns from the skulls of 29 killed lizards (found where they had been impaled) and 155 live lizards. Their results, shown in the graph in Figure 13.15, indicate that the average horn length and spread of live lizards is about 10% greater than that of killed lizards (note that each blue bar is about 10% taller than the corresponding orange bar). The researchers concluded that defensive behavior against predators is one factor driving natural selection of horn length among this lizard species. Thus, evolution—in this case of the length of lizard horns—is observable and measurable in the world around us today.

◄ Figure 13.16 **The effect of predation on the evolution of lizard horn length.** Researchers measured the horns of lizards killed by birds and compared them with the horns of live lizards. The fact that the length of the rear horns and the spread of the side horns are both significantly greater in live lizards than in killed lizards suggests that horn length is an adaptation that is evolving in response to predation by birds.

(a) A flat-tailed horned lizard. The lizards use the spiky horns that protrude from the back and sides of the skull to ward off attacks.

(b) The remains of a lizard impaled by a shrike. After killing a lizard, the bird often impales the lizard on a fence or branch.

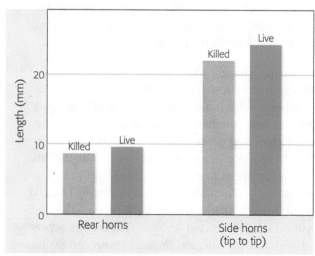

(c) Results of measurement of lizard horns.

Evolutionary Trees

In Darwin's view, the history of life is analogous to a tree. Patterns of descent branch off from a common trunk, the first organism, to the tips of millions of twigs representing the species living today. At each fork of the evolutionary tree is an ancestor common to all evolutionary branches extending from that fork. Closely related species share many traits because their lineage of common descent traces to a recent fork of the tree of life. Biologists represent these patterns of descent with an **evolutionary tree**, although today they usually turn the trees sideways as in Figure 13.17.

Homologous structures, both anatomical and molecular, can be used to determine the branching sequence of an evolutionary tree. Some homologous structures, such as the genetic code, are shared by all species because they date to the deep ancestral past. In contrast, traits that evolved more recently are shared by smaller groups of organisms. For example, all tetrapods (from the Greek *tetra*, four, and *pod*, foot) have the same basic limb bone structure illustrated in Figure 13.9, but their ancestors do not.

Figure 13.17 is an evolutionary tree of tetrapods (amphibians, mammals, and reptiles, including birds) and their closest living relatives, the lungfishes. In this diagram, each branch point represents the common ancestor of all species that descended from it. For example, lungfishes and tetrapods descended from ancestor ❶. Three homologies are shown by the blue dots on the tree—tetrapod limbs, the amnion (a protective embryonic membrane), and feathers. Tetrapod limbs were present in common ancestor ❷ and hence are found in its descendants (the tetrapods). The amnion was present in ancestor ❸ and thus is shared only by mammals and reptiles, which are known as amniotes. Feathers were present only in ancestor ❻ and hence are found only in birds.

Evolutionary trees are hypotheses reflecting our current understanding of patterns of evolutionary descent. Some trees are more speculative because sufficient data are not yet available. Other trees are based on a convincing combination of fossil, anatomical, and DNA data. ✓

✓ CHECKPOINT

In Figure 13.17, which number represents the most recent common ancestor of humans and canaries?

Answer: The most recent ancestor of humans (mammals) and canaries (birds) is ❸.

▼ Figure 13.17 **An evolutionary tree of tetrapods (four-limbed animals).**

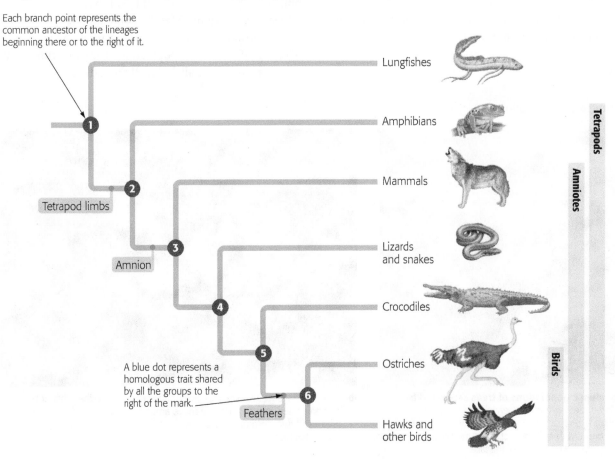

Each branch point represents the common ancestor of the lineages beginning there or to the right of it.

A blue dot represents a homologous trait shared by all the groups to the right of the mark.

Tetrapod limbs

Amnion

Feathers

Lungfishes

Amphibians

Mammals

Lizards and snakes

Crocodiles

Ostriches

Hawks and other birds

Tetrapods

Amniotes

Birds

The Modern Synthesis: Darwinism Meets Genetics

Natural selection requires hereditary processes that Darwin could not explain. How do the variations that are the raw material for natural selection arise in a population? And how are these variations passed along from parents to offspring? Darwin and Gregor Mendel lived and worked around the same time. In fact, by breeding peas in his abbey garden, Mendel illuminated the very hereditary processes required for natural selection to work. However, Mendel's discoveries went unappreciated by the scientific community during his lifetime. Mendelism and Darwinism finally came together in the mid-1900s, decades after both scientists had died. This fusion of genetics with evolutionary biology came to be known as the **modern synthesis** (here, the term *synthesis* means "combination"). One of its key elements is an emphasis on the biology of populations.

Populations as the Units of Evolution

As noted earlier, individual organisms do not evolve during their lifetimes. Although natural selection affects an organism's survival and reproductive success, the evolutionary impact is only apparent in the changes in a population over time.

One population may be isolated from other populations of the same species, with little interbreeding and thus little exchange of alleles between them. Such isolation is common for populations in geographically separated areas—for example, widely separated islands, unconnected lakes, or mountain ranges separated by lowlands. However, populations are not usually so isolated, and they rarely have sharp boundaries (Figure 13.18a). One population center may blur into another in a region of overlap, where members of both populations are present but less numerous. Nevertheless, individuals are more concentrated in the population centers and are more likely to breed with other locals (Figure 13.18b). Therefore, organisms of a population are generally more closely related to one another than to members of other populations.

A population is the smallest biological unit that can evolve. In the Biology and Society section and Figure 13.15, you saw that natural selection can affect pesticide resistance in populations of insects. That impact is measured by the change in the relative numbers of resistant insects over a span of generations, not by the ability of any individual insect to survive.

In studying evolution at the population level, biologists focus on what is called the **gene pool**, the total collection of alleles in a population at any one time (that is, the total of all the alleles in all the individuals making

▼ Figure 13.18 **Populations.**

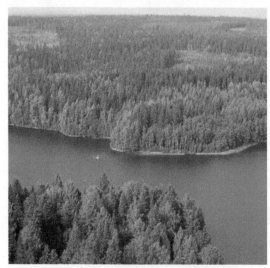

(a) Two dense populations of trees separated by a lake. Interbreeding occurs when wind blows pollen between the populations. Nevertheless, trees are more likely to breed with members of the same population than with trees on the other side of the lake.

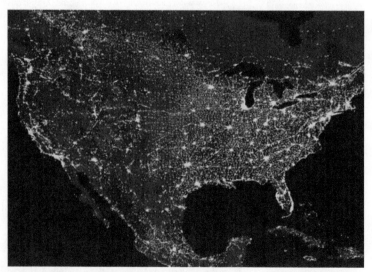

(b) A nighttime satellite view of North America. Notice the lights of human population centers, or cities. People move around, of course, and there are suburban and rural communities between cities, but people are more likely to choose mates locally.

up the population). For many genes, there are two or more alleles (versions of the gene) in the gene pool. For example, in an insect population, there may be one allele that codes for an enzyme that breaks down a certain pesticide and one for a version of the enzyme that does not. In fields sprayed with pesticide, the first allele will increase in frequency and the other allele will decrease in frequency. When the relative frequencies of alleles in a population change like this over a number of generations, evolution is occurring on its smallest scale. Later we'll look at the causes of evolution within a population. But first let's explore the sources of genetic variation. ☑

Genetic Variation in Populations

You have no trouble recognizing your friends in a crowd. People vary in appearance, reflecting the individual differences in their genomes. Individual variation abounds in all species (Figure 13.19). In addition to visible differences, most populations vary greatly at the molecular level. For example, you cannot tell someone's blood group (A, B, AB, or O) just by looking at that person, but biochemical analyses can reveal such variations.

If your parents spend a lot of money on orthodontia for you, will your children inherit nice, straight teeth?

Not all variation in a population is heritable. Phenotype—the expressed traits of an organism—results from a combination of the genotype, which is inherited, and many environmental influences. For instance, a strength-training program can build up your muscle mass beyond what would naturally occur from your genetic makeup. However, you would not pass this environmentally induced physique on to your offspring. Only the genetic component of variation is relevant to natural selection.

Many of the variable traits in a population result from the combined effect of several genes. This polygenic ("many genes") inheritance produces traits that vary more or less continuously—in human height, for instance, from very short individuals to very tall ones. By contrast, other features, such as human blood group, are determined by a single gene locus, with different alleles producing one of only a few distinct phenotypes; there are no in-between types. Next, we'll focus on the sources of different alleles.

Sources of Genetic Variation

Mutations and sexual reproduction, both involving random processes, produce genetic variation. Let's examine each of these processes in detail.

Mutations, random changes in the nucleotide sequence of DNA (see Figure 10.22), can result in new alleles. For example, a mutation in a gene may substitute one nucleotide for another. If such a change affects the protein's function, the mutation will probably be harmful. A random mutation is like a shot in the dark; it is not likely to improve a genome any more than shooting a bullet through the hood of a car is likely to improve engine performance.

☑ **CHECKPOINT**
What is the smallest biological unit that can evolve?

Answer: a population

▶ Figure 13.19 **Variation in a garter snake population.** These four garter snakes, which belong to the same species, were all captured in one Oregon field. The behavior of each physical type is correlated with its coloration. When approached, spotted snakes, which blend in with their background, generally freeze. In contrast, snakes with stripes, which make it difficult to judge the speed of motion, usually flee rapidly when approached.

Do mutations occur in response to a changing environment?

On rare occasions, however, a mutant allele may actually enhance reproductive success. This kind of effect is more likely when the environment is changing in such a way that alleles that were once disadvantageous are favorable under the new conditions. We already considered one example, the changing fortune of the DDT resistance allele in insect populations.

A new mutation that is transmitted in gametes can immediately change the gene pool of a population by replacing one allele with another. For any given gene locus, mutation alone has little effect on a large population in a single generation. This is because a mutation at any given gene locus is a very rare event. However, the cumulative impact of mutations across the genome can be significant because an individual has thousands of genes, and many populations have thousands or millions of individuals.

Organisms with very short generation spans, such as bacteria, can evolve rapidly with mutation as the only source of genetic variation. Bacteria multiply so quickly that natural selection can increase a population's frequency of a beneficial mutation in just hours or days. For most animals and plants, however, their long generation times prevent new mutations from significantly affecting overall genetic variation in the short term. Consequently, in sexually reproducing organisms, most of the genetic variation in a population results from the unique combination of alleles that each individual inherits. (Of course, the origin of the variation in those alleles is past mutation.)

Fresh assortments of existing alleles arise every generation from three random components of sexual reproduction: independent orientation of homologous chromosomes at metaphase I of meiosis (see Figure 8.16), random fertilization, and crossing over (see Figure 8.18).

During prophase I of meiosis, pairs of homologous chromosomes, one set inherited from each parent, trade some of their genes by crossing over, and then each pair separates into gametes independently of other chromosome pairs. Gametes from one individual vary extensively in their genetic makeup, and each zygote made by a mating pair has a unique assortment of alleles resulting from the random union of sperm and egg.

While the processes that generate genetic variation—mutation and events during sexual reproduction—are random, natural selection (and hence evolution) is not. The environment selectively promotes the propagation of those genetic combinations that enhance survival and reproductive success. ☑

Analyzing Gene Pools

As described earlier, a gene pool consists of all the alleles in a population at any one time. The gene pool is the reservoir from which the next generation of organisms draws its alleles.

Imagine a wildflower population with two varieties that are different colors **(Figure 13.20)**. An allele for red flowers, which we will symbolize by *R*, is dominant to an allele for white flowers, symbolized by *r*. These are the only two alleles for flower color in the gene pool of this hypothetical plant population. Now, let's say that 80%, or 0.8, of all flower-color loci in the gene pool have the *R* allele. We'll use the letter *p* to represent the relative frequency of the *R* allele in the population. Thus, *p* = 0.8. Because there are only two alleles in this example, the *r* allele must be present at the other 20% (0.2) of the gene pool's flower-color loci. Let's use the letter *q* for the frequency of the *r* allele in the population. For the wildflower population, *q* = 0.2. And since there are only two alleles for flower color, we can express their frequencies as follows:

$$p \quad + \quad q \quad = \quad 1$$

Frequency of one allele Frequency of alternate allele

Notice that if we know the frequency of either allele in the gene pool, we can subtract it from 1 to calculate the frequency of the other allele.

From the frequencies of alleles, we can also calculate the frequencies of different genotypes in the population if the gene pool is completely stable (not evolving). In the wildflower population, what is the probability of producing an *RR* individual by "drawing" two *R* alleles from the pool of gametes? Here we apply the rule of multiplication that you learned in Chapter 9 (review Figure 9.11). The probability of drawing an *R* sperm

▼ Figure 13.20 **A population of wildflowers with two varieties of color.**

multiplied by the probability of drawing an *R* egg is $p \times p = p^2$, or $0.8 \times 0.8 = 0.64$. In other words, 64% of the plants in the population will have the *RR* genotype. Applying the same math, we also know the frequency of *rr* individuals in the population: $q^2 = 0.2 \times 0.2 = 0.04$. Thus, 4% of the plants are *rr*, giving them white flowers. Calculating the frequency of heterozygous individuals, *Rr*, is trickier. That's because the heterozygous genotype can form in two ways, depending on whether the sperm or egg supplies the dominant allele. So the frequency of the *Rr* genotype is $2pq$, which is $2 \times 0.8 \times 0.2 = 0.32$. In our imaginary wildflower population, 32% of the plants are *Rr*, with red flowers. **Figure 13.21** reviews these calculations graphically.

Now we can write a general formula for calculating the frequencies of genotypes in a gene pool from the frequencies of alleles, and vice versa:

$$p^2 \; + \; 2pq \; + \; q^2 \; = \; 1$$

Frequency of homozygotes for one allele — Frequency of heterozygotes — Frequency of homozygotes for alternate allele

Notice that the frequencies of all genotypes in the gene pool must add up to 1. This formula is called the Hardy-Weinberg formula, named for the two scientists who derived it in 1908.

Population Genetics and Health Science

Public health scientists use the Hardy-Weinberg formula to calculate the percentage of a human population that carries the allele for certain inherited diseases. Consider phenylketonuria (PKU), which is an inherited inability to break down the amino acid phenylalanine. If untreated, the disorder causes severe mental retardation. PKU occurs in about 1 out of 10,000 babies born in the United States. New-born babies are now routinely tested for PKU, and symptoms can be prevented if individuals living with the disease follow a strict diet **(Figure 13.22)**.

PKU is caused by a recessive allele (that is, one that must be present in two copies to produce the phenotype). Thus, we can represent the frequency of individuals in the U.S. population born with PKU with the q^2 term in the Hardy-Weinberg formula. For one PKU occurrence per 10,000 births, $q^2 = 0.0001$. Therefore, q, the frequency of the recessive allele in the population, equals the square root of 0.0001, or 0.01. And p, the frequency of the dominant allele, equals $1 - q$, or 0.99.

Now let's calculate the frequency of carriers, who are heterozygous individuals who carry the PKU allele in a single copy and may pass it on to offspring. Carriers are represented in the formula by $2pq$: $2 \times 0.99 \times 0.01$, or 0.0198. Thus, the Hardy-Weinberg formula tells us that about 2% of the U.S. population are carriers for the PKU allele. Estimating the frequency of a harmful allele is essential for any public health program dealing with genetic diseases.

Microevolution as Change in a Gene Pool

As stated earlier, evolution can be measured as changes in the genetic composition of a population over time. It helps, as a basis of comparison, to know what to expect if a population is *not* evolving. A nonevolving population is in genetic equilibrium, which is also known as **Hardy-Weinberg equilibrium**. The population's gene pool remains constant. From generation to generation, the frequencies of alleles (p and q) and genotypes (p^2, $2pq$, and q^2) are unchanged. Sexual shuffling of genes cannot by itself change a large gene pool.

One of the products of the modern synthesis was a definition of evolution that is based on the genetics of populations: Evolution is a generation-to-generation change in a population's frequencies of alleles. Because this is evolution viewed on the smallest scale, it is sometimes referred to as **microevolution**. ☑

INGREDIENTS: SORBITOL, MAGNESIUM STEARATE, ARTIFICIAL FLAVOR, **ASPARTAME†** (SWEETENER), ARTIFICIAL COLOR (YELLOW 5 LAKE, BLUE 1 LAKE), ZINC GLUCONATE.
†PHENYLKETONURICS: CONTAINS PHENYLALANINE

▲ **Figure 13.22 A warning to individuals with PKU.** People with PKU (phenylketonuria) must strictly regulate their dietary intake of the amino acid phenylalanine. In addition to natural sources, phenylalanine is found in aspartame, a common artificial sweetener. The frequency of the PKU allele is high enough to warrant warnings on foods that contain phenylalanine.

▼ **Figure 13.21 A mathematical swim in the gene pool.** Each of the four boxes in the Punnett square corresponds to a probable "draw" of alleles from the gene pool.

Allele frequencies $p = 0.8$ $q = 0.2$
                         (R) (r)

Eggs

	R $p = 0.8$	r $q = 0.2$
R $p = 0.8$	RR $p^2 = 0.64$	Rr $pq = 0.16$
r $q = 0.2$	Rr $pq = 0.16$	rr $q^2 = 0.04$

Sperm

Genotype frequencies $p^2 = 0.64$ $2pq = 0.32$ $q^2 = 0.04$
                           (RR) (Rr) (rr)

☑ CHECKPOINT

1. Which term in the Hardy-Weinberg formula ($p^2 + 2pq + q^2 = 1$) corresponds to the frequency of individuals with *no* alleles for the recessive disease PKU?
2. Define microevolution.

Answers: 1. p^2 2. Microevolution is a change in a population's frequencies of alleles.

Mechanisms of Evolution

Now that we understand that evolution can be evident in changes in a population's genetic makeup from generation to generation (microevolution), we come to an obvious question: What mechanisms can change a gene pool? Natural selection is the most important, because it is the only process that promotes adaptation. But we'll also look at two other mechanisms of evolutionary change: genetic drift, which is due to chance, and gene flow, the exchange of alleles between neighboring populations.

Genetic Drift

Flip a coin 1,000 times, and a result of 700 heads and 300 tails would make you very suspicious about that coin. But flip a coin 10 times, and an outcome of 7 heads and 3 tails would seem within reason. With a smaller sample, there is a greater chance of deviation from an idealized result—in this case, an equal number of heads and tails.

Let's apply coin toss logic to a population's gene pool. If a new generation draws its alleles at random from the previous generation, then the larger the population (the sample size), the better the new generation will represent the gene pool of the previous generation. Thus,

one requirement for a gene pool to maintain the status quo is a large population size. The gene pool of a small population may not be accurately represented in the next generation because of sampling error. The changed gene pool is analogous to the erratic outcome from a small sample of coin tosses.

Figure 13.23 applies this concept of sampling error to a small population of wildflowers. Chance causes the frequencies of the alleles for red (R) and white (r) flowers to change over the generations. And that fits our definition of microevolution. This evolutionary mechanism, a change in the gene pool of a population due to chance, is called **genetic drift**. But what would cause a population to shrink down to a size where there is genetic drift? Two ways this can occur are the bottleneck effect and the founder effect.

The Bottleneck Effect

Disasters such as earthquakes, floods, and fires may kill large numbers of individuals, producing a small surviving population that is unlikely to have the same genetic makeup as the original population. By chance, certain alleles may be overrepresented among the survivors. Other

▼ **Figure 13.23 Genetic drift.** This hypothetical wildflower population consists of only ten plants. Due to random change over the generations, genetic drift can eliminate some alleles, as is the case for the *r* allele in generation 3 of this imaginary population.

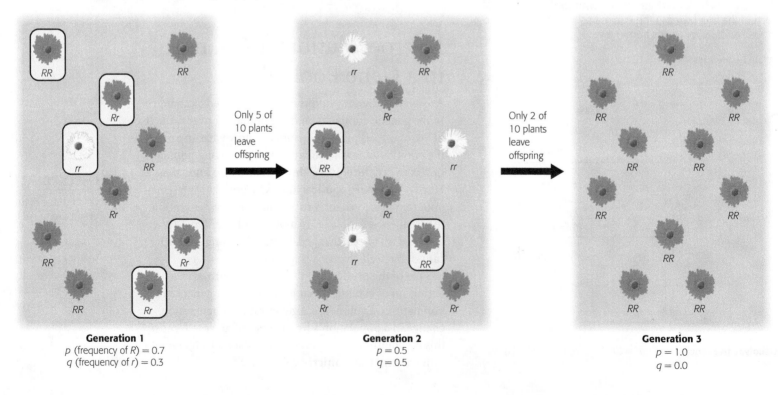

Generation 1
p (frequency of R) = 0.7
q (frequency of r) = 0.3

Generation 2
$p = 0.5$
$q = 0.5$

Generation 3
$p = 1.0$
$q = 0.0$

alleles may be underrepresented. And some alleles may be eliminated. Chance may continue to change the gene pool for many generations until the population is again large enough for sampling errors to be insignificant.

The analogy in **Figure 13.24** illustrates why genetic drift due to a drastic reduction in population size is called the **bottleneck effect**.

▼ Figure 13.24 **The bottleneck effect.** The colored marbles in this analogy represent three alleles in an imaginary population. Shaking just a few of the marbles through the bottleneck is like an environmental disaster that drastically reduces the size of a population. Compared with the predisaster population, purple marbles are overrepresented in the new population, green marbles are underrepresented, and orange marbles are absent—all by chance. Similarly, a population that passes through a "bottleneck" event emerges with reduced variability.

Original population   Bottleneck event   Surviving population

Passing through a "bottleneck"—a severe reduction in population size—decreases the overall genetic variability in a population because at least some alleles are likely to be lost from the gene pool. An important application of this concept is the potential loss of individual variation, and hence adaptability, in drastically reduced populations of endangered species, such as the cheetah **(Figure 13.25)**. The fastest of all running animals, cheetahs are magnificent cats that were once widespread in Africa and Asia. Like many African mammals, the number of cheetahs fell dramatically during the last ice age (around 10,000 years ago). At that time, the species suffered a severe bottleneck, possibly as a result of disease, human hunting, and periodic droughts. Evidence suggests that the South African cheetah population suffered a second bottleneck during the 1800s, when farmers hunted the animals to near extinction. Today, only a few small populations of cheetahs exist in the wild. Genetic variability in these populations is very low compared with populations of other mammals. This lack of variability, coupled with an increasing loss of habitat, makes the cheetah's future precarious. The cheetahs remaining in Africa are being crowded into nature preserves and parks as human demands on the land increase. Along with crowding comes an increased potential for the spread of disease. With so little variability, the cheetah has a reduced capacity to adapt to such environmental challenges. Captive breeding programs are already under way and may be required for the cheetah's long-term survival. However, the species' pre-bottleneck genetic diversity can never be restored. ☑

alleles may be underrepresented. And some alleles may be eliminated. Chance may continue to change the gene pool for many generations until the population is again large enough for sampling errors to be insignificant.

The analogy in **Figure 13.24** illustrates why genetic drift due to a drastic reduction in population size is called the **bottleneck effect**.

▼ Figure 13.24 **The bottleneck effect.** The colored marbles in this analogy represent three alleles in an imaginary population. Shaking just a few of the marbles through the bottleneck is like an environmental disaster that drastically reduces the size of a population. Compared with the predisaster population, purple marbles are overrepresented in the new population, green marbles are underrepresented, and orange marbles are absent—all by chance. Similarly, a population that passes through a "bottleneck" event emerges with reduced variability.

Original population   Bottleneck event   Surviving population

☑ **CHECKPOINT**

Which mechanism of microevolution has been most affected by the increased ease of people traveling throughout the world?

Answer: gene flow

The Founder Effect

Genetic drift is also likely when a few individuals colonize an isolated island, lake, or other new habitat. The smaller the colony, the less its genetic makeup will match the gene pool of the larger population from which the colonists emigrated. If the colony succeeds, random drift will continue to affect the frequency of alleles until the population is large enough for genetic drift to be minimal.

The type of genetic drift resulting from the establishment of a small, new population whose gene pool differs from that of the parent population is called the **founder effect**. The founder effect undoubtedly contributed to the evolutionary divergence of the finches and other organisms that arrived as strays on the remote Galápagos Islands that Darwin visited.

The founder effect also explains the relatively high frequency of certain inherited disorders in some small human populations. For example, in 1814, a group of 15 people founded a British colony on Tristan da Cunha, a cluster of small islands in the middle of the Atlantic Ocean (Figure 13.26). Apparently, one of the colonists carried a recessive allele for retinitis pigmentosa, a progressive form of blindness. Of the 240 descendants who still lived on the islands in the 1960s, 4 had retinitis pigmentosa, and 9 others were heterozygous carriers with one copy of the recessive allele. The frequency of the retinitis pigmentosa allele was ten times higher on Tristan da Cunha than in the British population from which the founders came.

▼ **Figure 13.26 Residents of Tristan da Cunha in the early 1900s.** The island of Tristan da Cunha, located in the middle of the Atlantic Ocean, is listed in *Guinness World Records* as the world's most remote inhabited island. The genetic isolation of the island's residents resulted in a disproportionately high rate of hereditary blindness.

Gene Flow

Another source of evolutionary change, separate from genetic drift, is **gene flow**, where a population may gain or lose alleles when fertile individuals move into or out of the population or when gametes (such as plant pollen) are transferred between populations (Figure 13.27). Gene flow tends to reduce differences between populations. For example, because people today move more freely about the world than in the past, gene flow has become an important agent of evolutionary change in previously isolated human populations. ☑

▲ **Figure 13.27 Gene flow.** The pollen of some plants can be carried by the wind for hundreds of miles, allowing gene flow to occur between distant populations.

Natural Selection: A Closer Look

Genetic drift, gene flow, and even mutation can cause evolution, but they do not necessarily lead to adaptation. In fact, random drift, migrant alleles, and shot-in-the-dark mutations are unlikely to improve a population's fit to its environment. Of all causes of evolution, only natural selection promotes adaptation. And such evolutionary adaptation, remember, is a blend of chance and sorting—chance in the random generation of genetic variability, and sorting in the unequal reproductive success among the varying individuals. Darwin explained the basics of natural selection. But it took the modern synthesis to fill in the details.

Hardy-Weinberg equilibrium, which defines a nonevolving population, demands that all individuals in a population be equal in their ability to survive and reproduce. This condition is probably never actually met. On average, individuals that function best in the environment leave the most offspring and therefore have a disproportionate impact on the gene pool. When farmers began spraying their fields with pesticides, resistant pests started outreproducing other members of the insect populations. The spraying increased the frequency of alleles for pesticide resistance in the insect gene pools. As a result, evolution by natural selection occurred.

Evolutionary Fitness

The phrases "struggle for existence" and "survival of the fittest" are misleading if we take them to mean direct competitive contests between individuals. There *are* animal species in which individuals lock horns or otherwise

South America

Africa

Tristan da Cunha

▲ **Figure 13.28** **Relative fitness of some flowering plants depends in part on competition in attracting pollinators.**

fight one another to determine mating privilege. But the causes of reproductive success are generally more subtle. Plants in a wildflower population, for example, may differ in reproductive success because some attract more pollinators—perhaps the result of slight differences in flower color, shape, or fragrance (Figure 13.28). A frog may produce more eggs than her neighbors because she is better at catching insects for food. These examples point to an evolutionary definition of **relative fitness**: the contribution an individual makes to the gene pool of the next generation *relative to* the contributions of other individuals. Thus, the fittest individuals in the context of evolution are those that produce the largest numbers of viable, fertile offspring and thus pass on the most alleles to the next generation. ☑

Three General Outcomes of Natural Selection

Imagine a population of mice with individuals ranging in fur color from very light to very dark gray. If we graph the number of mice in each color category, we get a bell-shaped curve like the one shown at the top of Figure 13.29. If natural selection favors certain fur-color phenotypes over others, the population of mice will change over the generations. Three general outcomes are possible, depending on which phenotypes are favored. These three modes of natural selection are called directional selection, disruptive selection, and stabilizing selection.

Directional selection shifts the overall makeup of a population by selecting in favor of one extreme phenotype—the darkest mice, for example (Figure 13.29a). Directional selection is most common when the local environment changes or when organisms migrate to a new

environment. An actual example is the shift of insect populations toward a greater frequency of pesticide-resistant individuals.

Disruptive selection can lead to a balance between two or more contrasting phenotypes in a population (Figure 13.29b). A patchy environment, which favors different phenotypes in different patches, is one situation associated with disruptive selection. The variations seen in the snake population in Figure 13.19 result from disruptive selection.

Stabilizing selection favors intermediate phenotypes (Figure 13.29c). It typically occurs in relatively stable environments, where conditions tend to reduce physical variation. This evolutionary conservatism works by selecting against the more extreme phenotypes. For example, stabilizing selection keeps the majority of human birth weights between 3 and 4 kg (approximately 6.5 to 9 pounds). For babies much lighter or heavier than this, infant mortality is greater.

☑ **CHECKPOINT**

What is the best measure of relative fitness?

Answer: the number of fertile offspring an individual leaves

◄ **Figure 13.29** **Three possible outcomes for selection working on fur color in imaginary populations of mice.** The large downward arrows symbolize the pressure of natural selection working against certain phenotypes.

Original population

Frequency of individuals

Phenotypes (fur color)

Original population | Evolved population

(a) Directional selection shifts the overall makeup of the population by favoring variants at one extreme. In this case, the trend is toward darker color, perhaps because the landscape has been shaded by the growth of trees, making darker mice less noticeable to predators.

(b) Disruptive selection favors variants at opposite extremes over intermediate individuals. Here, the relative frequencies of very light and very dark mice have increased. Perhaps the mice have colonized a patchy habitat where a background of light soil is studded with dark rocks.

(c) Stabilizing selection culls extreme variants from the population, in this case eliminating individuals that are unusually light or dark. The trend is toward reduced phenotypic variation and increased frequency of an intermediate phenotype.

Of the three selection modes, stabilizing selection prevails most of the time, resisting change in well-adapted populations. Evolutionary spurts occur when a population is stressed by a change in the environment or by migration to a new place. When challenged with a new set of environmental problems, a population either adapts through natural selection or dies off in that locale. The fossil record tells us that the population's extinction is the most common result. Those populations that do survive crises may change enough to be designated new species. (You'll learn more about this in Chapter 14.) ✔

Sexual Selection

Darwin was the first to explore the implications of **sexual selection**, a form of natural selection in which individuals with certain traits are more likely than other individuals to obtain mates. The males and females of an animal species obviously have different reproductive organs. But they may also have secondary sexual traits, noticeable differences not directly associated with reproduction or survival. This distinction in appearance, called **sexual dimorphism**, is often manifested in a size difference. Among male vertebrates, sexual dimorphism may also be evident in adornment, such as manes on lions, antlers on deer, or colorful plumage on peacocks and other birds **(Figure 13.30a)**.

In some species, secondary sex structures may be used to compete with members of the same sex (usually males) for mates. Contests may involve physical combat, but are more often ritualized displays **(Figure 13.30b)**. Such selection is common in species where the winner acquires a harem of mates—an obvious boost to that male's evolutionary fitness.

In a more common type of sexual selection, individuals of one sex (usually females) are choosy in selecting their mates. Males with the largest or most colorful adornments are often the most attractive to females. The extraordinary feathers of a peacock's tail are an example of this sort of "choose me!" statement. Every time a female chooses a mate based on a certain appearance or behavior, she perpetuates the alleles that caused her to make that choice and allows a male with that particular phenotype to perpetuate his alleles.

What is the advantage to females of being choosy? One hypothesis is that females prefer male traits that are correlated with "good" alleles. In several bird species, research has shown that traits preferred by females, such as bright beaks or long tails, are related to overall male health. This link—between alleles and health—brings us to this chapter's final example of evolution in action.

▼ Figure 13.30 **Sexual dimorphism.**

(a) Sexual dimorphism in a finch species. Among vertebrates, including this pair of green-winged Pytilia (native to Africa), males (right) are usually the showier sex.

(b) Competing for mates. Male Spanish ibex engage in nonlethal combat for the right to mate with females.

An Evolutionary Response to Malaria

Like all organisms, our own species has been shaped by natural selection. We can't observe human evolutionary change over a short time span, however. While organisms such as mosquitoes produce new generations of offspring in a matter of weeks, our generation span is measured in decades. Nevertheless, we can see the results of past natural selection in present-day humans.

Malaria, the devastating disease you learned about in the Biology and Society section of this chapter, must have had a powerful selective effect on human populations. The disease first emerged as a serious threat to people in Africa just 10,000 years ago, long after humans had established populations around the globe. Consequently, we expect to see an evolutionary response in populations from malarial regions, but not elsewhere.

What kind of adaptation could protect people against malaria? After the protozoan invades the human body, it enters red blood cells, using the hemoglobin (a protein that transports oxygen) within to fuel its own reproduction. Thus, a mutation that denies the parasite this critical resource would be beneficial. One such mutation results in an abnormal form of hemoglobin, called sickle hemoglobin, which distorts the shape of red blood cells (Figure 13.31). An individual who has one copy of this allele (a heterozygote) is relatively resistant to malaria. It is not an ideal solution—possessing two sickle-cell alleles is usually fatal, and even heterozygotes may have health problems under certain circumstances. But then, adaptations are often compromises.

On the map in Figure 13.31, the dotted areas indicate locations with a high incidence of malaria—environments where the sickle-cell allele should be favored. As you can see, the highest allele frequencies are indeed found in those regions. People whose ancestors came from malarial regions are also more likely to carry the sickle-cell allele. For example, about one in ten black Americans has a single copy of the allele, a vestige of west African roots. Other malarial regions also have a high frequency of the sickle-cell allele. And sickle hemoglobin is not the only evolutionary response to malaria. Several other mutations are thought to protect against the disease as well. One example is a group of inherited blood disorders called thalassemias, which are common in people from malarial regions of Africa, Asia, and the Mediterranean.

This example of the intersection of evolutionary biology and health science is a reminder that biology is the foundation of all medicine. And evolution is the foundation of all biology.

▼ Figure 13.31 **Mapping malaria and the sickle-cell allele.** The inset shows sickled red blood cells.

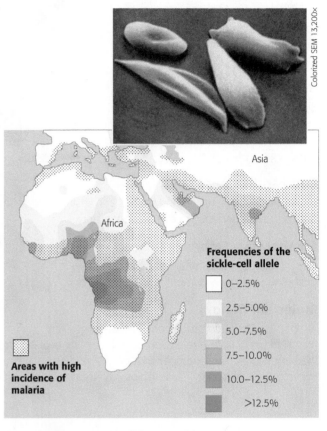

Colorized SEM 13,200×

Asia

Africa

Frequencies of the sickle-cell allele

- 0–2.5%
- 2.5–5.0%
- 5.0–7.5%
- 7.5–10.0%
- 10.0–12.5%
- >12.5%

Areas with high incidence of malaria

Chapter Review

SUMMARY OF KEY CONCEPTS

Go to **www.masteringbiology.com** for homework assignments, practice quizzes, Pearson eText, and more.

Charles Darwin and *The Origin of Species*

Charles Darwin established the ideas of evolution and natural selection in his 1859 publication *On the Origin of Species by Means of Natural Selection*.

Darwin's Cultural and Scientific Context

During his around-the-world voyage on the *Beagle*, Darwin observed adaptations of organisms that inhabited diverse environments. In particular,

Darwin was struck by the geographic distribution of organisms on the Galápagos Islands, off the South American coast. When Darwin considered his observations in light of new evidence for a very old Earth that changed slowly, he arrived at ideas that were at odds with the long-held notion of a young Earth populated by unchanging species.

Descent with Modification

Darwin made two proposals in *The Origin of Species*: (1) Existing species descended from ancestral species, and (2) natural selection is the mechanism of evolution.

Evidence of Evolution

The Fossil Record

The fossil record shows that organisms have appeared in a historical sequence, and many fossils link ancestral species with those living today.

Biogeography

Biogeography, the study of the geographic distribution of species, suggests that species evolved from ancestors that inhabited the same region.

Comparative Anatomy

Homologous structures among species and vestigial organs provide evidence of evolutionary history.

Comparative Embryology

Closely related species often have similar stages in their embryonic development.

Molecular Biology

All species share a common genetic code, suggesting that all forms of life are related through branching evolution from the earliest organisms. Comparisons of DNA and proteins provide evidence of evolutionary relationships.

Natural Selection

Darwin's Theory of Natural Selection

Individuals best suited for a particular environment are more likely to survive and reproduce than less fit individuals.

Natural Selection in Action

Natural selection can be observed in the evolution of pesticide-resistant insects, drug-resistant microbes, and horned lizards, among many other organisms.

Evolutionary Trees

An evolutionary tree represents a succession of related species, with the most recent at the tips of the branches. Each branch point represents a common ancestor of all species that radiate from it.

The Modern Synthesis: Darwinism Meets Genetics

The modern synthesis fused genetics (Mendelism) and evolutionary biology (Darwinism) in the mid-1900s.

Populations as the Units of Evolution

A population, members of the same species living in the same time and place, is the smallest biological unit that can evolve. Population genetics emphasizes the extensive genetic variation within populations and tracks the genetic makeup of populations over time.

Genetic Variation in Populations

Polygenic ("many genes") inheritance produces traits that vary continuously, whereas traits determined by one genetic locus may be present in two or more distinct forms. Mutation and sexual reproduction produce genetic variation. Individual mutations have little short-term effect on a large gene pool, but in the long term, mutation is the source of genetic variation.

Analyzing Gene Pools

A gene pool consists of all the alleles in all the individuals making up a population. The Hardy-Weinberg formula can be used to calculate the frequencies of genotypes in a gene pool from the frequencies of alleles, and vice versa:

$$p^2 + 2pq + q^2 = 1$$

Population Genetics and Health Science

The Hardy-Weinberg formula can be used to estimate the frequency of a harmful allele, which is useful information for public health programs dealing with genetic diseases.

Microevolution as Change in a Gene Pool

Microevolution is generation-to-generation change in allele frequencies in a population.

Mechanisms of Evolution

Genetic Drift

Genetic drift is a change in the gene pool of a small population due to chance. A bottleneck event (a drastic reduction in population size) and the founder effect (occurring in a new population started by a few individuals) are two situations leading to genetic drift.

Gene Flow

A population may gain or lose alleles by gene flow, which is genetic exchange with another population.

Natural Selection: A Closer Look

Of all causes of evolution, only natural selection promotes evolutionary adaptations. Relative fitness is the contribution an individual makes to the gene pool of the next generation relative to the contributions of other individuals. The outcome of natural selection may be directional, disruptive, or stabilizing.

Original population / Evolved population | Pressure of natural selection

Directional selection   **Disruptive selection**   **Stabilizing selection**

Sexual Selection

Secondary sexual traits (such as sex-specific plumage or behaviors) can promote sexual selection, a type of natural selection in which mating preferences are determined by inherited traits.

SELF-QUIZ

1. Which of the following is a true statement about Charles Darwin?
   a. He was the first to discover that living things can change, or evolve.
   b. He based his theory on the inheritance of acquired traits.
   c. He proposed natural selection as the mechanism of evolution.
   d. He was the first to realize that Earth is more than 6,000 years old.

2. How did the insights of Lyell and other geologists influence Darwin's thinking about evolution?

3. In a population with two alleles for a particular genetic locus, B and b, the allele frequency of B is 0.7. If this population is in Hardy-Weinberg equilibrium, the frequency of heterozygotes is _____, the frequency of homozygous dominants is _____, and the frequency of homozygous recessives is _____.

4. Define fitness from an evolutionary perspective.

5. The processes of _____ and _____ generate variation, and _____ produces adaptation to the environment.
   a. sexual reproduction . . . natural selection . . . mutation
   b. mutation . . . sexual reproduction . . . genetic drift
   c. genetic drift . . . mutation . . . sexual reproduction
   d. mutation . . . natural selection . . . sexual reproduction
   e. mutation . . . sexual reproduction . . . natural selection

6. As a mechanism of evolution, natural selection can be most closely equated with
   a. random mating.
   b. genetic drift.
   c. unequal reproductive success.
   d. gene flow.

7. Compare and contrast how the bottleneck effect and the founder effect can lead to genetic drift.

8. In a particular bird species, individuals with average-sized wings survive severe storms more successfully than other birds in the same population with longer or shorter wings. Of the three general outcomes of natural selection (directional, disruptive, or stabilizing), this example illustrates _____.

9. Which of the following statements is (are) true about a population in Hardy-Weinberg equilibrium? (More than one may be true.)
   a. The population is quite small.
   b. The population is not evolving.
   c. Gene flow between the population and surrounding populations does not occur.
   d. Natural selection is not occurring.

10. What environmental factor accounts for the relatively high frequency of the sickle-cell allele in tropical Africa?

Answers to these questions can be found in Appendix: Self-Quiz Answers.

THE PROCESS OF SCIENCE

11. A population of snails has recently become established in a new region. The snails are preyed on by birds that break the snails open on rocks, eat the soft bodies, and leave the shells. The snails occur in both striped and unstriped forms. In one area, researchers counted both live snails and broken shells. Their data are summarized here:

	Striped Shells	Unstriped Shells
Number of live snails	264	296
Number of broken snail shells	486	377
Total	750	673

Based on these data, which snail form is more subject to predation by birds? Predict how the frequencies of striped and unstriped individuals might change over the generations.

12. Imagine that the presence or absence of stripes on the snails from the previous question is determined by a single gene locus, with the dominant allele (S) producing striped snails and the recessive allele (s) producing unstriped snails. Combining the data from both the living snails and broken shells, calculate the following: the frequency of the dominant allele, the frequency of the recessive allele, and the number of heterozygotes in the observed groups.

BIOLOGY AND SOCIETY

13. To what extent are people in a technological society exempt from natural selection? Explain your answer.

Appendix A Metric Conversion Table

MEASUREMENT	UNIT AND ABBREVIATION	METRIC EQUIVALENT	APPROXIMATE METRIC-TO-ENGLISH CONVERSION FACTOR	APPROXIMATE ENGLISH-TO-METRIC CONVERSION FACTOR
Length	1 kilometer (km)	= 1,000 (10^3) meters	1 km = 0.6 mile	1 mile = 1.6 km
	1 meter (m)	= 100 (10^2) centimeters	1 m = 1.1 yards	1 yard = 0.9 m
		= 1,000 millimeters	1 m = 3.3 feet	1 foot = 0.3 m
			1 m = 39.4 inches	
	1 centimeter (cm)	= 0.01 (10^{-2}) meter	1 cm = 0.4 inch	1 foot = 30.5 cm
				1 inch = 2.5 cm
	1 millimeter (mm)	= 0.001 (10^{-3}) meter	1 mm = 0.04 inch	
	1 micrometer (μm)	= 10^{-6} meter (10^{-3} mm)		
	1 nanometer (nm)	= 10^{-9} meter (10^{-3} μm)		
	1 angstrom (Å)	= 10^{-10} meter (10^{-4} μm)		
Area	1 hectare (ha)	= 10,000 square meters	1 ha = 2.5 acres	1 acre = 0.4 ha
	1 square meter (m²)	= 10,000 square centimeters	1 m² = 1.2 square yards	1 square yard = 0.8 m²
			1 m² = 10.8 square feet	1 square foot = 0.09 m²
	1 square centimeter (cm²)	= 100 square millimeters	1 cm² = 0.16 square inch	1 square inch = 6.5 cm²
Mass	1 metric ton (t)	= 1,000 kilograms	1 t = 1.1 tons	1 ton = 0.91 t
	1 kilogram (kg)	= 1,000 grams	1 kg = 2.2 pounds	1 pound = 0.45 kg
	1 gram (g)	= 1,000 milligrams	1 g = 0.04 ounce	1 ounce = 28.35 g
			1 g = 15.4 grains	
	1 milligram (mg)	= 10^{-3} gram	1 mg = 0.02 grain	
	1 microgram (μg)	= 10^{-6} gram		
Volume (solids)	1 cubic meter (m³)	= 1,000,000 cubic centimeters	1 m³ = 1.3 cubic yards	1 cubic yard = 0.8 m³
			1 m³ = 35.3 cubic feet	1 cubic foot = 0.03 m³
	1 cubic centimeter (cm³ or cc)	= 10^{-6} cubic meter	1 cm³ = 0.06 cubic inch	1 cubic inch = 16.4 cm³
	1 cubic millimeter (mm³)	= 10^{-9} cubic meter (10^{-3} cubic centimeter)		
Volume (liquids and gases)	1 kiloliter (kL or kl)	= 1,000 liters	1 kL = 264.2 gallons	1 gallon = 3.79 L
	1 liter (L)	= 1,000 millimeters	1 L = 0.26 gallon	1 quart = 0.95 L
			1 L = 1.06 quarts	
	1 milliliter (mL or ml)	= 10^{-3} liter	1 mL = 0.03 fluid ounce	1 quart = 946 mL
		= 1 cubic centimeter	1 mL = approx. ¼ teaspoon	1 pint = 473 mL
			1 mL = approx. 15–16 drops	1 fluid ounce = 29.6 mL
				1 teaspoon = approx. 5 mL
	1 microliter (μl or μL)	= 10^{-6} liter (10^{-3} milliliters)		
Time	1 second (s)	= $\frac{1}{60}$ minute		
	1 millisecond (ms)	= 10^{-3} second		
Temperature	Degrees Celsius (°C)		°F = $\frac{9}{5}$°C + 32	°C = $\frac{5}{9}$(°F − 32)

Appendix B The Periodic Table

Atomic number (number of protons) → 6
C
Element symbol
Atomic mass (number of protons plus number of neutrons averaged over all isotopes) — 12.01

☐ Metals   ☐ Metalloids   ☐ Nonmetals

Representative elements

Groups: Elements in a vertical column have the same number of electrons in their valence (outer) shell and thus have similar chemical properties.

Periods: Each horizontal row contains elements with the same total number of electron shells. Across each period, elements are ordered by increasing atomic number.

Alkali metals — Alkaline earth metals

Halogens   Noble gases

Transition elements

*Lanthanides
†Actinides

NAME (SYMBOL)	ATOMIC NUMBER	NAME (SYMBOL)	ATOMIC NUMBER	NAME (SYMBOL)	ATOMIC NUMBER	NAME (SYMBOL)	ATOMIC NUMBER	NAME (SYMBOL)	ATOMIC NUMBER
Actinium (Ac)	89	Copernicium (Cn)	112	Iridium (Ir)	77	Palladium (Pd)	46	Sodium (Na)	11
Aluminum (Al)	13	Copper (Cu)	29	Iron (Fe)	26	Phosphorus (P)	15	Strontium (Sr)	38
Americium (Am)	95	Curium (Cm)	96	Krypton (Kr)	36	Platinum (Pt)	78	Sulfur (S)	16
Antimony (Sb)	51	Darmstadtium (Ds)	110	Lanthanum (La)	57	Plutonium (Pu)	94	Tantalum (Ta)	73
Argon (Ar)	18	Dubnium (Db)	105	Lawrencium (Lr)	103	Polonium (Po)	84	Technetium (Tc)	43
Arsenic (As)	33	Dysprosium (Dy)	66	Lead (Pb)	82	Potassium (K)	19	Tellurium (Te)	52
Astatine (At)	85	Einsteinium (Es)	99	Lithium (Li)	3	Praseodymium (Pr)	59	Terbium (Tb)	65
Barium (Ba)	56	Erbium (Er)	68	Lutetium (Lu)	71	Promethium (Pm)	61	Thallium (Tl)	81
Berkelium (Bk)	97	Europium (Eu)	63	Magnesium (Mg)	12	Protactinium (Pa)	91	Thorium (Th)	90
Beryllium (Be)	4	Fermium (Fm)	100	Manganese (Mn)	25	Radium (Ra)	88	Thulium (Tm)	69
Bismuth (Bi)	83	Fluorine (F)	9	Meitnerium (Mt)	109	Radon (Rn)	86	Tin (Sn)	50
Bohrium (Bh)	107	Francium (Fr)	87	Mendelevium (Md)	101	Rhenium (Re)	75	Titanium (Ti)	22
Boron (B)	5	Gadolinium (Gd)	64	Mercury (Hg)	80	Rhodium (Rh)	45	Tungsten (W)	74
Bromine (Br)	35	Gallium (Ga)	31	Molybdenum (Mo)	42	Roentgenium (Rg)	111	Uranium (U)	92
Cadmium (Cd)	48	Germanium (Ge)	32	Neodymium (Nd)	60	Rubidium (Rb)	37	Vanadium (V)	23
Calcium (Ca)	20	Gold (Au)	79	Neon (Ne)	10	Ruthenium (Ru)	44	Xenon (Xe)	54
Californium (Cf)	98	Hafnium (Hf)	72	Neptunium (Np)	93	Rutherfordium (Rf)	104	Ytterbium (Yb)	70
Carbon (C)	6	Hassium (Hs)	108	Nickel (Ni)	28	Samarium (Sm)	62	Yttrium (Y)	39
Cerium (Ce)	58	Helium (He)	2	Niobium (Nb)	41	Scandium (Sc)	21	Zinc (Zn)	30
Cesium (Cs)	55	Holmium (Ho)	67	Nitrogen (N)	7	Seaborgium (Sg)	106	Zirconium (Zr)	40
Chlorine (Cl)	17	Hydrogen (H)	1	Nobelium (No)	102	Selenium (Se)	34		
Chromium (Cr)	24	Indium (In)	49	Osmium (Os)	76	Silicon (Si)	14		
Cobalt (Co)	27	Iodine (I)	53	Oxygen (O)	8	Silver (Ag)	47		

Appendix C Credits

PHOTO CREDITS

FRONT MATTER: p. i, iv left Igor Siwanowicz/Fame Pictures, Inc.; **iv right** Ellen McKnight/Alamy; **p. v** NIBSC/Photo Researchers, Inc.; **p. vi left** Dr. Torsten Wittmann/Photo Researchers, Inc.; **vi right** Flirt/SuperStock; **vii left** All Canada Photos/SuperStock; **vii right** NHPA/SuperStock; **p. viii left** Adrian Sherratt/Alamy; **viii right** DASFA/ZJAH WENN Photos/Newscom; **p. ix left** OREDUN ANIMAL HEALTH LTD/Photo Researchers, Inc.; **ix right** Science Photo Library/Alamy; **p. xi** Beawiharta Beawiharta/REUTERS; **p. xii left** Steven Kazlowski/Photolibrary; **xii right** Richard Carey/Alamy; **p. xiii left** JAMES P. BLAIR/National Geographic Stock; **xiii right** GmbH & Co. KG/Alamy Images; **p. xiv left** Maridav/iStockphoto; **xiv right** Steve Lovegrove/iStockphoto; **p. xv** AJPhoto/Photo Researchers; **p. xvi left** Kitch Bain/AGE Fotostock; **xvi right** marco mayer/Shutterstock.com; **p. xvii** YOSHIKAZU TSUNO/AFP/Getty Images/Newscom.

UNIT OPENERS: Unit 1 left Dr. Torsten Wittmann/Photo Researchers, Inc. **Unit 1 top left** imagebroker.net/SuperStock; **Unit 1 top right** Bon Appetit/Alamy; **Unit 1 middle left** NIBSC/Photo Researchers, Inc.; **Unit 1 middle right** Dr. Torsten Wittmann/Photo Researchers, Inc.; **Unit 1 bottom left** Flirt/SuperStock; **Unit 1 bottom right** All Canada Photos/SuperStock; **Unit 2 left** Eye of Science/Photo Researchers, Inc.; **Unit 2 top left** NHPA/SuperStock; **Unit 2 top right** Adrian Sherratt/Alamy; **Unit 2 middle left** DASFA/ZJAH WENN Photos/Newscom; **Unit 2 middle right** OREDUN ANIMAL HEALTH LTD/Photo Researchers, Inc.; **Unit 2 bottom** Science Photo Library/Alamy; **Unit 3 left** Alex Mustard/Nature Picture Library; **Unit 3 top left** Ton Koene/Photolibrary; **Unit 3 top right** Tier und Naturfotografie/SuperStock; **Unit 3 middle left** Frans Lanting Studio/Alamy; **Unit 3 middle right** FILIPPO MONTEFORTE/AFP/Getty Images/Newscom; **Unit 3 bottom** Beawiharta Beawiharta/REUTERS; **Unit 4 left** Markus Varesvuo/Nature Picture Library; **Unit 4 top left** Steven Kazlowski/Photolibrary; **Unit 4 top right** Richard Carey/Alamy; **Unit 4 bottom** JAMES P. BLAIR/National Geographic Stock; **Unit 5 left** Exactostock/SuperStock; **Unit 5 top left** GmbH & Co. KG/Alamy Images; **Unit 5 top right** Maridav/iStockphoto; **Unit 5 middle left** Steve Lovegrove/iStockphoto; **Unit 5 middle right** RODGER BOSCH/AFP/Getty Images/Newscom; **Unit 5 bottom left** UPI Photo Service/Newscom; **Unit 5 bottom middle** AJPhoto/Photo Researchers; **Unit 5 bottom right** Kitch Bain/AGE Fotostock; **Unit 6 left** Dave Zubraski/AGE Fotostock; **Unit 6 top left** marco mayer/Shutterstock.com; **Unit 6 top right** YOSHIKAZU TSUNO/AFP/Getty Images/Newscom.

CHAPTER 1: Chapter opening photo Ellen McKnight/Alamy; **p. 3, 15, 18** Ellen McKnight/Alamy; **1.1a** Nikreates/Alamy; **1.1b** P. Narayan/The Image Bank/AGE Fotostock; **1.1c** Ingo Arndt/Nature Picture Library; **1.1d** Michael Lander/NordicPhotos/AGE Fotostock; **1.1e** Kim Taylor and Jane Burton/DK Images; **1.1f** Steve Bloom Images/Alamy; **1.1g** Mark Taylor/Nature Picture Library; **1.2 top left to bottom left** Goddard Space Flight Center/NASA;

Pete Oxford/Nature Picture Library; Dave G. Houser/Alamy; Manfred Kage/Peter Arnold Inc./Photolibrary; **1.3** Christopher Elwell/Shutterstock.com; **1.4 left** S. C. Holt/Biological Photo Service; **1.4 right** Steve Gschmeissner/Photo Researchers; **1.6** KK/AP Images; **1.7** Daniela Dirscherl/AGE Fotostock America Inc.; **1.8 top to bottom** Eye of Science/Photo Researchers, Inc.; Eye of Science/Photo Researchers, Inc.; Neil Fletcher/DK Images; Malcom Coulson/DK Images; Stockbyte/Getty Images; D. P. Wilson/Photo Researchers; **1.9** Richard T. Nowitz/Photo Researchers, Inc.; **1.11 clockwise from top left** Mike Hayward/Alamy; American Museum of Natural History; Michael Nolan/SpecialistStock; **1.13a from left to right** Simon Krzi/iStockphoto; Paul Rapson/Alamy; Foodcollection.com/Alamy; Suzannah Skelton/iStockphoto; iStockphoto; iStockphoto; **1.13b left** Eric Baccega/Nature Picture Library; **1.13b right** Erik Lam/Shutterstock.com; **1.14 left** Michael Nichols/National Geographic Image Collection; **1.14 right** Tim Ridley/DK Images; **1.15** Adrian Sherratt/Alamy; **1.16** ancroft/Shutterstock.com; **1.17** Jim Newcomb; **1.18** Scott Strazzante/MCT/Newscom; **1.19 bottom** Massachusetts Department of Public Health; **1.19 top** Eye of Science/Photo Researchers, Inc.

CHAPTER 2: Chapter opening photo imagebroker.net/SuperStock; **p. 23, 31, 33.1** imagebroker.net/SuperStock; **2.1** Clive Streeter/DK Images; **2.3 woman left** Ivan Polunin/Bruce Coleman/Photoshot Holdings Ltd; **montage clockwise from bottom left** Lukasz Panek/iStockphoto; Enrico Fianchini/iStockphoto; Howard Shooter/Dorling Kindersley; Alessio Cola/Shutterstock.com; **2.5** Will & Deni McIntyre/Photo Researchers; **2.10** Sylvain Cordier/Photolibrary, Inc.; **2.11 left** Stephen Alvarez/National Geographic Image Collection; **2.11 right** Andrew Syred/Photo Researchers; **2.12** Dietmar Nill/Photolibrary, Inc.; **2.13** Joe Fox/Alamy; **2.14** iStockphoto; **2.15** Kristin Piljay; **p. 31** Blend Images/SuperStock; **2.17 top to bottom** Beth Van Trees/Shutterstock.com; Monika Wisniewska/iStockphoto; VR Photos/Shutterstock.com; terekhov igor/Shutterstock.com; Jakub Semeniuk/iStockphoto; **2.18** J M Hall Spencer; **2.19 left** NASA Earth Observing System; **2.19 right** NASA.

CHAPTER 3: Chapter opening photo Bon Appetit/Alamy; **p. 37, 51** Bon Appetit/Alamy; **3.3 left** James M. Phelps, Jr./Shutterstock.com; **3.3 right** Dorling Kindersley; **3.5** Gerry Ellis/Getty/PhotoLibrary; **3.7** Bon Appetit/Alamy; **3.8 bottom** Kristin Piljay; **3.8 top** Sandra Caldwell/iStockphoto.com; **3.9 top left** Dougal Waters/Getty Images; **3.9 top right** Biophoto Associates/Photo Researchers, Inc.; **3.9 middle right** Dr. Lloyd M. Beidler; **3.9 bottom** Biophoto Associates/Photo Researchers, Inc.; **3.10** Martyn F. Chillmaid/SPL/Photo Researchers, Inc.; **3.12 left box from top left to bottom right** Hannamariah/Shutterstock.com; Joe Potato Photo/iStockphoto.com; Valentin Mosichev/Shutterstock; Thomas M. Perkins/Shutterstock.com; **3.12 right box from bottom left to bottom right** Multiart/Shutterstock.com; Dorling Kindersley; Juanmonino/iStockphoto.com; Oleksandr Staroseltsev/iStockphoto.com; Robyn Mackenzie/Shutterstock.com; vladm/Shutterstock.com; **3.13 left** EcoPrint/Shutterstock.com; **3.13 right** Stockbyte/

Getty Images; **3.14 left** Pool Getty Images/AP Images; **3.14 right** New York Daily News/WENN/Newscom; **3.15 left to right** Glow Images/Alamy; Dorling Kindersley; Dave King/Dorling Kindersley; Harry Taylor/Dorling Kindersley; kolvenbach/Alamy; Steve Gschmeissner/SPL/Photo Researchers, Inc.; Kristin Piljay; **3.19** Ingram Publishing/Photolibrary, Inc.; **3.28** SuperStock/Photolibrary, Inc.

CHAPTER 4: Chapter opening photo main NIBSC/Photo Researchers, Inc.; **left inset** Leonard Lessin/Photo Researchers, Inc.; **right inset** Dr. Tim Evans/Photo Researchers, Inc.; **p. 55, 61, 71** NIBSC/Photo Researchers, Inc.; **4.1 left to right** M.I. Walker/Photo Researchers, Inc.; SPL/Photo Researchers, Inc.; Educational Images LTD/Custom Medical Stock Photo; **4.2** Exactostock/SuperStock; **4.4** NIBSC/SPL/Photo Researchers, Inc.; **4.7** CDC/SPL/Photo Researchers, Inc.; **4.8 left** The Rockefeller University Press; **4.8 right** Richard Rodewald/Biological Photo Service; **4.10** Hybrid Medical Animation/Photo Researchers; **4.11** D. W. Fawcett/Photo Researchers, Inc.; **4.13** Barry King/Biological Photo Service; **4.15** SPL/Photo Researchers, Inc.; **4.16** Daniel S. Friend; **4.17a** Michael Abbey/Photo Researchers, Inc.; **4.17b** Dr. Jeremy Burgess/Photo Researchers, Inc.; **4.18** Garry Cole/Biological Photo Service; **4.19** Courtesy of W.P. Wergin and E.H. Newcomb, University of Wisconsin/BPS; **4.20** Daniel S. Friend; **4.21a** Dr. Torsten Wittmann/Photo Researchers, Inc.; **4.21b** Dr. D. J. Patterson/SPL/Photo Researchers, Inc.; **4.22a** Exactostock/SuperStock; **4.22b** Steve Gschmeissner/SPL/Photo Researchers, Inc.; **4.22c** Charles Daghlian/Photo Researchers, Inc.; **4.23 bottom** Centers for Disease Control and Prevention (CDC); **4.23 top** The Advertising Archives.

CHAPTER 5: Chapter opening photo Dr. Torsten Wittmann/Photo Researchers, Inc.; **p. 75, 81, 87** Dr. Torsten Wittmann/Photo Researchers, Inc.; **5.1** Thinkstock; **5.3a** Dave King/Dorling Kindersley; **5.3b** blickwinkel/Alamy; **5.8** The Protein Data Bank/RCSB; **5.15** David Cook/blueshiftstudios/Alamy; **5.19** Fuse/Getty Images; **5.20** Peter B. Armstrong.

CHAPTER 6: Flirt/SuperStock; **p. 91, 102, 103** Flirt/SuperStock; **6.1** Westend61/SuperStock; **6.2 left to right** Elena Elisseeva/iStockphoto.com; Eric Isselée/Shutterstock.com; Ultrashock/Shutterstock.com; **6.3** Belinda Images/SuperStock; **6.14** Chris Mole/Shutterstock.com; **6.16 left** stanislaff/iStockphoto.com; **6.16 right** stocksnapp/Shutterstock.com; **6.17** José Carlos Pires Pereira/iStockphoto.com.

CHAPTER 7: Chapter opening photo All Canada Photos/SuperStock; **p. 107, 111, 115** All Canada Photos/SuperStock; **7.1 left to right** Dorling Kindersley; Jeff Rotman/Nature Picture Library; Susan M. Barns, Ph.D.; **7.2 top to bottom** John Fielding/Dorling Kindersley; John Durham/Photo Researchers, Inc.; E.H. Newcomb & W.P. Wergin/Biological Photo Service; **7.5** Jamie Grill/Dorling Kindersley; **7.7** Corbis/SuperStock; **7.8** LQ/Alamy; **7.14 left** Dinodia/Pixtal/agefotostock.com; **7.14 right** ImageDJ/Jupiter Images.

CHAPTER 8: Chapter opening photo NHPA/SuperStock; **p. 121, 137, 140** NHPA/SuperStock; **8.1 left to right** Dr. Torsten Wittmann/Photo Researchers, Inc.; Dr. Yorgos

Nikas/Photo Researchers, Inc.; Biophoto Associates/Photo Researchers, Inc.; Roger Steene/Image Quest Marine; Eric J. Simon; **8.2 top to bottom** Eric Isselée/Shutterstock.com; Christian Musat/Shutterstock.com; Edyta Pawlowska/iStockphoto.com; Eric Isselée/Shutterstock.com; Milton H. Gallardo; **8.3** Ed Reschke/Photolibrary/Getty Images; **8.4 top** A.L. Olins/Biological Photo Service; **8.4 bottom** Biophoto Associates/Photo Researchers, Inc.; **8.7** Conly L. Rieder, Ph.D.; **8.8a** Don W. Fawcett/Photo Researchers, Inc.; **8.8b** Kent Wood/Photo Researchers, Inc.; **8.10** Big Cheese Photo/SuperStock; **8.11** Science Source/CNRI/SPL/Photo Researchers, Inc.; **8.12** iofoto/Shutterstock.com; **8.14** Ed Reschke/Peter Arnold, Inc./Photolibrary; **8.17** David M. Phillips/Photo Researchers, Inc.; **8.19** Dr. David Mark Welch; **8.22 bottom** SPL/Photo Researchers, Inc.; **8.22 top** Lauren Shear/Photo Researchers, Inc.; **8.24** David Hosking/FLPA; **p. 143** ARS/Agricultural Research Service/USDA.

CHAPTER 9: Chapter opening photo Adrian Sherratt/Alamy; **p. 145, 157, 167** Adrian Sherratt/Alamy; **9.1** Science Source/Photo Researchers, Inc.; **9.4** Patrick Lynch/Alamy; **9.5** James King-Holmes/Photo Researchers, Inc.; **9.8** Martin Shields/Photo Researchers, Inc.; **9.9 left to right** Tracy Morgan/Dorling Kindersley; Tracy Morgan/Dorling Kindersley; Eric Isselée/Shutterstock.com; Andrew Johnson/iStockphoto.com; **9.10 left** Tracy Morgan/Dorling Kindersley; **9.10 right** Eric Isselée/Shutterstock.com; **9.12 top left to right** James Woodson /Getty Images; ostill/Shutterstock.com; Jose Luis Pelaez, Inc./Blend Images/Getty Images; **9.12 bottom left to right** John Evans/iStockphoto.com; Image Source/Getty Images; Blend Images/Shutterstock.com; **9.13 left to right** Comstock Images; Blend Images/Shutterstock.com; Jose Luis Pelaez, Inc./Blend Images/Getty Images; **9.15** Michael Ciesielski Photography; **9.16** Will Binns, Pacificcoastnews/Newscom; **9.17 left** J-L. Klein & M-L. Hubert/Photolibrary, Inc.; **9.17 right** Vasiliy Khimenko/Shutterstock.com; **9.20** Mauro Fermariello/Photo Researchers, Inc.; **9.21 left** Oliver Meckes & Nicole Ottawa/Photo Researchers, Inc.; **9.21 right** Eye of Science/Photo Researchers, Inc.; **9.23** Eric J. Simon; **9.29 top left to right** iStockphoto.com; Yuri Arcurs/iStockphoto.com; Andrew Syred/Photo Researchers, Inc.; **9.29 bottom left to right** Dave King/Dorling Kindersley; Jo Foord/Dorling Kindersley; **9.32** Archive Pics/Alamy; **9.33 top left to bottom right** Jerry Young/Dorling Kindersley; Nikolay Titov/iStockphoto.com; Dave King/Dorling Kindersley; Dave King/Dorling Kindersley; Tracy Morgan/Dorling Kindersley; Dave King/Dorling Kindersley; Jerry Young/Dorling Kindersley; Dave King/Dorling Kindersley; Dave King/Dorling Kindersley; Tracy Morgan/Dorling Kindersley; Le Loft 1911/Shutterstock.com; **p. 167** Eric Simon; **p. 169 left** iStockphoto.com; **p. 169 right** Yuri Arcurs/iStockphoto.com; **p. 171** USDA/APHIS Animal And Plant Health Inspection Service.

CHAPTER 10: Chapter opening photo DASFA/ZJAH WENN Photos/Newscom; **p. 173, 192, 194** DASFA/ZJAH WENN Photos/Newscom; **10.3 left** Barrington Brown/Photo Researchers, Inc.; **10.3 top right** Courtesy of the Library of Congress; **10.3 bottom right** Cold Spring Harbor Laboratory Archives; **10.9** Woodfall Wild Images/Photoshot Holdings Ltd.; **10.12** Masaru Okabe; **10.23** Dennis Frates/Alamy; **10.24** MIXA/Alamy; **10.25** Oliver Meckes/Photo Researchers, Inc.; **10.26** Russell Kightley/SPL/Photo Researchers, Inc.; **10.27** N. Thomas/Photo Researchers, Inc.; **10.29** Hazel Appleton, Centre for Infections/Health Protection Agency/SPL/Photo Researchers, Inc.; **10.30** Jeff Zelevansky/Reuters; **10.32** NIBSC/Science Photo Library/Photo Researchers, Inc.; **10.33** Will & Deni McIntyre/SPL/Photo Researchers, Inc.; **10.34** Sinclair Stammers/Photo Researchers, Inc.; **10.35** CHINE NOUVELLE/SIPA/Newscom.

CHAPTER 11: Chapter opening photo OREDUN ANIMAL HEALTH LTD/Photo Researchers, Inc.; **p. 199, 212, 215** OREDUN ANIMAL HEALTH LTD/Photo Researchers, Inc.; **11.1 left to right** Steve Gschmeissner/Photo Researchers, Inc.; Science Photo Library/Alamy; Ed Reschke/Photolibrary; **11.4** Patrick A. Krost/istockphoto; **11.9** F. Rudolf Turner; **11.11** American Association for the Advancement of Science; **11.12** Videowokart/Shutterstock.com; **11.13** Courtesy of the Roslin Institute, Edinburgh; **11.14a** Pat Sullivan/AP Images; **11.14b** University of Missouri; **11.14c left to right** Pasqualino Loi; Robert Lanza; Robert Lanza; Lee Jae Woon/Reuters; **11.16 left** Cord Blood Registry; **11.16 right** Craig Hammell; **11.19 left** Blend Images/Alamy; **11.19 right** Simon Fraser/Royal Victoria Infirmary, Newcastle upon Tyne/Photo Researchers, Inc.; **11.20** GeoM/Shutterstock.com; **11.22** Chris Bjornberg/Photo Researchers, Inc.; **11.23** CNRI/Photo Researchers.

CHAPTER 12: Chapter opening photo Science Photo Library/Alamy; **p. 219, 233, 237** Science Photo Library/Alamy; **12.1** AP Images; **12.2** Copyright Eli Lilly and Company. Used with permission; **12.3** Volker Steger/SPL/Photo Researchers, Inc.; **12.4 left** USDA; **12.4 right** Christopher and Sally Gable/Dorling Kindersley; **12.5** International Rice Research Institute; **12.6** DNX/Peter Arnold, Inc./Photolibrary; **12.7 inset** Prof. S. Cohen/Photo Researchers, Inc.; **12.7** Huntington Potter, University of South Florida College of Medicine; **12.12** Hank Morgan/SPL/Photo Researchers, Inc.; **12.14 left** Michael Stephens/AP Images; **12.14 right** Kim Sayer/Dorling Kindersley; **12.15** Applied Biosystems; **12.20** CHUCK KENNEDY KRT/Newscom; **12.21 bottom** Scott Camazine/Photo Researchers, Inc.; **12.21 top** Newscom; **12.22 bottom** David Parker/Science Photo Library/Photo Researchers, Inc.; **12.22 top** Edyta Pawlowska/Shutterstock.com; **12.24** Phil Date/Shutterstock.com; **12.25** ER Productions/BrandX/Corbis Images; **12.26** AFP/Getty Images; **12.27** 23andMe, Inc.

CHAPTER 13: Ton Koene/Photolibrary; **p. 243, 254, 265** Ton Koene/Photolibrary; **13.1a** Curtis Strauss/Photolibrary; **13.1b** Barbara Jablonska/Shutterstock.com; **13.1c** Edward S. Ross, California Academy of Sciences; **13.2** Cambridge University Library; **13.3a** Chris Pole/Shutterstock.com; **13.3b** Sabena Jane Blackbird/Alamy; **13.4 left** George Richmond/Photo Researchers, Inc.; **13.4 right** Classic Image/Alamy; **13.5 left** Cathleen A. Clapper/Shutterstock.com; **13.5 right** David B. Fleetham/Photolibrary; **13.6** Corbis Images; **13.7** Dr. Philip D. Gingerich; **13.8 top left** Kim Taylor and Jane Burton/Dorling Kindersley; **13.8 center** Planetary Visions Ltd./Photo Researchers; **13.8 top right** Bill Ling/Dorling Kindersley; **13.8 bottom left** Geoff Dann/Dorling Kindersley; **13.8 bottom right** Rob Reichenfeld/Dorling Kindersley; **13.10 left** Dr. Keith Wheeler/Photo Researchers; **13.10 right** Scanpix Sweden AB; **13.12a** Tui DeRoy/Photoshot Holdings Ltd.; **13.12b** NHPA/SuperStock; **13.12c** Tui DeRoy/Photoshot Holdings Ltd.; **13.13** Alain Barrère/Photo Researchers, Inc.; **13.14** Laura Jesse; **13.16** American Association for the Advancement of Science; **13.18a** Photo Alto/Getty Images; **13.18b** NASA Images; **13.19** Edmund D. Brodie III; **13.20** Andy Levin/Photo Researchers, Inc.; **13.22** Anne Dowie; **13.25** Steve Bloom Images/Alamy; **13.26** Hulton-Deutsch Collection/Corbis; **13.27** Natural Visions/Alamy Images; **13.28** Rinusbaak/Dreamstime.com; **13.30a** Reinhard/ARCO/Nature Picture Library; **13.30b** John Cancalosi/AGE Fotostock.com; **13.31** Bill Longcore/Photo Researchers, Inc.

CHAPTER 14: Chapter opening photo Tier und Naturfotografie/SuperStock; **p. 269, 284, 289** Tier und Naturfotografie/SuperStock; **14.1** Papilio/Alamy; **14.2 Clockwise from far left** Bill Draker/Rolfnp/Alamy; David Kjaer/Nature Picture Library; Comstock; www.photos.com/Jupiter Images; Phil Date/Shutterstock.com; Robert Kneschke/iStockphoto.com; Comstock Images; Comstock Images; **14.4 p. 272 left to right** USDA/APHIS Animal And Plant Health Inspection Service; Brian Kentosh; Joe McDonald/Photoshot Holdings, Ltd.; Moses Michelsohn; **14.4 p. 273 left to right** J & C Sohns/Tier und Naturfotografie Collection/AGE Fotostock; Takahiro Asami; Richard Herrmann/Photolibrary; **14.5 left** Charles W. Brown; **14.5 center top to bottom** dogist/Shutterstock.com; Dorling Kindersley; Alistair Duncan/Dorling Kindersley; **14.5 right** Kazutoshi Okuno; **14.7** Corbis Images; **14.7 top left inset** John Shaw/Photoshot Holdings Ltd.; **14.7 top right inset** Michael Fogden/Photoshot Holdings Ltd.; **14.9** Zeljko Radojko/Shutterstock.com; **14.11** Chip Clark; **14.12** Jane Burton/Photoshot Holdings, Ltd.; **14.13 top** Michel Gunther/Photolibrary; **14.13 bottom** Hemera Technologies/Getty Images/AbleStock.com/JupiterImages; **14.14 top left** Francois Gohier/Photo Researchers, Inc.; **14.14 top right** George Gerster/Photo Researchers, Inc.; **14.14 center** Francois Gohier/Photo Researchers, Inc.; **14.14 bottom left** Pixtal/Superstock; **14.14 bottom right** Francis Latrielle/Mammuthus/Vostok; **14.16** ZUMA Press/Newscom; **14.18 right** Mark Pilkington/Geological Survey of Canada/SPL/Photo Researchers, Inc.; **14.19 top** Philip Dowell/Dorling Kindersley; **14.19 center left** Dave King/Dorling Kindersley; **14.19 center right** Dave King/Dorling Kindersley; **14.19 bottom** Philip Dowell/Dorling Kindersley; **14.20** Jeremy Woodhouse/Photolibrary; **14.22** Manfred Cage/Getty/Photolibrary; **14.26** Arco Images GmbH/Alamy.

CHAPTER 15: Chapter opening photo Frans Lanting Studio/Alamy; **p. 293, 297, 311** Frans Lanting Studio/Alamy; **15.3** National Museum of Natural History, Smithsonian Institution; **15.6.** George Luther; **15.7 left** Hemera Technologies/Jupiterimages; **15.7 right** Dr. Tony Brain and David Parker/Science Photo Library/Photo Researchers, Inc.; **15.8 left to right** Scimat/SPL/Photo Researchers, Inc.; NIAID/CDC/Photo Researchers, Inc.;

CNRI/SPL/Photo Researchers, Inc.; **15.9a** David M. Phillips/Science Source/Photo Researchers, Inc.; **15.9b** Susan M. Barns, Ph.D.; **15.9c** Heide Schulz/Max-Planck Institut Fur Marine Mikrobiologie; **15.10** Science Photo Library/Photolibrary; **15.11** H.S. Pankratz, T.C. Beaman/BPS; **15.12 top left** Martin Shields/Photo Researchers, Inc.; **15.12 top right** Alfred Pasieka/Photo Researchers, Inc.; **15.12 bottom left** Pasieka/SPL/Photo Researchers, Inc.; **15.12 bottom right** Westend61/SuperStock; **15.13a** Helen E. Carr/BiologicalPhoto Service; **15.13b** Russell Burden/Photolibrary; **15.14.** Dr. Tony Brain/Science Photo Library/Photo Researchers, Inc.; **15.15 bottom left to right** Centers for Disease Control and Prevention (CDC); Scott Camazine/Photo Researchers, Inc.; David M. Phillips/Photo Researchers, Inc.; **15.15 top** Stefan Sollfors/Alamy; **15.16** Centers for Disease Control and Prevention (CDC); **15.18** ExxonMobil Corporation; **15.20a** Carol Buchanan/AGEFotostock.com; **15.20b** Oliver Meckes/Photo Researchers, Inc.; **15.20c** blickwinkel/Alamy; **15.21** M. I. Walker/Photo Researchers, Inc.; **15.22 p. 308 left to right** Eye of Science/Photo Researchers, Inc.; David M. Phillips/Photo Researchers, Inc.; Biophoto Associates/Photo Researchers, Inc.; **15.22 p. 309 left to right** Manfred Kage/Getty/Photolibrary; **15.22** Dr. Masamichi Aikawa; Michael Abbey/Photo Researchers, Inc.; **15.23** The Hidden Forest, www.hiddenforest.co.nz; **15.24 left** Courtesy of Matt Springer, Stanford University; **15.24 right top to bottom** Courtesy of Robert Kay, MRC Cambridge; Courtesy of Robert Kay, MRC Cambridge; **15.25a** Biophoto Associates/Photo Researchers, Inc.; **15.25b** Kent Wood/Photo Researchers, Inc.; **15.25c** Microfield Scientific Ltd/SPL/Photo Researchers, Inc.; **15.25d** Manfred Kage/Photolibrary; **15.26 left to right** Marevision/AGEFotostock.com; Marevision/AGEFotostock.com; David Hall/Photo Researchers, Inc.

CHAPTER 16: Chapter opening photo FILIPPO MONTEFORTE/AFP/Getty Images/Newscom; **p. 315, 331, 332** FILIPPO MONTEFORTE/AFP/Getty Images/Newscom; **16.2** Dr. Jeremy Burgess/SPL/Photo Researchers, Inc.; **16.3** Dorling Kindersley; **16.4** Graham Kent; **16.5 left** Bob Gibbons/Alamy Images; **16.5 right** Linda Graham, University of Wisconsin-Madison; **16.7 left to right** Photolibrary; James Randklev/Getty Images/Photolibrary; V.J. Matthew/Shutterstock.com; Dale Wagler/Shutterstock.com; **16.8** Duncan Shaw/SPL/Photo Researchers, Inc.; **16.9** John Serrao/Photo Researchers, Inc.; **16.11 bottom left inset** Ed Reschke/Getty Images/Photolibrary; **16.11 bottom right inset** Kim Taylor and Jane Burton/Dorling Kindersley; **16.11 top right inset** Biophoto Associates/Photo Researchers, Inc.; **16.11 main** Photolibrary; **16.12** The Field Museum, Neg#CSGE075400c, Chicago; **16.13** Danilo Donadoni/AGE Fotostock; **16.15 left to right** Stephen P. Parker/Photo Researchers, Inc.; Morales/AGEFotostock.com; Gunter Marx/Alamy; **16.16** Gene Cox/Photo Researchers, Inc.; **16.18 left to right** Smart-foto/Shutterstock.com; Tyler Boyes/Shutterstock.com; Christopher Marin/Shutterstock.com; Howard Rice/Dorling Kindersley; **16.20 left** Jean Dickey; **16.20 top right** Scott Camazine/Photo Researchers, Inc.; **16.20 bottom right** Juniors Bildarchiv/Alamy; **16.21** Martin

Wendler/Photo Researchers, Inc.; **Table 16.1 top to bottom** Dorling Kindersley; Jon Rasmussen/iStockphoto.com; Ben Mcleish/iStockphoto.com; Radu Razvan/Shutterstock.com; Dorling Kindersley, Courtesy of the Natural History Museum, London; Greg Vaughn/Getty Images/Photolibrary; National Tropical Botanical Garden; Alle/Shutterstock.com; **16.22 left** Marc Anderson/Alamy; **16.22 top center** Stan Rohrer/Alamy; **16.22 bottom center** Elizabeth Peardon/iStockphoto.com; **16.22 inset** VEM/Photo Researchers, Inc.; **16.22 top right** J. Forsdyke/Gene Cox/Science Photo Library/Photo Researchers, Inc.; **16.22 bottom right** G.L. Barron & N. Allin/Biological Photo Service; **16.23 bottom** blickwinkel/Alamy; **16.23 top** Jupiter Images; **16.24a** Bedrich Grunzweig/Photo Researchers, Inc.; **16.24b** Nigel Cattlin/Photo Researchers, Inc.; **16.25** North Wind/North Wind Picture Archives; **16.26 top left** Ed Reschke/Photolibrary; **16.26 bottom left** imagebroker.net/SuperStock; **16.26 right** Will Heap, Dorling Kindersley; **16.27** Christine Case/Skyline College; **16.28 left** Jean Dickey; **16.28 right** Eye of Science/Photo Researchers, Inc.

CHAPTER 17: Chapter opening photo Beawiharta Beawiharta/REUTERS; **p. 337, 365, 367** Beawiharta Beawiharta/REUTERS; **17.1** Gunter Ziesler/Getty Images/Photolibrary; **17.2** Georgette Douwman/Nature Picture Library; **17.4 left** South Australian Museum; **17.4 right** Museum of Paleontology; **17.5 left** Publiphoto/Photo Researchers, Inc.; **17.5 right** Chip Clark; **17.9** James D. Watt/Image Quest Marine; **17.10 top left to right** Sue Daly/Nature Picture Library; Michael Klenetsky/Shutterstock.com; Kim Taylor/Nature Picture Library; **17.10 bottom** Jordi Chias/Image Quest Marine; **17.13 top left** Georgette Douwma/Nature Picture Library; **17.13 top** Georgette Douwma/Nature Picture Library; **bottom left** Jez Tryner/Image Quest Marine; **center left to right** Harold W. Pratt/Biological Photo Service; Marevision/AGEFotostock.com; Daniela Dirscherl/Photolibrary; **17.14 top** David Scharf/Photolibrary; **17.14 bottom left to right** Geoff Brightling/Dorling Kindersley; **17.14** Eye of Science/Photo Researchers, Inc.; **17.15 left to right** Photoshot/NHPA Limited; Carol Buchanan/Getty Images/Photolibrary; Wildlife/Getty Images/Photolibrary; **p. 346** Astrid & Hanns-Frieder Michler/Photo Researchers, Inc.; **17.17a** Steve Gschmeissner/Photo Researchers, Inc.; **17.17b** Eye of Science/Photo Researchers, Inc.; **17.17c** David Scharf/Photo Researchers, Inc.; **17.18 top to bottom** Callan Morgan/Getty Images/Photolibrary; Maximilian Weinzierl/Alamy Images; George Grall/National Geographic; ephotocorp/Alamy Images; **17.19** Dave King/Dorling Kindersley; **17.20 top left to right** Herbert Hopfensperger/AGEFotostock.com; Dorling Kindersley; Andrew Syred/Photo Researchers, Inc.; **17.20 bottom left to right** Callan Morgan/Getty Images/Photolibrary; Larry West/Photo Researchers, Inc.; **17.21 top** Dave King/Dorling Kindersley; **17.21 center left to right** Maximilian Weinzierl/Alamy; Tom McHugh/Photo Researchers, Inc.; Nature's Images/Photo Researchers, Inc.; **17.21 bottom left to right** Dietmar Nill/naturepl.com; Nancy Sefton/SPL/Photo Researchers, Inc.; **17.22 left** George Grall/National Geographic; **17.22 right** Tom McHugh/Photo Researchers, Inc.; **17.23** Radius Images/Alamy; **17.24 clockwise from top right** D & S Tollerton/Photolibrary;

Cordier-Huguet/agefotostock.com; Chris Mattison/Photolibrary; Jean Dickey; ephotocorp/Alamy; Joël Héras/Photolibrary; Kerstin Hinze/Photolibrary; Stuart Wilson/Photo Researchers, Inc.; **17.25 top** First Light/Alamy; **17.25 bottom** Keith Dannemiller/Alamy; **17.26 top left** Roger Steene/Image Quest Marine; **17.26 inset** Andrew J. Martinez/Photo Researchers, Inc.; **17.26 top right** Jose B. Ruiz/Nature Picture Library; **17.26 bottom left to right** tbkmedia.de/Alamy; Image Quest Marine; Roger Steene/Image Quest Marine; **17.27** Colin Keates/Dorling Kindersley; **17.29 left** Oxford Scientific/Photolibrary; **17.29 right** Roger Steene/Image Quest Marine; **17.31a** Tom McHugh/Photo Researchers, Inc.; **17.31b** F. Hecker/AGE Fotostock; **17.31b inset** A. Hartl/AGE Fotostock; **17.31c** George Grall/National Geographic; **17.31d** Christian Vinces/Shutterstock.com; **17.32a top** Gary Meszaros/Photo Researchers, Inc.; **17.32a bottom** Bill Brooks/Alamy; **17.32b left** Tom McHugh/Photo Researchers, Inc.; **17.32b right** Jack Goldfarb/agefotostock.com; **17.34 p. 358 left to right** Sylvain Cordier/Photolibrary, Inc.; © Universal Images Group Limited/Alamy; LYNN M. STONE/naturepl.com; **17.34 p. 359 left to right** Jerry Young/Dorling Kindersley; DLILL/Corbis Images; Miguel Periera/Dorling Kindersley; Adam Jones/Digital Vision/Getty Images; **17.36 left to right** Jean Phillipe Varin/Jacana/Photo Researchers, Inc.; Martin Rugner/Photolibrary; Barry Lewis/Alamy; **17.38 Clockwise from top left** Creative Studio Heinemann/Photolibrary; Siegfried Grassegger/Getty Images/Photolibrary; Arco Images GmbH/Alamy; Juan Carlos Munoz/agefotostock.com; Anup Shah/Nature Picture Library; John Kelly/Getty Images; Anup Shah/Nature Picture Library; Ingo Arndt/Nature Picture Library; P. Wegner/Arco Images/Getty Images/Photolibrary; **17.40b** John Reader/SPL/Photo Researchers, Inc.; **17.41** Rosino, http://www.flickr.com/people/rosino; **17.42** Photo Researchers, Inc.; **17.44** Hemis.fr/SuperStock; **17.45** Kablonk/SuperStock; **17.46** Stefan Espenhahn/AGE Fotostock America, Inc.

CHAPTER 18: Chapter opening photo Steven Kazlowski/Photolibrary; **p. 373, 396, 399** Steven Kazlowski/Photolibrary; **18.1** Philippe Psaila/Photo Researchers, Inc.; **18.2** JAY DIRECTO/AFP/GETTY IMAGES/Newscom; **18.3a** Barry Mansell/Nature Picture Library; **18.3b** Sue Flood/Alamy; **18.3c** Junior Bildarchiv/agefotostock.com; **18.3d** Jeremy Woodhouse/Getty Images; **18.4** David Wall/Alamy; **18.5** NASA Earth Observing System; **18.6 left** Verena Tunnicliffe, University of Victoria; **18.6 right** Woods Hole Oceanographic Institution; **18.7** John Cancalosi/Photolibrary; **18.8a** Picture Hooked/Malcolm Schuyl/Alamy; **18.8b** age fotostock/SuperStock; **18.9** Antti Leinonen/Johners; **18.11 left** Daniel Cox/Getty Images/Photolibrary; **18.11 right** J & C Sohns/agefotostock.com; **18.12** Ed Reschke/Photolibrary; **18.13** Robert Stainforth/Alamy; **18.14** Worldsat International Inc./SPL/Photo Researchers, Inc. **18.16** Ishbukar Yalilfatar/Shutterstock.com; **18.17** Kevin Schafer/Alamy; **18.18** Jean Dickey; **18.20** Getty Images; **18.21** Konrad Wothe/Photolibrary; **18.22** George McCarthy/naturepl.com; **18.29** age fotostock/SuperStock; **18.30** Eric Isselée/Shutterstock.com; **18.31** Juan Carlos Munoz/agefotostock.com; **18.32** The California Chaparral Institute; **18.33** All Canada Photos/SuperStock;

18.34 Visions of America, LLC/Alamy; **18.35** Jorma Luhta/Nature Picture Library; **18.36** PAUL NICKLEN/National Geographic Stock; **18.37** Gordon Wiltsie/National Geographic Image Collection; **18.39** UNEP/GRID - Sioux Falls (DEWA); **18.40** JUAN PABLO MOREIRAS/FFI/Photolibrary; **18.41a, b** UNEP/GRID - Sioux Falls (DEWA); **18.42** Jim West/Alamy; **18.43** Kamira/Shutterstock.com; **18.47** Chris Martin Bahr/Photo Researchers, Inc.; **18.48** Mike Meadows/AP Photos; **18.49** Drake Fleege/Alamy; **18.50** University of North Carolina; **18.51** Chris Cheadle/Getty Images/Photolibrary.com; **18.52a** William E. Bradshaw; **18.52b** Steven Kazlowski/naturepl.com.

CHAPTER 19: Chapter opening photo Richard Carey/Alamy; **p. 403, 415, 421** Richard Carey/Alamy; **19.1** Frans Lanting/National Geographic Stock; **19.2** Wave Royalty Free/Alamy; **19.3** WorldFoto/Alamy; **19.4 left to right** Yuri Arcurs/Shutterstock.com; Jane Burton/Dorling Kindersley; Roger Phillips/Dorling Kindersley; **p. 407 left** Achim Prill/Shutterstock.com; **p. 407 right** Anke van Wyk/Shutterstock.com; **19.5** Joshua Lewis/Shutterstock.com; **19.6** Tom Vezo/naturepl.com; **19.7 left** Joshua Lewis/Shutterstock.com; **19.7 right** WizData/Shutterstock.com; **19.8a** Marcin Perkowski/Shutterstock.com; **19.8b** Nigel Cattlin/Alamy; **19.9** Design Pics/SuperStock; **19.10** Meul/ARCO/Nature Picture Library; **19.11** Alan Carey/Photo Researchers, Inc.; **19.12 left to right** Rob Curtis/The Early Birder; USDA Forest Service; Gilbert S. Grant/Photo Researchers, Inc.; **19.13** Dan Burton/Nature Picture Library; **19.14** Ed Reschke/Photolibrary; **19.15** ZUMA Press/Newscom; **19.16** CHRIS JOHNS/National Geographic Stock; **19.17** David R. Frazier Photolibrary, Inc./Alamy; **19.18** Science Photo Library/Alamy; **19.19** Nigel Cattlin/Alamy; **19.20** Claudius Thiriet/Photolibrary; **19.24** Peter Menzel Photography; **19.26** franzfoto.com/Alamy.

CHAPTER 20: Chapter opening photo JAMES P. BLAIR/National Geographic Stock; **p. 425, 446, 448** JAMES P. BLAIR/National Geographic Stock; **20.1** James King-Holmes/Photo Researchers, Inc.; **20.2 left** Mark Carwardine/Getty Images/Photolibrary; **20.2 right** Michael Fogden/Photolibrary; **20.3** Andre Seale/AGE Fotostock; **20.4** American Folklife Center, Library of Congress; **20.5** Gerald Herbert/AP Photo; **20.6** Richard D. Estes/Photo Researchers, Inc.; **20.7a** Jim Zipp/Photo Researchers, Inc.; **20.7b** All Canada Photos/SuperStock; **20.8 bottom** M. I. Walker/SPL/Photo Researchers, Inc.; **20.8 top** M. I. Walker/Photo Researchers, Inc.; **20.9** Jurgen Freund/Nature Picture Library; **20.10** Eric Lemar/Shutterstock.com; **20.11** ARCO/P. Wegner/AGE Fotostock America, Inc.; **p. 430** Jean Dickey; **20.12 left** Steve Kaufman/Photolibrary; **20.12 right** Barry Mansell/Nature Picture Library; **20.13 left** Dante Fenolio/Photo Researchers, Inc.; **20.13 right** Peter J. Mayne; **20.14 top left** Bildagentur-Online/TH Photo/SPL/Photo Researchers, Inc.; **20.14 top right** Luca Invernizzi Tettoni/Getty Images/Photolibrary; **20.14 bottom** ImageState/Alamy; **20.16** Jim West/Photolibrary; **20.21** Visual&Written SL/Alamy; **20.22** Todd Sieling/Corvus Consulting; **20.23** Frans Lanting Studio/Alamy; **20.24** Jeff & Alexa Henry/Photolibrary; **20.30** Wing-Chi Poon; **20.35** Michael Marten/SPL/Photo Researchers, Inc.; **20.36 top** NASA/Goddard

Space Flight Center; **20.36 bottom left and right** NASA/Goddard Space Flight Center; **20.38 bottom** James P. Blair/NGS Image Collection; **20.38 top** Lee Foster/Alamy; **20.39** Joel Sartore/National Geographic; **20.40** R. O. Bierregaard, Jr., Biology Department, University of North Carolina, Charlotte; **20.41** United States Department of Agriculture; **20.42** Photo provided by Kissimmee Division staff, South Florida Water Management District (WPB); **20.43** Frans Lanting/National Geographic Stock; **20.44 left** WaterFrame/Alamy; **20.44 top right** Chad Ehlers/Photolibrary; **20.44 bottom left** Beanstock Images/Photolibrary; **20.44 bottom right** Image Source/Corbis Images; **p. 450 Biodiversity table left to right** James King-Holmes/Photo Researchers; Michael Fogden/Photolibrary; Andre Seale/AGE Fotostock; **p. 450 Interactions table left top to bottom** EOC.Jim Zipp/Photo Researchers, Inc.; All Canada Photos/SuperStock; Jurgen Freund/Nature Picture Library; **p. 450 Interactions table right top to bottom** Outdoor-Archiv/Alamy; Scott Camazine/Alamy; Renaud Visage/Getty Images.

CHAPTER 21: Chapter opening photo GmbH & Co. KG/Alamy Images; **p. 455, 468, 471** GmbH & Co. KG/Alamy Images; **21.1** Andy Crawford/Dorling Kindersley; **21.2a** Segey Nastenko/iStockphoto; **21.2b** Janice Sheldon; **21.2c** Thomas Deerinck, NCMIR/Photo Researchers, Inc.; **21.3** Blend Images/Alamy; **21.4a** Nina Zanetti; **21.4b** Nina Zanetti; **21.4c** Dr. Gopal Murti/SPL/Photo Researchers, Inc.; **21.4d** Biophoto Associates/Photo Researchers, Inc.; **21.4e** Chuck Brown/Photo Researchers, Inc.; **21.4f** Nina Zanetti; **21.4 left** Mike Kemp/Getty Images; **21.5a** Nina Zanetti; **21.5b** Manfred Kage/Getty Images/Photolibrary; **21.5c** Michael Abbey/Photo Researchers, Inc.; **21.5 middle** Blend Images/Alamy; **21.6 left** James Cavallini/Photo Researchers, Inc.; **21.6 right** John Davis/Dorling Kindersley; **21.7** Blend Images/Alamy; **21.8 p. 462 top left** Phil Date Photography/iStockphoto.com; **21.8 p. 462 top right** Douglas Pulsipher/Alamy; **21.8 p. 462 center** Sean Justice/Getty Images; **21.8 p. 462 bottom left** Andy Crawford/Dorling Kindersley; **21.8 p. 462 bottom right** Tim Tadder/Corbis; **21.8 p. 463 top left** Image100/Corbis; **21.8 p. 463 top right** Photodisc/Getty Images; **21.8 p. 463 bottom left to right** Goodshoot/Corbis; bonniej/iStockphoto.com; moodboard/Corbis; **21.9** James W. Evarts/Photo Researchers, Inc.; **21.10** SPL/Photo Researchers, Inc.; **21.12** Jane Burton/Dorling Kindersley; **21.16** Good Olga/iStockphoto; **21.17** Tim Tadder/Corbis Images; **21.20 top left** Goinyk Volodymyr/Dreamstime; **21.20 bottom left** vario images GmbH & Co.KG/Alamy; **21.20 middle** Vendla Stockdale/Shutterstock.com; **21.20 right** Regien Paassen/Shutterstock.com; **p. 472** Andy Crawford/Dorling Kindersley.

CHAPTER 22: Chapter opening photo Maridav/iStockphoto; **p. 475, 490, 491** Maridav/iStockphoto; **22.1 left to right** Arco Images GmbH/Alamy; Bence Mate/Nature Picture Library; Reggie Casagrande/Jupiter Images; **22.2** Corbis; **22.5** GeoM/Shutterstock; **22.17 top left** Lindsay Noechel/Shutterstock; **22.17 top right** Roger Phillips/DK Images; **22.17 bottom left to right** DK Images; DK Images; David Murray and Jules Selmes/DK Images; **p. 487** rebvt/Shutterstock.com; **22.18** Kristin Piljay; **22.19** Hartmut

Schwarzbach/Argus/Photolibrary; **22.21** Jackson Laboratory; **22.23** Stuart Gregory/Getty Images.

CHAPTER 23: Chapter opening photo Steve Lovegrove/iStockphoto; **p. 495, 504, 513** Steve Lovegrove/iStockphoto; **23.6b** Gustoimages/Photo Researchers; **23.8a** Scanpix Sweden AB; **23.10** Martyn F. Chillmaid/Photo Researchers; **23.11** Corbis/Photolibrary; **23.12 left to right** Susumu Nishinaga/Photo Researchers, Inc.; SPL/Photo Researchers, Inc.; Scimat/Photo Researchers; **23.12 right inset** The Gillette Co.; **23.14 left** Biophoto Associates/Photo Researchers, Inc.; **23.14 right** Biophoto Associates/Photo Researchers, Inc.; **23.17 left to right** ARCO/H Reinhard/AGE Fotostock; Matthew Oldfield, ScubaZoo/Photo Researchers; Dr. Keith Wheeler/Photo Researchers; Cordelia Molloy/Photo Researchers; **23.18** imagebroker.net/SuperStock; **23.19a** Douglas Pulsipher/Alamy; **23.24a** Creative Digital Visions; **23.24b** Medical-on-Line/Alamy; **23.25** Pep Roig/Alamy; **p. 514 Blood table left to right** Susumu Nishinaga/Photo Researchers, Inc.; SPL/Photo Researchers, Inc.; The Gillette Co.

CHAPTER 24: Chapter opening photo RODGER BOSCH/AFP/Getty Images/Newscom; **p. 517, 523, 530** RODGER BOSCH/AFP/Getty Images/Newscom; **24.1** Charles Daghlian/Photo Researchers, Inc.; **24.4.** Getty Images; **24.5** bonniej/iStockphoto.com; **24.8** Hank Morgan/Photo Researchers, Inc.; **24.10 bottom** Samuel Ashfield/Photo Researchers, Inc.; **24.10 top** Hazel Appleton, Health Protection Agency Centre for Infections/Photo Researchers, Inc.; **24.11** Biology Media/Science Source/Photo Researchers; **24.14** Ralph C. Eagle Jr./Photo Researchers, Inc.; **24.15** Dey L. P. Pharmaceuticals; **24.16 left** SPL/Photo Researchers; **24.16 right** Salisbury District Hospital/Photo Researchers; **24.17 left** Philippe Garo/Photo Researchers; **24.17 right** Chris Bjornberg/Photo Researchers.

CHAPTER 25: Chapter opening photo UPI Photo Service/Newscom; **p. 535, 546, 547** UPI Photo Service/Newscom; **25.1** Milos_Kula/iStockphoto; **25.4** Image100/Corbis; **25.6** Image100/Corbis; **25.7a** Zephyr/Photo Researchers, Inc.; **25.7b** AP Wide World Photos; **25.7c** Peter Kramer/AP Wide World Photos; **p. 451** David P. Smith/Shutterstock; **25.10 inset** Edward Kinsman/Photo Researchers; **25.10 left** Ian Hooton/Photo Researchers; **25.10 right** ZUMA Press/Newscom; **25.11** Image Source/Corbis; **25.13** Bob Evans/Photolibrary; **p. 540, 541, 543, 544, 546** Image100/Corbis.

CHAPTER 26: Chapter opening photo AJPhoto/Photo Researchers; **p. 551, 569, 570** AJPhoto/Photo Researchers; **26.1** Oxford Scientific/Photolibrary; **26.2** David Wrobel; **26.3** Adam Reitzel, John R. Finnerty, Boston University; **26.4** Alessandra Sarti/Alamy; **26.8** C. Edelman/La Vilette Petit Format/Photo Researchers; **26.10** Reuters NewMedia Inc.; **Table 26.2 clockwise from top left** David M. Phillips/Photo Researchers, Inc.; Kwangshin Kim/Photo Researchers; Chris Bjornberg/Science Photo Library/Photo Researchers; Hazel Appleton, Centre for Infections/Health Protection Agency/Photo Researchers; Dr. Linda Stannard, Uct/Photo Researchers; Photo Researchers; Eye of Science/Photo Researchers, Inc.; **26.12** David M. Phillips/Photo Researchers; **26.14 left** David Barlow Photographer;

26.14 right David Barlow/BBC Photo Library; 26.17 p. 566 Scanpix Sweden AB; 26.17 p. 567 left Scanpix Sweden AB; 26.17 p. 567 right Eric J. Simon; 26.18 Eric J. Simon; 26.18 Trevor Smith/Alamy; 26.21 Dr. Yorgos Nikas/Photo Researchers; 26.22 Design Pics Inc./Alamy.

CHAPTER 27: Chapter opening photo Kitch Bain/AGE Fotostock; p. 575, 598, 599 Kitch Bain/AGE Fotostock; 27.6 Edwin R. Lewis, Professor Emeritus; 27.7 John Davis/ Dorling Kindersley; 27.9 left 66North/iStockphoto; 27.9 right Pasieka/SPL/Photo Researchers, Inc.; 27.13 Johns Hopkins University; 27.14 The Dornsife Neuroscience Imaging Center; 27.15 WDCN/Univ. College London/ SPL/Photo Researchers; 27.16 Liaison/Getty Images; 27.22 Corbis; 27.25 Getty Images; 27.26 Phil Date Photography/ iStockphoto; 27.29 Jochen Tack/Alamy; 27.31 Professor Clara Franzini-Armstrong; 27.36 Danny Moloshok/AP Images; 27.37 Frank Greenaway/DK Images.

CHAPTER 28: Chapter opening photo marco mayer/ Shutterstock.com; p. 605, 616, 621 marco mayer/ Shutterstock.com; 28.1 Adam Hart-Davis/Photo Researchers, Inc.; page 606 Eric J. Simon; 28.2a Nigel Cattlin/Alamy; 28.2b Michael Fogden/Photolibrary; 28.3 left Smit/Shutterstock; 28.3 right bluemagenta/Alamy; 28.4a NHPA/SuperStock; 28.4b Donald Gregory Clever; 28.4c Datacraft/AGE Fotostock; 28.6a Yogesh S. More/AGE Fotostock; 28.6b PIXTAL/AGE Fotostock; 28.11 left top to bottom Ed Resckke/Photolibrary; Graham Kent; Graham Kent; 28.11 right top Andrew Syred/Photo Researchers; 28.11 right bottom Biophoto Associates/Photo Researchers; 28.12 left to right Jtb/Photolibrary; Andrew Lawson/DK Images; Terry Smith Images/Alamy; 28.14 Biology Pics/ Photo Researchers, Inc.; 28.15 Ray Hendley/AGE Fotostock; 28.17 Don Mason/Corbis; 28.18 Courtesy of David W. Stahle, Tree-Ring Laboratory, University of Arkansas; 28.19 bottom Dan Suzio/SPL/Photo Researchers; 28.19 top teft Tim Hill/Alamy; 28.19 top right Duncan Smith/Photo Researchers; 28.25 Walter H. Hodge/Photolibrary; 28.26 bottom Ewa Walicka/Shutterstock.com; 28.26 top ILYA GENKIN/Shutterstock.com; 28.27 Nigel Cattlin/Alamy; 28.28 Volodymyr Pylypchuk/Shutterstock.com.

CHAPTER 29: Chapter opening photo YOSHIKAZU TSUNO/AFP/Getty Images/Newscom; p. 625, 633, 637 YOSHIKAZU TSUNO/AFP/Getty Images/Newscom; 29.2 Eric J. Simon; 29.3 Educational Images LTD/Custom Medical Stock Photo/Newscom; 29.4 Paul Rapson/SPL/ Photo Researchers; 29.5 Brian Capon; 29.6 R. L. Peterson/ Biological Photo Service; 29.8 left David M. Dennis/ Photolibrary; 29.8 right E. H. Newcomb and S. R. Tandon/ Biological Photo Service; p. 606 Daniel Wiedemann/ Shutterstock.com; 29.10 left to right Frank Greenaway/ DK Images; Jeremy Bur/Photo Researchers; Jeremy Bur/ Photo Researchers; 29.11 Professor Ray F. Evert; 29.12 Lezh/ iStockphoto; 29.13 Dmitry Baevskiy/Dreamstime; 29.16 Kristin Piljay/Pearson Education/Pearson Science; 29.17 Fred Jensen; 29.18 Don Paulson Photography/Purestock/ SuperStock; 29.19 left to right Maryann Frazier/SPL/Photo Researchers; Scott Camazine/Photo Researchers; Michael Evans; 29.21 Igor Siwanowicz/Fame Pictures, Inc.

ILLUSTRATION AND TEXT CREDITS

CHAPTER 5: 5.3: Data from S. E. Gebhardt and R. G. Thomas, *Nutritive Values of Foods* (USDA, 2002); S. A. Plowman and D. L. Smith, *Exercise Physiology for Health, Fitness, and Performance,* 2nd ed. Copyright © 2003 Pearson Education, Inc. publishing as Pearson Benjamin Cummings.

CHAPTER 6: 6.5: Copyright © 2002 from *Molecular Biology of the Cell,* 4th ed. by Bruce Alberts et al., fig. 2.69, p. 92. Garland Science/Taylor & Francis Books, Inc. Reproduced by permission of Garland Science/Taylor & Francis LLC.

CHAPTER 7: 7.12: Adapted from Richard and David Walker, *Energy, Plants and Man,* fig. 4.1, p. 69. Oxygraphics. Copyright © Richard Walker. Used courtesy of Richard Walker, http://www.oxygraphics.co.uk.

CHAPTER 10: Page 194: Text quotation by Joshua Lederberg, from Barbara J. Culliton, "Emerging Viruses, Emerging Threat," *Science, 247,* p. 279, 1/19/1990. Copyright © 1990 American Association for the Advancement of Science.

CHAPTER 11: Table 11.1: Data from the American Cancer Society website, "Cancer Facts & Figures 2008" at http:// www.cancer.org/docroot/STT/stt_0.asp; 11.10: Adapted from an illustration by William McGinnis in Peter Radetsky, "The homeobox: Something very precious that we share with flies, from egg to adult." Bethesda, MD: Howard Hughes Medical Institute, 1992, p. 92. Reprinted by permission of William McGinnis.

CHAPTER 13: 13.16: Data for graph from K. V. Young et al., "How the horned lizards got its horns," in *Science, 304,* 4/2/2004, p. 65. American Association for the Advancement of Science; 13.31: Adapted from A. C. Allison, "Abnormal Hemoglobins and Erythrovute Enzyme-Deficiency Traits," in *Genetic Variation in Human Populations,* by G. A. Harrison, ed. (Oxford: Elsevier Science, 1961).

CHAPTER 15: 15.17: Adapted from G. J. Tortora, B. R. Funke, and C. L. Case, *Microbiology: An Introduction,* 9th ed. Copyright © 2007 Pearson Education, Inc., publishing as Pearson Benjamin Cummings. Reprinted and electronically reproduced by permission of Pearson Education, Inc., Upper Saddle River, New Jersey.

CHAPTER 17: 17.38: Drawn from photos of fossils: *A. ramidus* adapted from www.age-of-the-sage.org/ evolution/ardi_fossilized_skeleton.htm. *H. neanderthalensis* adapted from *The Human Evolution Coloring Book. P. boisei* drawn from a photo by David Bill; 17.43: Migration of modern H. sapiens, illustration by Bob Crimi from *Nature Genetics.* Authors L. Luca Cavalli-Sforza and M. W. Feldman. 2003. The application of molecular genetic approaches to the study of human evolution. Vol. 33: 266–275, fig. 3, copyright 2003. Reprinted by permission of Bob Crimi.

CHAPTER 18: 18.25: From J. H. Withgott and S. R. Brennan, *Environment: The Science Behind the Stories,* 3rd ed., fig, 6.30, p 169. Copyright © 2008 Pearson Education, Inc., Prentice Hall. Reprinted and electronically reproduced by permission of Pearson Education, Inc., Upper Saddle River, New Jersey; 18.44: From "Global Temperature Change," J. Hansen et al., *PNAS,* Sept. 26, 2006, Vol. 103, No. 39, Fig. 1B. Copyright 2006 National Academy of Sciences, U.S.A. Reprinted with permission; 18.45: Adapted from *Climate Change 2007: The Physical Science Basis.* Working Group I Contribution to the Fourth Assessment Report of the Intergovernmental Panel on Climate Change, FAQ 2.1, Fig. 1. Cambridge University Press. Reprinted by permission of IPCC, c/o World Meteorological Organization.

CHAPTER 19: 19.13: Data from Fisheries and Oceans, Canada, 1999; 19.21: Data from United Nations, the World at Six Billion, 2007; 19.22 and 19.23: Data from U. S. Census Bureau International Data Base; 19.25: From *The Ecological Footprint Atlas 2009* by B. Ewing et al., p. 31, Map 2. © 2009 Global Footprint Network. All rights reserved. Used by permission; Table 19.1: Data from Centers for Disease Control and Prevention website, "United States Life Tables, 2003," *National Vital Statistics Report,* vol. 50, no. 14, April 19, 2006. www.cdc.gov; Table 19.3: Data from Population Reference Bureau, 2008, www.prb.org.

CHAPTER 20: 20.42: Map by Patterson Clark, June 23, 2002. Copyright (c) 2002, The Washington Post. All rights reserved. Used by permission and protected by the Copyright Laws of the United States. The printing, copying, redistribution, or retransmission of the Material without express written permission is prohibited.

CHAPTER 21: 21.15: Adapted from fig. 2 in V. H. Hutchison et al. Thermoregulation in a brooding female Indian python, Python molurus bivittatus. *Science* 151: 694–695, fig. 2. Copyright © 1966. Reprinted with permission from AAAS.

CHAPTER 22: 22.20: Data adapted from *Clinical Guidelines on the Identification, Evaluation, and Treatment of Overweight and Obesity in Adults: The Evidence Report.* Data found at the National Heart, Lung, and Blood Institute: http://www.nhlbi.nih.gov/guidelines/obesity/bmi_tbl.htm; Table 22.1: Data from S. E. Gebhardt and R. G. Thomas, *Nutritive Values of Foods* (USDA, 2002); S. A. Plowman and D. L. Smith, *Exercise Physiology for Health, Fitness, and Performance,* 2nd ed. Copyright © 2003 Pearson Education, Inc. publishing as Benjamin Cummings.

CHAPTER 23: 23.23: Illustration of hemoglobin structure by Irving Geis. Image from Irving Geis Collection, HHMI. Rights owned by Howard Hughes Medical Institute (HHMI). Not to be reproduced without permission.

CHAPTER 26: Table 26.1: Data from R. Hatcher et al., *Contraceptive Technology: 1990—1992,* p. 134 (New York: Irvington, 1990).

CHAPTER 27: 27.5: Adapted from W. M. Becker and D. W. Deamer, *The World of the Cell,* 2e. fig. 20.16. Copyright © 1991 Pearson Education, Inc., publishing as Pearson Benjamin Cummings. Reprinted and electronically reproduced by permission of Pearson Education, Inc., Upper Saddle River, New Jersey.

Appendix D Self-Quiz Answers

CHAPTER 1

1. b (some living organisms are single-celled)
2. atom, molecule, cell, tissue, organ, organism, population, ecosystem, biosphere; the cell
3. Photosynthesis cycles nutrients by converting the carbon in carbon dioxide to sugar, which is then consumed by other organisms. Additionally, the oxygen in water is released as oxygen gas. Photosynthesis contributes to energy flow by converting sunlight to chemical energy, which is then also consumed by other organisms, and by producing heat.
4. a4, b1, c3, d2.
5. On average, those individuals with heritable traits best suited to the local environment produce the greatest number of offspring that survive and reproduce. This increases the frequency of those traits in the population over time. The result is the accumulation of evolutionary adaptations.
6. Without a control group, you don't know if the experimental outcome is due to the variable you are trying to test or to some other variable.
7. d
8. c
9. Evolution
10. a3, b2, c1, d4

CHAPTER 2

1. electrons; neutrons; protons
2. Nitrogen-14 has an atomic number of 7 and a mass number of 14. The radioactive isotope, nitrogen-16, has an atomic number of 7 and a mass number of 16.
3. Organisms incorporate radioactive isotopes of an element into their molecules just as they do the nonradioactive isotopes, and researchers can detect the presence of the radioactive isotopes.
4. two
5. Each carbon atom has only three covalent bonds instead of the required four.
6. The positively charged hydrogen regions would repel each other.
7. d
8. a

9. The positive and negative poles cause adjacent water molecules to become attracted to each other, forming hydrogen bonds. The properties of water such as cohesion, temperature regulation, and water's ability to act as a solvent all arise from this atomic stickiness.
10. The cola is an aqueous solution, with water as the solvent, sugar as the main solute, and the CO_2 making the solution acidic.

CHAPTER 3

1.

$$\begin{array}{ccc} H & & H \\ & \diagdown \quad \diagup & \\ & C=C & \\ & \diagup \quad \diagdown & \\ H & & H \end{array}$$

2. dehydration; water; hydrolysis
3. b
4. fatty acid; glycerol
5. b
6. c
7. d
8. Hydrophobic amino acids are most likely to be found within the interior of a protein, far from the watery environment.
9. a
10. starch (or glycogen or cellulose); nucleic acid
11. Both DNA and RNA are polynucleotides; both have the same phosphate group along the backbone; and both use A, C, and G bases. But DNA uses T while RNA uses U as a base; the sugar differs between them; and DNA is usually double-stranded, while RNA is usually single-stranded.
12. Structurally, a gene is a long stretch of DNA. Functionally, a gene contains the information needed to produce a protein.

CHAPTER 4

1. d
2. about 0.075 mm, which equals 75 µm
3. b
4. A membrane is fluid because its components are not locked into place. A membrane is mosaic because it contains a variety of embedded proteins.
5. endomembrane system
6. smooth ER; rough ER
7. rough ER, Golgi apparatus, plasma membrane

8. Both organelles use membranes to organize enzymes and both provide energy to the cell. But chloroplasts use pigments to capture energy from sunlight in photosynthesis, whereas mitochondria release energy from glucose using oxygen in cellular respiration. Chloroplasts are only in photosynthetic plants and protists, whereas mitochondria are in almost all eukaryotic cells.
9. a3, b1, c5, d2, e4
10. nucleus, nuclear pores, ribosomes, rough ER, Golgi apparatus
11. Both are motile appendages that extend from the surface of a cell and help in movement. Cells with flagella typically have one long flagellum that propels the cell in a whiplike motion; cilia are usually shorter, more numerous, and beat together.

CHAPTER 5

1. You convert the chemical energy from food to the kinetic energy of your upward climb. At the top of the stairs, some of the energy has been stored as potential energy because of your higher elevation. The rest has been converted to heat.
2. Energy; entropy
3. 10,000 g (or 10 kg); remember that 1 Calorie on a food label equals 1,000 calories of heat energy.
4. The three phosphate groups store chemical energy, a form of potential energy. The release of a phosphate group makes some of this potential energy available to cells to perform work.
5. Hydrolases are enzymes that participate in hydrolysis reactions, breaking down large molecules into the smaller molecules that make them up.
6. An inhibitor's binding to another site on the enzyme can cause the enzyme's active site to change shape.
7. b
8. a
9. *Hypertonic* and *hypotonic* are relative terms. A solution that is hypertonic to tap water could be hypotonic to seawater. In using these terms, you must provide a comparison, as in "The solution is hypertonic to the cell's cytoplasm."

10. Passive transport moves atoms or molecules along their concentration gradient (from higher to lower concentration), while active transport moves them against their concentration gradient.
11. b
12. signal transduction pathway

CHAPTER 6

1. d
2. Plants produce organic molecules by photosynthesis. Consumers must acquire organic material by consuming it rather than making it.
3. In breathing, your lungs exchange CO_2 and O_2 between your body and the atmosphere. In cellular respiration, your cells consume the O_2 in extracting energy from food and release CO_2 as a waste product.
4. the electron transport chain
5. glucose; NAD^+
6. O_2
7. The majority of the energy provided by cellular respiration is generated during the electron transport chain. Shutting down that pathway will deprive cells of energy very quickly.
8. b
9. Glycolysis
10. b
11. Because fermentation supplies only 2 ATP per glucose molecule compared with about 32 from cellular respiration, the yeast will have to consume 19 times as much glucose to produce the same amount of ATP.

CHAPTER 7

1. thylakoids; stroma
2. The Calvin cycle, which consumes the NADPH and ATP, occurs in the stroma.
3. inputs: a, d, e; outputs: b, c
4. Green light is reflected by chlorophyll, not absorbed, and therefore cannot drive photosynthesis.
5. H_2O
6. c
7. The reactions of the Calvin cycle require the outputs of the light reactions (ATP and NADPH).
8. In hot, dry environments, most plants close their stomata, which saves water but decreases the amount of CO_2 available inside the leaves.

9. C_4 and CAM plants can close their stomata and save water without shutting down photosynthesis.

10. c

CHAPTER 8

1. c

2. They have identical genes (DNA).

3. They are in the form of very long, thin strands.

4. b

5. prophase and telophase

6. a. 1,1; b. 1, 2; c. 2, 4; d. $2n$, n; e. individually, by homologous pair; f. identical, unique; g. repair, growth, asexual reproduction; gamete formation

7. c

8. 39

9. Prophase II or metaphase II; it cannot be during meiosis I because then you would see an even number of chromosomes; it cannot be during a later stage of meiosis II because then you would see the sister chromatids separated.

10. benign; malignant

11. 16 ($2n = 8$, so $n = 4$ and $2^n = 2^4 = 16$)

12. Nondisjunction would create just as many gametes with an extra copy of chromosome 3 or 16, but extra copies of chromosome 3 or 16 are probably fatal.

CHAPTER 9

1. genotype; phenotype

2. Statement **a.** is the law of independent assortment; statement **b.** is the law of segregation.

3. c

4. c

5. d

6. d

7. d

8. $\frac{1}{4}$ ($\frac{1}{2}$ chance the child will be male times $\frac{1}{2}$ chance that he will inherit the X carrying the disease allele)

9. The two parental-type gametes, *WS* and *ws*, are produced through meiosis. The process of recombination (due to crossing over) can produce two kinds of recombinant gametes, *Ws* and *wS*.

10. Height appears to result from polygenic inheritance, like human skin color. See Figure 9.22.

11. The brown allele appears to be dominant, the white allele recessive.

The brown parent appears to be homozygous dominant, *BB*, and the white mouse is homozygous recessive, *bb*. The F_1 mice are all heterozygous, *Bb*. If two of the F_1 mice are mated, $\frac{3}{4}$ of the F_2 mice will be brown.

12. The best way to find out whether a brown F_2 mouse is homozygous dominant or heterozygous is to do a testcross: Mate the brown mouse with a white mouse. If the brown mouse is homozygous, all the offspring will be brown. If the brown mouse is heterozygous, you would expect half the offspring to be brown and half to be white.

13. Freckles are dominant, so Tim and Jan must both be heterozygous. There is a $\frac{3}{4}$ chance that they will produce a child with freckles, a $\frac{1}{4}$ chance that they will produce a child without freckles. The probability that the next two children will have freckles is $\frac{3}{4} \times \frac{3}{4} = \frac{9}{16}$.

14. According to the odds, half their children will be heterozygous and have elevated cholesterol levels. There is a $\frac{1}{4}$ chance that their next child will be homozygous, *hh*, and have an extremely high cholesterol level, like Katerina.

15. The bristle-shape alleles are sex-linked, carried on the X chromosome. Normal bristles is dominant (*F*) and forked is recessive (*f*). The genotype of the female parent is $X^f X^f$. The genotype of the male parent is $X^F Y$. Their female offspring are $X^F X^f$; their male offspring are $X^f Y$.

16. The mother is a heterozygous carrier, and the father is normal. See Figure 9.32 for a pedigree. $\frac{1}{4}$ of their children will be boys suffering from hemophilia; $\frac{1}{4}$ will be female carriers.

17. For a woman to be colorblind, she must inherit X chromosomes bearing the colorblindness allele from both parents. Her father has only one X chromosome, which he passes on to all his daughters, so he must be colorblind. A male only needs to inherit the colorblindness allele from a carrier mother; both his parents are usually phenotypically normal.

CHAPTER 10

1. polynucleotides; nucleotides; sugar (deoxyribose); phosphate; nitrogenous base

2. b

3. Each daughter DNA molecule will have half the radioactivity of the parent molecule, since one polynucleotide from the original parental DNA molecule winds up in each daughter DNA molecule.

4. CAU; GUA; histidine (His)

5. A gene is the polynucleotide sequence with information for making one polypeptide. Each codon—a triplet of bases in DNA or RNA—codes for one amino acid. Transcription occurs when RNA polymerase produces mRNA using one strand of DNA as a template. A ribosome is the site of translation, or polypeptide synthesis, and tRNA molecules serve as interpreters of the genetic code. Each tRNA molecule has an amino acid attached at one end and a three-base anticodon at the other end. Beginning at the start codon, mRNA moves relative to the ribosome a codon at a time. A tRNA with a complementary anticodon pairs with each codon, adding its amino acid to the polypeptide chain. The amino acids are linked by peptide bonds. Translation stops at a stop codon, and the finished polypeptide is released. The polypeptide folds to form a functional protein, sometimes in combination with other polypeptides.

6. a3, b3, c1, d2, e2 and 3

7. d

8. d

9. The genetic material of these viruses is RNA, which is replicated inside the infected cell by special enzymes encoded by the virus. The viral genome (or its complement) serves as mRNA for the synthesis of viral proteins.

10. reverse transcriptase

11. The process of reverse transcription occurs only in infections by RNA-containing retroviruses like HIV. Cells do not require reverse transcriptase (their RNA molecules do not undergo reverse transcription), so reverse

transcriptase can be knocked out without harming the human host.

CHAPTER 11

1. c

2. operon

3. b

4. a

5. DNA polymerase and other proteins required for transcription do not have access to tightly packed DNA.

6. the ability of these cells to produce entire organisms through cloning

7. nuclear transplantation

8. which genes are active in a particular sample of cells

9. b

10. embryonic tissue (ES cells), umbilical cord blood, and bone marrow (adult stem cells)

11. Proto-oncogenes are normal genes involved in the control of the cell cycle. Mutation or viruses can cause them to be converted to oncogenes, or cancer-causing genes. Proto-oncogenes are necessary for normal control of cell division.

12. Master control genes, called homeotic genes, regulate many other genes during development.

CHAPTER 12

1. c, d, b, a

2. because it does not contain introns

3. vector

4. Such an enzyme creates DNA fragments with "sticky ends," single-stranded regions whose unpaired bases can hydrogen-bond to the complementary sticky ends of other fragments created by the same enzyme.

5. PCR

6. Different people tend to have different numbers of repeats at each STR site. DNA fragments prepared from the STR sites of different people will thus have different lengths, causing them to migrate to different locations on a gel.

7. a

8. b

9. Chop the genome into fragments using restriction enzymes, clone and sequence each fragment, and reassemble the short sequences into

a continuous sequence for every chromosome.

10. c, b, a, d

CHAPTER 13

1. c
2. Lyell and other geologists presented evidence for the gradual change of geologic features over millions of years. Darwin applied this idea to suggest that species evolve through the slow accumulation of small changes over long periods of time.
3. *Bb*: 0.42; *BB*: 0.49; *bb*: 0.09
4. The fitness of an individual (or of a particular genotype) is measured by the relative number of alleles that it contributes to the gene pool of the next generation compared with the contribution of others. Thus the number of fertile offspring produced determines an individual's fitness.
5. e
6. c
7. Both effects result in populations small enough for significant sampling error in the gene pool for the first few generations. A bottleneck event reduces the size of an existing population in a given location. The founder effect occurs when a new, small population colonizes a new territory.
8. stabilizing selection
9. b, c, d
10. the prevalence of malaria

CHAPTER 14

1. Microevolution is a change in the gene pool of a population, often associated with adaptation. Speciation is an evolutionary process in which one species splits into two or more species. Macroevolution is evolutionary change above the species level, including the origin of evolutionary novelty and new taxonomic groups and the impact of mass extinctions on the diversity of life and its subsequent recovery. Macroevolution is marked by major changes in the history of life, including the origin of new species, and these changes are often noticeable enough to be evident in the fossil record.
2. b

3. prezygotic: a, b, c, e; postzygotic: d
4. because a small gene pool is more likely to be changed substantially by genetic drift and natural selection
5. exaptations
6. d
7. d
8. species, genus, family, order, class, phylum, kingdom, domain
9. 2.6
10. Archaea and Bacteria

CHAPTER 15

1. g, d, f, c, b, a, e
2. d, c, a, b, e
3. DNA polymerase is a protein, which must be transcribed from a gene. But a DNA gene requires DNA polymerase to be replicated. This creates a paradox about which came first—DNA or protein. But RNA can act as both an information storage molecule and an enzyme, suggesting that dual-role RNA may have preceded both DNA and proteins.
4. Exotoxins are poisons secreted by pathogenic bacteria; endotoxins are components of the outer membrane of pathogenic bacteria.
5. Autotrophs make their own organic compounds from CO_2, while heterotrophs must obtain at least one type of organic compound from another organism.
6. They can form endospores.
7. Both you and a mushroom are chemoheterotrophs.
8. because the first eukaryotes were protists, and these ancient protists were ancestral to all other eukaryotes, including plants, fungi, animals, and modern protists
9. c
10. b

CHAPTER 16

1. cuticle
2. flowers
3. a. sporophyte b. cones; angiosperms c. fruit
4. b
5. b
6. a fern
7. Because the plants do not lose their leaves during autumn and winter, the leaves are already fully developed for photosynthesis when the short growing season begins in spring.
8. vascular plant

9. a
10. a ripened ovary of a flower that protects and aids in the dispersal of seeds contained in the fruit
11. algae; fungi
12. A fungus digests its food externally by secreting digestive juices into the food and then absorbing the small nutrients that result from digestion. In contrast, humans and most other animals ingest relatively large pieces of food and digest the food within their bodies.

CHAPTER 17

1. c
2. coelom; pseudocoelom
3. arthropod
4. amphibians
5. b
6. Chordata; notochord; cartilage disks between your vertebrae
7. bipedalism
8. a
9. *Australopithecus* species, *Homo habilis*, *Homo erectus*, *Homo sapiens*
10. a4, b5, c1, d2, e3

CHAPTER 18

1. organismal ecology, population ecology, community ecology, ecosystem ecology
2. light, water temperature, chemicals added
3. physiological; behavioral
4. d
5. a. desert; b. grassland; c. tropical rain forest; d. temperate broadleaf forest; e. coniferous forest; f. tundra
6. chaparral
7. permafrost, very cold winters, and high winds
8. agriculture
9. Carbon dioxide and other gases in the atmosphere absorb heat energy radiating from Earth and reflect it back toward Earth. This is called the greenhouse effect. As the carbon dioxide concentration in the atmosphere increases, more heat is retained, causing global warming.
10. c
11. populations of organisms that have high genetic variability and short life spans

CHAPTER 19

1. the number of people and the land area in which they live

2. III; I
3. O; O; E; O; E
4. a. The *x*-axis is time; the *y*-axis is the number of individuals; the red curve represents exponential growth; the blue curve represents logistic growth.
   b. carrying capacity
   c. In exponential growth, the population growth rate continues to increase as long as the population size increases. In logistic growth, the population grows fastest when it is about ½ the carrying capacity.
   d. exponential growth curve, though the worldwide growth rate is slowing
5. d
6. opportunistic
7. c
8. The large population segment, the baby boomers, are currently in the workforce and are in their peak earning years.
9. d

CHAPTER 20

1. habitat destruction
2. d
3. c
4. a2, b5, c5, d3 or d4, e1
5. because the pesticides become concentrated in their prey
6. succession
7. Only 10% of the energy trapped by photosynthesis is turned into biomass by the plant, and only 10% of that energy is turned into the meat of a grazing animal. Therefore, eating grain-fed beef obtains only about 1% of the energy captured by photosynthesis.
8. Many nutrients come from the soil, but carbon comes from the air.
9. landscape
10. b

CHAPTER 21

1. atom, molecule, organelle, cell, tissue, organ, organ system, organism
2. A very thin or flat organism may have all of its body cells in contact with the environment and therefore would not need a circulatory system. In contrast, a thicker organism will require a circulatory system to transport substances to all body cells.
3. c

4. interstitial fluid
5. positive; negative
6. Endotherms get most of their body heat from metabolic processes, whereas ectotherms get most of their body heat from the environment.
7. osmoregulator; osmoconformer
8. d
9. b
10. Most of the water is reabsorbed into the blood; the rest is excreted in the urine.

CHAPTER 22

1. Large food items could not be digested; it would be difficult to eliminate wastes; and it would be difficult to nourish the many cells that compose a large animal.
2. Yes, absorption is the uptake of nutrients into body cells. Without it, you would never gain any calories (or nutritional value) from your food.
3. Digestion; absorption
4. because peristalsis pushes the food along
5. proteins; pepsin
6. bacteria (specifically, *Helicobacter pylori*); by using antibiotics and bismuth
7. d
8. The antibiotics kill the bacteria that synthesize vitamin K in the colon.
9. b
10. because cellular respiration requires oxygen to break down food
11. Many plant proteins are incomplete, meaning that they lack certain essential amino acids. Animal products tend to have complete proteins that contain all the essential amino acids. Vegetarians must therefore eat a variety of plant products to receive all the essential amino acids.
12. a (Overdoses of fat-soluble vitamins can be dangerous because the body cannot rid itself of them quickly.)

CHAPTER 23

1. In an open circulatory system, vessels have open ends and the circulating fluid flows directly around the body cells. In a closed circulatory system, the circulating fluid stays within a closed system of vessels.
2. Arteries carry oxygen-rich blood to the body, but they carry oxygen-poor blood to the lungs. Veins carry oxygen-poor blood from the body to the heart, but they carry oxygen-rich blood from the lungs to the heart. Arteries are defined as vessels that carry blood away from the heart; veins carry blood to the heart.
3. a3, b1, c4, d2
4. Oxygen levels are reduced, as oxygen-depleted blood mixes with oxygen-rich blood.
5. anemia
6. a3, b4, c1, d2
7. fruits, vegetables, and whole grains; cholesterol, saturated fats, and trans fats
8. Gills (the respiratory organ of fishes) extend outward from the body into the surrounding environment, whereas lungs (the respiratory organ of humans) are internal.
9. alveoli
10. b
11. b

CHAPTER 24

1. antigens; antibodies
2. innate: a, b, d, e; adaptive: c, f, g
3. b
4. It takes several days for a clone of effector cells to be formed during the primary response. In a secondary response, memory cells can respond more quickly.
5. a4, b1, c6, d3, e2, f5
6. Swelling dilutes toxins, delivers more oxygen, promotes scabbing; pain changes behavior to discourage further damage; fever may inhibit bacterial growth.
7. HIV destroys helper T cells, thereby impairing both the cell-mediated and the humoral immune response.
8. B cells
9. In a person with lupus, the immune system makes antibodies against the person's own (self) molecules.
10. memory cells; clonal selection

CHAPTER 25

1. d
2. b
3. The first two cells could have membrane receptors for that hormone, but they might trigger different signal transduction pathways. The third cell could lack membrane receptors for that particular hormone.
4. b

5. Alcohol slows the release of antidiuretic hormone (ADH) from the pituitary. Decreased levels of ADH result in decreased levels of water reabsorption by the kidneys, increasing urine output.
6. The patient has hypothyroidism. The thyroid cannot produce its metabolism-regulating hormones without iodine.
7. d
8. c
9. At high levels, glucocorticoids suppress the immune system. Although this is good for relieving pain and inflammation, the immune system can no longer respond appropriately to threats such as infection. Additionally, glucocorticoids may mask pain, leading to behaviors that aggravate the injury.
10. androgens
11. a. endorphins b. human growth hormone (HGH) c. estrogens

CHAPTER 26

1. Asexual reproduction is favorable in a stable environment with many resources. Sexual reproduction may enhance success in a changing environment by producing genetically variable offspring.
2. the seminal vesicles and/or the prostate
3. a4, b6, c3, d1, e5, f2
4. b
5. Inhibiting FSH and LH after ovulation ensures that another egg will not be released during this cycle. Estrogen and progesterone inhibit FSH and LH.
6. They also help prevent the spread of sexually transmitted diseases.
7. a
8. c
9. The nerve cells may follow chemical trails to the muscle cells (induction).
10. oxytocin
11. in vitro fertilization; fertilization "in glass"

CHAPTER 27

1. cell body; dendrites; axon; synaptic terminal
2. It speeds up conduction of signals along an axon.
3. central nervous system; peripheral nervous system; brain; spinal cord

4. cerebrospinal fluid; meninges
5. activation of the sympathetic branch of the peripheral nervous system
6. The cerebral cortex deals with sensory information, while structures in the brainstem maintain vital functions. If a person suffers a severe head injury, the cerebral cortex may be damaged while the brainstem is still able to function, leaving the person unresponsive but alive.
7. An action potential (used by neurons) is an all-or-none situation; it doesn't vary in intensity. A receptor potential (used by sensory receptor cells) conveys information about the strength of the stimulus.
8. photoreceptor, chemoreceptor, mechanoreceptor, chemoreceptor
9. c (He can hear the tuning fork against his skull, so the cochlea, nerve, and brain are all functioning properly. Apparently, sounds are not being transmitted to the cochlea; therefore, the bones of the middle ear are the problem.)
10. axial; appendicular
11. d
12. a (Each neuron controls a smaller number of muscle fibers.)

CHAPTER 28

1. b, c, d, e
2. When most plants grow naturally, they exhibit apical dominance, which inhibits the outgrowth of the axillary buds. If your friend were to pinch back the terminal buds, there would be increased growth from the axillary buds. This would result in more branches and leaves, which would increase next year's yield.
3. ovary; ovule
4. a4, b2, c5, d6, e3, f1
5. sexual, because it generates genetic variation among the offspring, enhancing the potential for adaptation to a changing environment
6. a. fruit (ripened ovary); b. fruit; c. leaf; d. root; e. fruit
7. c
8. e
9. b; a
10. vascular cambium

CHAPTER 29

1. Excessive amounts of fungicides could destroy mycorrhizae,

symbiotic associations of fungi and plant root hairs. The fungal filaments provide lots of surface area for absorption of water and nutrients. Destroying the mycorrhizae could cause a water or nutrient deficiency in the plant.

2. c

3. Phloem; Xylem

4. Cohesion is the sticking together of identical molecules—water molecules in the case of xylem sap. Adhesion is the sticking together of different kinds of molecules, as in the adhesion of water to the cellulose of xylem walls. Cohesion enables transpiration to pull xylem sap up without the water in the vessels separating; adhesion helps to support the sap against the downward pull of gravity.

5. b

6. auxins; cytokinins

7. The terminal bud produces auxins, which counter the effects of cytokinins from the roots and inhibit the growth of axillary buds. If the terminal bud is removed, the cytokinins predominate, and branching occurs at the axillary buds.

8. a1; b4; c2; d5; e3

9. a4; b3; c1; d2

10. The room lights will inhibit flowering in the chrysanthemums.

Glossary

A

abiotic factor (ā′bī-ot′-ik)
A nonliving component of an ecosystem, such as air, water, light, minerals, or temperature.

abiotic reservoir
The part of an ecosystem where a chemical, such as carbon or nitrogen, accumulates or is stockpiled outside of living organisms.

ABO blood groups
Genetically determined classes of human blood that are based on the presence or absence of carbohydrates A and B on the surface of red blood cells. The ABO blood group phenotypes, also called blood types, are A, B, AB, and O.

abscisic acid (ab-sis′-ik)
A plant hormone that inhibits cell division and promotes dormancy. Abscisic acid interacts with gibberellins in regulating seed germination.

absorption
The uptake of small nutrient molecules by an organism's own body. In animals, absorption is the third main stage of food processing, following digestion; in fungi, it is acquisition of nutrients from the surrounding medium.

acclimation (ak-li-mā-shun)
Physiological adjustment that occurs gradually, though still reversibly, in response to an environmental change.

achondroplasia (uh-kon′-druh-plā′-zhuh)
A form of human dwarfism caused by a single dominant allele. The homozygous condition is lethal.

acid
A substance that increases the hydrogen ion (H⁺) concentration in a solution.

action potential
A self-propagating change in the voltage across the plasma membrane of a neuron; a nerve signal.

activation energy
The amount of energy that reactants must absorb before a chemical reaction will start.

activator
A protein that switches on a gene or group of genes by binding to DNA.

active site
The part of an enzyme molecule where a substrate molecule attaches (by means of weak chemical bonds); typically, a pocket or groove on the enzyme's surface.

active transport
The movement of a substance across a biological membrane against its concentration gradient, aided by specific transport proteins and requiring the input of energy (often as ATP).

adaptive defense
An immune system defense that is found only in vertebrates and that must be activated by exposure to a specific invader.

adenine (A) (ad′-uh-nēn)
A double-ring nitrogenous base found in DNA and RNA.

adhesion
The attraction between different kinds of molecules.

adipose tissue
A type of connective tissue in which the cells contain fat.

ADP
Adenosine diphosphate (a-den′-ō-sēn dī-fos′-fāt)
A molecule composed of adenosine and two phosphate groups. The molecule ATP is made by combining a molecule of ADP with a third phosphate in an energy-consuming reaction.

adrenal cortex (uh-drē′-nul)
The outer portion of an adrenal gland, controlled by ACTH from the anterior pituitary; secretes hormones called glucocorticoids.

adrenal gland
One of a pair of endocrine glands, located atop each kidney in mammals, composed of an outer cortex and a central medulla.

adrenal medulla (uh-drē′-nul muh-dul′-uh)
The central portion of an adrenal gland, controlled by nerve signals; secretes the fight-or-flight hormones epinephrine and norepinephrine.

adult stem cell
A cell present in adult tissues that generates replacements for nondividing differentiated cells.

aerobic (ār-ō′-bik)
Containing or requiring molecular oxygen (O₂).

age structure
The relative number of individuals of each age in a population.

AIDS
Acquired immunodeficiency syndrome; the late stages of HIV infection, characterized by a reduced number of T cells; usually results in death caused by opportunistic infections.

alga (al′-guh)
(plural, **algae**) An informal term that describes a great variety of protists, most of which are unicellular or colonial photosynthetic autotrophs with chloroplasts. Heterotrophic and multicellular protists closely related to unicellular autotrophs are also regarded as algae.

alimentary canal (al′-uh-men′-tuh-rē)
A digestive tube running between a mouth and an anus; also called a digestive tract.

allele (uh-lē′-ul)
An alternative version of a gene.

allergen (al′-er-jen)
An otherwise harmless antigen that causes an allergic reaction.

allergy
An exaggerated sensitivity to an antigen. Symptoms are triggered by histamines released from mast cells.

allopatric speciation
The formation of a new species in populations that are geographically isolated from one another. *See also* sympatric speciation.

alternation of generations
A life cycle in which there is both a multicellular diploid form, the sporophyte, and a multicellular haploid form, the gametophyte; a characteristic of plants and multicellular green algae.

alternative RNA splicing
A type of regulation at the RNA-processing level in which different mRNA molecules are produced from the same primary transcript, depending on which RNA segments are treated as exons and which as introns.

alveolus (al-vē′-oh-lus)
(plural, **alveoli**) One of millions of tiny sacs within the vertebrate lungs where gas exchange occurs.

Alzheimer's disease
A form of mental deterioration, or dementia, characterized by confusion and memory loss.

amino acid (uh-mēn′-ō)
An organic molecule containing a carboxyl group, an amino group, a hydrogen atom, and a variable side group (also called a radical group or R group); serves as the monomer of proteins.

amniote
Member of a clade of tetrapods that has an amniotic egg containing specialized membranes that protect the embryo. Amniotes include mammals and reptiles (including birds).

amniotic egg (am′-nē-ot′-ik)
A shelled egg in which an embryo develops within a fluid-filled amniotic sac and is nourished by yolk. Produced by reptiles (including birds) and egg-laying mammals, it enables them to complete their life cycles on dry land.

amoeba (uh-mē′-buh)
A general term for a protozoan (animal-like protist) characterized by great structural flexibility and the presence of pseudopodia.

amphibian
Member of a class of vertebrate animals that includes frogs and salamanders.

anaerobic (an′-ār-ō′-bik)
Lacking or not requiring molecular oxygen (O₂).

analogy
The similarity between two species that is due to convergent evolution rather than to descent from a common ancestor with the same trait.

anaphase
The third stage of mitosis, beginning when sister chromatids separate from each other and ending when a complete set of daughter chromosomes has arrived at each of the two poles of the cell.

anatomy
The study of the structure of an organism and its parts.

androgen (an'-drō-jen)
A sex hormone secreted by the gonads that promotes the development and maintenance of the male reproductive system and male body features.

anemia (uh-nē'-me-ah)
A condition in which an abnormally low amount of hemoglobin or a low number of red blood cells results in the body cells not receiving enough oxygen.

angiosperm (an'-jē-ō-sperm)
A flowering plant, which forms seeds inside a protective chamber called an ovary.

animal
A eukaryotic, multicellular, heterotrophic organism that obtains nutrients by ingestion.

annelid (an'-uh-lid)
A segmented worm. Annelids include earthworms, polychaetes, and leeches.

annual
A plant that completes its life cycle in a single year or growing season.

anorexia nervosa
An eating disorder that results in self-starvation due to an intense fear of gaining weight, even when the person is underweight.

antagonistic hormones
Two hormones that have opposite effects.

anterior pituitary (puh-tū'-uh-tār-ē)
An endocrine gland, adjacent to the hypothalamus and the posterior pituitary, that synthesizes and secretes several hormones, including some that control the activity of other endocrine glands.

anther
A sac in which pollen grains develop, located at the tip of a flower's stamen.

anthropoid (an'-thruh-poyd)
Member of a primate group made up of the apes (gibbons, orangutans, gorillas, chimpanzees, and bonobos), monkeys, and humans.

antibody (an'-tih-bod'-ē)
A protein that is secreted by a B cell and attaches to a specific kind of antigen, helping counter its effects.

anticodon (an'-tī-kō'-don)
On a tRNA molecule, a specific sequence of three nucleotides that is complementary to a codon triplet on mRNA.

antigen (an'-tuh-jen)
Any molecule that elicits a response from a lymphocyte.

anus
The digestive system opening through which undigested materials are expelled.

aphotic zone (ā-fō'-tik)
The region of an aquatic ecosystem beneath the photic zone, where light levels are too low for photosynthesis to take place.

apical dominance (ā'-pik-ul)
In a plant, the hormonal inhibition of axillary buds by a terminal bud.

apical meristem (ā'-pik-ul mer'-uh-stem)
A meristem at the tip of a plant root or in the terminal or axillary bud of a shoot.

apicomplexan (ap'-ē-kom-pleks'-un)
A type of parasitic protozoan (animal-like protist). Some apicomplexans cause serious human disease.

appendicular skeleton (ap'-en-dik'-yū-ler)
Components of the skeletal system that support the arms and legs of a land vertebrate; bones of the limbs, shoulders, and pelvis. See also axial skeleton.

appendix (uh-pen'-dix)
A small, finger-like extension near the union of the small and large intestines.

aqueous humor (ā'-kwē-us hyū'-mer)
A liquid in the space between the lens and cornea in the vertebrate eye that helps maintain the shape of the eye, supplies nutrients and oxygen to its tissues, and disposes of its wastes.

aqueous solution (ā'-kwē-us)
A solution in which water is the solvent.

arachnid
Member of a major arthropod group that includes spiders, scorpions, ticks, and mites.

Archaea (ar-kē'-uh)
One of two prokaryotic domains of life, the other being Bacteria.

archaean (ar-kē'-uhn)
(plural, **archaea**) An organism that is a member of the domain Archaea.

arteriole (ar-tar'-ē-ōl)
A small vessel that conveys blood between an artery and a capillary bed.

artery
A vessel that carries blood away from the heart to other parts of the body.

arthritis (ar-thrī'-tis)
A skeletal disorder characterized by inflamed joints and deterioration of the cartilage between bones.

arthropod (ar'-thruh-pod)
Member of the most diverse phylum in the animal kingdom; includes the horseshoe crab, arachnids (for example, spiders, ticks, scorpions, and mites), crustaceans (for example, crayfish, lobsters, crabs, and barnacles), millipedes, centipedes, and insects. Arthropods are characterized by a chitinous exoskeleton, molting, jointed appendages, and a body formed of distinct groups of segments.

asexual reproduction
The creation of genetically identical offspring by a single parent, without the participation of gametes (sperm and egg).

association areas
Areas of the cerbral cortex where different types of incoming sensory information are integrated.

astigmatism (uh-stig'-muh-tizm)
Blurred vision caused by a misshapen lens or cornea.

atherosclerosis (ath'-uh-rō'-skluh-rō'-sis)
A cardiovascular disease in which a buildup of fatty deposits called plaques develop on the inner walls of the arteries, narrowing the passageways through which blood can flow.

atom
The smallest unit of matter that retains the properties of an element.

atomic number
The number of protons in each atom of a particular element.

ATP Adenosine triphosphate (a-den'-ō-sēn trī-fos'-fāt)
A molecule composed of adenosine and three phosphate groups; the main energy source for cells. A molecule of ATP can be broken down to a molecule of ADP (adenosine diphosophate) and a free phosphate; this reaction releases energy that can be used for cellular work.

ATP synthase
A protein cluster, found in a cellular membrane (including the inner membrane of mitochondria, the thylakoid membrane of chloroplasts, and the plasma membrane of prokaryotes), that uses the energy of a hydrogen ion concentration gradient to make ATP from ADP. An ATP synthase provides a port through which hydrogen ions (H^+) diffuse.

atrium (ā'-trē-um)
(plural, **atria**) A heart chamber that receives blood from the body or lungs via veins.

auditory canal
The part of the outer ear that channels sound waves from the pinna, or outer body surface, to the eardrum.

autoimmune disease
An immunological disorder in which the immune system improperly attacks the body's own molecules.

autonomic nervous system (ot'-ō-nom'-ik)
A component of the peripheral nervous system of vertebrates that regulates the internal environment. The autonomic nervous system is made up of the sympathetic and parasympathetic subdivisions. The autonomic nervous system is primarily under involuntary control.

autosome
A chromosome not directly involved in determining the sex of an organism; in mammals, for example, any chromosome other than X or Y.

autotroph (ot'-ō-trōf)
An organism that makes its own food from inorganic ingredients, thereby sustaining itself without eating other organisms or their molecules. Plants, algae, and photosynthetic bacteria are autotrophs.

auxin (ok'-sin)
Any of a group of plant hormones whose chief effect is to promote the growth and development of shoots.

AV (atrioventricular) node
A region of muscle tissue between the heart's right atrium and right ventricle. It generates electrical impulses that primarily cause the ventricles to contract.

axial skeleton (ak'-sē-ul)
Components of the skeletal system that support the central trunk of the body; the skull, backbone, and rib cage in a vertebrate. *See also* appendicular skeleton.

axillary bud (ak'-sil-ār-ē)
An embryonic shoot present in the angle formed by a leaf and stem.

axon (ak'-son)
A neuron fiber that extends from the cell body and conducts signals to another neuron or to an effector cell.

B

B cell
A type of lymphocyte that matures in the bone marrow and later produces antibodies; responsible for the humoral immune response. *See also* T cell.

bacillus (buh-sil'-us)
(plural, **bacilli**) A rod-shaped prokaryotic cell.

Bacteria
One of two prokaryotic domains of life, the other being Archaea.

bacteriophage (bak-tēr'-ē-ō-fāj)
A virus that infects bacteria; also called a phage.

bacterium
(plural, **bacteria**) An organism that is a member of the domain Bacteria.

ball-and-socket joint
A joint that allows rotation and movement in several planes. Examples in humans are the shoulder and hip joints.

bark
All the tissues external to the vascular cambium in a plant with secondary growth. Bark is made up of secondary phloem, cork cambium, and cork.

basal metabolic rate (BMR)
The number of kilocalories a resting animal requires to fuel its essential body processes for a given time.

base
A substance that decreases the hydrogen ion (H^+) concentration in a solution.

benign tumor
An abnormal mass of cells that remains at its original site in the body.

benthic realm
A seafloor or the bottom of a freshwater lake, pond, river, or stream. The benthic realm is occupied by communities of organisms known as benthos.

biennial
A plant that completes its life cycle in two years.

bilateral symmetry
An arrangement of body parts such that an organism can be divided equally by a single cut passing longitudinally through it. A bilaterally symmetric organism has mirror-image right and left sides.

bile
A solution of salts secreted by the liver that emulsifies fats and aids in their digestion.

binary fission
A means of asexual reproduction in which a parent organism, often a single cell, divides into two individuals of about equal size.

binomial
A two-part Latinized name of a species; for example, *Homo sapiens*.

biodiversity
The variety of living things; includes genetic diversity, species diversity, and ecosystem diversity.

biodiversity hot spot
A small geographic area that contains a large number of threatened or endangered species and an exceptional concentration of endemic species (those found nowhere else).

biofilm
A surface-coating cooperative colony of prokaryotes.

biogenesis
The principle that all life arises by the reproduction of preexisting life.

biogeochemical cycle
Any of the various chemical circuits occurring in an ecosystem, involving both biotic and abiotic components of the ecosystem.

biogeography
The study of the geographic distribution of species.

biological control
The intentional release of a natural enemy to attack a pest population.

biological magnification
The accumulation of persistent chemicals in the living tissues of consumers in food chains.

biological species concept
The definition of a species as a population or group of populations whose members have the potential in nature to interbreed and produce fertile offspring.

biology
The scientific study of life.

biomass
The amount, or mass, of living organic material in an ecosystem.

biome (bī'-ōm)
A major terrestrial or aquatic life zone, characterized by vegetation type in terrestrial biomes and the physical environment in aquatic biomes.

biophilia
The human desire to affiliate with other life in its many forms.

bioremediation
The use of living organisms to detoxify and restore polluted and degraded ecosystems.

biosphere
The global ecosystem; the entire portion of Earth inhabited by life; all of life and where it lives.

biotechnology
The manipulation of living organisms to perform useful tasks. Today, biotechnology often involves DNA technology.

biotic factor (bī-ot'-ik)
A living component of a biological community; any organism that is part of an individual's environment.

bipolar disorder
Depressive mental illness characterized by extreme mood swings; also called manic-depressive disorder.

bird
Member of a group of reptiles with feathers and adaptations for flight.

birth control pill
A chemical contraceptive that inhibits ovulation, retards follicular development, or alters a woman's cervical mucus to prevent sperm from entering the uterus.

bivalve
Member of a group of molluscs that includes clams, mussels, scallops, and oysters.

blade
The flattened portion of a typical leaf.

blastula (blas'-tyū-luh)
An embryonic stage that marks the end of cleavage during animal development; a hollow ball of cells in many species.

blood
A type of connective tissue with a fluid matrix called plasma in which blood cells are suspended.

blood pressure
The force that blood exerts against the walls of the blood vessels.

body cavity
A fluid-filled space separating the digestive tract from the outer body wall.

body mass index (BMI)
A ratio of weight to height used as a measure of obesity.

body segmentation
Subdivision of an animal's body into a series of repeated parts called segments.

bone
A type of connective tissue consisting of living cells held in a rigid matrix of collagen fibers embedded in calcium salts.

bony fish
A fish that has a stiff skeleton reinforced by calcium salts.

bottleneck effect
Genetic drift resulting from a drastic reduction in population size.

brain
The master control center of the central nervous system, which is involved in regulating and controlling body activity and interpreting information from the senses.

brainstem
A functional unit of the vertebrate brain, composed of the midbrain, medulla oblongata, and pons; serves mainly as a sensory filter, selecting which information reaches higher brain centers.

breathing
The ventilation of the lungs by alternate inhalation and exhalation, supplying a lung or gill with O_2-rich air or water and expelling CO_2-rich air or water.

bronchiole (brong'-kē-ōl)
A thin breathing tube that branches from a bronchus within a lung.

bronchus (*brong'-kus*)
(plural, **bronchi**) One of a pair of breathing tubes that branch from the trachea into the lungs.

bryophyte (*brī'-uh-fīt*)
A type of plant that lacks xylem and phloem; a nonvascular plant. Bryophytes include mosses and their close relatives.

budding
A means of asexual reproduction in which a new individual splits off after developing from an outgrowth of a parent.

buffer
A chemical substance that resists changes in pH by accepting hydrogen ions from or donating hydrogen ions to solutions.

bulimia
An eating disorder characterized by episodic binge eating followed by purging through induced vomiting, abuse of laxatives, or excessive exercise.

C

C_3 plant
A plant that used the Calvin cycle for the initial steps that incorporate CO_2 into organic material, forming a three-carbon compound as the first stable intermediate.

C_4 plant
A plant that prefaces the Calvin cycle with reactions that incorporate CO_2 into four-carbon compounds, the end product of which supplies CO_2 for the Calvin cycle.

calcitonin (*kal'-sih-tōn'-in*)
A peptide hormone, secreted by the thyroid gland, that lowers blood calcium level.

calorie
The amount of energy that raises the temperature of 1 g of water by 1°C.

Calvin cycle
The second of two stages of photosynthesis; a cyclic series of chemical reactions that occur in the stroma of a chloroplast, using the carbon in CO_2 and the ATP and NADPH produced by the light reactions to make the energy-rich sugar molecule G3P, which is later used to produce glucose.

CAM plant
A plant that uses the following adaptation for photosynthesis in arid conditions: Carbon dioxide entering open stomata during the night is converted to organic compounds, which release CO_2 for the Calvin cycle during the day, when stomata are closed.

cancer
A malignant growth or tumor caused by abnormal and uncontrolled cell division.

cap
Extra nucleotides added to the beginning of an RNA transcript in the nucleus of a eukaryotic cell.

capillary (*kap'-il-ar-ē*)
A microscopic blood vessel that conveys blood between an artery and a vein or between an arteriole and a venule; enables the exchange of nutrients and dissolved gases between the blood and interstitial fluid.

carbohydrate (*kar'-bō-hī'-drāt*)
A biological molecule consisting of a simple sugar (a monosaccharide), two monosaccharides joined into a double sugar (a disaccharide), or a chain of monosaccharides (a polysaccharide).

carbon fixation
The initial incorporation of carbon from CO_2 into organic compounds by autotrophic organisms such as photosynthetic plants, algae, or bacteria.

carbon footprint
The amount of greenhouse gas emitted as a result of the actions of a person, nation, or other entity.

carcinogen (*kar-sin'-uh-jin*)
A cancer-causing agent, either high-energy radiation (such as X-rays or UV light) or a chemical.

cardiac cycle (*kar'-dē-ak*)
The alternating contractions and relaxations of the heart.

cardiac muscle
Striated muscle that forms the contractile tissue of the heart.

cardiovascular disease
(*kar'-dē-ō-vas'-kyū-ler*)
A set of diseases of the heart and blood vessels.

cardiovascular system
A closed circulatory system, found in vertebrates, with a heart and a branching network of arteries, capillaries, and veins.

carnivore
An animal that mainly eats other animals. *See also* herbivore; omnivore.

carpel (*kar'-pul*)
The egg-producing part of a flower, consisting of a stalk with an ovary at the base and a stigma, which traps pollen, at the tip.

carrier
An individual who is heterozygous for a recessively inherited disorder and who therefore does not show symptoms of that disorder.

carrying capacity
The maximum population size that a particular environment can sustain.

cartilage (*kar'-ti-lij*)
A type of connective tissue consisting of living cells embedded in a rubbery matrix with collagen fibers.

cartilaginous fish (*kar-ti-laj'-uh-nus*)
A fish that has a flexible skeleton made of cartilage.

cell body
The part of a cell, such as a neuron, that houses the nucleus and other organelles.

cell cycle
An ordered sequence of events (including interphase and the mitotic phase) that extends from the time a eukaryotic cell is first formed from a dividing parent cell until its own division into two cells.

cell cycle control system
A cyclically operating set of proteins that triggers and coordinates events in the eukaryotic cell cycle.

cell division
The reproduction of a cell.

cell junction
A structure that connects animal cells to one another in a tissue.

cell plate
A membranous disk that forms across the midline of a dividing plant cell. During cytokinesis, the cell plate grows outward, accumulating more cell wall material and eventually fusing into a new cell wall.

cell theory
The theory that all living things are composed of cells and that all cells come from other cells.

cell wall
A protective layer external to the plasma membrane in plant cells, bacteria, fungi, and some protists; protects the cell and helps maintain its shape.

cell-mediated immune response
The type of adaptive immune response that involves T cells, lymphocytes that fight body cells infected with pathogens. *See also* humoral immune response.

cellular differentiation
Specialization in the structure and function of cells that occurs during the development of an organism; results from selective activation and deactivation of the cells' genes.

cellular respiration
The aerobic harvesting of energy from food molecules; the energy-releasing chemical breakdown of food molecules, such as glucose, and the storage of potential energy in a form that cells can use to perform work; involves glycolysis, the citric acid cycle, the electron transport chain, and chemiosmosis.

cellular slime mold
A type of protist that has unicellular amoeboid cells and a multicellular reproductive body in its life cycle.

cellulose (*sel'-yū-lōs*)
A large polysaccharide composed of many glucose monomers linked into cable-like fibrils that provide structural support in plant cell walls. Because cellulose cannot be digested by animals, it acts as fiber, or roughage, in the diet.

centipede
A carnivorous terrestrial arthropod that has one pair of long legs for each of its numerous body segments, with the front pair modified as poison claws.

central nervous system (CNS)
The integration and command center of the nervous system; the brain and, in vertebrates, the spinal cord.

central vacuole (*vak'-yū-ōl*)
A membrane-enclosed sac occupying most of the interior of a mature plant cell, having diverse roles in reproduction, growth, and development.

centromere (sen'-trō-mer)
The region of a chromosome where two sister chromatids are joined and where spindle microtubules attach during mitosis and meiosis. The centromere divides at the onset of anaphase during mitosis and anaphase II of meiosis.

centrosome (sen'-trō-sōm)
Material in the cytoplasm of a eukaryotic cell that gives rise to microtubules; important in mitosis and meiosis; functions as a microtubule-organizing center.

cephalopod
Member of a group of molluscs that includes squids and octopuses.

cerebellum (sar'-ruh-bel'-um)
Part of the vertebrate hindbrain; mainly a planning center that interacts closely with the cerebrum in coordinating body movement.

cerebral cortex (suh-rē'-brul kor'-teks)
A highly folded layer of tissue that forms the surface of the cerebrum. In humans, it contains integrating centers for higher brain functions, such as reasoning, speech, language, and imagination.

cerebrospinal fluid (suh-rē'-brō-spī'-nul)
Fluid that surrounds, cushions, and nourishes the brain and spinal cord and protects them from infection.

cerebrum (suh-rē'-brum)
The largest, most sophisticated, and most dominant part of the vertebrate forebrain, made up of right and left cerebral hemispheres. The cerebrum contains the cerebral cortex.

cervix (ser'-viks)
The narrow neck at the bottom of the uterus, which opens into the vagina.

chaparral (shap-uh-ral')
A terrestrial biome limited to coastal regions where cold ocean currents circulate offshore, creating mild, rainy winters and long, hot, dry summers; also known as the Mediterranean biome. Chaparral vegetation is adapted to fire.

character
A heritable feature that varies among individuals within a population, such as flower color in pea plants.

charophyte (kar'-uh-fīt')
A member of the green algal group that shares features with land plants. Charophytes are considered the closest relatives of land plants; modern charophytes and modern plants likely evolved from a common ancestor.

chemical bond
An attraction between two atoms resulting from a sharing of outer-shell electrons or the presence of opposite charges on the atoms. The bonded atoms gain complete outer electron shells.

chemical cycling
The use and reuse of chemical elements such as carbon within an ecosystem.

chemical energy
Energy stored in the chemical bonds of molecules; a form of potential energy.

chemical reaction
A process leading to chemical changes in matter, involving the making and/or breaking of chemical bonds.

chemoreceptor (kē'-mō-rē-sep'-ter)
A sensory receptor that detects chemical changes within the body or a specific kind of chemical in the external environment; chemoreceptors are involved in our senses of taste and smell.

chemotherapy (kē'-mo-ther'-uh-pē)
Treatment for cancer in which drugs are administered to disrupt cell division of the cancer cells.

chiasma (kī-az'-muh)
(plural, **chiasmata**) The microscopically visible site where crossing over has occurred between chromatids of homologous chromosomes during prophase I of meiosis.

chlamydia
A common sexually transmitted disease caused by a bacterial infection. Its primary symptoms are genital discharge and burning during urination. It is easily treatable with antibiotics.

chlorophyll (klor'-ō-fil)
A light-absorbing pigment in chloroplasts that plays a central role in converting solar energy to chemical energy.

chlorophyll a (klor'-ō-fil ā)
A green pigment in chloroplasts that participates directly in the light reactions.

chloroplast (klō'-rō-plast)
An organelle found in plants and photosynthetic protists. Enclosed by two concentric membranes, a chloroplast absorbs sunlight and uses it to power the synthesis of organic food molecules (sugars).

chordate (kor'-dāt)
An animal that at some point during its development has a dorsal, hollow nerve cord, a notochord, pharyngeal slits, and a post-anal tail. Chordates include lancelets, tunicates, and vertebrates.

chorion (kōr'-ē-on)
In animals, the outermost membrane protecting an embryo. In mammals, the chorion becomes part of the placenta.

chorionic villus (kōr'-ē-on'-ik vil'-us)
(plural, **villi**) An outgrowth of the chorion, containing embryonic blood vessels. As part of the placenta, chorionic villi absorb nutrients and oxygen from the mother's bloodstream and pass wastes into the mother's bloodstream.

chromatin (krō'-muh-tin)
The combination of DNA and proteins that constitutes chromosomes; often used to refer to the diffuse, very extended form taken by the chromosomes when a eukaryotic cell is not dividing.

chromosome (krō'-muh-sōm)
A gene-carrying structure found in the nucleus of a eukaryotic cell and most visible during mitosis and meiosis; also, the main gene-carrying structure of a prokaryotic cell. Each chromosome consists of one very long threadlike DNA molecule and associated proteins. See also chromatin.

chromosome theory of inheritance
A basic principle in biology stating that genes are located on chromosomes and that the behavior of chromosomes during meiosis accounts for inheritance patterns.

chyme (kīm)
A mixture of recently swallowed food and gastric juice.

ciliate (sil'-ē-it)
A type of protozoan (animal-like protist) that moves and feeds by means of cilia.

cilium (sil'-ē-um)
(plural, **cilia**) A short appendage that propels some protists through the water and moves fluids across the surface of many tissue cells in animals.

circulatory system
The organ system that transports materials such as nutrients, O_2, and hormones to body cells and transports CO_2 and other wastes from body cells.

citric acid cycle
The metabolic cycle that is fueled by acetyl CoA formed after glycolysis in cellular respiration. Chemical reactions in the cycle complete the metabolic breakdown of glucose molecules to carbon dioxide. The cycle occurs in the matrix of mitochondria and supplies most of the NADH molecules that carry energy to the electron transport chains. Also referred to as the Krebs cycle.

clade
An ancestral species and all its descendants—a distinctive branch in the tree of life.

cladistics (kluh-dis'-tiks)
The study of evolutionary history; specifically, an approach to systematics in which organisms are grouped by common ancestry.

class
In classification, the taxonomic category above order.

cleavage (klē-vij)
(1) Cytokinesis in animal cells and in some protists, characterized by pinching in of the plasma membrane. (2) In animal development, the succession of rapid cell divisions without cell growth, converting the animal zygote to a ball of cells.

cleavage furrow
The first sign of cytokinesis during cell division in an animal cell; a shallow groove in the cell surface near the old metaphase plate.

clitoris (klit'-uh-ris)
An organ in the female that engorges with blood and becomes erect during sexual arousal.

clonal selection (klōn'-ul)
The production of a population of genetically identical lymphocytes (white blood cells) that recognize

and attack the specific antigen that stimulated their proliferation. Clonal selection is the mechanism that underlies the immune system's specificity and memory of antigens.

clone
As a verb, to produce genetically identical copies of a cell, organism, or DNA molecule. As a noun, the collection of cells, organisms, or molecules resulting from cloning; also (colloquially), a single organism that is genetically identical to another because it arose from the cloning of a somatic cell.

closed circulatory system
A circulatory system in which blood is confined to vessels and is kept separate from the interstitial fluid.

cnidarian (*nī-dār'-ē-an*)
An animal characterized by cnidocytes, radial symmetry, a gastrovascular cavity, and a polyp or medusa body form. Cnidarians includes hydras, jellies, sea anemones, and corals.

coccus (*kok'-us*)
(plural, **cocci**) A spherical prokaryotic cell.

cochlea (*kok'-lē-uh*)
A coiled tube in the inner ear that contains the hearing organ, the organ of Corti.

codominant
Expressing two different alleles of a gene in a heterozygote.

codon (*kō'-don*)
A three-nucleotide sequence in mRNA that specifies a particular amino acid or polypeptide termination signal; the basic unit of the genetic code.

coelom (*sē'-lōm*)
A body cavity completely lined by tissue derived from mesoderm.

cohesion (*kō-hē'-zhun*)
The attraction between molecules of the same kind.

collenchyma cell (*kuh-leng'-kuh-muh*)
In plants, a type of cell with a thick primary wall and no secondary wall, functioning mainly in supporting growing parts.

colon (*kō'-lun*)
Most of the length of the large intestine, the tubular portion of the vertebrate alimentary canal between the small intestine and the rectum;

functions mainly in water absorption and the formation of feces.

community
All the organisms inhabiting and potentially interacting in a particular area; an assemblage of populations of different species.

community ecology
The study of how interactions between species affect community structure and organization.

comparative anatomy
The comparison of body structures in different species.

competitive exclusion principle
The concept that populations of two species cannot coexist in a community if their niches are nearly identical. Using resources more efficiently and having a reproductive advantage, one of the populations will eventually outcompete and eliminate the other.

complement protein
A defensive blood protein that attacks pathogens directly as part of innate internal defense. Complement proteins can enhance phagocytosis and cut holes in microbial membranes, causing the cells to burst.

complementary DNA (cDNA)
A DNA molecule made in vitro using mRNA as a template and the enzyme reverse transcriptase. A cDNA molecule therefore corresponds to a gene but lacks the introns present in the DNA of the genome.

complete digestive tract
A digestive tube with two openings, a mouth and an anus.

compost
A soil-like mixture of decomposed organic matter used to fertilize plants.

compound
A substance containing two or more elements in a fixed ratio; for example, table salt (NaCl) consists of one atom of the element sodium (Na) for every atom of chlorine (Cl).

concentration gradient
An increase or decrease in the density of a chemical substance within a given region. Cells often maintain concentration gradients of hydrogen ions across their membranes. When a gradient exists,

the ions or other chemical substances involved tend to move from where they are more concentrated to where they are less concentrated.

condom
A flexible sheath, usually made of thin rubber or latex, designed to cover the penis during sexual intercourse for contraceptive purposes or as a means of preventing sexually transmitted diseases.

cone
(1) In vertebrates, a photoreceptor cell in the retina, stimulated by bright light and enabling color vision. (2) In conifers, a reproductive structure bearing pollen or ovules.

conifer (*kon'-uh-fer*)
A gymnosperm, or naked-seed plant, most of which produce cones.

coniferous forest (*kō-nif'-rus*)
A terrestrial biome characterized by conifers, cone-bearing evergreen trees.

connective tissue
Tissue consisting of cells held in an abundant extracellular matrix.

conservation biology
A goal-oriented science that seeks to understand and counter the loss of biodiversity.

conservation of energy
The principle that energy can neither be created nor destroyed.

consumer
An organism that obtains its food by eating plants or by eating animals that have eaten plants.

contraception
The deliberate prevention of pregnancy.

controlled experiment
A component of the process of science whereby a scientist carries out two parallel tests, an experimental test and a control test. The experimental test differs from the control by one factor, the variable.

convergent evolution
The evolution of similar features in different evolutionary lineages, which can result from living in very similar environments.

coral reef
Tropical marine biome characterized by hard skeletal structures secreted primarily by the resident cnidarians.

cork
The outermost protective layer of a plant's bark, produced by the cork cambium.

cork cambium
Meristem tissue that produces cork cells during secondary growth of a plant.

cornea (*kor'-nē-uh*)
The transparent front portion of the sclera that admits light into the vertebrate eye.

coronary artery (*kōr'-uh-nār-ē*)
A large blood vessel that conveys blood from the aorta to the tissues of the heart.

corpus callosum (*kor'-pus kuh-lō'-sum*)
A thick band of nerve fibers that connects the right and left cerebral hemispheres, enabling them to process information together.

corpus luteum (*kor'-pus lū'-tē-um*)
A small body of endocrine tissue that develops from an ovarian follicle after ovulation. The corpus luteum secretes progesterone and estrogen during pregnancy.

cortex
In plants, the ground tissue system of a root, which stores food and absorbs water and minerals that have passed through the epidermis. *See also* adrenal cortex; cerebral cortex.

corticosteroid
One of a family of steroid hormones, including glucocorticoids, synthesized and secreted by the adrenal cortex.

cotyledon (*kot'-uh-lē'-don*)
The first leaf that appears on an embryo of a flowering plant; a seed leaf. Monocot embryos have one cotyledon; dicot embryos have two.

covalent bond (*kō-vā'-lent*)
An attraction between atoms that share one or more pairs of outer-shell electrons.

crista (*kris'-tuh*)
(plural, **cristae**) A fold of the inner membrane of a mitochondrion. Enzyme molecules embedded in cristae make ATP.

cross
The cross-fertilization of two different varieties of an organism or of two different species; also called hybridization.

crossing over
The exchange of segments between chromatids of homologous chromosomes during prophase I of meiosis.

crustacean
Member of a major arthropod group that includes lobsters, crayfish, crabs, shrimps, and barnacles.

cryptic coloration
Adaptive coloration that makes an organism difficult to spot against its background.

culture
The accumulated knowledge, customs, beliefs, arts, and other human products that are socially transmitted over the generations.

cuticle (*kyū'-tuh-kul*)
(1) In animals, a tough, nonliving outer layer of the skin. (2) In plants, a waxy coating on the surface of stems and leaves that helps retain water.

cystic fibrosis (*sis'-tik fī-brō'-sis*)
A genetic disease that occurs in people with two copies of a certain recessive allele; characterized by an excessive secretion of mucus and consequent vulnerability to infection; fatal if untreated.

cytokinesis (*sī-tō-kuh-nē'-sis*)
The division of the cytoplasm to form two separate daughter cells. Cytokinesis usually occurs during telophase of mitosis, and the two processes (mitosis and cytokinesis) make up the mitotic (M) phase of the cell cycle.

cytokinin (*sī-tō-kī'-nin*)
Any of a family of plant hormones that promote cell division, retard aging in flowers and fruits, and may counter the effects of auxins in regulating plant growth and development.

cytoplasm (*sī-tō-plaz'-um*)
Everything inside a eukaryotic cell between the plasma membrane and the nucleus; consists of a semifluid medium and organelles; can also refer to the interior of a prokaryotic cell.

cytosine (C) (*sī'-tuh-sēn*)
A single-ring nitrogenous base found in DNA and RNA.

cytoskeleton
A meshwork of fine fibers in the cytoplasm of a eukaryotic cell; includes microfilaments, intermediate filaments, and microtubules.

cytosol (*sī'-tuh-sol*)
The fluid part of the cytoplasm, in which organelles are suspended.

cytotoxic T cell (*sī'-tō-tok'-sik*)
A type of lymphocyte that directly attacks body cells infected by pathogens.

D

decomposer
An organism that secretes enzymes that digest molecules in organic material and convert them to inorganic form.

dehydration (*dē-hī-drā'-shun*)
A chemical process in which a polymer forms when monomers are linked by the removal of water molecules. One molecule of water is removed for each pair of monomers linked. A dehydration reaction is essentially the reverse of a hydrolysis reaction.

denaturation (*dē-nā'-chuh-rā'-shun*)
A process in which a protein unravels, losing its specific conformation and hence its function; can be caused by changes in pH or salt concentration or by high temperature; also refers to the separation of the two strands of the DNA double helix, caused by similar factors.

dendrite (*den'-drīt*)
A short, branched neuron fiber that receives signals and conveys them from its tip inward, toward the rest of the neuron.

density-dependent factor
A limiting factor whose effects intensify with increasing population density.

density-independent factor
A limiting factor whose occurrence and effects are not related to population density.

dermal tissue system
In plants, the tissue system that forms an outer protective covering.

desert
A terrestrial biome characterized by low and unpredictable rainfall (less than 30 cm per year).

determinate growth
Termination of growth after reaching a certain size, as in most animals. *See also* indeterminate growth.

detritivore (*di-trī'-tuh-vor*)
An organism that consumes dead organic matter (detritus).

detritus (*di-trī'-tus*)
Dead organic matter.

diabetes mellitus (*dī'-uh-bē'-tis mel'-uh-tus*)
A human hormonal disease in which body cells cannot absorb enough glucose from the blood and become energy starved. Body fats and proteins are then consumed for their energy. Insulin-dependent diabetes results when the pancreas does not produce insulin. Non-insulin-dependent diabetes results when body cells fail to respond to insulin. A third type of diabetes, called gestational diabetes, can affect any pregnant woman, even one who has never shown symptoms of diabetes before.

dialysis (*dī-al'-uh-sis*)
Separation and disposal of metabolic wastes from the blood by mechanical means; an artificial method of performing the functions of the kidneys.

diaphragm (*dī'-uh-fram*)
(1) The sheet of muscle separating the chest cavity from the abdominal cavity in mammals. Its contraction expands the chest cavity, and its relaxation reduces it. (2) A dome-shaped rubber cap that covers a woman's cervix, serving as a barrier method of contraception.

diastole (*dī-as'-tuh-lē*)
The stage of the cardiac cycle in which the heart muscle is relaxed, allowing the chambers to fill with blood. *See also* systole.

diatom (*dī'-uh-tom*)
A unicellular photosynthetic alga with a unique glassy cell wall containing silica.

dicot (*dī'-kot*)
A flowering plant whose embryos have two seed leaves, or cotyledons.

diffusion
The spontaneous movement of particles of any kind down a concentration gradient; that is, movement of particles from where they are more concentrated to where they are less concentrated.

digestion
The mechanical and chemical breakdown of food into molecules small enough for the body to absorb; the second stage of food processing, following ingestion.

digestive tract
A digestive compartment with two openings: a mouth for the entrance of food and an anus for the exit of undigested wastes. Most animals, including humans, have a digestive tract, more commonly called an alimentary canal.

dihybrid cross (*dī'-hī'-brid*)
A mating of individuals differing at two genetic loci.

dinoflagellate (*dī'-nō-flaj'-uh-let*)
A unicellular photosynthetic alga with two flagella situated in perpendicular grooves in cellulose plates covering the cell.

diploid (*dip'-loid*)
Containing two sets of chromosomes (pairs of homologous chromosomes) in each cell, one set inherited from each parent; referring to a 2*n* cell.

directional selection
Natural selection that acts in favor of the individuals at one end of a phenotypic range.

disaccharide (*dī-sak'-uh-rīd*)
A sugar molecule consisting of two monosaccharides linked by a dehydration reaction.

discovery science
The process of scientific inquiry that focuses on using observations to describe nature. *See also* hypothesis-driven science.

disruptive selection
Natural selection that favors extreme over intermediate phenotypes.

disturbance
In an ecological sense, a force that damages a biological community, at least temporarily, by destroying organisms and altering the availability of resources needed by organisms in the community. Disturbances such as fires and storms play a pivotal role in structuring many biological communities.

DNA Deoxyribonucleic acid (*dē-ok'-si-rī'-bō-nū-klā'-ik*)

The genetic material that organisms inherit from their parents; a double-stranded helical macromolecule consisting of nucleotide monomers with deoxyribose sugar, a phosphate group, and the nitrogenous bases adenine (A), cytosine (C), guanine (G), and thymine (T). *See also* gene.

DNA ligase (*lī'-gās*)

An enzyme, essential for DNA replication, that catalyzes the covalent bonding of adjacent DNA nucleotides; used in genetic engineering to paste a specific piece of DNA containing a gene of interest into a bacterial plasmid or other vector.

DNA microarray

A glass slide containing thousands of different kinds of single-stranded DNA fragments arranged in an array (grid). Tiny amounts of DNA fragments, representing different genes, are attached to the glass slide. These fragments are tested for hybridization with various samples of cDNA molecules, thereby measuring the expression of thousands of genes at one time.

DNA polymerase (*puh-lim'-er-ās*)

An enzyme that assembles DNA nucleotides into polynucleotides using a preexisting strand of DNA as a template.

DNA profiling

A procedure that analyzes an individual's unique collection of genetic markers using PCR and gel electrophoresis. DNA profiling can be used to determine whether two samples of genetic material were derived from the same individual.

DNA technology

Methods used to study or manipulate genetic material.

domain

A taxonomic category above the kingdom level. The three domains of life are Archaea, Bacteria, and Eukarya.

dominant allele

In a heterozygote, the allele that determines the phenotype with respect to a particular gene.

dorsal, hollow nerve cord

One of the four hallmarks of chordates; the chordate brain and spinal cord.

double circulation system

A circulation scheme with separate pulmonary and systemic circuits.

double fertilization

In flowering plants, the formation of both a zygote and a cell with a triploid nucleus, which develops into the endosperm.

double helix

The form assumed by DNA in living cells, referring to its two adjacent polynucleotide strands wound into a spiral shape.

Down syndrome

A human genetic disorder resulting from a condition called trisomy 21, the presence of an extra chromosome 21; characterized by heart and respiratory defects and varying degrees of mental retardation.

duodenum (*dū-ō-dē'-num*)

The first portion of the vertebrate small intestine after the stomach, where chyme from the stomach is mixed with bile and digestive enzymes.

E

eardrum

A sheet of connective tissue separating the outer ear from the middle ear. The eardrum vibrates when stimulated by sound waves and passes the vibrations to the middle ear.

earthworm

A type of annelid, or segmented worm, that extracts nutrients from soil.

echinoderm (*ih-kī'-nuh-derm*)

Member of a group of slow-moving or stationary marine animals characterized by a rough or spiny skin, a water vascular system, typically an endoskeleton, and radial symmetry in adults. Echinoderms include sea stars, sea urchins, and sand dollars.

ecological footprint

An estimate of the amount of land required to provide the raw materials an individual or a population consumes, including food, fuel, water, housing, and waste disposal.

ecological niche

The sum of a species' use of the biotic and abiotic resources in its environment.

ecological succession

The process of biological community change resulting from disturbance; transition in the species composition of a biological community, often following a flood, fire, or volcanic eruption. *See also* primary succession; secondary succession.

ecology

The scientific study of the interactions between organisms and their environments.

ecosystem (*ē'-kō-sis-tem*)

All the organisms in a given area, along with the nonliving (abiotic) factors with which they interact; a biological community and its physical environment.

ecosystem ecology

The study of energy flow and the cycling of chemicals among the various biotic and abiotic factors in an ecosystem.

ecosystem services

Functions performed by an ecosystem that directly or indirectly benefit people.

ectotherm (*ek'-tō-therm*)

An animal that warms itself mainly by absorbing heat from its surroundings.

effector cell

A short-lived lymphocyte that has an immediate effect against a specific pathogen; a cell capable of carrying out some action in response to a command from the nervous system.

egg

A female gamete.

ejaculation (*ih-jak'-yū-lā'-shun*)

The expulsion of sperm-containing fluid (semen) from the penis.

electrocardiogram (ECG or EKG)

A record of the electrical impulses that travel through heart muscle during the cardiac cycle.

electromagnetic receptor

A sensory receptor that detects energy of different wavelengths, such as magnetism and light.

electromagnetic spectrum

The full range of radiation, from the very short wavelengths of gamma rays to the very long wavelengths of radio signals.

electron

A subatomic particle with a single unit of negative electrical charge.

One or more electrons move around the nucleus of an atom.

electron microscope (EM)

An instrument that focuses an electron beam through or onto the surface of a specimen. An electron microscope achieves a thousandfold greater resolving power than a light microscope; the most powerful EM can distinguish objects as small as 0.2 nm (2×10^{-10} m).

electron transport

A redox (oxidation-reduction) reaction in which one or more electrons are transferred to carrier molecules. A series of such reactions, called an electron transport chain, can release the energy stored in high-energy molecules such as glucose. *See also* electron transport chain.

electron transport chain

A series of electron carrier molecules that shuttle electrons during the redox reactions that release energy used to make ATP; located in the inner membrane of mitochondria, the thylakoid membrane of chloroplasts, and the plasma membrane of prokaryotes.

element

A substance that cannot be broken down into other substances by chemical means. Scientists recognize 92 chemical elements occurring in nature.

elimination

The passing of undigested material out of the digestive compartment; the fourth stage of food processing, following absorption.

embryo (*em'-brē-ō*)

A developing stage of a multicellular organism. In humans, the stage in the development of offspring from the first division of the zygote until body structures begin to appear, about the 9th week of pregnancy.

embryo sac

The female gametophyte contained in the ovule of a flowering plant.

embryonic stem cell (ES cell)

Any of the cells in the early animal embryo that differentiate during development to give rise to all the kinds of specialized cells in the body.

emerging virus

A virus that has appeared suddenly or has recently come to the attention of medical scientists.

endangered species

As defined in the U.S. Endangered Species Act, a species that is in danger of extinction throughout all or a significant portion of its range.

endemic species

A species whose distribution is limited to a specific geographic area.

endocrine gland (en'-dō-krin)

A gland that synthesizes hormone molecules and secretes them directly into the bloodstream.

endocrine system

The body's main system for internal chemical regulation, consisting of all hormone-secreting cells; cooperates with the nervous system in regulating body functions and maintaining homeostasis.

endocytosis (en'-dō-sī-tō'-sis)

The movement of materials from the external environment into the cytoplasm of a cell via vesicles or vacuoles.

endodermis

The innermost layer (a one-cell-thick cylinder) of the cortex of a plant root. The endodermis forms a selective barrier, determining which substances pass from the cortex into the vascular tissue.

endomembrane system

A network of organelles that partitions the cytoplasm of eukaryotic cells into functional compartments. Some of the organelles are structurally connected to each other, whereas others are structurally separate but functionally connected by the traffic of vesicles among them.

endometrium (en'-dō-mē'-trē-um)

The inner lining of the uterus in mammals, richly supplied with blood vessels that provide the maternal part of the placenta and nourish the developing embryo.

endoplasmic reticulum (ER) (reh-tik'-yuh-lum)

An extensive membranous network in a eukaryotic cell, continuous with the outer nuclear membrane and composed of ribosome-studded (rough) and ribosome-free (smooth)

regions. *See also* rough ER; smooth ER.

endorphin (en-dōr'-fin)

A pain-inhibiting hormone produced by the anterior pituitary; also serves as a neurotransmitter.

endoskeleton

A hard interior skeleton located within the soft tissues of an animal; found in all vertebrates and a few invertebrates (such as echinoderms).

endosperm

In flowering plants, a nutrient-rich mass formed by the union of a sperm cell with the diploid central cell of the embryo sac during double fertilization; provides nourishment to the developing embryo in the seed.

endospore

A thick-coated, protective cell produced within a prokaryotic cell exposed to harsh conditions.

endosymbiosis (en'-dō-sim-bē-ō'-sis)

Symbiotic relationship in which one species resides within another species. The mitochondria and chloroplasts of eukaryotic cells probably evolved from symbiotic associations between small prokaryotic cells living inside larger ones.

endotherm

An animal that derives most of its body heat from its own metabolism.

endotoxin

A poisonous component of the outer membrane of certain bacteria.

energy

The capacity to cause change, or to move matter in a direction it would not move if left alone.

energy flow

The passage of energy through the components of an ecosystem.

enhancer

A eukaryotic DNA sequence that helps stimulate the transcription of a gene at some distance from it. An enhancer functions by means of a transcription factor called an activator, which binds to it and then to the rest of the transcription apparatus. *See also* silencer.

entropy (en'-truh-pē)

A measure of disorder, or randomness. One form of disorder is heat, which is random molecular motion.

enzyme (en'-zīm)

A protein that serves as a biological catalyst, changing the rate of a chemical reaction without itself being changed in the process.

enzyme inhibitor

A chemical that interferes with an enzyme's activity by changing the enzyme's shape, either by plugging up the active site or by binding to another site on the enzyme.

epinephrine (ep'-uh-nef'-rin)

An amine hormone (also called adrenaline) that is secreted by the adrenal medulla and that prepares body organs for "fight or flight"; also serves as a neurotransmitter.

epithelial tissue (ep'-uh-thē'-lē-ul)

A sheet of tightly packed cells lining organs and cavities; also called epithelium.

epithelium

(plural, **epithelia**) *See* epithelial tissue.

equilibrial life history (ē-kwi-lib'-rē-ul)

The pattern of reaching sexual maturity slowly and producing few offspring but caring for the young; often seen in long-lived, large-bodied species.

erythrocyte (ih-rith'-ruh-sīt)

See red blood cell.

esophagus (ih-sof'-uh-gus)

The channel through which food passes in a digestive tube, connecting the pharynx to the stomach.

essential amino acid

Any amino acid that an animal cannot synthesize itself and must obtain from food. Eight amino acids are essential for the human adult.

essential element

In plants, a chemical element required for the plant to complete its life cycle (to grow from a seed and produce another generation of seeds).

essential fatty acid

An unsaturated fatty acid that animals need but cannot make.

essential nutrient

A substance that an organism must absorb in preassembled form because it cannot synthesize the nutrient from any other material. Humans require vitamins, minerals, essential amino acids, and essential fatty acids.

estrogen (es'-trō-jen)

One of several chemically similar sex hormones secreted by the gonads. Estrogen maintains the female reproductive system and promotes the development of female body features.

estuary (es'-chuh-wār-ē)

The area where a freshwater stream or river merges with seawater.

ethylene

A gas that functions as a hormone in plants, triggering aging responses such as fruit ripening and leaf drop.

eudicot (yū-dī'-kot)

Member of a group consisting of the vast majority of flowering plants that have two cotyledons (embryonic seed leaves).

Eukarya (yū-kār'-yuh)

The domain of eukaryotes, organisms made up of eukaryotic cells; includes all of the protists, plants, fungi, and animals.

eukaryote (yū-kār'-ē-ōt)

An organism characterized by eukaryotic cells. *See also* eukaryotic cell.

eukaryotic cell (yū-kār-ē-ot'-ik)

A type of cell that has a membrane-enclosed nucleus and other membrane-enclosed organelles. All organisms except bacteria and archaea are composed of eukaryotic cells.

Eustachian tube (yū-stā'-shun)

An air passage between the middle ear and throat that equalizes air pressure on either side of the eardrum.

eutherian (yū-thēr'-ē-un)

See placental mammal.

evaporative cooling

A property of water whereby a body becomes cooler as water evaporates from it.

evo-devo

Evolutionary developmental biology, which studies the evolution of developmental processes in multicellular organisms.

evolution

Descent with modification; genetic change in a population or species over generations; the heritable changes that have produced Earth's diversity of organisms.

evolutionary adaptation

A population's increase in the frequency of traits suited to the environment.

evolutionary tree

A branching diagram that reflects a hypothesis about evolutionary relationships between groups of organisms.

excretion (ek-skrē'-shun)

The disposal of nitrogen-containing metabolic wastes.

exocytosis (ek'-sō-sī-tō'-sis)

The movement of materials out of the cytoplasm of a cell via membranous vesicles or vacuoles.

exon (ek'-son)

In eukaryotes, a coding portion of a gene. *See also* intron.

exoskeleton

A hard, external skeleton that protects an animal and provides points of attachment for muscles.

exotoxin

A poisonous protein secreted by certain bacteria.

exponential population growth

A model that describes the expansion of a population in an ideal, unlimited environment.

extracellular matrix

The meshwork that surrounds animal cells, consisting of a web of protein and polysaccharide fibers embedded in a liquid, jelly, or solid.

F

F$_1$ generation

The offspring of two parental (P generation) individuals. F$_1$ stands for first filial.

F$_2$ generation

The offspring of the F$_1$ generation. F$_2$ stands for second filial.

facilitated diffusion

The passage of a substance across a biological membrane down its concentration gradient, aided by specific transport proteins.

family

In classification, the taxonomic category above genus.

farsightedness

An inability to focus on close objects; occurs when the eyeball is shorter

than normal and the focal point of the lens is behind the retina; also called hyperopia.

fat

A large lipid molecule made from an alcohol called glycerol and three fatty acids; a triglyceride. Most fats function as energy-storage molecules.

feces

The wastes of the digestive tube.

fermentation

The anaerobic harvest of food by some cells.

fern

Any of a group of seedless vascular plants.

fertilization

The union of a haploid sperm cell with a haploid egg cell, producing a zygote.

fertilizer

A compound applied to the soil to promote plant growth.

fetus (fē'-tus)

A developing human from the 9th week of pregnancy until birth. The fetus has all the major structures of an adult.

fever

An abnormally high internal body temperature, usually the result of an infection.

fibrin (fī'-brin)

The activated form of the blood-clotting protein fibrinogen, which aggregates into threads that form the fabric of a blood clot.

fibrinogen (fī-brin'-uh-jen)

The plasma protein that is activated to form a clot when a blood vessel is injured.

fibrous connective tissue

A dense tissue with large numbers of collagen fibers organized into parallel bundles. This is the dominant tissue in tendons and ligaments.

filtrate

Fluid extracted by the excretory system from the blood or body cavity. The excretory system produces urine from the filtrate after extracting valuable solutes from it and concentrating it.

filtration

In the vertebrate kidney, the extraction of water and small solutes, including metabolic wastes, from the blood by the nephrons.

fission

A means of asexual reproduction whereby a parent separates into two or more genetically identical individuals of about equal size.

flagellate (flaj'-uh-lit)

A protozoan (animal-like protist) that moves by means of one or more flagella.

flagellum (fluh-jel'-um)

(plural, **flagella**) A long appendage that propels protists through the water and moves fluids across the surface of many tissue cells in animals. A cell may have one or more flagella.

flatworm

A bilateral animal with a thin, flat body form, a gastrovascular cavity with a single opening, and no body cavity. Flatworms include planarians, flukes, and tapeworms.

flower

In an angiosperm, a short stem with four sets of modified leaves, bearing structures that function in sexual reproduction.

fluid mosaic

A description of membrane structure, depicting a cellular membrane as a mosaic of diverse protein molecules embedded in a fluid bilayer of phospholipid molecules.

follicle (fol'-uh-kul)

A cluster of cells surrounding, protecting, and nourishing a developing egg cell in the ovary. The follicle also secretes estrogen.

food chain

The sequence of food transfers between the trophic levels of a community, beginning with the producers.

food web

A network of interconnecting food chains.

foram

A marine protozoan (animal-like protist) that secretes a shell and extends pseudopodia through pores in its shell.

forensics

The scientific analysis of evidence for crime scene investigations and other legal proceedings.

fossil

A preserved imprint or remains of an organism that lived in the past.

fossil fuel

An energy deposit formed from the fossilized remains of long-dead plants and animals.

fossil record

The ordered sequence of fossils as they appear in the rock layers, marking the passing of geologic time.

founder effect

The genetic drift resulting from the establishment of a small, new population whose gene pool differs from that of the parent population.

fruit

A ripened, thickened ovary of a flower, which protects dormant seeds and aids in their dispersal.

functional group

A group of atoms that form the chemically reactive part of an organic molecule. A particular functional group usually behaves similarly in different chemical reactions.

fungus

(plural, **fungi**) A chemo-heterotrophic eukaryote that digests its food externally and absorbs the resulting small nutrient molecules. Most fungi consist of a netlike mass of filaments called hyphae. Molds, mushrooms, and yeasts are examples of fungi.

G

gallbladder

An organ that stores bile and releases it as needed into the small intestine.

gametangium (gam'-uh-tan'-jē-um)

(plural, **gametangia**) A reproductive organ that houses and protects the gametes of a plant.

gamete (gam'-ēt)

A sex cell; a haploid egg or sperm. The union of two gametes of opposite sex (fertilization) produces a zygote.

gametogenesis

The creation of gametes within the gonads.

gametophyte (guh-mē'-tō-fīt)

The multicellular haploid form in the life cycle of organisms undergoing alternation of generations; results from a union of spores and mitotically produces haploid gametes that unite and grow into the sporophyte generation.

gastric juice
The collection of fluids secreted by the epithelium lining the stomach.

gastropod
Member of the largest group of molluscs, including snails and slugs.

gastrovascular cavity
A digestive compartment with a single opening that serves as both the entrance for food and the exit for undigested wastes; may also function in circulation, body support, and gas exchange. Jellies and hydras are examples of animals with a gastrovascular cavity.

gastrula (*gas'-trū-luh*)
The embryonic stage resulting from gastrulation in animal development. Most animals have a gastrula made up of three layers of cells: ectoderm, endoderm, and mesoderm.

gastrulation (*gas'-trū-lā'-shun*)
The phase of embryonic development that transforms the blastula (blastocyst in mammals) into a gastrula. Gastrulation adds more cells to the embryo and sorts the cells into distinct cell layers.

gel electrophoresis (*jel' e-lek'-trō-fōr-ē'-sis*)
A technique for sorting macromolecules. A mixture of molecules is placed on a gel between a positively charged electrode and a negatively charged one; negative charges on the molecules are attracted to the positive electrode, and the molecules migrate toward that electrode. The molecules separate in the gel according to their rates of migration.

gene
A unit of inheritance in DNA (or RNA, in some viruses) consisting of a specific nucleotide sequence that programs the amino acid sequence of a polypeptide. Most of the genes of a eukaryote are located in its chromosomal DNA; a few are carried by the DNA of mitochondria and chloroplasts.

gene cloning
The production of multiple copies of a gene.

gene expression
The process whereby genetic information flows from genes to proteins; the flow of genetic information from the genotype to the phenotype: DNA → RNA → protein.

gene flow
The gain or loss of alleles from a population by the movement of individuals or gametes into or out of the population.

gene pool
All the genes in a population at any one time.

gene regulation
The turning on and off of specific genes within a living organism.

genetic code
The set of rules giving the correspondence between nucleotide triplets (codons) in mRNA and amino acids in protein.

genetic drift
A change in the gene pool of a population due to chance.

genetic engineering
The direct manipulation of genes for practical purposes.

genetic recombination
The production of offspring with gene combinations that differ from that found in either parent.

genetically modified (GM) organism
An organism that has acquired one or more genes by artificial means. If the gene is from another organism, typically of another species, the recombinant organism is also known as a transgenic organism.

genetics
The scientific study of heredity (inheritance).

genital herpes
A common sexually transmitted disease caused by a virus. The primary symptom is sores on the genitalia. Although outbreaks can be controlled with medication, genital herpes is incurable.

genomic library (*juh-nō'-mik*)
The entire collection of DNA segments from an organism's genome. Each segment is usually carried by a plasmid or phage.

genomics
The study of whole sets of genes and their interactions.

genotype (*jē'-nō-tīp*)
The genetic makeup of an organism.

genus (*jē'-nus*)
(plural, **genera**) In classification, the taxonomic category above species; the first part of a species' binomial; for example, *Homo*.

geologic time scale
A time scale established by geologists that reflects a consistent sequence of geologic periods, grouped into four divisions: Precambrian, Paleozoic, Mesozoic, and Cenozoic.

germinate
To initiate growth, as in a plant seed.

gestation (*jes-tā'-shun*)
Pregnancy; the state of carrying developing young within the female reproductive tract.

gibberellin (*jib'-uh-rel'-in*)
Any of a family of plant hormones that trigger the germination of seeds and interact with auxins in regulating growth and fruit development.

gill
An extension of the body surface of an aquatic animal, specialized for gas exchange and/or suspension feeding.

glucagon (*glū'-kuh-gon*)
A protein hormone, secreted by islet cells in the pancreas, that raises the level of glucose in the blood.

glucocorticoid (*glū'-kuh-kor'-tih-koyd*)
A corticosteroid hormone, secreted by the adrenal cortex, that increases the blood glucose level and helps maintain the body's response to long-term stress.

glycogen (*glī'-kō-jen*)
A complex, extensively branched polysaccharide made up of many glucose monomers; serves as an energy-storage molecule in liver and muscle cells.

glycolysis (*glī-kol'-uh-sis*)
The multistep chemical breakdown of a molecule of glucose into two molecules of pyruvic acid; the first stage of cellular respiration in all organisms; occurs in the cytoplasmic fluid.

Golgi apparatus (*gol'-jē*)
An organelle in eukaryotic cells consisting of stacks of membranous sacs that modify, store, and ship products of the endoplasmic reticulum.

gonad
An animal sex organ that produces gametes; an ovary or a testis.

granum (*gran'-um*)
(plural, **grana**) A stack of hollow disks formed of thylakoid membrane in a chloroplast. Grana are the sites where light energy is trapped by chlorophyll and converted to chemical energy during the light reactions of photosynthesis.

gravitropism (*grav'-uh-trō'-pizm*)
A plant's directional growth in response to gravity.

green alga
One of a group of photosynthetic protists that includes unicellular, colonial, and multicellular species. Green algae are the photosynthetic protists most closely related to plants.

greenhouse effect
The warming of the atmosphere caused by CO_2, CH_4, and other gases that absorb heat radiation and slow its escape from Earth's surface.

greenhouse gas
Any of the gases in the atmosphere that absorb heat radiation, including CO_2, methane, water vapor, and synthetic chlorofluorocarbons.

ground tissue system
A tissue that makes up the bulk of a plant, filling the space between the epidermis and the vascular tissue system. The ground tissue system fulfills a variety of functions, including storage, photosynthesis, and support.

growth factor
A protein secreted by certain body cells that stimulates other cells to divide.

guanine (G) (*gwa'-nēn*)
A double-ring nitrogenous base found in DNA and RNA.

guard cell
A specialized epidermal cell in plants that regulates the size of a stoma, allowing gas exchange between the surrounding air and the photosynthetic cells in the leaf.

gymnosperm (*jim'-nō-sperm*)
A naked-seed plant. Its seed is said to be naked because it is not enclosed in an ovary.

H

habitat
A place where an organism lives; a specific environment in which an organism lives.

haploid
Containing a single set of chromosomes; referring to an *n* cell.

Hardy-Weinberg equilibrium
The condition describing a nonevolving population (one that is in genetic equilibrium).

heart
(1) The chambered muscular organ in vertebrates that pumps blood received from the veins into the arteries, thereby maintaining the flow of blood through the entire circulatory system. (2) A similarly functioning structure in invertebrates.

heart attack
Damage or death of heart muscle tissue and the resulting failure of the heart to deliver enough blood to the body.

heart murmur
A hissing sound emitted by an abnormal heart, usually caused by a defective heart valve.

heart rate
The number of heartbeats per minute.

heat
The amount of kinetic energy contained in the movement of the atoms and molecules in a body of matter. Heat is energy in its most random form.

helper T cell
A type of lymphocyte that helps activate other T cells and helps stimulate B cells to produce antibodies.

hemoglobin (*hē'-muh-glō-bin*)
An iron-containing protein in red blood cells that reversibly binds O_2 and transports it to body tissues.

hemophilia (*hē'-muh-fil'-ē-uh*)
A human genetic disease caused by a sex-linked recessive allele and characterized by excessive bleeding following injury.

herbivore
An animal that eats mainly plants, algae, or phytoplankton. *See also* carnivore; omnivore.

herbivory
The consumption of plant parts or algae by an animal.

heredity
The transmission of traits from one generation to the next.

hermaphrodite (*her-maf'-rō-dīt*)
An individual that has both female and male reproductive systems, producing both sperm and eggs.

heterotroph (*het'-er-ō-trōf*)
An organism that cannot make its own organic food molecules from inorganic ingredients and must obtain them by consuming other organisms or their organic products; a consumer or a decomposer in a food chain.

heterozygous (*het'-er-ō-zī'-gus*)
Having two different alleles for a given gene.

hinge joint
A joint that allows movement in only one plane. In humans, examples include the elbow and knee.

histamine (*his'-tuh-mēn*)
A chemical alarm signal released by injured cells that causes blood vessels to dilate during an inflammatory response.

histone (*his'-tōn*)
A small protein molecule associated with DNA and important in DNA packing in the eukaryotic chromosome.

HIV
Human immunodeficiency virus; the retrovirus that attacks the human immune system and causes AIDS.

homeostasis (*hō'-mē-ō-stā'-sis*)
The steady state of body functioning; the tendency to maintain relatively constant conditions in the internal environment even when the external environment changes.

homeotic gene (*hō'-mē-ot'-ik*)
A master control gene that determines the identity of a body structure of a developing organism, presumably by controlling the developmental fate of groups of cells. (In plants, such genes are called organ identity genes).

hominin (*hah'-mi-nin*)
Any anthropoid on the human branch of the evolutionary tree, more closely related to humans than to chimpanzees.

homologous chromosomes (*hō-mol'-uh-gus*)
The two chromosomes that make up a matched pair in a diploid cell. Homologous chromosomes are of the same length, centromere position, and staining pattern and possess genes for the same characteristics at corresponding loci. One homologous chromosome is inherited from the organism's father, the other from the mother.

homology (*hō-mol'-uh-jē*)
Anatomical similarity due to common ancestry.

homozygous (*hō'-mō-zī'-gus*)
Having two identical alleles for a given gene.

hormone
In multicellular organisms, a regulatory chemical that travels in body fluids from its production site to other sites, where target cells respond to the regulatory signal.

host
An organism that is exploited by a parasite or pathogen.

human gene therapy
A recombinant DNA procedure intended to treat disease by altering an afflicted person's genes.

Human Genome Project
An international collaborative effort that sequenced the DNA of the entire human genome.

human growth hormone (HGH)
A protein hormone, secreted by the anterior pituitary, that promotes development and growth and stimulates metabolism.

humoral immune response
The type of adaptive immune response that involves secretion of antibodies into the blood and lymph by effector B cells. These antibodies fight bacteria and viruses in body fluids. *See also* cell-mediated immune response.

Huntington's disease
A human genetic disease caused by a dominant allele; characterized by uncontrollable body movements and degeneration of the nervous system; usually fatal 10 to 20 years after the onset of symptoms.

hybrid
The offspring of parents of two different species or of two different varieties of one species; the offspring of two parents that differ in one or more inherited traits; an individual that is heterozygous for one or more pairs of genes.

hydrocarbon
A chemical compound composed only of the elements carbon and hydrogen.

hydrogen bond
A type of weak chemical bond formed when a partially positive hydrogen atom from one polar molecule is attracted to the partially negative atom in another molecule (or in another part of the same molecule).

hydrogenation
The process of converting unsaturated fats to saturated fats by adding hydrogen.

hydrolysis (*hī-drol'-uh-sis*)
A chemical process in which macromolecules are broken down by the chemical addition of water molecules to the bonds linking their monomers; an essential part of digestion. A hydrolysis reaction is the opposite of a dehydration reaction.

hydrophilic (*hī'-drō-fil'-ik*)
"Water-loving"; pertaining to polar, or charged, molecules (or parts of molecules), which are soluble in water.

hydrophobic (*hī'-drō-fō'-bik*)
"Water-fearing"; pertaining to nonpolar molecules (or parts of molecules), which do not dissolve in water.

hymen
A thin membrane that partly covers the vaginal opening in the human female and is ruptured by sexual intercourse or other vigorous activity.

hypercholesterolemia (*hī'-per-kō-les'-tur-ah-lēm'-ē-uh*)
An inherited human disease characterized by an excessively high level of cholesterol in the blood.

hypertension
Abnormally high blood pressure consisting of a persistent systolic blood pressure higher than 140 and/or diastolic blood pressure higher than 90. This condition can lead to a variety of serious cardiovascular disorders.

hypertonic
In comparing two solutions, referring to the one with the greater concentration of solutes.

hypha (*hī'-fuh*)
(plural, **hyphae**) One of many filaments making up the body of a fungus.

hypothalamus (*hī'-pō-thal'-uh-mus*)
The main control center of the endocrine system, located in the vertebrate forebrain. The hypothalamus functions in maintaining homeostasis, especially in coordinating the endocrine and nervous systems. It synthesizes hormones secreted by the posterior pituitary and regulates the secretion of hormones by the anterior pituitary.

hypothesis (*hī-poth'-uh-sis*)
(plural, **hypotheses**) A tentative explanation that a scientist proposes for a specific phenomenon that has been observed.

hypothesis-driven science
The process of scientific inquiry that uses the steps of the scientific method to answer questions about nature. *See also* discovery science; scientific method.

hypotonic
In comparing two solutions, referring to the one with the lower concentration of solutes.

I

immune system
The body's system of defenses against infectious disease.

immunodeficiency disease
An immunological disorder in which the body lacks one or more components of the immune system, making a person susceptible to infectious agents that would not ordinarily cause a problem.

impotence
The inability to maintain an erection; also called erectile dysfunction.

in vitro fertilization (IVF) (*vē'-tro*)
Uniting sperm and egg in a laboratory container, followed by the placement of a resulting early embryo into the mother's uterus.

inbreeding
The mating of close relatives.

incomplete dominance
A type of inheritance in which the phenotype of a heterozygote (*Aa*) is intermediate between the phenotypes of the two types of homozygotes (*AA* and *aa*).

indeterminate growth
Growth that continues throughout life, as in most plants. *See also* determinate growth.

induced fit
The interaction between a substrate molecule and the active site of an enzyme, which changes shape slightly to embrace the substrate and catalyze the reaction.

induction
During embryonic development, the influence of one group of cells on an adjacent group of cells.

infertility
The inability to conceive after one year of regular, unprotected sexual intercourse.

inflammatory response
An example of internal innate defense involving the release of histamine and other chemical alarm signals, which trigger increased blood flow, a local increase in white blood cells, and fluid leakage from the blood. The results include redness, heat, and swelling in the affected tissues.

ingestion
The act of eating; the first stage of food processing.

innate defense
An immune system defense that is always present in its final form and ready to act.

inner ear
One of three main regions of the human ear; includes the cochlea, which contains the organ of Corti, the hearing organ.

insect
An arthropod that usually has three body segments (head, thorax, and abdomen), three pairs of legs, and one or two pairs of wings.

insulin
A protein hormone, secreted by islet cells in the pancreas, that lowers the level of glucose in the blood.

integration
The interpretation of sensory signals and the formulation of responses within the central nervous system.

interferon (*in'-ter-fēr'-on*)
A defensive protein that is produced by virus-infected cells and that helps other cells resist viruses as part of internal innate defense.

interneuron (*in'-ter-nūr'-on*)
A nerve cell, entirely within the central nervous system, that integrates sensory signals and may relay command signals to motor neurons.

internode
The portion of a plant stem between two nodes.

interphase
The phase in the eukaryotic cell cycle when the cell is not actually dividing. During interphase, cellular metabolic activity is high, chromosomes and organelles are duplicated, and cell size may increase. Interphase accounts for 90% of the cell cycle. *See also* mitosis.

interspecific competition
Competition between populations of two or more species that require similar limited resources.

interspecific interaction
Any interaction between members of different species.

interstitial fluid (*in'-ter-stish'-ul*)
An aqueous solution that surrounds body cells and through which materials pass back and forth between the blood and the body tissues.

intertidal zone (*in'-ter-tīd'-ul*)
A shallow zone where the waters of an estuary or ocean meet land.

intraspecific competition
Competition between individuals of the same species for the same limited resources.

intron (*in'-tron*)
In eukaryotes, a nonexpressed (noncoding) portion of a gene that is excised from the RNA transcript. *See also* exon.

invasive species
A non-native species that has spread far beyond the original point of introduction and causes environmental or economic damage by colonizing and dominating suitable habitats.

invertebrate
An animal that does not have a backbone.

ion (*ī'-on*)
An atom or molecule that has gained or lost one or more electrons, thus acquiring an electrical charge.

ionic bond (*ī-on'-ik*)
An attraction between two ions with opposite electrical charges. The electrical attraction of the opposite charges holds the ions together.

iris
The colored part of the vertebrate eye, formed by the anterior portion of the pigmented layer called the choroid.

isomer (*ī'-sō-mer*)
One of two or more molecules with the same molecular formula but different structures and thus different properties.

isotonic (*ī-sō-ton'-ik*)
Having the same solute concentration as another solution.

isotope (*ī'-sō-tōp*)
A variant form of an atom. Isotopes of an element have the same number of protons and electrons but different numbers of neutrons.

K

karyotype (*kār'-ē-ō-tīp*)
A display of micrographs of the metaphase chromosomes of a cell, arranged by size and centromere position.

keystone species
A species whose impact on its community is much larger than its biomass or abundance indicates.

kilocalorie (kcal)
A quantity of heat equal to 1,000 calories. Used to measure the energy content of food, it is usually called a "Calorie."

kinetic energy (*kuh-net'-ik*)
Energy of motion. Moving matter performs work by transferring its motion to other matter, such as leg muscles pushing bicycle pedals.

kingdom
In classification, the broad taxonomic category above phylum.

L

labia majora (*lā'-bē-uh muh-jor'-uh*)
A pair of outer thickened folds of skin that protect the female genital region.

labia minora (*lā'-bē-uh mi-nor'-uh*)
A pair of inner folds of skin bordering and protecting the female genital region.

labor
A series of strong, rhythmic uterine contractions that expels a baby out of the uterus and vagina during childbirth.

lancelet
One of a group of bladelike invertebrate chordates.

landscape
A regional assemblage of interacting ecosystems.

landscape ecology
The application of ecological principles to the study of land-use patterns; the scientific study of the biodiversity of interacting ecosystems.

large intestine
The tubular portion of the vertebrate alimentary canal between the small intestine and the anus. *See also* colon.

larynx (*lār'-inks*)
The voice box, containing the vocal cords.

lateral line system
A row of sensory organs along each side of a fish's body. Sensitive to changes in water pressure, it enables a fish to detect minor vibrations in the water.

law of independent assortment
A general rule of inheritance, first proposed by Gregor Mendel, that states that when gametes form during meiosis, each pair of alleles for a particular character segregate (separate) independently of each other pair.

law of segregation
A general rule of inheritance, first proposed by Gregor Mendel, that states that the two alleles in a pair segregate (separate) into different gametes during meiosis.

leaf
The main site of photosynthesis in a plant; consists of a flattened blade and a stalk (petiole) that joins the leaf to the stem.

leech
A type of annelid, or segmented worm, that typically lives in fresh water.

lens
The disklike structure in an eye that focuses light rays onto the retina.

leukemia (*lū-kē'-mē-ah*)
Cancer of the white blood cells (leukocytes), characterized by excessive production of these cells, resulting in an abnormally high number in the blood.

leukocyte (*lū'-kō-sīt*)
See white blood cell.

lichen (*lī'-ken*)
A mutually beneficial symbiotic association between a fungus and an alga or between a fungus and a cyanobacterium.

life
The set of common characteristics that distinguish living organisms from non-living matter, including such properties and processes as order, regulation, growth and development, energy utilization, response to the environment, reproduction, and the capacity to evolve over time.

life cycle
The entire sequence of stages in the life of an organism, from the adults of one generation to the adults of the next.

life history
The traits that affect an organism's schedule of reproduction and survival.

life table
A listing of survivals and deaths in a population in a particular time period and predictions of how long, on average, an individual of a given age will live.

ligament
A type of fibrous connective tissue that joins bones together at joints.

light microscope (LM)
An optical instrument with lenses that refract (bend) visible light to magnify images and project them into a viewer's eye or onto photographic film.

light reactions
The first of two stages in photosynthesis, the steps in which solar energy is absorbed and converted to chemical energy in the form of ATP and NADPH. The light reactions power the sugar-producing Calvin cycle but produce no sugar themselves.

lignin (*lig'-nin*)
A chemical that hardens the cell walls of plants. Lignin makes up most of what we call wood.

limiting factor
An environmental factor that restricts the number of individuals that can occupy a particular habitat, thus holding population growth in check.

linkage map
A map of a chromosome showing the relative positions of genes.

linked genes
Genes located close enough together on a chromosome that they are usually inherited together.

lipid
An organic compound consisting mainly of carbon and hydrogen atoms linked by nonpolar convalent bonds and therefore mostly hydrophobic and insoluble in water. Lipids include fats, waxes, phospholipids, and steroids.

liver
The largest organ in the vertebrate body. The liver performs diverse functions, such as producing bile, preparing nitrogenous wastes for disposal, and detoxifying poisonous chemicals in the blood.

lobe-finned fish
A bony fish with strong, muscular fins supported by bones.

locus
(plural, **loci**) The particular site where a gene is found on a chromosome. Homologous chromosomes have corresponding gene loci.

logistic population growth
A model that describes population growth that decreases as population size approaches carrying capacity.

loose connective tissue
The most widespread connective tissue in the vertebrate body. It binds epithelia to underlying tissues and functions as packing material, holding organs in place.

lung
An internal sac, lined with moist epithelium, where gases are exchanged between inhaled air and the blood.

lymph
A fluid similar to interstitial fluid that circulates in the lymphatic system.

lymph node
A small organ that is located along a lymph vessel and that filters lymph.

lymphatic system (*lim-fat'-ik*)
The organ system through which lymph circulates; includes lymph vessels, lymph nodes, and several other organs. The lymphatic system helps remove toxins and pathogens from the blood and interstitial fluid and returns fluid and solutes from the interstitial fluid to the circulatory system.

lymphocyte (*lim'-fuh-sīt*)
A type of white blood cell that carries out adaptive defenses—recognizing and responding to specific invading pathogens. There are two types of lymphocytes: B cells and T cells. *See also* B cell; T cell.

lysogenic cycle (*lī-sō-jen'-ik*)
A bacteriophage reproductive cycle in which the viral genome is incorporated into the bacterial host chromosome as a prophage. New phages are not produced, and the host cell is not killed or lysed unless the viral genome leaves the host chromosome.

lysosome (*lī'-sō-sōm*)
A digestive organelle in eukaryotic cells; contains enzymes that digest the cell's food and wastes.

lytic cycle (*lit'-ik*)
A viral reproductive cycle resulting in the release of new viruses by lysis (breaking open) of the host cell.

M

macroevolution
Evolutionary change above the species level, including the origin of evolutionary novelty and new taxonomic groups and the impact of mass extinctions on the diversity of life and its subsequent recovery.

macromolecule
A giant molecule formed by joining smaller molecules. Examples of macromolecules include proteins, polysaccharides, and nucleic acids.

macronutrient
A chemical element that an organism must obtain in relatively large amounts. *See also* micronutrient.

magnification
An increase in the apparent size of an object.

major depression
Depressive mental illness characterized by persistent sadness and loss of interest in pleasurable activities.

malignant tumor
An abnormal tissue mass that spreads into neighboring tissue and to other parts of the body; a cancerous tumor.

malnutrition
The absence of one or more essential nutrients from the diet.

mammal
Member of a class of endothermic amniotes that possesses mammary glands and hair.

mantle
In molluscs, the outgrowth of the body surface that drapes over the animal. The mantle produces the shell and forms the mantle cavity.

marsupial (mar-sū'-pē-ul)
A pouched mammal, such as a kangaroo, opossum, or koala. Marsupials give birth to embryonic offspring that complete development while housed in a pouch and attached to nipples on the mother's abdomen.

mass
A measure of the amount of material in an object.

mass number
The sum of the number of protons and neutrons in an atom's nucleus.

matrix
The thick fluid contained within the inner membrane of the mitochondrion.

matter
Anything that occupies space and has mass.

mechanoreceptor (mek'-uh-nō-ri-sep'-ter)
A sensory receptor that detects physical changes in the environment, associated with pressure, touch, stretch, motion, and sound.

medulla oblongata (meh-duh'-luh ob'-long-got'-uh)
Part of the vertebrate hindbrain continuous with the spinal cord; passes data between the spinal cord and forebrain and controls autonomic, homeostatic functions, including breathing, heart rate, swallowing, and digestion.

medusa (med-ū'-suh)
(plural, **medusae**) One of two types of cnidarian body forms; a floating, umbrella-like body form; also called a jelly.

meiosis (mī-ō'-sis)
In a sexually reproducing organism, the process of cell division that produces haploid gametes from diploid cells within the reproductive organs.

memory cell
A long-lived lymphocyte that responds to subsequent exposures to a specific pathogen. A memory cell is formed during the primary immune response and is activated by exposure to the same antigen that triggered its formation. When activated, a memory cell forms large clones of effector cells and memory cells that mount the secondary immune response.

meninges (muh-nin'-jēz)
Layers of connective tissue that enwrap and protect the brain and spinal cord.

menstrual cycle (men'-stru-ul)
The hormonally synchronized cyclic buildup and breakdown of the endometrium in some primates, including humans.

menstruation (men'-stru-ā'-shun)
Uterine bleeding resulting from the breakdown of the endometrium during a menstrual cycle.

meristem (mār'-eh-stem)
Plant tissue consisting of undifferentiated cells that divide and generate new cells and tissues.

mesophyll (mes'-ō-fil)
The green tissue in the interior of a leaf; a leaf's ground tissue system, the main site of photosynthesis.

messenger RNA (mRNA)
The type of ribonucleic acid that encodes genetic information from DNA and conveys it to ribosomes, where the information is translated into amino acid sequences.

metabolic rate
Energy expended by the body per unit time.

metabolism (muh-tab'-uh-liz-um)
The total of all the chemical reactions in an organism.

metamorphosis (met'-uh-mōr'-fuh-sis)
The transformation of a larva into an adult.

metaphase (met'-eh-fāz)
The second stage of mitosis. During metaphase, the centromeres of all the cell's duplicated chromosomes are lined up on an imaginary plate equidistant between the poles of the mitotic spindle.

metastasis (muh-tas'-tuh-sis)
The spread of cancer cells beyond their original site.

microevolution
A change in a population's gene pool over a succession of generations; evolutionary changes in species over relatively brief periods of geologic time.

micronutrient
A chemical element that an organism needs in very small amounts. *See also* macronutrient.

microtubule
The thickest of the three main kinds of fibers making up the cytoskeleton of a eukaryotic cell; a straight, hollow tube made of globular proteins called tubulins. Microtubules form the basis of the structure and movement of cilia and flagella.

middle ear
One of three main regions of the human ear; a chamber containing three small bones (the hammer, anvil, and stirrup) that convey vibrations from the eardrum to the inner ear.

millipede
A terrestrial arthropod that has two pairs of short legs for each of its numerous body segments and that eats decaying plant matter.

mineral
In nutrition, an inorganic chemical element (other than carbon, hydrogen, oxygen, or nitrogen) that an organism requires for proper body functioning.

mitochondrion (mī'-tō-kon'-drē-on)
(plural, **mitochondria**) An organelle in eukaryotic cells where cellular respiration occurs. Enclosed by two concentric membranes, it is where most of the cell's ATP is made.

mitosis (mī'-tō-sis)
The division of a single nucleus into two genetically identical daughter nuclei. Mitosis and cytokinesis make up the mitotic (M) phase of the cell cycle.

mitotic (M) phase
The phase of the cell cycle when mitosis divides the nucleus and distributes its chromosomes to the daughter nuclei and cytokinesis divides the cytoplasm, producing two daughter cells.

mitotic spindle
A spindle-shaped structure formed of microtubules and associated proteins that is involved in the movement of chromosomes during mitosis and meiosis. (A spindle is shaped roughly like a football.)

modern synthesis
A comprehensive theory of evolution that incorporates genetics and includes most of Darwin's ideas, focusing on populations as the fundamental units of evolution.

molecular biology
The study of the molecular basis of heredity; molecular genetics.

molecule
A group of two or more atoms held together by covalent bonds.

mollusc (mol'-lusk)
A soft-bodied animal characterized by a muscular foot, mantle, mantle cavity, and radula. Molluscs include gastropods (snails and slugs), bivalves (clams, oysters, and scallops), and cephalopods (squids and octopuses).

monocot (mon'-uh-kot)
A flowering plant whose embryos have a single seed leaf, or cotyledon.

monohybrid cross
A mating of individuals differing at one genetic locus.

monomer (mon'-uh-mer)
A chemical subunit that serves as a building block of a polymer.

monosaccharide (mon'-uh-sak'-uh-rīd)
The smallest kind of sugar molecule; a single-unit sugar; also known as a

simple sugar. Monosaccharides are the building blocks of more complex sugars and polysaccharides.

monotreme (*mon'-uh-trēm*)
An egg-laying mammal, such as the duck-billed platypus.

morning-after pill (MAP)
A birth control pill taken within three days of unprotected intercourse to prevent fertilization or implantation.

moss
Any of a group of seedless nonvascular plants.

motor neuron
A nerve cell that conveys command signals from the central nervous system to effector cells, such as muscle cells or gland cells.

motor output
The conduction of signals from the central nervous system to effector cells.

motor system
A component of the peripheral nervous system of vertebrates composed of neurons that carry signals to skeletal muscles, mainly in response to external stimuli. The motor system is primarily under voluntary control.

motor unit
A motor neuron and all the muscle fibers it controls.

mouth
See oral cavity.

movement corridor
A series of small clumps or a narrow strip of quality habitat (usable by organisms) that connects otherwise isolated patches of quality habitat.

muscle tissue
Tissue consisting of long muscle cells that are capable of contracting when stimulated by nerve impulses. *See also* skeletal muscle; cardiac muscle; smooth muscle.

muscular system
All the skeletal muscles in the body. (Cardiac muscle and smooth muscle are components of other organ systems.)

mutagen (*myū'-tuh-jen*)
A chemical or physical agent that interacts with DNA and causes a mutation.

mutation
A change in the nucleotide sequence of DNA; a major source of genetic diversity.

mutualism
An interspecific interaction in which both partners benefit.

mycelium (*mī-sē'-lē-um*)
(plural, **mycelia**) The densely branched network of hyphae in a fungus.

mycorrhiza (*mī'-kō-rī'-zuh*)
(plural, **mycorrhizae**) A mutually beneficial symbiotic association of a plant root and fungus.

myelin sheath (*mī'-uh-lin*)
A chain of bead-like supporting cells that insulate the axon of a nerve cell in vertebrates. This insulation helps to speed electrical transmission along the axon.

myofibril (*mī'-ō-fī'-bril*)
A contractile unit in a muscle cell (fiber) made up of many arcomeres. Longitudinal bundles of myofibrils make up a muscle fiber.

N

NADH
An electron carrier (a molecule that carries electrons) involved in cellular respiration and photosynthesis. NADH carries electrons from glucose and other fuel molecules and deposits them at the top of an electron transport chain. NADH is generated during glycolysis and the citric acid cycle.

NADPH
An electron carrier (a molecule that carries electrons) involved in photosynthesis. Light drives electrons from chlorophyll to $NADP^+$, forming NADPH, which provides the high-energy electrons for the reduction of carbon dioxide to sugar in the Calvin cycle.

natural family planning
See rhythm method.

natural killer (NK) cell
A white blood cell that attacks cancer cells and infected body cells as part of internal innate defense.

natural selection
A process in which organisms with certain inherited characteristics are more likely to survive and reproduce than are organisms with other characteristics; unequal reproductive success.

nearsightedness
An inability to focus on distant objects; occurs when the eyeball is longer than normal and the lens focuses distant objects in front of the retina; also called myopia.

negative feedback
A control mechanism in which a chemical reaction, metabolic pathway, or hormone-secreting gland is inhibited by the products of the reaction, pathway, or gland. As the concentration of the products builds up, the product molecules themselves inhibit the process that produced them.

negative pressure breathing
A breathing system in which lower air pressure in the lungs causes air to enter the lungs.

nematode (*nem'-uh-tōd*)
An animal characterized by a pseudocoelom, a cylindrical, wormlike body form, and a complete digestive tract; also called a roundworm.

nephron
The tubular excretory unit and associated blood vessels of the vertebrate kidney. The nephron extracts filtrate from the blood and refines it into urine.

nerve
A communication line made up of cable-like bundles of neuron fibers (axons and dendrites) tightly wrapped in connective tissue.

nervous system
The organ system that forms a communication and coordination network throughout an animal's body.

nervous tissue
Tissue made up of neurons and supportive cells.

neuron (*nūr'-on*)
A nerve cell; the fundamental structural and functional unit of the nervous system, specialized for carrying signals from one location in the body to another.

neurotransmitter
A chemical messenger that carries information from a transmitting neuron to a receiving cell, either another neuron or an effector cell.

neutron
An electrically neutral particle (a particle having no electrical charge), found in the nucleus of an atom.

nitrogen fixation
The conversion of atmospheric nitrogen (N_2) to nitrogen compounds (NH_4, NO_3) that plants can absorb and use.

node
The point of attachment of a leaf on a stem.

nondisjunction
An accident of meiosis or mitosis in which a pair of homologous chromosomes or a pair of sister chromatids fail to separate at anaphase.

norepinephrine (*nor'-ep-uh-nef'-rin*)
An amine hormone (also called noradrenaline) that is secreted by the adrenal medulla and that prepares body organs for "fight or flight"; also serves as a neurotransmitter.

notochord (*nō'-tuh-kord*)
A flexible, cartilage-like, longitudinal rod located between the digestive tract and nerve cord in chordate animals, present only in embryos in many species.

nuclear envelope
A double membrane, perforated with pores, that encloses the nucleus and separates it from the rest of the eukaryotic cell.

nuclear transplantation
A technique in which the nucleus of one cell is placed into another cell that already has a nucleus or in which the nucleus has been previously destroyed. The cell is then stimulated to grow, producing an embryo that is a genetic copy of the nucleus donor.

nucleic acid (*nū-klā'-ik*)
A polymer consisting of many nucleotide monomers; serves as a blueprint for proteins and, through the actions of proteins, for all cellular structures and activities. The two types of nucleic acids are DNA and RNA.

nucleic acid probe (*nū-klā'-ik*)
In DNA technology, a labeled single-stranded nucleic acid molecule used to find a specific gene or other nucleotide sequence within a mass of

DNA. The probe hydrogen-bonds to the complementary sequence in the targeted DNA.

nucleoid
A non–membrane-enclosed region in a prokaryotic cell where the DNA is concentrated.

nucleolus (nū-klē'-ō-lus)
A structure within the nucleus of a eukaryotic cell where ribosomal RNA is made and assembled with proteins to make ribosomal subunits; consists of parts of the chromatin DNA, RNA transcribed from the DNA, and proteins imported from the cytoplasm.

nucleosome (nū'-klē-ō-sōm)
The bead-like unit of DNA packing in a eukaryotic cell; consists of DNA wound around a protein core made up of eight histone molecules.

nucleotide (nū'-klē-ō-tīd)
An organic monomer consisting of a five-carbon sugar covalently bonded to a nitrogenous base and a phosphate group. Nucleotides are the building blocks of nucleic acids.

nucleus
(plural, **nuclei**) (1) An atom's central core, containing protons and neutrons. (2) The genetic control center of a eukaryotic cell.

O

obesity
An excessively high body mass index, a ratio of weight to height.

omnivore
An animal that eats both plants and animals. *See also* carnivore; herbivore.

oncogene (on'-kō-jēn)
A cancer-causing gene; usually contributes to malignancy by abnormally enhancing the amount or activity of a growth factor made by the cell.

oogenesis (ō'-uh-jen'-uh-sis)
The formation of egg cells within the ovaries.

open circulatory system
A circulatory system in which the circulating fluid is pumped through open-ended vessels and out among the body cells. In an animal with

an open circulatory system, the circulating fluid and interstitial fluid are the same.

open system
Any system that exchanges chemicals and energy with its surroundings. All organisms are open systems.

operator
In prokaryotic DNA, a sequence of nucleotides near the start of an operon to which an active repressor can attach. The binding of repressor prevents RNA polymerase from attaching to the promoter and transcribing the genes of the operon.

operculum (ō-per'-kyū-lum)
(plural, **opercula**) A protective flap on each side of a bony fish's head that covers a chamber housing the gills.

operon (op'-er-on)
A unit of genetic regulation common in prokaryotes; a cluster of genes with related functions, along with the promoter and operator that control their transcription.

opportunistic life history
The pattern of reproducing when young and producing many offspring that receive little or no parental care; often seen in short-lived, small-bodied species.

optic nerve
A nerve that arises from the retina in each eye and carries visual information to the brain.

oral cavity
An opening through which food is taken into an animal's body; also known as the mouth.

order
In classification, the taxonomic category above family.

organ
A structure consisting of two or more tissues that coordinate to perform specific functions.

organ system
A group of organs that work together in performing vital body functions.

organelle (ōr-guh-nel')
A membrane-enclosed structure with a specialized function within a eukaryotic cell.

organic compound
A chemical compound containing the element carbon and usually synthesized by cells.

organic farming
A method of farming intended to promote environmental sustainability through such practices as crop rotation, water conservation, and avoidance of synthetic fertilizers, pesticides, and genetically modified organisms.

organism
An individual living thing, such as a bacterium, fungus, protist, plant, or animal.

organismal ecology
The study of the evolutionary adaptations that enable individual organisms to meet the challenges posed by their abiotic environments.

osmoconformer (oz'-mō-con-form'-er)
An organism whose body fluids have a solute concentration equal to that of its surroundings. Osmoconformers do not have a net gain or loss of water by osmosis.

osmoregulation
The control of the gain or loss of water and dissolved solutes in an organism.

osmoregulator
An organism whose body fluids have a solute concentration different from that of its environment and that must use energy in controlling water loss or gain.

osmosis (oz-mō'-sis)
The diffusion of water across a selectively permeable membrane.

osteoporosis (os'-tē-ō-puh-rō'-sis)
A skeletal disorder characterized by thinning, porous, and easily broken bones. Osteoporosis is common among women after menopause and is often related to low estrogen levels.

outer ear
One of three main regions of the ear in humans and some other animals. The outer ear is made up of the auditory canal and the pinna.

ovarian cycle (ō-vār'-ē-un)
Hormonally synchronized cyclic events in the mammalian ovary, culminating in ovulation.

ovary
(1) In animals, the female gonad, which produces egg cells and reproductive hormones. (2) In flowering plants, the base of a carpel in which the egg-containing ovules develop.

oviduct (ō'-vuh-dukt)
The tube that conveys egg cells away from an ovary; also called a fallopian tube.

ovulation (ah'-vyū-lā'-shun)
The release of an egg cell from an ovarian follicle.

ovule (ō'-vyūl)
In a seed plant, a reproductive structure that contains the female gametophyte and the developing egg. An ovule develops into a seed.

oxidation
The loss of electrons from a substance involved in a redox reaction; always accompanies reduction.

P

P generation
The parent individuals from which offspring are derived in studies of inheritance. P stands for parental.

pacemaker
The SA (sinoatrial) node; a region of cardiac muscle that maintains the heart's pumping rhythm (heartbeat) by setting the rate at which the heart contracts.

paedomorphosis (pē'-duh-mōr'-fuh-sis)
The retention in the adult of features that were juvenile in ancestral species.

pain receptor
A sensory receptor that detects painful stimuli.

pancreas (pan'-krē-us)
A gland with dual functions: The nonendocrine portion secretes digestive enzymes and an alkaline solution into the small intestine via a duct; the endocrine portion secretes the hormones insulin and glucagon into the blood.

parasite
An organism that lives in or on another organism (the host) from which it obtains nourishment; an organism that benefits at the expense of another organism, which is harmed in the process.

parasympathetic division
One of two sets of neurons in the autonomic nervous system; generally promotes body activities that gain and conserve energy ("rest

and digest"). *See also* sympathetic division.

parathyroid gland (*pār'-uh-thī'-royd*) One of four endocrine glands embedded in the surface of the thyroid gland that secrete parathyroid hormone; functions in calcium homeostasis.

parathyroid hormone (PTH) A peptide hormone, secreted by the parathyroid glands, that raises blood calcium level.

parenchyma cell (*puh-reng'-kuh-muh*) In plants, an abundant and relatively unspecialized type of cell with a thin primary wall and no secondary wall; functions in photosynthesis, food storage, and aerobic respiration and may differentiate into other cell types.

passive transport The diffusion of a substance across a biological membrane without any input of energy.

pathogen A disease-causing virus or organism.

pedigree A family tree representing the occurrence of heritable traits in parents and offspring across a number of generations.

pelagic realm (*puh-laj'-ik*) The open-water region of an ocean.

penis The structure in male mammals that functions in sexual intercourse.

pepsin An enzyme present in gastric juice that begins the hydrolysis of proteins.

peptide bond The covalent linkage between two amino acid units in a polypeptide, formed by a dehydration reaction between two amino acids.

perennial (*puh-ren'-ē-ul*) A plant that lives for many years.

peripheral nervous system (PNS) The network of nerves carrying signals into and out of the central nervous system.

peristalsis (*par'-uh-stal'-sis*) Rhythmic waves of contraction of smooth muscles. Peristalsis propels food through a digestive tube and also enables many animals, such as earthworms, to crawl.

permafrost Continuously frozen subsoil found in the arctic tundra.

petal A modified leaf of a flowering plant. Petals are the often colorful parts of a flower that advertise it to insects and other pollinators.

petiole (*pet'-ē-ōl*) The stalk of a leaf, which joins the leaf to a node of the stem.

pH scale A measure of the relative acidity of a solution, ranging in value from 0 (most acidic) to 14 (most basic). pH stands for potential hydrogen and refers to the concentration of hydrogen ions (H^+).

phage (*fāj*) *See* bacteriophage.

phagocytic cell (*fag'-ō-si-tik*) A white blood cell that engulfs bacteria, foreign proteins, and the remains of dead body cells as part of internal innate defense.

phagocytosis (*fag'-ō-sī-tō'-sis*) Cellular "eating"; a type of endocytosis whereby a cell engulfs large molecules, other cells, or particles into its cytoplasm.

pharyngeal slit (*fuh-rin'-jē-ul*) A gill structure in the pharynx, found in chordate embryos and some adult chordates.

pharynx (*far'-inks*) The organ in a digestive tract that receives food from the oral cavity; in terrestrial vertebrates, the throat region where the air and food passages cross.

phenotype (*fē'-nō-tīp*) The expressed traits of an organism.

phloem (*flō'-um*) The portion of a plant's vascular system that conveys sugars, nutrients, and hormones throughout a plant. Phloem is made up of live food-conducting cells.

phloem sap The solution of sugars, other nutrients, and hormones conveyed throughout a plant via phloem tissue.

phospholipid (*fos'-fō-lip'-id*) A molecule that is a constituent of the inner bilayer of biological membranes, having a hydrophilic head and a hydrophobic tail.

phospholipid bilayer A double layer of phospholipid molecules (each molecule consisting of a phosphate group bonded to two fatty acids) that is the primary component of all cellular membranes.

photic zone (*fō'-tik*) Shallow water near shore or the upper layer of water away from the shore; region of an aquatic ecosystem where sufficient light is available for photosynthesis.

photon (*fō'-ton*) A fixed quantity of light energy. The shorter the wavelength of light, the greater the energy of a photon.

photoperiod The length of the day relative to the length of the night; an environmental stimulus that plants use to detect the time of year.

photoreceptor A type of electromagnetic receptor that detects light.

photosynthesis (*fō'-tō-sin'-thuh-sis*) The process by which plants, algae, and some bacteria transform light energy to chemical energy stored in the bonds of sugars. This process requires an input of carbon dioxide (CO_2) and water (H_2O) and produces oxygen gas (O_2) as a waste product.

photosystem A light-harvesting unit of a chloroplast's thylakoid membrane; consists of several hundred molecules, a reaction-center chlorophyll, and a primary electron acceptor.

phototropism (*fō'-tō-trō'-pizm*) The directional growth of a plant shoot in response to light.

phylogenetic tree (*fī'-lō-juh-net'-ik*) A branching diagram that represents a hypothesis about evolutionary relationships between organisms.

phylum (*fī'-lum*) (plural, **phyla**) In classification, the taxonomic category above class and below kingdom. Members of a phylum all have a similar general body plan.

physiology (*fi'-zē-ol'-uh-jē*) The study of the function of an organism's structural equipment.

phytoplankton (*fī'-tō-plank'-ton*) Algae and photosynthetic bacteria that drift passively in aquatic environments.

pinna (*pin'-uh*) The flap-like part of the outer ear in humans and some other animals. The pinna collects sound waves and channels them to the auditory canal.

pith Part of the ground tissue system of a eudicot plant. Pith fills the center of a stem and may store food.

pituitary gland (*puh-tū'-uh-tār'-ē*) An endocrine gland at the base of the hypothalamus; consists of a posterior lobe, which stores and releases two hormones produced by the hypothalamus, and an anterior lobe, which produces and secretes many hormones that regulate diverse body functions.

pivot joint A joint that allows precise rotations in multiple planes. An example in humans is the elbow.

placenta (*pluh-sen'-tuh*) In most mammals, the organ that provides nutrients and oxygen to the embryo and helps dispose of its metabolic wastes. The placenta is formed of the embryo's chorion and the mother's endometrial blood vessels.

placental mammal (*pluh-sen'-tul*) Mammal whose young complete their embryonic development in the uterus, nourished via the mother's blood vessels in the placenta; also called a eutherian.

plankton Communities of organisms, mostly microscopic, that drift passively in ponds, lakes, and oceans.

plant A multicellular eukaryote that carries out photosynthesis and has a set of structural and reproductive terrestrial adaptations, including a multicellular, dependent embryo.

plasma The yellowish liquid of the blood in which the blood cells are suspended.

plasma membrane The thin layer of lipids and proteins that sets a cell off from its surroundings and acts as a selective barrier to the passage of ions and molecules into and out of the cell; consists of a phospholipid bilayer in which proteins are embedded.

plasmid
A small ring of self-replicating DNA separate from the chromosome(s). Plasmids are found in prokaryotes and yeasts.

plasmodial slime mold (*plaz-mō'-dē-ul*)
A type of protist named for an amoeboid plasmodial feeding stage in its life cycle.

platelet
A piece of cytoplasm from a large cell in the bone marrow; a blood-clotting element.

pleiotropy (*plī'-uh-trō-pē*)
The control of more than one phenotypic character by a single gene.

polar ice
A terrestrial biome that includes regions of extremely cold temperature and low precipitation located at high latitudes north of the arctic tundra and in Antarctica.

polar molecule
A molecule containing an uneven distribution of charge due to the presence of polar covalent bonds (bonds having opposite charges on opposite ends).

pollen grain
In a seed plant, the male gametophyte that develops within the anther of a stamen. It houses cells that will develop into sperm.

pollination
In seed plants, the delivery, by wind or animals, of pollen from the male parts of a plant to the stigma of a carpel on the female.

polychaete
A type of annelid, or segmented worm, that typically lives on the seafloor.

polygenic inheritance (*pol'-ē-jen'-ik*)
The additive effect of two or more genes on a single phenotypic characteristic.

polymer (*pol'-uh-mer*)
A large molecule consisting of many identical or similar molecular units, called monomers, covalently joined together in a chain.

polymerase chain reaction (PCR) (*puh-lim'-uh-rās*)
A technique used to obtain many copies of a DNA molecule or many copies of part of a DNA molecule. A small amount of DNA mixed with the enzyme DNA polymerase, DNA nucleotides, and a few other ingredients replicates repeatedly in a test tube.

polynucleotide (*pol'-ē-nū'-klē-ō-tīd*)
A polymer made up of many nucleotides covalently bonded together.

polyp (*pol'-ip*)
One of two types of cnidarian body forms; a stationary (sedentary), columnar, hydra-like body.

polypeptide
A chain of amino acids linked by peptide bonds.

polysaccharide (*pol'-ē-sak'-uh-rīd*)
A carbohydrate polymer consisting of many monosaccharides (sugars) linked by covalent bonds.

population
A group of interacting individuals belonging to one species and living in the same geographic area at the same time.

population density
The number of individuals of a species per unit area or volume of the habitat.

population ecology
The study of how members of a population interact with their environment, focusing on factors that influence population density and growth.

population momentum
In a population in which the fertility rate averages two children per female (replacement rate), the continuation of population growth as girls reach their reproductive years.

positive feedback
A control mechanism in which the products of a process stimulate the process that produced them.

post-anal tail
A tail posterior to the anus, found in chordate embryos and most adult chordates.

posterior pituitary
An extension of the hypothalamus composed of nervous tissue that secretes hormones made in the hypothalamus; a temporary storage site for hypothalamic hormones.

postzygotic barrier (*pōst'-zī-got'-ik*)
A reproductive barrier that operates if interspecies mating occurs and forms hybrid zygotes.

potential energy
Stored energy; the energy that an object has due to its location and/or arrangement. Water behind a dam and chemical bonds both possess potential energy.

predation
An interaction between species in which one species, the predator, kills and eats the other, the prey.

prepuce (*prē'-pyūs*)
A fold of skin covering the head of the clitoris or penis.

pressure-flow mechanism
The method by which phloem sap is transported through a plant from a sugar source, where sugars are produced, to a sugar sink, where sugars are used. The mechanism relies on building up water pressure at the source end of the phloem tube and reducing water pressure at the sink end.

prezygotic barrier (*prē'-zī-got'-ik*)
A reproductive barrier that impedes mating between species or hinders fertilization of eggs if members of different species attempt to mate.

primary consumer
An organism that eats only autotrophs; an herbivore.

primary electron acceptor
A molecule in the reaction center of a photosystem that traps the light-excited electron from the reaction-center chlorophyll.

primary growth
Growth in the length of a plant root or shoot produced by an apical meristem.

primary immune response
The initial immune response to an antigen, which includes production of effector cells that respond to the antigen within a few days and also memory cells that will respond to future exposure to the antigen.

primary oocyte (*ō'-uh-sīt*)
A diploid cell, in prophase I of meiosis, that can be hormonally triggered to develop into an ovum.

primary production
The amount of solar energy converted to chemical energy (organic compounds) by autotrophs in an ecosystem during a given time period.

primary spermatocyte (*sper-mat'-eh-sīt'*)
A diploid cell in the testis that undergoes meiosis I.

primary structure
The first level of protein structure; the specific sequence of amino acids making up a polypeptide chain.

primary succession
A type of ecological succession in which a biological community begins in an area without soil. *See also* secondary succession.

primate
Member of the mammalian group that includes lorises, pottos, lemurs, tarsiers, monkeys, apes, and humans.

prion
An infectious form of protein that may multiply by converting related proteins to more prions. Prions cause several related diseases in different animals, including scrapie in sheep, mad cow disease, and Creutzfeldt-Jakob disease in humans.

producer
An organism that makes organic food molecules from carbon dioxide, water, and other inorganic raw materials: a plant, alga, or autotrophic bacterium; the trophic level that supports all others in a food chain or food web.

product
An ending material in a chemical reaction.

progestin (*prō-jes'-tin*)
One of a family of sex hormones, including progesterone, produced by the mammalian ovary. Progestins prepare the uterus for pregnancy.

programmed cell death
The timely death (and disposal of the remains) of certain cells, triggered by certain genes; an essential process in normal development.

prokaryote (*prō-kār'-ē-ōt*)
An organism characterized by prokaryotic cells. *See also* prokaryotic cell.

prokaryotic cell (*prō-kār'-ē-ot'-ik*)
A type of cell lacking a nucleus and other organelles. Prokaryotic cells are found only in the domains Bacteria and Archaea.

promoter
A specific nucleotide sequence in DNA, located at the start of a gene,

that is the binding site for RNA polymerase and the place where transcription begins.

prophage (*prō'-fāj*)
Phage DNA that has inserted into the DNA of a prokaryotic chromosome.

prophase
The first stage of mitosis. During prophase, duplicated chromosomes condense to form structures visible with a light microscope, and the mitotic spindle forms and begins moving the chromosomes toward the center of the cell.

prostate gland (*pros'-tāt*)
A gland in human males that secretes an acid-neutralizing component of semen.

protein
A biological polymer constructed from amino acid monomers.

proteomics
The systematic study of the full protein sets (proteomes) encoded by genomes.

protist (*prō'-tist*)
Any eukaryote that is not a plant, animal, or fungus.

proton
A subatomic particle with a single unit of positive electrical charge, found in the nucleus of an atom.

proto-oncogene (*prō'-tō-on'-kō-jēn*)
A normal gene that can be converted to a cancer-causing gene.

protozoan (*prō'-tō-zō'-un*)
A protist that lives primarily by ingesting food; a heterotrophic, animal-like protist.

provirus
Viral DNA that inserts into a host genome.

pseudocoelom (*sū'-dō-sē'-lōm*)
A body cavity that is not completely lined by tissue derived from mesoderm.

pseudopodium (*sū'-dō-pō'-dē-um*)
(plural, **pseudopodia**) A temporary extension of an amoeboid cell. Pseudopodia function in moving cells and engulfing food.

pulmonary circuit
One of two main blood circuits in terrestrial vertebrates; conveys blood between the heart and the lungs. *See also* systemic circuit.

pulse
The rhythmic stretching of the arteries caused by the pressure of blood forced through the arteries by contractions of the ventricles during systole.

punctuated equilibria
In the fossil record, long periods of little apparent change (equilibria) interrupted (punctuated) by relatively brief periods of sudden change.

Punnett square
A diagram used in the study of inheritance to show the results of random fertilization.

pupil
The opening in the iris that admits light into the interior of the vertebrate eye. Muscles in the iris regulate its size.

pyramid of production
A diagram depicting the cumulative loss of energy with each transfer in a food chain.

Q

quaternary consumer (*kwot'-er-nār-ē*)
An organism that eats tertiary consumers.

R

radial symmetry
An arrangement of the body parts of an organism like pieces of a pie around an imaginary central axis. Any slice passing longitudinally through a radially symmetric organism's central axis divides the organism into mirror-image halves.

radiation therapy
Treatment for cancer in which parts of the body that have cancerous tumors are exposed to high-energy radiation to disrupt cell division of the cancer cells.

radioactive isotope
An isotope whose nucleus decays spontaneously, giving off particles and energy.

radiometric dating
A method for determining the age of fossils and rocks from the

ratio of a radioactive isotope to the nonradioactive isotope(s) of the same element in the sample.

radula (*rad'-yū-luh*)
A file-like organ found in many molluscs, used to scrape up or shred food.

ray-finned fish
A bony fish having fins supported by thin, flexible skeletal rays. All but one living species of bony fishes are ray-fins. *See* lobe-finned fish.

reabsorption
In the vertebrate kidney, the reclaiming of water and valuable solutes from the filtrate.

reactant
A starting material in a chemical reaction.

reaction center
In a photosystem in a chloroplast, the chlorophyll *a* molecule and primary electron acceptor that trigger the light reactions of photosynthesis. The chlorophyll donates an electron excited by light energy to the primary electron acceptor, which passes an electron to an electron transport chain.

receptor potential
The change in membrane potential of a sensory receptor cell that results from sensory transduction.

recessive allele
In heterozygotes, the allele that has no noticeable effect on the phenotype.

recombinant DNA
A DNA molecule carrying genes derived from two or more sources, often from different species.

recombination frequency
With respect to two given genes, the number of recombinant progeny from a mating divided by the total number of progeny. Recombinant progeny carry combinations of alleles different from that seen in either of the parents as a result of independent assortment of chromosomes and crossing over.

rectum
The terminal portion of the large intestine, where the feces are stored until they are eliminated.

red blood cell
A blood cell containing hemoglobin, which transports O_2; also called an erythrocyte.

red-green colorblindness
A common sex-linked human disorder involving several genes on the X chromosome and characterized by a malfunction of light-sensitive cells in the eyes; affects mostly males but also homozygous females.

redox reaction
Short for reduction-oxidation reaction; a chemical reaction in which electrons are lost from one substance (oxidation) and added to another (reduction). Oxidation and reduction always occur together.

reduction
The gain of electrons by a substance involved in a redox reaction; always accompanies oxidation.

regeneration
The regrowth of body parts from pieces of an organism.

relative abundance
The proportional representation of a species in a biological community; one component of species diversity.

relative fitness
The contribution an individual makes to the gene pool of the next generation relative to the contribution of other individuals in the population.

repetitive DNA
Nucleotide sequences that are present in many copies in the DNA of a genome. The repeated sequences may be long or short and may be located next to each other or dispersed in the DNA.

repressor
A protein that blocks the transcription of a gene or operon.

reproduction
The creation of new individuals from existing ones.

reproductive barrier
Anything that prevents individuals of closely related species from interbreeding, even when populations of the two species live together.

reproductive cloning
Using a somatic cell from a multicellular organism to make one or more genetically identical individuals.

reproductive cycle
In females, a recurring series of events that produces gametes, makes

them available for fertilization, and prepares the body for pregnancy.

reptile
Member of the clade of amniotes that includes snakes, lizards, turtles, crocodiles, alligators, birds, and a number of extinct groups (most of the dinosaurs).

resolving power
A measure of the clarity of an image; the ability of an optical instrument to show two objects as separate.

respiratory surface
The part of an animal where gases are exchanged with the environment.

respiratory system
The organ system that functions in exchanging gases with the environment, taking in O_2 and disposing of CO_2.

resting potential
The voltage across the plasma membrane of a resting neuron.

restoration ecology
A field of ecology that develops methods of returning degraded ecosystems to their natural state.

restriction enzyme
A bacterial enzyme that cuts up foreign DNA at one very specific nucleotide sequence, thus protecting bacteria against intruding DNA from phages and other organisms. Restriction enzymes are used in DNA technology to cut DNA molecules in reproducible ways.

restriction fragment
A molecule of DNA produced from a longer DNA molecule cut up by a restriction enzyme; used in genome mapping and other applications.

restriction site
A specific sequence on a DNA strand that is recognized and cut by a restriction enzyme.

retina (ret'-uh-nuh)
The light-sensitive layer in an eye, made up of photoreceptor cells and sensory neurons.

retrovirus
An RNA virus that reproduces by means of a DNA molecule. It reverse-transcribes its RNA into DNA, inserts the DNA into a cellular chromosome, and then transcribes more copies of the RNA from the viral DNA. HIV and a number

of cancer-causing viruses are retroviruses.

reverse transcriptase (tran-skrip'-tās)
An enzyme that catalyzes the synthesis of DNA on an RNA template.

rheumatoid arthritis
An autoimmune disease in which the joints become highly inflamed.

rhizome (rī'-zōm)
A horizontal stem that grows below the ground.

rhythm method
A form of contraception that relies on refraining from sexual intercourse when conception is most likely to occur; also called natural family planning.

ribosomal RNA (rRNA) (rī'-buh-sōm'-ul)
The type of ribonucleic acid that, together with proteins, makes up ribosomes; the most abundant type of RNA.

ribosome (rī'-buh-sōm)
A cellular structure consisting of RNA and protein organized into two subunits and functioning as the site of protein synthesis in the cytoplasm. The ribosomal subunits are constructed in the nucleolus.

RNA
Ribonucleic acid (rī'-bō-nū-klā'-ik) A type of nucleic acid consisting of nucleotide monomers, with a ribose sugar, a phosphate group, and the nitrogenous bases adenine (A), cytosine (C), guanine (G), and uracil (U); usually single-stranded; functions in protein synthesis and as the genome of some viruses.

RNA polymerase (puh-lim'-uh-rās)
An enzyme that links together the growing chain of RNA nucleotides during transcription, using a DNA strand as a template.

RNA splicing
The removal of introns and joining of exons in eukaryotic RNA, forming an mRNA molecule with a continuous coding sequence; occurs before mRNA leaves the nucleus.

rod
A photoreceptor cell in the vertebrate retina, enabling vision in dim light (but only in shades of gray).

root
The underground organ of a plant. Roots anchor the plant in the soil,

absorb and transport minerals and water, and store food.

root cap
A cone of cells at the tip of a plant root that protects the root's apical meristem.

root hair
An outgrowth of an epidermal cell on a root, which increases the root's absorptive surface area.

root system
All of a plant's roots, which anchor it in the soil, absorb and transport minerals and water, and store food.

rough ER (rough endoplasmic reticulum) (reh-tik'-yuh-lum)
A network of interconnected membranous sacs in a eukaryotic cell's cytoplasm. Rough ER membranes are studded with ribosomes that make membrane proteins and secretory proteins. The rough ER constructs membrane from phospholipids and proteins.

roundworm
See nematode.

rule of multiplication
A rule stating that the probability of a compound event is the product of the separate probabilities of the independent events.

S

SA (sinoatrial) node (sī'-nō-ā'-trē-ul)
The pacemaker of the heart, located in the wall of the right atrium. At the base of the wall separating the two atria is another patch of nodal tissue called the atrioventricular (AV) node. See also pacemaker.

salivary gland
A gland associated with the oral cavity that secretes substances that lubricate food and begin the process of chemical digestion.

sarcomere (sar'-kō-mēr)
The fundamental unit of muscle contraction, composed of thin filaments and thick filaments; the region between two narrow, dark lines in the myofibril.

saturated
Pertaining to fats and fatty acids the hydrocarbon chains of which contain the maximum number of hydrogens and therefore have no

double covalent bonds. Because of their straight, flat shape, saturated fats and fatty acids tend to be solid at room temperature.

savanna
A terrestrial biome dominated by grasses and scattered trees. Frequent fires and seasonal drought are significant abiotic factors.

scanning electron microscope (SEM)
A microscope that uses an electron beam to study the surface architecture of a cell or other specimen.

scavenger
An animal that feeds on the carcasses of dead animals.

science
Any method of learning about the natural world that follows the scientific method. See discovery science; hypothesis-driven science.

scientific method
Scientific investigation involving the observation of phenomena, the formulation of a hypothesis concerning the phenomena, experimentation to demonstrate the truth or falseness of the hypothesis, and results that validate or modify the hypothesis.

sclera (sklār'-uh)
A tough, whitish layer of connective tissue forming the outer surface of the vertebrate eye. The cornea is the front part of the sclera.

sclerenchyma cell (skli-reng'-kuh-muh)
In plants, a supportive type of cell with a rigid secondary wall hardened with lignin.

scrotum
A pouch of skin outside the abdomen that houses a testis. The scrotum functions in cooling the sperm, thereby keeping them viable.

seaweed
A large, multicellular marine alga.

secondary consumer
An organism that eats primary consumers.

secondary growth
An increase in a plant's girth, involving cell division in the vascular cambium and cork cambium.

secondary immune response
The immune response elicited by memory cells upon exposure to a previously encountered antigen. The

secondary immune response is more rapid, of greater magnitude, and of longer duration than the primary immune response.

secondary oocyte (ō'-uh-sīt')
A haploid cell that results from meiosis I in oogenesis and that will become an ovum after meiosis II.

secondary spermatocyte (sper-mat'-uh-sīt')
A haploid cell that results from meiosis I in spermatogenesis and that will become a sperm cell after meiosis II.

secondary succession
A type of ecological succession that occurs where a disturbance has destroyed an existing biological community but left the soil intact. *See also* primary succession.

secretion
In the vertebrate kidney, the transport of certain substances, such as some ions and drugs, from the blood into the filtrate.

seed
A plant embryo packaged with a food supply within a protective covering.

seed coat
A tough outer covering of a seed, formed from the outer coat of an ovule. In a flowering plant, it encloses and protects the embryo and endosperm.

semen (sē'-mun)
The sperm-containing fluid that is ejaculated by the male during orgasm.

seminal vesicle (sem'-uh-nul ves'-uh-kul)
A gland in males that secretes a fluid component of semen that lubricates and nourishes sperm.

seminiferous tubule (sem'-uh-nif'-uh-rus)
A coiled sperm-producing tube in a testis.

sensory adaptation
The tendency of some sensory receptors to become less sensitive when they are stimulated repeatedly.

sensory input
The conduction of signals from sensory receptors to integration centers in the central nervous system.

sensory neuron
A nerve cell that receives information from sensory receptors and conveys

signals into the central nervous system.

sensory transduction
The conversion of a stimulus signal to an electrical signal by a sensory receptor cell.

sepal (sē'-pul)
A modified leaf of a flowering plant. A whorl of sepals encloses and protects the flower bud before it opens.

sex chromosome
A chromosome that determines whether an individual is male or female; in mammals, for example, the X or Y chromosome.

sex-linked gene
A gene located on a sex chromosome.

sexual dimorphism
Distinction in appearance based on secondary sexual characteristics, noticeable differences not directly associated with reproduction or survival.

sexual reproduction
The creation of genetically distinct offspring by the fusion of two haploid sex cells (gametes: sperm and egg), forming a diploid zygote.

sexual selection
A form of natural selection in which individuals with certain characteristics are more likely than other individuals to obtain mates.

sexually transmitted disease (STD)
A contagious disease spread by sexual contact.

shoot
The aerial organ of a plant, consisting of stem and leaves. Leaves are the main photosynthetic structures of most plants.

shoot system
All of a plant's stems, leaves, and reproductive structures.

short tandem repeat (STR)
DNA consisting of tandem (in a row) repeats of a short sequence of nucleotides.

sickle-cell disease
A genetic disorder in which the red blood cells have abnormal hemoglobin molecules and take on an abnormal shape.

signal transduction pathway
A series of molecular changes that converts a signal received on a target

cell's surface to a specific response inside the cell.

silencer
A eukaryotic DNA sequence that inhibits the start of gene transcription; may act analogously to an enhancer, binding a repressor.

sister chromatid (krō'-muh-tid)
One of the two identical parts of a duplicated chromosome. While joined, two sister chromatids make up one chromosome; chromatids are eventually separated during mitosis or meiosis II.

skeletal muscle
Striated muscle attached to the skeleton. The contraction of striated muscle produces voluntary movements of the body.

skeletal system
The organ system that provides body support, protects body organs such as the brain, heart, and lungs, and anchors the muscles.

small intestine
The longest section of the alimentary canal. It is the principal site of the enzymatic hydrolysis of food molecules and absorption of nutrients.

smooth ER (smooth endoplasmic reticulum) (reh-tik'-yuh-lum)
A network of interconnected membranous tubules in a eukaryotic cell's cytoplasm. Smooth ER lacks ribosomes. Enzymes embedded in the smooth ER membrane function in the synthesis of certain kinds of molecules, such as lipids.

smooth muscle
Muscle made up of cells without striations, found in the walls of organs such as the digestive tract, urinary bladder, and arteries.

solute (sol'-yūt)
A substance that is dissolved in a liquid (which is called the solvent) to form a solution.

solution
A liquid consisting of a homogeneous mixture of two or more substances: a dissolving agent, the solvent, and a substance that is dissolved, the solute.

solvent
The dissolving agent in a solution. Water is the most versatile known solvent.

somatic cell (sō-mat'-ik)
Any cell in a multicellular organism except a sperm or egg cell or a cell that develops into a sperm or egg; a body cell.

speciation (spē'-sē-ā'-shun)
An evolutionary process in which one species splits into two or more species.

species
A group of populations whose members possess similar anatomical characteristics and have the ability to interbreed. *See also* biological species concept.

species diversity
The variety of species that make up a biological community; the number and relative abundance of species in a biological community.

species richness
The total number of different species in a community; one component of species diversity.

sperm
A male gamete.

spermatogenesis (sper-mat'-ō-jen'-uh-sis)
The formation of sperm cells.

spermicide
A sperm-killing chemical, in the form of a cream, jelly, or foam, that works with a barrier device as a method of contraception.

spinal cord
In vertebrates, a jellylike bundle of nerve fibers located within the vertebral column. The spinal cord and the brain together make up the central nervous system.

sponge
An aquatic stationary animal characterized by a highly porous body, choanocytes, and no true tissues.

spontaneous generation
The incorrect notion that life can emerge from nonliving matter.

spore
(1) In plants and algae, a haploid cell that can develop into a multicellular haploid individual, the gametophyte, without fusing with another cell. (2) In fungi, a haploid cell that germinates to produce a mycelium.

sporophyte (spōr'-uh-fīt)
The multicellular diploid form in the life cycle of organisms undergoing alternation of generations; results from

a union of gametes and meiotically produces haploid spores that grow into the gametophyte generation.

stabilizing selection
Natural selection that favors intermediate variants by acting against extreme phenotypes.

stamen (*stā'-men*)
A pollen-producing part of a flower, consisting of a stalk (filament) and an anther.

starch
A storage polysaccharide found in the roots of plants and certain other cells; a polymer of glucose.

start codon (*kō'-don*)
On mRNA, the specific three-nucleotide sequence (AUG) to which an initiator tRNA molecule binds, starting translation of genetic information.

stem
That part of a plant's shoot system that generally grows above the ground and supports the leaves and reproductive structures.

stem cell
A relatively unspecialized cell that can give rise to one or more types of specialized cells. *See* embryonic stem cell (ES cell); adult stem cell.

steroid (*stir'-oyd*)
A type of lipid whose carbon skeleton is in the form of four fused rings: three 6-sided rings and one 5-sided ring. Examples are cholesterol, testosterone, and estrogen.

stigma (*stig'-muh*)
(plural, **stigmata**) The sticky tip of a flower's carpel that traps pollen.

stimulus
(plural, **stimuli**) In a nervous system, a factor that triggers a nerve signal.

stoma (*stō'-muh*)
(plural, **stomata**) A pore surrounded by guard cells in the epidermis of a leaf. When stomata are open, CO_2 enters the leaf, and water and O_2 exit. A plant conserves water when its stomata are closed.

stomach
A pouch-like organ in a digestive tube that grinds and churns food and may store it temporarily.

stop codon (*kō'-don*)
In mRNA, one of three triplets (UAG, UAA, UGA) that signal gene translation to stop.

STR analysis
A method of DNA profiling that compares the lengths of STR sequences at specific sites in the genome.

stroma (*strō'-muh*)
A thick fluid enclosed by the inner membrane of a chloroplast. Sugars are made in the stroma by the enzymes of the Calvin cycle.

substrate
(1) A specific substance (reactant) on which an enzyme acts. Each enzyme recognizes only the specific substrate of the reaction it catalyzes. (2) A surface in or on which an organism lives.

sugar sink
A plant organ that is a net consumer or storer of sugar. Growing roots, shoot tips, stems, and fruits are sugar sinks supplied by phloem.

sugar source
A plant organ in which sugar is being produced by either photosynthesis or the breakdown of starch. Mature leaves are the primary sugar sources of plants.

sugar-phosphate backbone
The alternating chain of sugar and phosphate to which DNA and RNA nitrogenous bases are attached.

supporting cell
In the nervous system, a cell that protects, insulates, and reinforces a neuron.

survivorship curve
A plot of the number of individuals that are still alive at each age in the maximum life span; one way to represent age-specific mortality.

sustainability
The goal of developing, managing, and conserving Earth's resources in ways that meet the needs of people today without compromising the ability of future generations to meet their needs.

sustainable development
The long-term prosperity of human societies and the ecosystems that support them.

swim bladder
A gas-filled internal sac that helps bony fishes maintain buoyancy.

symbiosis (*sim'-bē-ō'-sis*)
An interaction between organisms of different species in which one

species, the symbiont, lives in or on another species, the host.

sympathetic division
One of two sets of neurons in the autonomic nervous system; generally prepares the body for energy-consuming activities ("fight or flight"). *See also* parasympathetic division.

sympatric speciation
The formation of a new species in populations that live in the same geographic area. *See also* allopatric speciation.

synapse (*sin'-aps*)
A junction, or relay point, between two neurons or between a neuron and an effector cell. Electrical and chemical signals are relayed from one cell to another at a synapse.

synaptic cleft (*sin-ap'-tik*)
A narrow gap separating the synaptic terminal of a transmitting neuron from a receiving neuron or an effector cell.

synaptic terminal
The bulb-like structure at the tip of a transmitting neuron's axon, where signals are sent to another neuron or to an effector cell.

systematics
A discipline of biology that focuses on classifying organisms and determining their evolutionary relationships.

systemic circuit
One of two main blood circuits in terrestrial vertebrates; conveys blood between the heart and the rest of the body. *See also* pulmonary circuit.

systole (*sis'-tō-lē*)
The contraction stage of the cardiac cycle, when the heart chambers actively pump blood. *See also* diastole.

T

T cell
A type of lymphocyte that matures in the thymus and is responsible for the cell-mediated immune response. *See also* B cell.

taiga (*tī'-guh*)
The northern coniferous forest, characterized by long, snowy winters and short, wet summers. Taiga

extends across North America and Eurasia, to the southern border of the arctic tundra; it is also found just below alpine tundra on mountainsides in temperate zones.

tail
Extra nucleotides added at the end of an RNA transcript in the nucleus of a eukaryotic cell.

target cell
A cell that responds to a regulatory signal, such as a hormone.

taxonomy
The branch of biology concerned with identifying, naming, and classifying species.

telophase
The fourth and final stage of mitosis, during which daughter nuclei form at the two poles of a cell. Telophase usually occurs together with cytokinesis.

temperate broadleaf forest
A terrestrial biome located throughout midlatitude regions where there is sufficient moisture to support the growth of large, broadleaf deciduous trees.

temperate grassland
A terrestrial biome located in the temperate zone and characterized by low rainfall and nonwoody vegetation. Tree growth is hindered by occasional fires and periodic severe drought.

temperate rain forest
A coniferous forest of coastal North America (from Alaska to Oregon) supported by warm, moist air from the Pacific Ocean.

temperate zones
Latitudes between the tropics and the Arctic Circle in the north and the Antarctic Circle in the south; regions with milder climates than the tropics or polar regions.

temperature
A measure of the intensity of heat, reflecting the average kinetic energy or speed of molecules.

tendon
Fibrous connective tissue connecting a muscle to a bone.

terminal bud
Embryonic tissue at the tip of a shoot, made up of developing leaves and a compact series of nodes and internodes.

terminator

A special sequence of nucleotides in DNA that marks the end of a gene. It signals RNA polymerase to release the newly made RNA molecule, which then departs from the gene.

tertiary consumer (ter'-shē-ār-ē)

An organism that eats secondary consumers.

testcross

The mating between an individual of unknown genotype for a particular character and an individual that is homozygous recessive for that same character.

testicle

A structural component of the male reproductive system consisting of a testis and scrotum.

testis

(plural, **testes**) The male gonad in an animal. The testis produces sperm and, in many species, reproductive hormones.

tetrapod

A vertebrate with four limbs. Tetrapods include mammals, amphibians, and reptiles (including birds).

theory

A widely accepted explanatory idea that is broad in scope and supported by a large body of evidence.

therapeutic cloning

The cloning of human cells by nuclear transplantation for therapeutic purposes, such as the replacement of body cells that have been irreversibly damaged by disease or injury. *See also* nuclear transplantation; reproductive cloning.

thermoreceptor

A sensory receptor that detects heat or cold.

thermoregulation

The maintenance of internal temperature within a range that allows cells to function efficiently.

thick filament

The thicker of the two types of filaments that make up a sarcomere, consisting of the protein myosin.

thigmotropism (thig'-mō-trō'-pizm)

Growth of a plant in response to touch.

thin filament

The thinner of the two types of filaments that make up a sarcomere, consisting of the protein actin.

threatened species

As defined in the U.S. Endangered Species Act, a species that is likely to become endangered in the foreseeable future throughout all or a significant portion of its range.

three-domain system

A system of taxonomic classification based on three basic groups: Bacteria, Archaea, and Eukarya.

threshold

The minimum change in a membrane's voltage that must occur to generate a nerve signal (action potential).

thylakoid (thī'-luh-koyd)

One of a number of disk-shaped membranous sacs inside a chloroplast. Thylakoid membranes contain chlorophyll and the enzymes of the light reactions of photosynthesis. A stack of thylakoids is called a granum.

thymine (T) (thī'-mēn)

A single-ring nitrogenous base found in DNA.

thyroid gland (thī'-royd)

An endocrine gland, located in the neck, that secretes hormones that increase oxygen consumption and metabolic rate and help regulate development and maturation.

tissue

An integrated group of similar cells that performs a specific function within a multicellular organism.

tissue system

An organized collection of plant tissues. The organs of plants (such as roots, stems, and leaves) are formed from the dermal, vascular, and ground tissue systems.

tongue

A muscular organ of the mouth that helps to taste and swallow food.

trace element

An element that is essential for the survival of an organism but is needed in only minute quantities.

trachea (trā'-kē-uh)

(plural, **tracheae**) (1) The windpipe; the portion of the respiratory tube between the larynx and the bronchi. (2) One of many tiny tubes that branch throughout an insect's body, enabling gas exchange between outside air and body cells.

tracheal system

In insects, an extensive network of branching internal tubes called tracheae, used in respiration.

tracheid (trā'-kē-id)

A tapered, porous, water-conducting, supportive cell in plants. Chains of tracheids or vessel elements make up the water-conducting, supportive tubes in xylem.

trait

A variant of a character found within a population, such as purple flowers in pea plants.

trans fats

An unsaturated fatty acid produced by the partial hydrogenation of vegetable oils and present in hardened vegetable oils, most margarines, many commercial baked foods, and many fried foods.

transcription

The synthesis of RNA on a DNA template.

transcription factor

In the eukaryotic cell, a protein that functions in initiating or regulating transcription. Transcription factors bind to DNA or to other proteins that bind to DNA.

transfer RNA (tRNA)

A type of ribonucleic acid that functions as an interpreter in translation. Each tRNA molecule has a specific anticodon, picks up a specific amino acid, and conveys the amino acid to the appropriate codon on mRNA.

transgenic organism

An organism that contains genes from another organism, typically of another species.

translation

The synthesis of a polypeptide using the genetic information encoded in an mRNA molecule. There is a change of "language" from nucleotides to amino acids.

transmission electron microscope (TEM)

A microscope that uses an electron beam to study the internal structure of thinly sectioned specimens.

transpiration

The evaporative loss of water from a plant.

transpiration-cohesion-tension mechanism

The transport mechanism of xylem sap whereby transpiration exerts a pull that is relayed downward along a string of water molecules held together by cohesion and helped upward by adhesion.

transport protein

A membrane protein that helps move substances across a cell membrane.

transport vesicle

A tiny membranous sphere in a cell's cytoplasm carrying molecules produced by the cell. The vesicle buds from the endoplasmic reticulum or Golgi apparatus and eventually fuses with another organelle or the plasma membrane, releasing its contents.

triglyceride (trī-glis'-uh-rīd)

A dietary fat that consists of a molecule of glycerol linked to three molecules of fatty acids.

trimester

In human development, one of three 3-month-long periods of pregnancy.

trisomy 21

See Down syndrome.

trophic structure (trō'-fik)

The feeding relationships among the various species in a community.

trophoblast (trōf'-ō-blast)

In mammalian development, the outer portion of a blastocyst. Cells of the trophoblast secrete enzymes that enable the blastocyst to implant in the endometrium of the mother's uterus.

tropical forest

A terrestrial biome characterized by warm temperatures year-round.

tropics

Region between the Tropic of Cancer and the Tropic of Capricorn; latitudes between 23.5° north and south.

tropism (trō'-pizm)

A growth response that makes a plant grow toward or away from a stimulus.

tubal ligation

A means of sterilization in which a woman's two oviducts (fallopian tubes) are tied closed to prevent eggs from reaching the uterus. A segment of each oviduct is removed.

tuber
An enlargement at the end of a rhizome, in which food is stored.

tubule
A thin tube within the internal structure of the human kidney.

tumor
An abnormal mass of cells that forms within otherwise normal tissue.

tumor-suppressor gene
A gene whose product inhibits cell division, thereby preventing uncontrolled cell growth.

tundra
A terrestrial biome characterized by bitterly cold temperatures. Plant life is limited to dwarf woody shrubs, grasses, mosses, and lichens. Arctic tundra has permanently frozen subsoil (permafrost); alpine tundra, found at high elevations, lacks permafrost.

tunicate
One of a group of stationary invertebrate chordates.

U

umbilical cord
A structure containing arteries and veins that connects a developing embryo to the placenta of the mother.

unsaturated
Pertaining to fats and fatty acids of which hydrocarbon chains lack the maximum number of hydrogen atoms and therefore have one or more double covalent bonds. Because of their bent shape, unsaturated fats and fatty acids tend to stay liquid at room temperature.

uracil (U) (yū'-ruh-sil)
A single-ring nitrogenous base found in RNA.

ureter (yū-rē'-ter or yū'-reh-ter)
A duct that conveys urine from the kidney to the urinary bladder.

urethra (yū-rē'-thruh)
A duct that conveys urine from the urinary bladder to outside the body. In the male, the urethra also conveys semen out of the body during ejaculation.

urinary bladder
The pouch where urine is stored before elimination.

urine
Concentrated filtrate produced by the kidneys and excreted via the bladder.

uterus (yū'-ter-us)
In the reproductive system of a mammalian female, the organ where the development of young occurs; the womb.

V

vaccination (vak'-suh-nā'-shun)
A procedure that presents the immune system with a harmless version of a pathogen, thereby stimulating an adaptive defense when the pathogen itself is encountered.

vaccine (vak-sēn')
A harmless version or piece of a pathogen (a disease-causing virus or organism) used to stimulate a host organism's immune system to mount a long-term defense against the pathogen.

vacuole (vak'-ū-ōl)
A membrane-enclosed sac, part of the endomembrane system of a eukaryotic cell, having diverse functions.

vagina (vuh-jī'-nuh)
Part of the female reproductive system between the uterus and the outside opening; the birth canal in mammals. The vagina accommodates the male's penis and receives sperm during copulation.

vas deferens (vas def'-er-enz)
(plural, **vasa deferentia**) Part of the male reproductive system that conveys sperm away from the testis; the sperm duct; in humans, the tube that conveys sperm between the epididymis and the common duct that leads to the urethra.

vascular cambium
(vas'-kyū-ler kam'-bē-um)
In plants, a cylinder of meristem tissue found between the primary xylem and phloem. During secondary growth, the vascular cambium produces secondary xylem and phloem.

vascular tissue
Plant tissue consisting of cells joined into tubes that transport water and nutrients throughout the plant body.

Xylem and phloem make up vascular tissue.

vascular tissue system
A system formed by xylem and phloem throughout a plant, serving as a long-distance transport system for water and nutrients, respectively.

vasectomy (vuh-sek'-tuh-mē)
Surgical removal of a section of the two sperm ducts (vasa deferentia) to prevent sperm from reaching the urethra; a means of sterilization in the male.

vector
A piece of DNA, usually a plasmid or a viral genome, that is used to move genes from one cell to another.

vein
(1) In animals, a vessel that returns blood to the heart. (2) In plants, a vascular bundle in a leaf, composed of xylem and phloem.

ventricle (ven'-truh-kul)
A heart chamber that pumps blood out of the heart to the body or lungs via arteries.

venule (ven'-yūl)
A small vessel that conveys blood between a capillary bed and a vein.

vertebrate (ver'-tuh-brāt)
A chordate animal with a backbone. Vertebrates include lampreys, cartilaginous fishes, bony fishes, amphibians, reptiles (including birds), and mammals.

vessel element
A short, open-ended, water-conducting, supportive cell in plants. Chains of vessel elements or tracheids make up the water-conducting, supportive tubes in xylem.

vestigial structure
A structure of marginal, if any, importance to an organism. Vestigial structures are historical remnants of structures that had important functions in ancestors.

virus
A microscopic particle capable of infecting cells of living organisms and inserting its genetic material. Viruses have a very simple structure and are generally not considered to be alive because they do not display all of the characteristics associated with life.

vitamin
An organic nutrient that an organism requires in very small quantities.

Vitamins generally function as coenzymes.

vitreous humor (vit'-rē-us hyū'-mer)
A jellylike substance that fills the space behind the lens in the vertebrate eye and helps maintain the shape of the eye.

vocal cord
One of a pair of tissues in the larynx. Air rushing past the tensed vocal cords makes them vibrate, producing sounds.

vulva
The outer features of the female reproductive anatomy.

W

warning coloration
The bright color pattern, often yellow, red, or orange in combination with black, of animals that have effective chemical defenses.

water vascular system
In echinoderms, a radially arranged system of water-filled canals that branch into extensions called tube feet. The system provides movement and circulates water, facilitating gas exchange and waste disposal.

wavelength
The distance between crests of adjacent waves, such as those of the electromagnetic spectrum.

wetland
An ecosystem intermediate between an aquatic ecosystem and a terrestrial ecosystem. Wetland soil is saturated with water permanently or periodically.

white blood cell
A blood cell that functions in defending the body against infections; also called a leukocyte.

whole-genome shotgun method
A method for determining the DNA sequence of an entire genome by cutting it into small fragments, sequencing each fragment, and then placing the fragments in the proper order.

wild-type trait
The trait most commonly found in nature.

wood
Secondary xylem of a plant.

X

X chromosome inactivation
In female mammals, the inactivation of one X chromosome in each somatic cell. Once X inactivation occurs in a given cell (during embryonic development), all descendants of that cell will have the same copy of the X chromosome inactivated.

xylem (*zī'-lum*)
The portion of a plant's vascular system that provides support and conveys water and inorganic nutrients from the roots to the rest of the plant. Xylem consists mainly of vessel elements and/or tracheids, water-conducting cells.

xylem sap
The solution of inorganic nutrients conveyed in xylem tissue from a plant's roots to its shoots.

Z

zooplankton
In aquatic environments, free-floating animals, including many microscopic ones.

zygote (*zī'-gōt*)
The fertilized egg, which is diploid, that results from the union of haploid gametes (sperm and egg) during fertilization.

Index

Page numbers with *f* indicate figure, *t* indicate table, and those in bold indicate page where defined as key term.

A

Abdomen, arthropod, 347*f*, 350*f*
Abiotic factors, **375**
  in biogeochemical cycles, 440
  of biosphere, 376–77
  in ecology, 375
  in ecosystem ecology, 437 (*see also* Chemical cycling; Energy flow)
  limiting population growth, 411
  in terrestrial biomes, 386
Abiotic reservoirs, **440**. *See also* Chemical cycling
Abiotic synthesis of life, 296–98
ABO blood groups, **159**, 503
Abortion, RU-486 and, 560
Abscisic acid, **635**
Absolute age, fossil, 282
Absorption, **329**, **476**, 482–84*f*
Abstinence, sexual, 559–61
Acclimation, **378**
Acetic acid, 98
Acetylcholine, 580
Acetyl CoA, 98
Achondroplasia (dwarfism), **156**, 236, 541
Acidification, ocean, 33
Acid precipitation, 391, 428
Acid reflux, 481
Acids, **32**
  bases, pH, and, 32–33
  in human gastric juice, 480–81
Acquired defenses. *See* Adaptive defenses
Acromegaly, 541
Acrosome, 562
ACTH (adrenocorticotropic hormone), 545
Actin, 596
Actinomycetes, 300*f*
Action potentials, **577**
  in nervous system signal transmission, 577–80
  in vision, 590
Activation energy, enzymes and, **80**
Activators, DNA, **203**
Active site, enzyme, **82**
Active transport, **86**
Adam's apples, 480
Adaptations, evolutionary. *See* Evolutionary adaptations
Adaptive coloration, predation and, 430
Adaptive defenses, **518**, 521–27
  B cells and humoral immune response of, 526
  case study on HIV as cause of AIDS and, 523

  clonal selection and multiplication of lymphocytes by, 524
  innate defenses vs., 518
  memory cells and secondary immune response of, 525
  recognition of invading antigens by, 522
  T cell and B cell lymphocytes of, 521
  T cells and cell-mediated immune response of, 526–27
  vaccination and, 525
Addiction
  hypothalamus pleasure center and, 583
  smooth ER and, 65
Adélie penguins, effect of global climate change on, 373, 399
Adenine (A), 7, 49–50, 174–**75**
Adenoviruses, 188*f*
ADH (antidiuretic hormone), 470, 540
ADHD (attention deficit hyperactivity disorder), 580
Adhesion, **629**–30
Adipose tissue, 16, 43, **459**
ADP (adenosine diphosphate), **79**–80
Adrenal cortex, 539*t*, **544**–45
Adrenal glands, **544**
  in cell signaling, 87
  endocrine system functions of, 539*t*, 544–45
Adrenaline. *See* Epinephrine (adrenaline)
Adrenal medulla, 539*t*, **544**–45
Adrenocorticotropic hormone (ACTH), 545
Adult stem cells, therapeutic cloning using, **210**. *See also* Stem cells
Aerobic capacity, high-altitude athletic training for, 504
Aerobic endosymbionts, 306
Aerobic exercise case study, 31–32
Aerobic processes, **94**. *See also* Aerobic vs. anaerobic lifestyles; Cellular respiration
Aerobic vs. anaerobic lifestyles
  evolution of glycolysis and, 103
  muscle fatigue as lactic acid accumulation from fermentation, 102
  slow-twitch vs. fast-twitch muscle fibers and, 91
Africa, origin of *Homo sapiens* in, 366
African mega mantises, 637
Afterbirth, 568
Agar gel, 310
Age structure, population, **405**, 418–19

Aggressive behavior, androgens and male, 547
Agriculture
  angiosperms in, 326
  auxins in, 633–34
  biological control of pests in, 414–15
  case study on drought and failure of, in Lost Colony of Roanoke, 616
  cheatgrass as invasive species and, 413–14
  deforestation for, 389, 392
  effects of bee colony collapse disorder on, 621
  fungal pests and, 330
  history of cultivation of coffee plants in, 604–5
  insects as pests in, 352
  integrated pest management in, 416
  loss of plant diversity through slash-and-burn, 327
  nutrient pollution by, 443
  organic farming and sustainable, 627, 634
  phosphorus and nitrogen in, 441–42
  plant cloning in, 207
  roundworms as pests in, 346
  in temperate grassland biomes, 388
AIDS (acquired immunodeficiency syndrome), **192**
  HIV and, 190, 192–94, 523 (*see also* HIV (human immunodeficiency virus))
  search for vaccine for, 516–17
  as sexually transmitted disease, 561
Ain, Dr. Michael C., 156*f*
Air pollution
  declining biodiversity and, 428
  effects of, on human lungs, 510
  tobacco smoke as, 512–13
Air pressure, breathing and, 511
Alcohol
  effects of, on fetal development, 565
  effects of, on human brain, 580
Alcoholic fermentation, 103, 107
Algae, **307**, 310
  in coral reef mutualism, 430
  in freshwater biomes, 380
  in lichens, 332
  in marine biomes, 382
  nutrient pollution and, 443
  photosynthetic, 108
  as photosynthetic protists, 307
  reproduction of, 317
  structural adaptations of, 316*f*
  unicellular and colonial, 310
Ali, Muhammad, 231*f*
Alimentary canal, **478**–79, 482
Alkaptonuria, 178

Allantois, 565
Alleles, **148**. *See also* Genes
  ABO blood groups as example of codominant, 159
  dominant vs. recessive, 148
  gene pools of, 256–59
  human genetic disorders and, 154–56
  law of segregation and, 148–49
  sickle-cell disease as example of pleiotropy by, 160
Allergens, **528**
Allergies, **528**
Alligators, 358
Allopatric speciation, **274**–75
Alprazolam, 580
Alternation of generations, **320**, 322–23
Alternative RNA splicing, **204**
Altitude
  athletic training at high, 504
  human adaptations to high, 513
  vegetation types and, 384
Alvarez, Luis and Walter, 284–85
Alveoli, **510**, 512
Alvin research submarine, 299*f*
Alzheimer's disease, 48, 231, **586**
Amazonian forest fragmentation case study, 446
American bison, 428
American elm trees, 330
American pika, 377
Amine hormones, 537
Amine neurotransmitters, 580
Amino acids, **46**
  case study on abiotic formation of, 297
  genes and sequences of, 48
  human essential, 486
  as monomers of proteins, 46 (*see also* Proteins)
  neurotransmitters derived from, 580
  synthesis of, in gene expression, 182–83 (*see also* Gene expression)
  systematics and sequences of, 287
  triplet genetic code for, 179–80
Amino groups, 46
Ammonifying bacteria, 628
Ammonium, nitrogen fixation and, 442, 628–29
Amniocentesis, 157
Amnion, 565
Amniotes, **358**
  reptiles and mammals as, 358
  vertebrates as, 355*f*
Amniotic eggs, 355*f*, **358**
Amniotic fluid, 565
Amoebas, 69, **308**, 464
Amoebic dysentery, 308

H